Handbook
of
NOISE
MEASUREMENT

**by Arnold P. G. Peterson
and Ervin E. Gross, Jr.**

Price: $9.00

EIGHTH EDITION

Form No. 5301-8111-N

 **GenRad**

PRINTED IN U.S.A.

Preface

A new chapter on hearing conservation is a particularly noteworthy addition to this handbook. It reflects the increased concern for hearing damage from noise exposure, which is now subject to extensive monitoring as a result of the Occupational Safety and Health Act.

The increased availability and use of more sophisticated noise measurement systems has led us to expand the section on analysis into a separate chapter, which includes information on digital as well as analog systems.

Many new instruments and an electret transducer that is new in the measurement field are reviewed here.

Many of the other sections have been revised to bring them up to date and to present a picture of the present state of the art from our point of view. Those areas that are still controversial should be evident from our comments and the references.

In this edition the references are more specific and more extensive in order to make it easier for the reader to pursue a particular subject area more thoroughly than is possible here, but we have not attempted to produce a comprehensive listing.

We appreciate the comments and corrections received from users of the previous editions and from our colleagues. In particular, we gratefully acknowledge the extensive help received from R. A. Boole, W. R. Kundert, and W. E. Collins in the preparation of this edition.

Arnold P. G. Peterson
Ervin E. Gross

Table of Contents

Chapter 1

Introduction

During the past decade more and more people have become concerned with the problem of noise in everyday life. There is danger of permanent hearing loss when exposure to an intense sound field is long and protective measures are not taken. This is important to millions of workers, to most industrial corporations, labor unions, and insurance companies.

The noise problem near many airports has become so serious that many people have moved out of nearby areas that were once considered pleasant. The din of high-powered trucks, motorcycles, and "hot" cars annoys nearly everyone, and one cannot so readily move away from them as from the airport, because they are almost everywhere.

The increasingly large number of people living in apartments, and the relatively light construction of most modern dwellings, has accentuated the problems of sound isolation. In addition, some of the modern appliances, for example dishwashers, are noisy for relatively long periods, which can be very vexing, if it interferes with a favorite TV program.

Lack of proper sound isolation and acoustical treatment in the classroom may lead to excessive noise levels and reverberation, with resulting difficulties in communication between teacher and class. The school teacher's job may become a nightmare because the design was inadequate or altered to save on the initial cost of the classroom.

High-power electronic amplifiers have brought deafening "music" within the reach of everyone, and many young people may eventually regret the hearing loss that is accelerated by frequent exposure to the extremely loud music they find stimulating.

Of all these problems, noise-induced hearing loss is the most serious. Those who are regularly exposed to excessive noise should have their hearing checked periodically, to determine if they are adequately protected. This approach is discussed in more detail in Chapter IV. In addition, for this problem as well as the others mentioned, reduction of noise at its source is often essential. The further step of providing direct protection for the individual may also be needed.

Much can be done by work on noise sources to reduce the seriousness of these noise problems. It is not often so simple as turning down the volume control on the electronic amplifier. But good mufflers are available for trucks, motorcycles and automobiles; and household appliances can be made quieter by the use of proper treatment for vibrating surfaces, adequately sized pipes and smoother channels for water flow, vibration-isolation mounts, and mufflers. The engineering techniques for dealing with noise are developing rapidly, and every designer should be alert to using them.

In many instances, the quieter product can function as well as the noisier one, and the increased cost of reducing the noise may be minor. But the aircraft-noise problem is an example where the factors of safety, performance, and cost must all be considered in determining the relative benefits to the public of changes made to cut down the noise.

In any of these, sound-measuring instruments and systems can help to assess the nature of the problem, and they can help in determining what to do to subdue the troublesome noise.

The study of mechanical vibration is closely related to that of sound, because sound is produced by the transfer of mechanical vibration to air. Hence, the process of quieting a machine or device often includes a study of the vibrations involved.

Conversely, high-energy acoustical noise, such as generated by powerful jet or rocket engines, can produce vibrations that can weaken structural members of a vehicle or cause electronic components to fail.

Other important effects of vibration include: human discomfort and fatigue from excessive vibration of a vehicle, fatigue and rupture of structural members, and increased maintenance of machines, appliances, vehicles, and other devices.

Vibration, then, is a source not only of noise, annoyance, and discomfort, but often of danger as well. The present refinement of high-speed planes, ships, and automobiles could never have been achieved without thorough measurement and study of mechanical vibration.

The instruments used in sound and vibration measurement are mainly electronic. Furthermore, some of the concepts and techniques developed by electronics engineers and physicists for dealing with random or interfering signals (for which they have borrowed the term "noise") are now used in sound and vibration studies.

The purpose of this book is to help those who are faced, possibly for the first time, with the necessity of making noise measurements. It attempts to clarify the terminology and definitions used in these measurements, to describe the measuring instruments and their use, to aid the prospective user in selecting the proper equipment for the measurements he must make, and to show how these measurements can be interpreted to solve typical problems.

Although some may wish to read the chapters of this book in sequence, many will find it more convenient to consult the table of contents or the index to find the sections of immediate interest. They then can refer to the other sections of the book as they need further information. For example, if hearing conservation is of primary concern, Chapter 4 could be read first. Chapter 7 ("What Noise and Vibration Measurements Should be Made") could be consulted if a specific noise problem is at hand. The reader can then find further details on the instruments recommended (Chapter 6) and on the techniques of use (Chapter 8).

Some sections of this book are marked by a diamond to indicate that they might well be omitted during an initial reading, since they are highly specialized or very technical.

Chapter 2

What are Noise
and Vibration

2.1 INTRODUCTION.

When an object moves back and forth, it is said to vibrate. This vibration disturbs the air particles near the object and sets them vibrating, producing a variation in normal atmospheric pressure. The disturbance spreads and, when the pressure variations reach our ear drums, they too are set to vibrating. This vibration of our ear drums is translated by our complicated hearing mechanisms into the sensation we call "sound."

To put it in more general terms, sound in the physical sense is a vibration of particles in a gas, a liquid, or a solid. The measurement and control of airborne sound is the basic subject of this book. Because the chief sources of sounds in air are vibrations of solid objects, the measurement and control of vibration will also be discussed. Vibrations of and in solids often have important effects other than those classified as sound, and some of these will also be included.

We have mentioned that a sound disturbance spreads. The speed with which it spreads depends on the mass and on the elastic properties of the material. In air the speed is about 1100 feet/second (about 750 miles/hour) or about 340 meters/second; in sea water it is about 1490 meters/second. The speed of sound has been popularized in aerodynamic concepts of the sound barrier and the supersonic transport, and its effects are commonly observed in echoes and in the apparent delay between a flash of lightning and the accompanying thunder.

The variation in normal atmospheric pressure that is a part of a sound wave is characterized by the rate at which the variation occurs and the extent of the variation. Thus, the standard tone "A" occurs when the pressure changes through a complete cycle 440 times per second. The frequency of this tone is then said to be 440 hertz, or 440 cycles per second (abbreviated "Hz" and "c/s", respectively). "Hertz" and "cycles per second" are synonymous terms, but most standardizing agencies have adopted "hertz" as the preferred unit of frequency.

Many prefixes are used with the unit of frequency, but the one that is common in acoustics and vibrations is "kilo-," abbreviated "k", which stands for a factor of 1000. Thus, 8000 Hz or 8000 c/s becomes 8 kHz or 8 kc/s.

The extent of the variation in pressure is measured in terms of a unit called the "microbar*", which is approximately one-millionth of the normal atmospheric pressure (standard atmospheric pressure = 1,013,250 microbars), or in terms of newtons per square meter, which is 10 microbars. Actually, these units are not often mentioned in noise measurement. Results are stated in decibels.

---

*Here, the prefix "micro" stands for a factor of one-millionth, and that prefix is abbreviated by the use of the Greek letter "μ" (mu). Thus "μN" stands for 0.000001 newton.

2.2 THE DECIBEL — WHAT IS IT?

Although to many laymen the decibel (abbreviated "dB") is uniquely associated with noise measurements, it is a term borrowed from electrical-communication engineering, and it represents a relative quantity. When it is used to express noise level, a reference quantity is implied. Usually, this reference value is a sound pressure of 20 micronewtons per square meter (abbreviated 20 μN/m^2). For the present, the reference level can be referred to as "0 decibels," the starting point of the scale of noise levels. This starting point is about the level of the weakest sound that can be heard by a person with very good hearing in an extremely quiet location. Other typical points on this scale of noise levels are shown in Figure 2-1. For example, the noise

TYPICAL A-WEIGHTED SOUND LEVELS

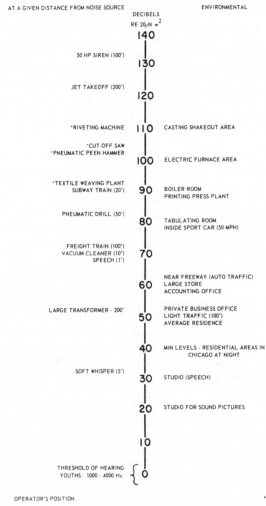

Figure 2-1. Typical A-weighted sound levels measured with a sound-level meter. These values are taken from the literature. Sound-level measurements give only part of the information usually necessary to handle noise problems, and are often supplemented by analysis of the noise spectra.

4

level in a large office usually is between 50 and 60 decibels. Among the very loud sounds are those produced by nearby airplanes, railroad trains, riveting machines, thunder, and so on, which are in the range near 100 decibels. These typical values should help the newcomer to develop a feeling for this term "decibel" as applied to sound level.

For some purposes it is not essential to know more about decibels than the above general statements. But when we need to modify or to manipulate the measured decibels, it is desirable to know more specifically what the term means. There is then less danger of misusing the measured values. From a strictly technical standpoint, the decibel is a logarithm of a ratio of two values of power, and equal changes in decibels represent equal ratios.

Although we shall use decibels for giving the results of power-level calculations, the decibel is most often used in acoustics for expressing the sound-pressure level and the sound level. These are extensions of the original use of the term, and all three expressions will be discussed in the following sections. First, however, it is worthwhile to notice that the above quantities include the word "level." Whenever level is included in the name of the quantity, it can be expected that the value of this level will be given in decibels or in some related term and that a reference power, pressure, or other quantity is stated or implied.

2.3 POWER LEVEL.

Because the range of acoustic powers that are of interest in noise measurements is about one-billion-billion to one (10^{18}:1), it is convenient to relate these powers on the decibel scale, which is logarithmic. The correspondingly smaller range of numerical values is easier to use and, at the same time, some calculations are simplified.

The decibel scale can be used for expressing the ratio between any two powers; and tables for converting from a power ratio to decibels and vice versa are given in Appendix I of this book. For example, if one power is four times another, the number of decibels is 6; if one power is 10,000 times another, the number is 40 decibels.

It is also convenient to express the power as a power level with respect to a reference power. Throughout this book the reference power will be 10^{-12} watt. Then the power level (PWL) is defined as

$$ PWL = 10 \log \frac{W}{10^{-12}} \text{ dB re } 10^{-12} \text{ watt} $$

where W is the acoustic power in watts, the logarithm is to the base 10, and re means referred to. This power level is conveniently computed from

$$ PWL = 10 \log W + 120 $$

since 10^{-12} as a power ratio corresponds to -120 dB. The quantity 10 log W, which is the number of decibels corresponding to the numerical value of watts, can be readily obtained from the decibel tables in the Appendix. For example, 0.02 watt corresponds to a power level of

$$ -17 + 120 = 103 \text{ dB}. $$

5

ACOUSTIC POWER

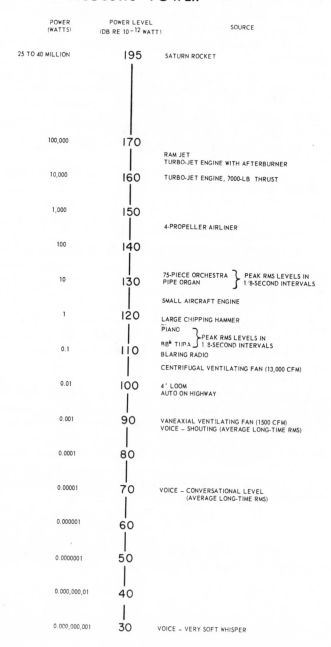

Figure 2-2. Typical power levels for various acoustic sources. These levels bear no simple relation to the sound levels of Figure 2-1.

Some typical power levels for various acoustic sources are shown in Figure 2-2.

No instrument for directly measuring the power level of a source is available. Power levels can be computed from sound-pressure measurements.

2.4 SOUND-PRESSURE LEVEL.

It is also convenient to use the decibel scale to express the ratio between any two sound pressures; tables for converting from a pressure ratio to decibels and vice versa are given in the Appendix. Since sound pressure is usually proportional to the square root of the sound power, the sound-pressure ratio for a given number of decibels is the square root of the corresponding power ratio. For example, if one sound pressure is twice another, the number of decibels is 6; if one sound pressure is 100 times another, the number is 40 decibels.

The sound pressure can also be expressed as a sound-pressure level with respect to a reference sound pressure. For airborne sounds this reference sound pressure is generally 20 μN/m^2. For some purposes a reference pressure of one microbar (0.1 N/m^2) has been used, but throughout this book the value of 20 μN/m^2 will always be used as the reference for sound-pressure level. Then the definition of sound-pressure level (SPL) is

$$ SPL = 20 \log \frac{P}{.00002} \text{ dB re 20 micronewtons/meter squared} $$

where P is the root-mean-square sound pressure in newtons/meter squared for the sound in question. For example, if the sound pressure is 1 N/m^2, then the corresponding sound-pressure ratio is

$$ \frac{1}{.00002} \text{ or } 50000. $$

From the tables, we find that the pressure level is 94 dB re 20 μN/m^2. If decibel tables are not available, the level can, of course, be determined from a table of logarithms.

The instrument used to measure sound-pressure level consists of a microphone, attenuator, amplifier, and indicating meter. This instrument must have an over-all response that is uniform ("flat") as a function of frequency, and the instrument is calibrated in decibels according to the above equation.

The position of the selector switch of the instrument for this measurement is often called "FLAT" or "20-kHz" to indicate the wide frequency range that is covered. The result of a measurement of this type is also called "over-all sound-pressure level."

2.5 SOUND LEVEL.

The apparent loudness that we attribute to a sound varies not only with the sound pressure but also with the frequency (or pitch) of the sound. In addition, the way it varies with frequency depends on the sound pressure. If this effect is taken into account to some extent for pure tones, by "weighting" networks included in an instrument designed to measure sound-pressure level, then the instrument is called a sound-level meter. In order to assist in obtaining reasonable uniformity among different instruments of this type, the American National Standards Institute (formerly, USA Standards Institute and American Standards Association), in collaboration with scientific and engineering societies, has established a standard to which sound-level meters should conform.

7

The current American National Standard Specification for Sound-Level Meters (ANSI S1.4-1971) requires that three alternate frequency-response characteristics be provided in instruments designed for general use (see Figure 2-3)*. These three responses are obtained by weighting networks designated as A, B, and C. Responses A, B, and C selectively discriminate against low and high frequencies in accordance with certain equal-loudness contours, which will be described in a later section.

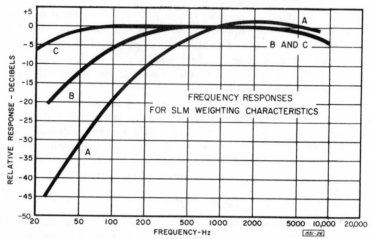

Figure 2-3. Frequency-response characteristics in the American National Standard Specification for Sound-Level Meters, ANSI-S1.4-1971.

Whenever one of these networks is used, the reading obtained should be described as in the following examples: the "A-weighted sound level is 45 dB" "sound level (A) = 45 dB," or "SLA = 45 dB". In a table, the abbreviated form "L_A" with the unit "dB" is suggested, or where exceptional compactness is necessary, "dB(A)." The form "dBA" has also been used, but this notation implies that a new unit has been introduced and is therefore not recommended. Note that when a weighting characteristic is used, the reading obtained is said to be the "sound level.**" Only when the over-all frequency response of the instrument is flat are sound-pressure levels measured. Since the reading obtained depends on the weighting characteristic used, the characteristic that was used must be specified or the recorded level may be useless. A common practice is to assume A-weighting if not otherwise specified.

It is often recommended that readings on all noises be taken with *all three* weighting positions. The three readings provide some indication of the frequency distribution of the noise. If the level is essentially the same on all three networks, the sound probably predominates in frequencies above 600 Hz. If the level is greater on the C network than on the A and B networks by several decibels, much of the noise is probably below 600 Hz.

In the measurement of the noise produced by distribution and power transformers, the difference in readings of level with C-weighting and A-

---

*The current international standards and most national standards on sound-level meters specify these same three responses.

** It was customary, if a single sound-level reading was desired, to select the weighting position according to level, as follows: for levels below 55 dB, A weighting, for levels from 55 dB to 85 dB, B weighting; and for levels above 85 dB. C weighting. Now, however, the A-weighted sound level is the one most widely used regardless of level. See paragraph 3.16.3.

weighting networks (L_C-L_A) is frequently noted. (This difference in decibels is called the "harmonic index" in that application only.) It serves, as indicated above, to give some idea of the frequency distribution of the noise. This difference is also used in other noise-rating techniques in conjunction with the A-weighted sound level.

2.6 COMBINING DECIBELS.

A number of possible situations require the combining of several noise levels stated in decibels. For example, we may want to predict the effect of adding a noisy machine in an office where there is already a significant noise level, to correct a noise measurement for some existing background noise, to predict the combined noise level of several different noise sources, or to obtain a combined total of several levels in different frequency bands.

In none of these situations should the numbers of decibels be added directly. The method that is usually correct is to combine them on an energy basis. The procedure for doing this is to convert the numbers of decibels to relative powers, to add or subtract them, as the situation may require, and then convert back to the corresponding decibels. By this procedure it is easy to see that a noise level of 80 decibels combined with a noise level of 80 decibels yields 83 decibels and not 160 dB. A table showing the relation between power ratio and decibels appears in Appendix I. A chart for combining or subtracting different decibel levels is shown in Appendix II.

The single line chart of Figure 2-4 is particularly convenient for adding noise levels. For example, a noisy factory space has a present A-weighted level at a given location of 82 dB. Another machine is to be added 5 feet away. Assume it's known from measurements on the machine, that at that location in that space, it alone will produce an A-weighted level of about 78 dB. What will the over-all level be when it is added? The difference in levels is 4 dB. If this value is entered on the line chart, one finds that 1.5 dB should be added to the higher level to yield 83.5 dB as the resultant level.

2.7 VIBRATION.

Vibration is the term used to describe continuing or steady-state periodic motion. The motion may be simple harmonic motion like that of a pendulum, or it may be complex like a ride in the "whip" at an amusement park.

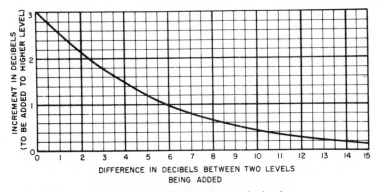

Figure 2-4. Chart for combining noise levels.

9

The motion may involve tiny air particles that produce sound when the rate of vibration is in the audible frequency range (20 to 20,000 Hz), or it may involve, wholly or in part, structures found in machinery, bridges, or battleships. Usually the word vibration is used to describe motions of the latter types, and is classed as solid-borne, or mechanical, vibration.

Many important mechanical vibrations lie in the frequency range of 1 to 2,000 Hz (corresponding to rotational speeds of 60 to 120,000 rpm). In some specialized fields, however, both lower and higher frequencies are important. For example, in seismological work, vibration studies may extend down to a small fraction of a Hz, while in loudspeaker-cone design, vibrations up to 20,000 Hz must be studied.

2.7.1 Nature of Vibratory Motion. Vibration problems occur in so many devices and operations that a listing of these would be impractical. Rather, we shall give a classification on the basis of the vibratory motion, together with numerous examples of where that motion occurs, to show the practical application. The classes of vibratory motion that have been selected are given in Table 2-1. They are not mutually exclusive and, furthermore, most devices and operations involve more than one class of vibratory motion.

----------------- Table 2-1 -----------------
NATURE OF VIBRATORY MOTION

Torsional or twisting vibration
Examples:
  Reciprocating devices
  Gasoline and diesel engines
  Valves
  Compressors
  Pumps
  Rotating devices
  Electric motors
  Fans
  Turbines
  Gears
  Turntables
  Pulleys
  Propellers

Bending vibration
Examples:
  Shafts in motors, engines
  String instruments
  Springs
  Belts
  Chains
  Tape in recorders
  Pipes
  Bridges
  Propellers
  Transmission lines
  Aircraft wings
  Reeds on reed instruments
  Rails
  Washing machines

Flexural and plate-mode vibration
Examples:
  Aircraft
  Circular saws
  Loudspeaker cones
  Sounding boards
  Ship hulls and decks
  Turbine blades
  Gears
  Bridges
  Floors
  Walls

Translational, axial, or rigid-body vibration
Examples:
  Reciprocating devices
  Gasoline and diesel engines
  Compressors
  Air hammers
  Tamping machines
  Shakers
  Punch presses
  Autos
  Motors
  Devices on vibration mounts

Extensional and shear vibration
Examples:
  Transformer hum
  Hum in electric motors
    and generators
  Moving tapes

  Belts
  Punch presses
  Tamping machines

Intermittent vibration (mechanical shock)
Examples:
  Blasting
  Gun shots
  Earthquakes
  Drop forges
  Heels impacting floors
  Typewriters
  Ratchets
  Geneva mechanisms
  Stepping motors
  Autos
  Catapults
  Planers
  Shapers
  Chipping hammers
  Riveters
  Impact wrenches

Random and miscellaneous motions
Examples:
  Combustion
  Ocean waves
  Tides
  Tumblers
  Turbulence
  Earthquakes
  Gas and fluid motion
    and their interaction
    with mechanisms

2.7.2 Vibration Terms. Vibration can be measured in terms of displacement, velocity, acceleration and jerk. The easiest measurement to understand is that of displacement, or the magnitude of motion of the body being studied. When the rate of motion (frequency of vibration) is low enough, the displacement can be measured directly with the dial-gauge micrometer. When the motion of the body is great enough, its displacement can be measured with the common scale.

In its simplest case, displacement may be considered as simple harmonic motion, like that of the bob of a pendulum, that is, a sinusoidal function having the form

$$x = A \sin \omega t \qquad (1)$$

where A is a constant, ω is 2π times the frequency, and t is the time, as shown in Figure 2-5. The maximum peak-to-peak displacement, also called double amplitude, (a quantity indicated by a dial gauge) is 2A, and the root-mean-square (rms) displacement is $A/\sqrt{2}$ (=0.707A). The average (full-wave rectified average) value of the displacement is $2A/\pi$ (=0.636A), while the "average double amplitude" (a term occasionally encountered) would be $4A/\pi$ (=1.272A). Displacement measurements are significant in the study of deformation and bending of structures.

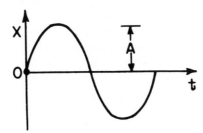

Figure 2-5. A simple sinusoidal function.

When a pure tone is propagated in air, the air particles oscillate about their normal position in a sinusoidal fashion. We could then think of sound in terms of the instantaneous particle displacement and specify its peak and rms value. But these displacements are so very small that they are very difficult to measure directly.

In many practical problems displacement is not the important property of the vibration. A vibrating mechanical part will radiate sound in much the same way as does a loudspeaker. In general, velocities of the radiating part (which corresponds to the cone of the loudspeaker) and the air next to it will be the same, and if the distance from the front of the part to the back is large compared with one-half the wavelength of the sound in air, the actual sound pressure in air will be porportional to the velocity of the vibration. The sound energy radiated by the vibrating surface is the product of the velocity squared and the resistive component of the air load. Under these conditions it is the velocity of the vibrating part and not its displacement that is of greater importance.

Velocity has also been shown by practical experience to be the best single criterion for use in preventive maintenance of rotating machinery. Peak-to-peak displacement has been widely used for this purpose, but then the

11

amplitude selected as a desirable upper limit varies markedly with rotational speed.

Velocity is the time rate of change of displacement, so that for the sinusoidal vibration of equation (1) the velocity is:

$$v = \omega A \cos \omega t \qquad (2)$$

Thus velocity is proportional to displacement and to frequency of vibration.

The analogy cited above covers the case where a loudspeaker cone or baffle is large compared with the wavelength of the sound involved. In most machines this relation does not hold, since relatively small parts are vibrating at relatively low frequencies. This situation can be compared to a small loudspeaker without a baffle. At low frequencies the air may be pumped back and forth from one side of the cone to the other with a high velocity, but without building up much of a pressure or radiating much sound energy because of the very low air load, which has a reactive mechanical impedance. Under these conditions an acceleration measurement provides a better measure of the amount of noise radiated than does a velocity measurement.

In many cases of mechanical vibration, and especially where mechanical failure is a consideration, the actual forces set up in the vibrating parts are important factors. The acceleration of a given mass is proportional to the applied force, and a reacting force equal but opposite in direction results. Members of a vibrating structure, therefore, exert forces on the total structure that are a function of the masses and the accelerations of the vibrating parts. For this reason, acceleration measurements are important when vibrations are severe enough to cause actual mechanical failure.

Acceleration is the time rate of change of velocity, so that for a sinusoidal vibration,

$$a = \omega^2 A \sin \omega t \qquad (3)$$

It is proportional to the displacement and to the square of the frequency or the velocity and the frequency.

Jerk is the time rate of change of acceleration. At low frequencies this change is related to riding comfort of autos and elevators and to bodily injury. It is also important for determining load tiedown in planes, trains, and trucks.

2.7.3 Acceleration and Velocity Level. Some use is now being made of "acceleration level" and "velocity level," which, as the names imply, express the acceleration and velocity in decibels with respect to a reference acceleration and velocity. The reference value of 10^{-8} m/s (10^{-6} cm/s) for velocity and 10^{-5} m/s^2 (10^{-3} cm/s^2) for acceleration are now used, although other references have been proposed.

2.7.4 Nonsinusoidal Vibrations. Equations (1), (2), and (3) represent only sinusoidal vibrations but, as with other complex waves, complex periodic vibrations can also be represented as a combination of sinusoidal vibrations often called a Fourier series. The simple equations may, therefore, be expanded to include as many terms as desirable in order to express any particular type of vibration. For a given sinusoidal displacement, velocity is proportional to frequency and acceleration is proportional to the square of the frequency, so that the higher-frequency components in a vibration are progressively more important in velocity and acceleration measurements than in displacement readings.

2.8 SUMMARY.

2.8.1 Sound. Reference quantities (ANSI S1.8-1969) and relations presented in this chapter included the following:

Reference sound pressure: 20 micronewtons/square meter (20 μN/m^2)*

Reference power: 10^{-12} watt.**

Power level PWL = 10 log $\dfrac{W}{10^{-12}}$ dB re 10^{-12} watt.

where W is the acoustic power in watts.

Sound pressure level: SPL = 20 log $\dfrac{P}{.00002}$ dB re 20 μN/m^2

where P is the root-mean-square sound pressure in newtons/square meter.

(Logarithms are taken to the base 10 in both PWL and SPL calculations.)

Important concepts that aid in interpreting noise measurement results can be summarized as follows:

To measure sound level, use a sound-level meter with one or more of its frequency-response weightings (A, B, and C).

To measure sound-pressure level, use a sound-level meter with the controls set for as uniform a frequency response as possible.

Decibels are usually combined on an energy basis, not added directly.

Speed of sound in air:

at 0°C is 1087 ft/s or 331.4 m/s

at 20°C is 1127 ft/s or 343.4 m/s

Pressure	Pressure Level re 20 μN/m^2
1 Newton/m^2	94 dB
1 microbar	74 dB
1 pound/ft.^{2}	127.6 dB
1 pound/in.^{2}	170.8 dB
1 atmosphere	194.1 dB

NOTE: The reference pressure and the reference power have been selected independently because they are not uniquely related.

2.8.2 Vibration. Displacement is magnitude of the motion.

Velocity is the time rate of change of displacement.

Acceleration is the time rate of change of velocity.

Jerk is the time rate of change of acceleration.

Reference quantities:

Velocity: 10^{-8} meters/second (10^{-6} cm/s)

Acceleration: 10^{-5} meters/second/second (10^{-3} cm/s^2)

*At one time the reference for a sound-level meter was taken as 10^{-12} watt/square meter. For most practical purposes, this reference is equivalent to the presently used pressure. This earlier reference value is *not* a reference for power, since it is power divided by an area. The pressure 20 μN/m^2 is also expressed as 2 x 10^{-5} newton/square meter, 0.0002 microbar, or 0.0002 dyne/cm^2.

**A reference power of 10^{-13} watt is also used in the USA, and has been used in very early editions of this handbook, but the reference power of 10^{-12} watt is preferred (ANSI S1.8-1969).

REFERENCES

Standards

ANSI S1.1-1960, Acoustical Terminology.
ANSI S1.8-1969, Preferred Reference Quantities for Acoustical Levels.
ANSI S1.4-1971, Sound-Level Meters.
ANSI S1.13-1971, Methods for the Measurement of Sound Pressure Levels.

Other

L. L. Beranek (1949), *Acoustic Measurements*, John Wiley & Sons, Inc., New York.

L. L. Beranek (1954), *Acoustics*, McGraw-Hill Book Company, Inc., New York.

L. L. Beranek, ed. (1971), *Noise and Vibration Control*, McGraw-Hill Book Company, Inc., New York.

R.E.D. Bishop (1965), *Vibration*, Cambridge University Press, Cambridge, England.

C. E. Crede (1951), *Vibration and Shock Isolation*, John Wiley & Sons, Inc., New York.

J. P. Den Hartog (1956), *Mechanical Vibrations*, McGraw-Hill Book Company Inc., New York.

C. M. Harris, ed. (1957), *Handbook of Noise Control*, McGraw-Hill Book Company, Inc., New York.

C. M. Harris and C. E. Crede, ed. (1961), *Shock and Vibration Handbook*, McGraw-Hill Book Company, Inc., New York.

L. E. Kinsler and A. R. Frey (1962), *Fundamentals of Acoustics*, John Wiley & Sons, Inc., New York.

C. T. Morrow (1963), *Shock and Vibration Engineering*, John Wiley & Sons, Inc., New York.

P. M. Morse and K. U. Ingard (1968), *Theoretical Acoustics*, McGraw-Hill Book Company, Inc., New York. (A graduate text.)

H. F. Olson (1957), *Acoustical Engineering*, D. Van Nostrand Company, Inc., New York, 3rd Edition.

J. R. Pierce and E. E. David, Jr.,(1958), *Man's World of Sound*, Doubleday & Company, Inc., Garden City, New York.

R. H. Randall (1951), *An Introduction to Acoustics*, Addison-Wesley Press, Cambridge, Mass.

R. W. B. Stephens and A. E. Bate (1966), *Acoustics and Vibrational Physics*, Arnold, London, St. Martin's Press, New York, 2nd Edition.

G. W. Swenson, Jr. (1953), *Principles of Modern Acoustics*, D. Van Nostrand Company, Inc., New York.

G. W. Van Santen (1953), *Mechanical Vibration*, Elsevier, Houston.

W. Wilson (1959), *Vibration Engineering*, Charles Griffin, London.

L. F. Yerges (1969), *Sound, Noise and Vibration Control*, Van Nostrand-Reinhold Company, New York.

R. W. Young (1955), *"A Brief Guide to Noise Measurement and Analysis,"* Research and Development Report 609, 16 May 1955, US Navy Electronics Laboratory, PB118036.

Chapter 3

What Noise and Vibration Do and How Much Is Acceptable

3.1 WHY WE MEASURE NOISE.

That very intense noise may cause hearing loss, that we are annoyed by a noisy device and a noisy environment, or that noise may interfere with our sleep, our work, and our recreation is frequently the basic fact that leads to noise measurements and attempts at quieting. In order to make the most significant measurements and to do the job of quieting most efficiently, it is clearly necessary to learn about these effects of noise. We seek to estimate from these effects what levels of noise are acceptable, and thus establish suitable noise criteria. Then if we measure the existing noise level, the difference between this level and the acceptable level is the noise reduction necessary.

Unfortunately, not all the factors involved in annoyance, interference, and hearing loss are known at present. Nor are we yet sure how the known factors can best be used. But a brief discussion of our reactions to sounds will serve to show some of the factors and their relative significance. This information will be useful as a guide for selecting electronic equipment to make the most significant measurements for the problem at hand.

3.2 PSYCHOACOUSTICAL EXPERIMENTS.

Scientists and engineers have investigated many aspects of man's reactions to sounds (Stevens, 1951). For example, they have measured the levels of the weakest sounds that various observers could just hear in a very quiet room (threshold of hearing), they have measured the levels of the sounds that are sufficiently high in level to cause pain (threshold of pain), and they have measured the least change in level and in frequency that various observers could detect (differential threshold). These experimenters have also asked various observers to set the levels of some sounds so that they are judged equal in loudness to reference sounds (equal loudness), and they have asked the observers to rate sounds for loudness on a numerical scale.

In order to get reliable measures of these reactions, the experimenters have to simplify the conditions under which people react to sounds. This simplification is mainly one of maintaining unchanged as many conditions as possible while a relatively few characteristics of the sound are varied. Some of the conditions that have to be controlled and specified are the following: the physical environment of the observer, particularly the background or ambient level; the method of presenting the changing signals, including the order of presentation, duration, frequency, and intensity; the selection of the observers; the instructions to the observers; the experience of the observers in the specific test procedure; the normal hearing characteristics of the observers; the responses; and the method of handling the data.

Variations in the conditions of the measurement will affect the result. Such interaction is the reason for requiring controlled and specified conditions. It is desirable to know, however, how much the various conditions do affect the result. For example, small changes in room temperature are usually of little significance. But if the observer is exposed to a noise of even moderate level just before a threshold measurement, the measured threshold level will, temporarily, be significantly higher than normal.

The basic method used by the observer to present his reaction to the signals is also important in the end result. Numerous methods have been developed for this presentation. Three of these psychophysical methods are as follows:

1. In the method of adjustment, the observer sets an adjustable control to the level he judges suitable for the test.
2. In the method of the just-noticeable difference, the observer states when two signals differ sufficiently, so that he can tell they are different.
3. In the method of constant stimuli, the observer states whether two signals are the same, or which is the greater, if they seem to differ.

The approach an observer takes in making a decision is significant. If an observer attempts to detect a signal that is sometimes present in a background of noise, four possible conditions exist. With the signal present or absent, he may respond that it is or is not present. The choice he makes can be influenced by the instructions. On the one hand, he may be told that false alarms are serious errors and that he should respond that the signal is present only if he is very certain of it. Or he may be told that occasional false alarms are unimportant. These different instructions will produce different approaches to the decision problem and will affect the results of the experiment. These factors have been organized in modern detection theory (Green and Swets, 1966) to permit a quantitative approach to such psychoacoustic problems by the use of a "receiver-operating characteristic," usually called "ROC." Experiments based on this theory have also shown that earlier concepts of a "threshold" are oversimplified. We shall, however, use the term threshold here without attempting to define it accurately, since it is a readily accepted concept, and it is adequate for the present discussion.

When psychoacoustical experiments are performed, the resultant data show variability in the judgments of a given observer as well as variability in the judgments of a group of observers. The data must then be handled by statistical methods, to obtain an average result as well as a measure of the deviations from the average. In general, it is the average result that is of most interest but the extent of the deviations is also of value, and in some experiments these deviations are of major interest.

The deviations are not usually shown on graphs of averaged psychoacoustical data, but they should be kept in mind. To picture these deviations one might think of the curves as if they were drawn with a wide brush instead of a fine pen.

The measured psychoacoustical responses also have a certain degree of stability, although it is not the degree of stability that we find in physical measurements. In the normal course of events, if one's threshold of hearing is measured today, a similar measurement tomorrow should give the same threshold level within a few decibels.

In the process of standardizing the measurement conditions for the sake of reliability and stability, the experiments have been controlled to the point

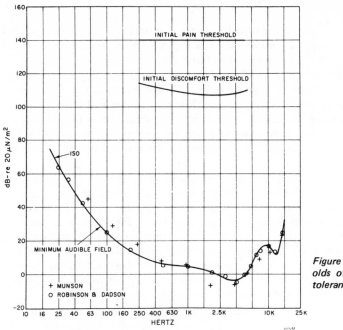

Figure 3-1. Thresh-olds of hearing and tolerance.

where they do not duplicate the conditions encountered in actual practice. They are then useful mainly as a guide in interpreting objective measurements in subjective terms, provided one allows for those conditions that seriously affect the result. As a general rule, the trend of human reactions to changes in the sound is all that can be estimated with validity. A conservative approach in using psychoacoustical data, with some margin as an engineering safety factor, is usually essential in actual practice.

3.3 THRESHOLDS OF HEARING AND TOLERANCE.

Many experimenters have made measurements of the threshold of hearing of various observers. When young persons with good hearing are tested, a characteristic similar to that labeled minimum audible field (MAF) in Figure 3-1 is usually obtained. This shows the level of the simple tone that can just be heard in an exceptionally quiet location under free-field conditions (see Chapter 8 for an explanation of "free-field") as a function of the frequency of the tone. For example, if a simple tone having a frequency of 250 Hz (about the same as the fundamental frequency of middle C) is sounded in a very quiet location, and if its sound-pressure level is greater than 12 dB re 20 $\mu N/m^2$ at the ear of the listener, it will usually be heard by a young person.

The results of two of the classical determinations of the minimum audible field are shown in the figure. Both were very carefully done. The values shown by the crosses were obtained by Munson on a group of 8 men and 2 women, average age of 24 (Sivian and White, 1933), when only a few laboratories could make accurate acoustical measurements. The values shown by the circles are a result of the extensive set of measurements made by Robinson and Dadson (1956) on 51 young people, average age of 20. The smooth curve is the one given in the international standard, ISO R226-1967.

Some variation in the threshold of a person can be expected even if the experiments are carefully controlled. Threshold determinations made in rapid succession may possibly differ by as much as 5 dB, and with longer intervals more variation between particular values is possible. But the average of a number of threshold measurements will generally be consistent with the average of another set to within less than 5 dB.

The variability among individuals is, of course, much greater than the day-to-day variability of a single individual. For example, the sensitivity of some young people is slightly better than that shown in Figure 3-1 as the minimum audible field, and, at the other extreme, some people have no usable hearing. Most noise-quieting problems, however, involve people whose hearing characteristics, on the average, are only somewhat poorer than shown in Figure 3-1.

The threshold curve (Figure 3-1) shows that at low frequencies the sound-pressure level must be comparatively high before the tone can be heard. In contrast we can hear tones in the frequency range from 200 to 10,000 Hz even though the levels are very low. This variation in acuity of hearing with frequency is one of the reasons that in most noise problems it is essential to know the frequency composition of the noise. For example, is it made up of a number of components all below 100 Hz? Or are they all between 1000 and 5000 Hz? The importance of a given sound-pressure level is significantly different in those two examples.

The upper limit of frequency at which we can hear air-borne sounds depends primarily on the condition of our hearing and on the intensity of the sound. This upper limit is usually quoted as being somewhere between 16,000 and 20,000 Hz. For most practical purposes the actual figure is not important.

Many hearing-threshold measurements are made by otologists and audiologists and other hearing specialists in the process of analyzing the condition of a person's hearing. An instrument known as an "audiometer" is used for this purpose. Why and how this instrument is used is covered in Chapter 4.

When a sound is very high in level, one can feel very uncomfortable listening to it. The "Discomfort Threshold" (Silverman, 1947), shown in Figure 3-1 at about 120 dB, is drawn in to show the general level at which such a reaction is to be expected for pure tones. At still higher levels the sound will become painful and the order of magnitude of these levels (Silverman, 1947) is also shown in Figure 3-1. The thresholds for discomfort are significantly lower (about 10 dB) on initial exposure and rise after repeated exposures to such high levels.

3.3.1 Hearing Loss with Age — Presbycusis. The expected loss in hearing sensitivity with age has been determined by statistical analysis of hearing-threshold measurements on many people. An analysis of such data has given the results shown in Figure 3-2 (Spoor, 1967). This set of curves shows, for a number of simple tones of differing frequencies, the extent of the shift in threshold that we can expect, on the average, as we grow older. It is shown there that the loss becomes increasingly severe at higher frequencies, and it is obvious that an upper hearing-frequency-limit of 20,000 Hz applies only to young people.

The curves shown are given in terms of the shift with respect to the 25-year age group. The shifts in hearing sensitivity represent the effects of a combination of aging (presbycusis) and the normal stresses and nonoccupational noises of modern civilization (sociocusis) (Glorig, 1958). Such curves are usually called "presbycusis curves," even though they do not represent

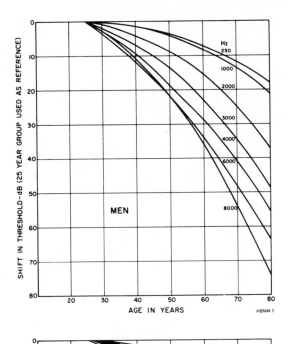

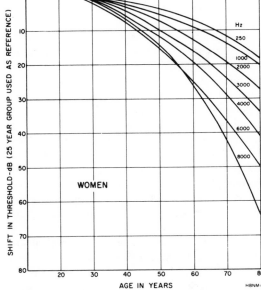

Figure 3-2. The average shifts with age of the threshold of hearing for pure tones of persons with "normal" hearing. (Spoor, 1967).

pure physiological aging, and they are used to help determine if the hearing of an older person is about what would be expected.

3.3.2 Hearing Loss From Noise Exposure. Exposure to loud noise may lead to a loss in hearing, which will appear as a shift in the hearing threshold. This effect of noise is so important that the next chapter is devoted to it.

3.3.3 Other Causes of Hearing Loss. There are so many possible contributing factors to hearing loss (Davis and Silverman, 1970) that we cannot review them here. But to remind one that aging and noise are only two of the many possible factors, here are some of the more obvious contributors — congenital defects, anatomical injuries, and disease.

3.4 "WHAT NOISE ANNOYS AN OYSTER?"

No adequate measures of the annoyance levels of noises have yet been devised. Various aspects of the problem have been investigated, but the psychological difficulties in making these investigations are very great. For example, the extent of our annoyance depends greatly on what we are trying to do at the moment, it depends on our previous conditioning, and it depends on the character of the noise.

The annoyance level of a noise is sometimes assumed to be related directly to the loudness level of the noise. Although not completely justifiable, this assumption is sometimes helpful because a loud sound is usually more annoying than one of similar character that is not so loud.

This approach is one of the reasons that many experiments have been made on judged loudness of various sounds, and procedures have been developed for predicting the loudness of noise from physical measurements. Some of the results of these experiments will be reviewed in the next section. In addition other experiments have been made in which listeners have been asked to judge noises for their "noisiness," "unacceptability," "objectionability," "annoyingness," or on how "disturbing" they were. Some of these experiments have led to the concept of "perceived noise level" and "noisiness." Since perceived noise level has been used widely, it too is described in more detail below.

In a comprehensive review of such experiments Stevens (1972) shows how remarkably similar most of the results are. One is led to the conclusions that these distinct terms do not produce really significant differences in judgment at least for the controlled experimental conditions. He has used the available evidence to produce a new, but related, procedure for predicting the "perceived level" and the "perceived magnitude" from physical measurements of a noise. This procedure, called "Mark VII," is also described below.

One conclusion that can be drawn from these experiments is that high-frequency sounds (in the vicinity of 5000 Hz) are usually louder, more annoying or disturbing than are lower-frequency sounds of the same sound-pressure level. Therefore, when it is determined, by methods to be explained later, that a significant portion of the noise is in this higher-frequency region, considerable effort at reducing these levels from the viewpoint of annoyance may be justified.

A rather different effect that may determine some of the annoying quality of a sound concerns its localization. When a large office has acoustically hard walls, floor, and ceiling, the room is "live," reverberant. The noise from any office machinery then is reflected back and forth, and the workers are immersed in the noise with the feeling that it comes from everywhere. If the office is heavily treated with absorbing material, the reflected sound is reduced, and the workers then feel that the noise is coming directly from the machine. This localized noise seems to be less annoying. While no adequate measures of this effect have been developed, the general principle discussed here seems to be accepted by many who are experienced in noise problems.

3.5 RATING THE LOUDNESS OF A SOUND.

Many psychoacoustical experiments have been made in which listeners have been asked to rate the loudness of a sound. As a result of these experiments, involving all sorts of sounds in various arrangements, much has been learned about the concept of loudness in laboratory situations. The way in which the judgment of loudness is obtained seems to affect the results sufficiently, however, so that we cannot reliably scale all the sounds of everyday life on an absolute basis. In particular, it does not seem possible to give a numerical value to the loudness ratio of two sounds and have this ratio be reasonably independent of the conditions of comparison. It does seem possible, however, to rank a sound with satisfactory reliability according to its loudness. For example, if sound A is judged louder than sound B and if sound B is judged louder than sound C, then, in general, sound A will also be judged louder than sound C.

3.5.1 Equal-Loudness Contours. One step in the direction of rating the loudness of a sound has been to determine the sound-pressure levels of simple tones of various frequencies that sound just as loud to an observer as a 1000-Hz tone of a given sound-pressure level. The results of this determination by Robinson and Dadson based on the averages of many observations, are given as equal-loudness contours in Figure 3-3. The number on each curve

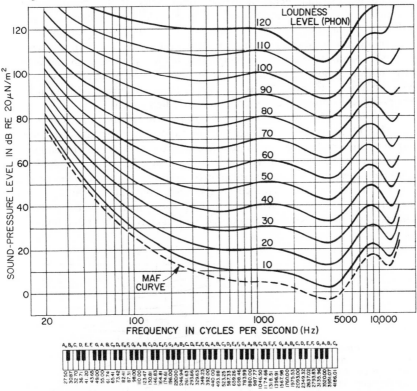

Figure 3-3. Free-field equal-loudness contours for pure tones (observer facing source), determined by Robinson and Dadson 1956 at the National Physical Laboratory, Teddington, England. (ISO/R226-1961) Piano keyboard helps identify the frequency scale. Only the fundamental frequency of each piano key is indicated.

21

is the sound-pressure level of the 1000-Hz tone used for comparison for that curve. To use the contours for determining the equally loud levels at other frequencies, we find the point on the curve corresponding to the desired frequency and read off the corresponding sound-pressure level as the ordinate. For example, the 60-dB contour line shows that a 67-dB level at 100 Hz is just as loud as a 60-dB 1000-Hz tone. We can also interpolate to find that a 60-dB 100-Hz tone is equal in loudness to a 51-dB 1000-Hz tone. The corresponding sound-pressure level in dB for the 1000-Hz tone has been defined as the *loudess level* in *phons*. Therefore, a 100-Hz tone at a sound-pressure level of 60 dB has a loudness level of 51 phons.

The weighting networks for the standard sound-level meter are based on similar contours developed much earlier by Fletcher and Munson (1933). The "A" and "B" weighting characteristics are in accordance with the 40- and 70-phon Fletcher-Munson contours, but with modifications to take into account the usually random nature of the sound field in a room and to simplify their simulation with electrical networks.

A set of equal-loudness contours (Pollack, 1952) for bands of random noise is shown in Figure 3-4. Random noise is a common type of noise that occurs in ventilating systems, jets, blowers, combustion chambers, etc. It does not have a well-defined pitch, such as characterizes a tone with the energy concentrated in components of definite frequencies. Rather, random noise has energy distributed over a band of frequencies. If the noise energy is uniform over a wide range, it is called "white noise," being analogous in spectrum characteristics to white light. When the energy is distributed over a very wide band, it is a sort of "hishing" sound. When the broadband noise has little energy at low frequencies, it is more of a hissing sound. When it is concentrated in narrower bands, the sound takes on some aspects of pitch. For example, low-frequency random noise may be a sort of roar.

The contours shown in Figure 3-4 are for relatively narrow bands of noise, such that 11 bands cover the range from 60 to 5800 Hz. They are distributed uniformly on a scale of pitch for simple tones (see 3.15.2). The numbers on the curves are phons, that is, the sound-pressure levels of equally loud 1000-Hz tones, and the levels are plotted according to the centers of the bands. For example, one band covers the range from 350 to 700 Hz. From the curves we can see that when the sound-pressure level of the noise in that band is 43 dB re 20 μN/m^2, the indicated loudness level is about 34 phons.

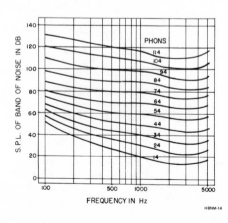

Figure 3-4. Equal-loudness contours for relatively narrow bands of random noise. The center frequency of the band is shown as the abscissa, and the numbers on the curves are phons (Pollack, 1952).

22

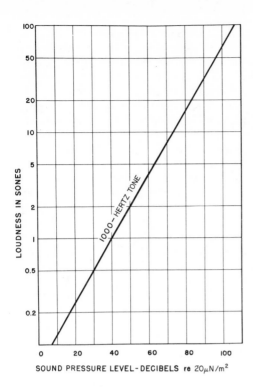

LOUDNESS IN SONES

SOUND PRESSURE LEVEL- DECIBELS re 20μN/m²

Figure 3-5. Loudness vs sound-pressure level for a pure tone of 1000 Hz.

3.5.2 Loudness and Loudness Level. Although we may remark that some sounds are louder than others, we do not ordinarily rate sounds for loudness on a numerical basis. Experimenters have asked observers to make judgments of the loudness ratio of sounds, that is, to state when one sound is twice, four times, one-half, etc., as loud as another. The resultant judgments depend to a considerable extent on how the problem is presented to the observer. But on the basis of such judgments, several scales of loudness have been devised, which rate sounds from "soft" to "loud" in units of *sones.* As a reference, the loudness of a 1000-Hz tone with a sound-pressure level of 40 dB re 20 μN/m² (a loudness level of 40 phons) is taken to be 1 sone. A tone that sounds twice as loud has a loudness of 2 sones. This scale is shown on the vertical axis of Figure 3-5, and the horizontal scale is the sound-pressure level of the sound in decibels. The curve shown in this figure relates the loudness in sones to the sound-pressure level for a 1000-Hz simple tone. This relation was developed as a useful engineering approximation by Stevens as a result of his analysis of the data reported by many experimenters, who used a wide variety of techniques. He also performed a series of experiments in which the loudness estimates were made on an unusually direct basis, and these experiments confirmed the relation shown. Robinson has also suggested this relation, which is published as a Recommendation of the International Standards Organization (ISO R131-1959).

Incidentally, the relation shown in Figure 3-5 tends to refute the point of view that the decibel is used in acoustics because we respond to sound pressure in a logarithmic manner. Actually, the loudness is approximately proportional to the sound pressure raised to the 0.6 power.

23

3.5.3 Loudness-Level Calculations.

If the sound to be measured is known to be a simple tone, the procedure for determination of loudness level is relatively easy. The sound-pressure level and the frequency of the tone are determined, and the equal-loudness contours of Figure 3-3 then indicate the loudness level. Since the weighting networks on a sound-level meter approximate two of the equal-loudness contours, a determination of the weighted level (sound level) can be used to give an estimate of the loudness level of a simple tone.

For any other type of sound, however, the measured sound level will be lower than the loudness level. The error in estimating loudness level will depend on the type of sound and for many noises will be more than 10 phons. For example, if we have a uniform wide-band noise from 20 to 6000 Hz of 80-dB sound-pressure level, the B-weighted sound level would be about 79 dB and the A-weighted sound level would be about 80 dB, whereas the actual loudness level of such a noise is about 95 phons. Here we see that the sound level is not only misleading, but is no nearer the loudness level than is the sound-pressure level. This result, for most noises, illustrates the fact that we need to know more about a sound than just its sound-pressure level or its sound level. If we know how the energy in a sound is distributed as a function of frequency, we can make a more useful estimate of its probable subjective effect than we can by knowing just its sound-pressure level. One of the ways such knowledge is used is the calculation of loudness level.

A number of workers in noise measurements have found it useful to translate their noise measurements into such loudness terms. Then they can say the measured sound is, for example, about equal in loudness to another, more familiar, sound. To some groups, such as executive and lay clients, this type of statement is seemingly more meaningful than levels quoted in decibels.

For steady, wide-band noises, a technique developed by Stevens has been found to give good results. The sound is divided by an analyzer into frequency bands covering the audio spectrum. The loudness level is then calculated according to the procedure given in the next section.

A set of 8 or 9 octave bands is most often used for this purpose. These have center frequencies of 31.5, 63, 125, 250, 500, 1000, 2000, 4000 and 8000 Hz, with each band actually covering a 2:1 frequency range. A more detailed division provided by a third-octave analysis is also widely used. Both of these band divisions are described in more detail in Chapter 5.

♦ **3.5.4 Procedure for Calculating Loudness*.** Table 3-1 is used to calculate the loudness for octave-band levels of the preferred series. The procedure is as follows:

1. From the table find the proper loudness index for each band level.
2. Add all the loudness indexes (ΣS).
3. Multiply this sum by 0.3.
4. Add this product to 0.7 of the index for that band that has the largest index ($0.3 \Sigma S + 0.7 S_{max}$). This value is the total loudness in sones.
5. This total loudness is then converted to loudness level in phons by the relation shown in the two columns at the right of the table.

---

*The method used here is that standardized in ANSI S3.4-1968 and originally given by S. S. Stevens (1961). Chart paper No. 31460-A (Codex Book Company, Norwood, Massachusetts 02062) is available for this calculation when the older series of octave bands is used.

24

Table 3-1.
BAND LEVEL CONVERSION TO LOUDNESS INDEX

Band Level	Band Loudness Index									Loudness	Loudness Level
dB	31.5	63	125	250	500	1000	2000	4000	8000	Sones	Phons
20						.18	.30	.45	.61	.25	20
21						.22	.35	.50	.67	.27	21
22					.07	.26	.40	.55	.73	.29	22
23					.12	.30	.45	.61	.80	.31	23
24					.16	.35	.50	.67	.87	.33	24
25					.21	.40	.55	.73	.94	.35	25
26					.26	.45	.61	.80	1.02	.38	26
27					.31	.50	.67	.87	1.10	.41	27
28				.07	.37	.55	.73	.94	1.18	.44	28
29				.12	.43	.61	.80	1.02	1.27	.47	29
30				.16	.49	.67	.87	1.10	1.35	.50	30
31				.21	.55	.73	.94	1.18	1.44	.54	31
32				.26	.61	.80	1.02	1.27	1.54	.57	32
33				.31	.67	.87	1.10	1.35	1.64	.62	33
34			.07	.37	.73	.94	1.18	1.44	1.75	.66	34
35			.12	.43	.80	1.02	1.27	1.54	1.87	.71	35
36			.16	.49	.87	1.10	1.35	1.64	1.99	.76	36
37			.21	.55	.94	1.18	1.44	1.75	2.11	.81	37
38			.26	.62	1.02	1.27	1.54	1.87	2.24	.87	38
39			.31	.69	1.10	1.35	1.64	1.99	2.38	.93	39
40		.07	.37	.77	1.18	1.44	1.75	2.11	2.53	1.00	40
41		.12	.43	.85	1.27	1.54	1.87	2.24	2.68	1.07	41
42		.16	.49	.94	1.35	1.64	1.99	2.38	2.84	1.15	42
43		.21	.55	1.04	1.44	1.75	2.11	2.53	3.0	1.23	43
44		.26	.62	1.13	1.54	1.87	2.24	2.68	3.2	1.32	44
45		.31	.69	1.23	1.64	1.99	2.38	2.84	3.4	1.41	45
46	.07	.37	.77	1.33	1.75	2.11	2.53	3.0	3.6	1.52	46
47	.12	.43	.85	1.44	1.87	2.24	2.68	3.2	3.8	1.62	47
48	.16	.49	.94	1.56	1.99	2.38	2.84	3.4	4.1	1.74	48
49	.21	.55	1.04	1.69	2.11	2.53	3.0	3.6	4.3	1.87	49
50	.26	.62	1.13	1.82	2.24	2.68	3.2	3.8	4.6	2.00	50
51	.31	.69	1.23	1.96	2.38	2.84	3.4	4.1	4.9	2.14	51
52	.37	.77	1.33	2.11	2.53	3.0	3.6	4.3	5.2	2.30	52
53	.43	.85	1.44	2.24	2.68	3.2	3.8	4.6	5.5	2.46	53
54	.49	.94	1.56	2.38	2.84	3.4	4.1	4.9	5.8	2.64	54
55	.55	1.04	1.69	2.53	3.0	3.6	4.3	5.2	6.2	2.83	55
56	.62	1.13	1.82	2.68	3.2	3.8	4.6	5.5	6.6	3.03	56
57	.69	1.23	1.96	2.84	3.4	4.1	4.9	5.8	7.0	3.25	57
58	.77	1.33	2.11	3.0	3.6	4.3	5.2	6.2	7.4	3.48	58
59	.85	1.44	2.27	3.2	3.8	4.6	5.5	6.6	7.8	3.73	59
60	.94	1.56	2.44	3.4	4.1	4.9	5.8	7.0	8.3	4.00	60
61	1.04	1.69	2.62	3.6	4.3	5.2	6.2	7.4	8.8	4.29	61
62	1.13	1.82	2.81	3.8	4.6	5.5	6.6	7.8	9.3	4.59	62
63	1.23	1.96	3.0	4.1	4.9	5.8	7.0	8.3	9.9	4.92	63
64	1.33	2.11	3.2	4.3	5.2	6.2	7.4	8.8	10.5	5.28	64
65	1.44	2.27	3.5	4.6	5.5	6.6	7.8	9.3	11.1	5.66	65
66	1.56	2.44	3.7	4.9	5.8	7.0	8.3	9.9	11.8	6.06	66
67	1.69	2.62	4.0	5.2	6.2	7.4	8.8	10.5	12.6	6.50	67
68	1.82	2.81	4.3	5.5	6.6	7.8	9.3	11.1	13.5	6.96	68
69	1.96	3.0	4.7	5.8	7.0	8.3	9.9	11.8	14.4	7.46	69
70	2.11	3.2	5.0	6.2	7.4	8.8	10.5	12.6	15.3	8.00	70
71	2.27	3.5	5.4	6.6	7.8	9.3	11.1	13.5	16.4	8.6	71
72	2.44	3.7	5.8	7.0	8.3	9.9	11.8	14.4	17.5	9.2	72
73	2.62	4.0	6.2	7.4	8.8	10.5	12.6	15.3	18.7	9.8	73
74	2.81	4.3	6.6	7.8	9.3	11.1	13.5	16.4	20.0	10.6	74
75	3.0	4.7	7.0	8.3	9.9	11.8	14.4	17.5	21.4	11.3	75
76	3.2	5.0	7.4	8.8	10.5	12.6	15.3	18.7	23.0	12.1	76
77	3.5	5.4	7.8	9.3	11.1	13.5	16.4	20.0	24.7	13.0	77
78	3.7	5.8	8.3	9.9	11.8	14.4	17.5	21.4	26.5	13.9	78
79	4.0	6.2	8.8	10.5	12.6	15.3	18.7	23.0	28.5	14.9	79
80	4.3	6.7	9.3	11.1	13.5	16.4	20.0	24.7	30.5	16.0	80
81	4.7	7.2	9.9	11.8	14.4	17.5	21.4	26.5	32.9	17.1	81
82	5.0	7.7	10.5	12.6	15.3	18.7	23.0	28.5	35.3	18.4	82
83	5.4	8.2	11.1	13.5	16.4	20.0	24.7	30.5	38	19.7	83
84	5.8	8.8	11.8	14.4	17.5	21.4	26.5	32.9	41	21.1	84
85	6.2	9.4	12.6	15.3	18.7	23.0	28.5	35.3	44	22.6	85

Table 3-1 (Continued)

Band Level	Band Loudness Index									Loudness	Loudness Level
dB	31.5	63	125	250	500	1000	2000	4000	8000	Sones	Phons
86	6.7	10.1	13.5	16.4	20.0	24.7	30.5	38	48	24.3	86
87	7.2	10.9	14.4	17.5	21.4	26.5	32.9	41	52	26.0	87
88	7.7	11.7	15.3	18.7	23.0	28.5	35.3	44	56	27.9	88
89	8.2	12.6	16.4	20.0	24.7	30.5	38	48	61	29.9	89
90	8.8	13.6	17.5	21.4	26.5	32.9	41	52	66	32.0	90
91	9.4	14.8	18.7	23.0	28.5	35.3	44	56	71	34.3	91
92	10.1	16.0	20.0	24.7	30.5	38	48	61	77	36.8	92
93	10.9	17.3	21.4	26.5	32.9	41	52	66	83	39.4	93
94	11.7	18.7	23.0	28.5	35.3	44	56	71	90	42.2	94
95	12.6	20.0	24.7	30.5	38	48	61	77	97	45.3	95
96	13.6	21.4	26.5	32.9	41	52	66	83	105	48.5	96
97	14.8	23.0	28.5	35.3	44	56	71	90	113	52.0	97
98	16.0	24.7	30.5	38	48	61	77	97	121	55.7	98
99	17.3	26.5	32.9	41	52	66	83	105	130	59.7	99
100	18.7	28.5	35.3	44	56	71	90	113	139	64.0	100
101	20.3	30.5	38	48	61	77	97	121	149	68.6	101
102	22.1	32.9	41	52	66	83	105	130	160	73.5	102
103	24.0	35.3	44	56	71	90	113	139	171	78.8	103
104	26.1	38	48	61	77	97	121	149	184	84.4	104
105	28.5	41	52	66	83	105	130	160	197	90.5	105
106	31.0	44	56	71	90	113	139	171	211	97	106
107	33.9	48	61	77	97	121	149	184	226	104	107
108	36.9	52	66	83	105	130	160	197	242	111	108
109	40.3	56	71	90	113	139	171	211	260	119	109
110	44	61	77	97	121	149	184	226	278	128	110
111	49	66	83	105	130	160	197	242	298	137	111
112	54	71	90	113	139	171	211	260	320	147	112
113	59	77	97	121	149	184	226	278	343	158	113
114	65	83	105	130	160	197	242	298	367	169	114
115	71	90	113	139	171	211	260	320		181	115
116	77	97	121	149	184	226	278	343		194	116
117	83	105	130	160	197	242	298	367		208	117
118	90	113	139	171	211	260	320			223	118
119	97	121	149	184	226	278	343			239	119
120	105	130	160	197	242	298	367			256	120
121	113	139	171	211	260	320				274	121
122	121	149	184	226	278	343				294	122
123	130	160	197	242	298	367				315	123
124	139	171	211	260	320					338	124
125	149	184	226	278	343					362	125

The calculated loudness is labeled sones (OD) and the loudness level is labeled phons (OD) to designate that they have been calculated from octave-band levels (O) and for a diffuse field (D).

A similar calculation can be made for third-octave bands, and they are labeled (TD).

For steady noises having a broad frequency spectrum, the loudness calculated by means of the tables, which are based on Steven's* method agrees reasonably well with direct assessments made by loudness balances against a 1000-Hz tone.

To illustrate this procedure, consider the calculations based on octave-band measurements of the noise in a factory (Table 3-2).

For a quick check to find which band contributes most to the loudness, add 3 dB to the band level in the second octave, 6 dB to the third, 9 dB to the fourth, and so on. Then the highest shifted level is usually the dominant band. This check will often be all that is needed to tell where to start in a noise-reduction program, if one doesn't have the loudness calculation charts at hand. This check is not reliable if the levels are low and the low-frequency bands dominate.

*Loc. cit.

26

Table 3-2

SAMPLE BAND LEVEL-TO-LOUDNESS-
INDEX CONVERSIONS

Octave Band No.	Octave Band (Hz)	Band Level (dB)	Band Loudness Index
15	31.5	78	4
18	63	76	5
21	125	78	8
24	250	82	13
27	500	81	14
30	1000	80	16
33	2000	80	20
36	4000	73	15
39	8000	65	11

ΣS = Sum of Band Loudness Indexes   = 106
S_m = Maximum Band Loudness Index   = 20
$0.3\ \Sigma S$ = 31.8
$0.7\ S_m$ = 14

$0.3\ \Sigma S + 0.7\ S_m$ = 46 sones (OD)*
or computed loudness level   = 95 phons (OD)*

*OD = Octave Diffuse (an octave-band analysis for a diffuse field).

Another and more elaborate loudness calculation procedure has been developed by Zwicker (1960) for third-octave analysis. It is not at all clear, however, that this more difficult calculation results in a calculated loudness that is in better agreement with subjective data.

Bauer and his associates (1971) have developed a simpler loudness meter that has been applied to broadcast program monitoring.

3.6 PERCEIVED-NOISE LEVEL.

Kryter (1970) and his co-workers (Kryter and Pearsons, 1963) have followed a procedure similar to that used for loudness, but they asked the observer to compare noises on the basis of their acceptability or their "noisiness." The resulting judgments were found to be similar to those for loudness, but enough difference was noticed to give a somewhat different rating for various sounds. On the basis of these results, Kryter has set up a calculation procedure for "perceived noise level," PNL in dB, also called "PNdB." The corresponding "noisiness" is given in units called "noys."

Ratings in terms of perceived noise level are now widely used for aircraft noise, particularly for aircraft flying overhead. The calculations for aircraft noise are based on levels in third-octave bands and the detailed procedures used are given in FAA regulations and in ISO recommendations.

A number of versions of the perceived-noise-level-calculation procedure have been proposed. The one used here is for octave-band levels (Kryter, 1970). Proceed as follows:

1. Combine on a power basis (use the chart of Figure 2-4), the levels in the 63-Hz and 125-Hz bands. Replace the 125-Hz level by this new level and ignore the 63-Hz level, unless the 63-Hz level was greater than the original 125-Hz level. In the latter case, replace the 63-Hz level by the combined level, and ignore the 125-Hz level.

2. In the frequency range from 500 Hz and up, note if any band level projects above the level in adjacent bands. If the difference between this projecting level and the average level in the two adjacent bands is 3 dB or greater, a correction is required, often called a tone correction.
3. Find the noy values from the appropriate table given by Kryter (1970), table 78 in his book, for the summed bands, the corrected band levels, and the remaining band levels.
4. Add all these noy values (Σ N).
5. Multiply the sum by 0.3.
6. Add this product to 0.7 of the noy value for that band that has the largest noy value ($0.3 \Sigma N + 0.7 N_{max}$).
7. Convert this summed noy value to PNL in dB, by the use of the 1000-Hz noy-to-dB column.

   Here is a sample calculation for the factory noise used previously for a loudness calculation:

Octave Band Center (Hz)	Band Level (dB)	Band Noisiness (noys)
63	76 ⎱ 80.1	
125	78 ⎰	11
250	82	16
500	81	18
1000	80	16
2000	80	28
4000	73	21
8000	65	9

$$\Sigma N = 119$$
$$0.3 \times 119 = 35.7$$
$$0.7 \times 28 = \underline{19.6}$$
$$55.3$$

55.3 noys correspond to 98-dB perceived noise level.

3.7 PERCEIVED LEVEL — STEVENS'S MARK VII.

As a result of his extensive review of the available evidence on "loudness," "annoyance," "noisiness," "acceptability," "objectionability," etc of noise, Stevens (1972) has revised his earlier calculation procedure in a number of important respects.

A 1/3-octave band of noise centered at 3150 Hz is used as the reference sound instead of a 1000-Hz tone, and this sound at a level of 32 dB re 20 μN/m^2 is assigned a perceived magnitude of 1 sone.

An increase in level of 9 dB (it was 10 dB before) in the reference tone doubles the perceived magnitude in sones.

The contours of equal perceived magnitude have been modified and the masking factor in the calculation procedure now varies with level.

Table 3-3*

PERCEIVED MAGNITUDE IN SONES AS A FUNCTION OF BAND PRESSURE LEVEL.

Band Freq (dB)	17 / 50	18 / 63	19 / 80	20 / 100	21 / 125	22 / 160	23 / 200	24 / 250	25 / 315	26–31 / 400–1250	32 / 1600	33 / 2000	34 / 2500	35–39 / 3150–8000	40 / 10 000	41 / 12 500
1														0.078		
2														0.087		
3													0.078	0.097		
4													0.087	0.107		
5												0.078	0.097	0.118	0.078	
6												0.087	0.107	0.129	0.087	
7											0.078	0.097	0.118	0.141	0.097	
8											0.087	0.107	0.129	0.153	0.107	
9										0.078	0.097	0.118	0.141	0.166	0.118	0.078
10										0.087	0.107	0.129	0.153	0.181	0.129	0.087
11										0.097	0.118	0.141	0.166	0.196	0.141	0.097
12										0.107	0.129	0.153	0.181	0.212	0.153	0.107
13									0.077	0.118	0.141	0.166	0.196	0.230	0.166	0.118
14									0.087	0.129	0.153	0.181	0.212	0.248	0.181	0.129
15									0.097	0.141	0.166	0.196	0.230	0.269	0.196	0.141
16									0.107	0.153	0.181	0.212	0.248	0.290	0.212	0.153
17								0.076	0.119	0.166	0.196	0.230	0.269	0.314	0.230	0.166
18								0.086	0.130	0.181	0.212	0.248	0.290	0.339	0.248	0.181
19								0.097	0.143	0.196	0.230	0.269	0.314	0.367	0.269	0.196
20								0.108	0.156	0.212	0.248	0.290	0.339	0.396	0.290	0.212
21							0.075	0.120	0.169	0.230	0.269	0.314	0.367	0.428	0.314	0.230
22							0.086	0.131	0.185	0.248	0.290	0.339	0.396	0.463	0.339	0.248
23							0.097	0.144	0.201	0.269	0.314	0.367	0.428	0.500	0.367	0.269
24							0.108	0.158	0.219	0.290	0.339	0.396	0.463	0.540	0.396	0.290
25						0.074	0.121	0.173	0.237	0.314	0.367	0.428	0.500	0.583	0.428	0.314
26						0.085	0.134	0.190	0.256	0.339	0.396	0.463	0.540	0.630	0.463	0.339
27						0.097	0.147	0.207	0.279	0.367	0.428	0.500	0.583	0.680	0.500	0.367
28						0.110	0.162	0.224	0.302	0.396	0.463	0.540	0.630	0.735	0.540	0.396
29					0.073	0.122	0.178	0.244	0.329	0.428	0.500	0.583	0.680	0.794	0.583	0.428
30					0.085	0.136	0.194	0.267	0.356	0.463	0.540	0.630	0.735	0.857	0.630	0.463
31					0.097	0.149	0.212	0.290	0.384	0.500	0.583	0.680	0.794	0.926	0.680	0.500
32					0.110	0.165	0.233	0.316	0.418	0.540	0.630	0.735	0.857	1.00	0.735	0.540
33				0.072	0.123	0.182	0.254	0.345	0.452	0.583	0.680	0.794	0.926	1.08	0.794	0.583
34				0.084	0.137	0.201	0.277	0.375	0.490	0.630	0.735	0.857	1.00	1.17	0.857	0.630
35				0.097	0.153	0.221	0.304	0.406	0.531	0.680	0.794	0.926	1.08	1.26	0.926	0.680
36				0.111	0.169	0.241	0.332	0.442	0.576	0.735	0.857	1.00	1.17	1.36	1.00	0.735
37			0.070	0.125	0.187	0.264	0.361	0.481	0.624	0.794	0.926	1.08	1.26	1.47	1.08	0.794
38			0.084	0.140	0.207	0.290	0.396	0.523	0.676	0.857	1.00	1.17	1.36	1.59	1.17	0.857
39			0.097	0.156	0.228	0.319	0.431	0.570	0.732	0.926	1.08	1.26	1.47	1.72	1.26	0.926
40			0.112	0.173	0.250	0.350	0.470	0.618	0.794	1.00	1.17	1.36	1.59	1.85	1.36	1.00
41			0.126	0.193	0.277	0.381	0.511	0.672	0.860	1.08	1.26	1.47	1.71	2.00	1.47	1.08
42			0.142	0.214	0.304	0.418	0.561	0.729	0.933	1.17	1.36	1.59	1.85	2.16	1.59	1.17
43			0.160	0.237	0.337	0.459	0.611	0.794	1.01	1.26	1.47	1.71	2.00	2.33	1.71	1.26
44		0.079	0.178	0.262	0.370	0.504	0.665	0.864	1.10	1.36	1.59	1.85	2.16	2.52	1.85	1.36

*From S. S. Stevens, "Perceived Level of Noise by Mark VII and Decibels (E)", *The Journal of Acoustical Society of America*, Vol. 51 No. 2 (Part 2) Feb, 1972, pp 594-596. Reprinted with permission.

Table 3-3 (Continued)
PERCEIVED MAGNITUDE IN SONES AS A FUNCTION OF BAND PRESSURE LEVEL.

Band Freq	17 50	18 63	19 30	20 100	21 125	22 160	23 200	24 250	25 315	26–31 400–1250	32 1600	3.3 2000	34 2500	35–39 3150–8000	40 10 000	41 12 500
45		0.092	0.199	0.290	0.406	0.552	0.727	0.938	1.18	1.47	1.71	2.00	2.33	2.72	2.00	1.47
46		0.107	0.222	0.321	0.448	0.606	0.794	1.02	1.28	1.59	1.85	2.16	2.52	2.94	2.16	1.59
47		0.121	0.246	0.356	0.492	0.660	0.866	1.10	1.39	1.71	2.00	2.33	2.72	3.18	2.33	1.71
48		0.138	0.275	0.393	0.540	0.724	0.945	1.20	1.50	1.85	2.16	2.52	2.94	3.43	2.52	1.85
49		0.156	0.307	0.435	0.597	0.794	1.03	1.31	1.64	2.00	2.33	2.72	3.18	3.70	2.72	2.00
50	0.072	0.176	0.341	0.481	0.655	0.871	1.12	1.42	1.77	2.16	2.52	2.94	3.43	4.00	2.94	2.16
51	0.086	0.197	0.378	0.531	0.724	0.955	1.23	1.55	1.91	2.33	2.72	3.18	3.70	4.32	3.18	2.33
52	0.101	0.222	0.422	0.588	0.794	1.04	1.34	1.69	2.08	2.52	2.94	3.43	4.00	4.67	3.43	2.52
53	0.117	0.250	0.468	0.649	0.871	1.14	1.46	1.82	2.26	2.72	3.18	3.70	4.32	5.04	3.70	2.72
54	0.134	0.279	0.519	0.718	0.962	1.25	1.59	1.98	2.44	2.94	3.43	4.00	4.67	5.44	4.00	2.94
55	0.152	0.314	0.579	0.794	1.06	1.37	1.74	2.16	2.64	3.18	3.70	4.32	5.04	5.88	4.32	3.18
56	0.175	0.347	0.643	0.877	1.17	1.50	1.90	2.35	2.85	3.43	4.00	4.67	5.44	6.35	4.67	3.43
57	0.197	0.390	0.714	0.970	1.28	1.65	2.06	2.56	3.10	3.70	4.32	5.04	5.88	6.86	5.04	3.70
58	0.222	0.435	0.794	1.07	1.40	1.80	2.26	2.78	3.35	4.00	4.67	5.44	6.35	7.41	5.44	4.00
59	0.250	0.488	0.882	1.18	1.55	1.97	2.46	3.01	3.65	4.32	5.04	5.88	6.86	8.00	5.88	4.32
60	0.282	0.544	0.977	1.31	1.70	2.16	2.68	3.27	3.94	4.67	5.44	6.35	7.41	8.64	6.35	4.67
61	0.319	0.611	1.09	1.45	1.87	2.37	2.94	3.56	4.27	5.04	5.88	6.86	8.00	9.33	6.86	5.04
62	0.358	0.686	1.21	1.60	2.06	2.60	3.20	3.88	4.63	5.44	6.35	7.41	8.64	10.1	7.41	5.44
63	0.402	0.762	1.34	1.77	2.26	2.83	3.48	4.22	5.00	5.88	6.86	8.00	9.33	10.9	8.00	5.88
64	0.454	0.851	1.49	1.95	2.50	3.10	3.79	4.58	5.44	6.35	7.41	8.64	10.1	11.8	9.64	6.35
65	0.511	0.952	1.66	2.16	2.74	3.40	4.16	4.98	5.88	6.86	8.00	9.33	10.9	12.7	9.33	6.86
66	0.574	1.06	1.84	2.39	3.01	3.73	4.52	5.40	6.37	7.41	8.64	10.1	11.8	13.7	10.1	7.41
67	0.649	1.18	2.05	2.64	3.32	4.09	4.94	5.88	6.91	8.00	9.33	10.9	12.7	14.8	10.9	8.00
68	0.729	1.33	2.28	2.92	3.65	4.47	5.40	6.40	7.48	8.64	10.1	11.8	13.7	16.0	11.8	8.64
69	0.818	1.48	2.54	3.22	4.02	4.89	5.88	6.96	8.10	9.33	10.9	12.7	14.8	17.3	12.7	9.33
70	0.921	1.66	2.81	3.56	4.42	5.36	6.40	7.55	8.78	10.1	11.8	13.7	16.0	18.7	13.7	10.1
71	1.03	1.87	3.13	3.94	4.85	5.88	7.00	8.21	9.51	10.9	12.7	14.8	17.3	20.2	14.8	10.9
72	1.16	2.08	3.48	4.35	5.34	6.45	7.64	8.91	10.3	11.8	13.7	16.0	18.7	21.8	16.0	11.8
73	1.32	2.33	3.85	4.81	5.88	7.07	8.33	9.70	11.1	12.7	14.8	17.3	20.2	23.5	17.3	12.7
74	1.48	2.58	4.29	5.32	6.47	7.70	9.09	10.6	12.1	13.7	16.0	18.7	21.8	25.4	18.7	13.7
75	1.66	2.90	4.76	5.88	7.13	8.46	9.92	11.5	13.1	14.8	17.3	20.2	23.5	27.4	20.2	14.8
76	1.87	3.24	5.28	6.50	7.82	9.26	10.8	12.5	14.1	16.0	18.7	21.8	25.4	29.6	21.8	16.0
77	2.10	3.62	5.88	7.18	8.61	10.2	11.8	13.5	15.4	17.3	20.2	23.5	27.4	32.0	23.5	17.3
78	2.37	4.03	6.53	7.94	9.48	11.1	12.9	14.7	16.6	18.7	21.8	25.4	29.6	34.6	25.4	18.7
79	2.66	4.52	7.26	8.78	10.4	12.2	14.0	16.0	18.0	20.2	23.5	27.4	32.0	37.3	27.4	20.2
80	2.99	5.05	8.06	9.70	11.5	13.3	15.3	17.3	19.4	21.8	25.4	29.6	34.6	40.3	29.6	21.8
81	3.35	5.64	8.95	10.7	12.6	14.6	16.6	18.7	21.0	23.5	27.4	32.0	37.3	43.5	32.0	23.5
82	3.79	6.31	9.96	11.8	13.8	16.0	18.0	20.2	22.6	25.4	29.6	34.6	40.3	47.0	34.6	25.4
83	4.25	7.05	11.1	13.1	15.3	17.3	19.4	21.8	24.4	27.4	32.0	37.3	43.5	50.8	37.3	27.4
84	4.79	7.88	12.3	14.5	16.6	18.7	21.0	23.5	26.4	29.6	34.6	40.3	47.0	54.9	40.3	29.6

Table 3-3 (Continued)
PERCEIVED MAGNITUDE IN SONES AS A FUNCTION OF BAND PRESSURE LEVEL.

Band Freq	17 50	18 63	19 80	20 100	21 125	22 160	23 200	24 250	25 315	26–31 400–1250	32 1600	33 2000	34 2500	35–39 3150–8000	40 10 000	41 12 500
85	5.40	8.81	13.7	16.0	18.0	20.2	22.6	25.4	28.5	32.0	37.3	43.5	50.8	59.3	43.5	32.0
86	6.06	9.85	15.2	17.3	19.4	21.8	24.4	27.4	30.8	34.6	40.3	47.0	54.9	64.0	47.0	34.6
87	6.82	11.0	16.6	18.7	21.0	23.5	26.4	29.6	33.3	37.3	43.5	50.8	59.3	69.1	50.8	37.3
88	7.68	12.3	18.0	20.2	22.6	25.4	28.5	32.0	35.9	40.3	47.0	54.9	64.0	74.7	54.9	40.3
89	8.64	13.8	19.4	21.8	24.4	27.4	30.8	34.6	38.8	43.5	50.8	59.3	69.1	80.6	59.3	43.5
90	9.71	15.4	21.0	23.5	26.4	29.6	33.3	37.3	41.9	47.0	54.9	64.0	74.9	87.1	64.0	47.0
91	10.9	16.8	22.6	25.4	28.5	32.0	35.9	40.3	45.2	50.8	59.3	69.1	80.6	94.1	69.1	50.8
92	12.3	18.3	24.4	27.4	30.8	34.6	38.8	43.5	48.9	54.9	64.0	74.7	87.1	102	74.7	54.9
93	13.8	19.8	26.4	29.6	33.3	37.3	41.9	47.0	52.8	59.3	69.1	80.6	94.1	110	80.6	59.3
94	15.6	21.5	28.5	32.0	35.9	40.3	45.2	50.8	57.1	64.0	74.7	87.1	102	119	87.1	64.0
95	17.1	23.3	30.8	34.6	38.8	43.5	48.9	54.9	61.6	69.1	80.6	94.1	110	128	94.1	69.1
96	18.6	25.3	33.3	37.3	41.9	47.0	52.8	59.3	66.6	74.7	87.1	102	119	138	102	74.7
97	20.3	27.4	35.9	40.3	45.3	50.8	57.1	64.0	71.9	80.6	94.1	110	128	149	110	80.6
98	22.1	29.8	38.8	43.5	48.9	54.9	61.6	69.1	77.6	87.1	102	119	138	161	119	87.1
99	24.1	32.3	41.9	47.0	52.8	59.3	66.6	74.7	83.8	94.1	110	128	149	174	128	94.1
100	26.3	35.1	45.3	50.8	57.1	64.0	71.9	80.6	90.6	102	119	138	161	188	138	102
101	28.6	38.0	48.9	54.9	61.6	69.1	77.6	87.1	98.0	110	128	149	174	203	149	110
102	31.2	41.2	52.8	59.3	66.6	74.7	83.8	94.1	106	119	138	161	188	219	161	119
103	34.0	44.7	57.0	64.0	71.9	80.6	90.6	102	114	128	149	174	203	237	174	128
104	37.0	48.5	61.6	69.1	77.6	87.1	98.0	110	124	138	161	188	219	256	188	138
105	40.4	52.4	66.5	74.7	83.8	94.1	106	119	133	149	174	203	237	276	203	149
106	44.0	57.0	71.8	80.6	90.6	102	114	128	144	161	188	219	256	299	219	161
107	48.0	61.8	77.6	87.1	98.0	110	124	138	155	174	203	237	276	323	237	174
108	52.3	67.1	83.8	94.1	106	119	133	149	168	188	219	256	299	348	256	188
109	57.0	72.8	90.5	102	114	128	144	161	181	203	237	276	323	376	276	203
110	62.1	78.9	97.8	110	124	138	155	174	196	219	256	299	348	406	299	219
111	67.5	85.6	106	119	133	149	168	188	211	237	276	323	376	439	323	237
112	73.8	92.9	114	128	144	161	181	203	228	256	299	348	406	474	348	256
113	80.5	101	123	138	155	174	196	219	246	276	323	376	439	512	376	276
114	87.8	109	133	149	168	188	211	237	266	299	348	406	474	553	406	299
115	95.6	119	144	161	181	203	228	256	288	323	376	439	512	597	439	323
116	104	129	155	174	196	219	246	276	311	348	406	474	553	645	474	348
117	114	139	168	188	211	237	266	299	336	376	439	512	597	697	512	376
118	124	152	181	203	228	256	288	323	362	406	474	553	645	752	553	406
119	135	164	196	219	246	276	311	348	391	439	512	597	697	813	597	439
120	147	178	211	237	266	299	336	376	422	474	553	645	752	878	645	474
121	160	193	228	256	288	323	362	406	456	512	597	697	813	948	697	512
122	175	209	246	276	311	348	391	439	493	553	645	752	878	1024	752	553
123	190	227	266	299	336	376	422	474	532	597	697	813	948	1106	813	597
124	207	246	287	323	362	406	456	512	575	645	752	878	1024	1194	878	645

Table 3-4*[†]
F vs SONES IN ONE-THIRD O.B.

Sones	F	Sones	F
0.181	0.10	8.64	0.230
0.196	0.122	9.33	0.226
0.212	0.140	10.1	0.222
0.230	0.158	10.9	0.217
0.248	0.174	11.8	0.212
0.269	0.187	12.7	0.208
0.290	0.200	13.7	0.204
0.314	0.212	14.8	0.200
0.339	0.222	16.0	0.197
0.367	0.232	17.3	0.195
0.396	0.241	18.7	0.194
0.428	0.250	20.2	0.193
0.463	0.259	21.8	0.192
0.500	0.267	23.5	0.191
0.540	0.274	25.4	0.190
0.583	0.281	27.4	0.190
0.630	0.287	29.6	0.190
0.680	0.293	32.0	0.190
0.735	0.298	34.6	0.190
0.794	0.303	37.3	0.190
0.857	0.308	40.3	0.191
0.926	0.312	43.5	0.191
1.00	0.316	47.0	0.192
1.08	0.319	50.8	0.193
1.17	0.320	54.9	0.194
1.26	0.322	59.3	0.195
1.36	0.322	64.0	0.197
1.47	0.320	69.1	0.199
1.59	0.319	74.7	0.201
1.72	0.317	80.6	0.203
1.85	0.314	87.1	0.205
2.00	0.311	94.1	0.208
2.16	0.308	102	0.210
2.33	0.304	110	0.212
2.52	0.300	119	0.215
2.72	0.296	128	0.217
2.94	0.292	138	0.219
3.18	0.288	149	0.221
3.43	0.284	161	0.223
3.70	0.279	174	0.224
4.00	0.275	188	0.225
4.32	0.270	203	0.226
4.67	0.266	219	0.227
5.04	0.262	237	0.227
5.44	0.258	256	0.227
5.88	0.253	.	
6.35	0.248	.	
6.86	0.244	.	
7.41	0.240	.	
8.00	0.235	.	

*The factor F as a function of the number of sones in the 1/3-octave band that is maximally loud or noisy. The value of F remains constant above 219 sones.

[†]From S. S. Stevens, "Perceived Level of Noise by Mark VII and Decibels (E)," *The Journal of Acoustical Society of America,* Vol 51 No. 2 (Part 2) Feb 1972, p 597. Reprinted with permission.

To calculate the perceived level and magnitude of a noise by the Mark VII procedure, proceed as follows:

1. From Table 3-3 find the proper perceived magnitude in sones for each band level.
2. From the maximum of these perceived magnitudes, Sm, find the factor, F, from Table 3-4. If octave-band levels are used, subtract 4.9 dB from the level of the loudest band; find the corresponding sone value; use this value for finding the factor F; double the value found in the table, and use it as F.
3. Add all the perceived magnitudes (ΣS); subtract the maximum, S_m.
4. Multiply the sum by the factor F.
5. Add this product to the maximum perceived magnitude, $S_t = (1-F) \bullet S_m + F \Sigma S$. This value is the total perceived magnitude in sones.
6. Convert this magnitude to perceived level in dB from Table 3-3 by the use of the 3150-Hz column.

This new perceived level will be about 8 dB less than that obtained for the loudness level in the Mark VI calculation procedure. This shift is a result of the use of a reference signal at 3150 Hz.

Here is a sample calculation for the factory noise used previously for the loudness calculation:

Octave Band Center (Hz)	Band Level (dB)	Perceived Magnitude (sones)
31.5	78	
63	76	3.2
125	78	9.5
250	82	20.2
500	81	23.5
1000	80	21.8
2000	80	29.6
4000	73	23.5
8000	65	12.7

ΣS = 144.0

ΣS - S_m = 114.4

Adjusted band level = 80 - 4.9 = 75.1 dB

Corresponding perceived

magnitude at 2000 Hz = 20.4 sones

2 X F = 2 X .193 = .386

.386 X 114.4 = 44.2

S_m = 29.6

S_t = 73.8 sones

PL = 87.8 dB

3.8 EFFECT OF TONAL COMPONENTS.

When a noise is a mixture of random noise and audible tonal components, the loudness or annoyance may be somewhat greater than expected from the direct analysis and calculation schemes (Kryter and Pearsons, 1963; Wells, 1969). The effect is usually taken into account by a correction of the calculated level, but it normally requires a detailed analysis of the sound at least equivalent to that of a third-octave analysis.

3.9 EFFECT OF DURATION.

If we are talking with someone and we are interrupted by a noise that interferes seriously with speech, it is more annoying if it lasts for a long time than if it is very brief. In order to take this effect into account a number of procedures have been suggested (Pietrasanta and Stevens, 1958; Young, 1968; Kryter, 1968). Most of them are, in effect, an integration (on a power basis) of the loudness, perceived noise, or A-weighted sound pressure over time.

These procedures are still not well validated. Some qualifying term, for example, "Effective Perceived Noise Level" is often used to indicate that a correction for duration has been made.

3.10 NC CURVES.

Another rating procedure, which uses "noise-criterion curves," was developed by Beranek (1957) for design goals for satisfactory background noise inside office buildings and in rooms and halls of various types. It is helpful in deciding where in the spectrum additional effort is required in noise reduction, in order to make the noise acceptable.

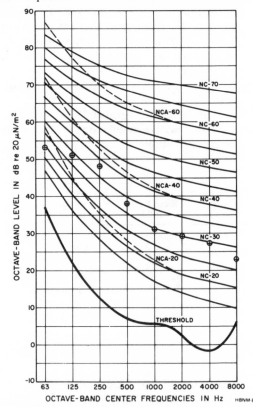

Figure 3-6. Noise-criteria curves.

A set of these NC Curves (Schultz, 1968; ASHRAE, 1967) are shown in Figure 3-6. A threshold curve for octave bands of noise (Robinson and Whittle, 1964), is also shown for reference.

In use, the measured spectrum is plotted on the chart. Each band level is then compared with the NC curves to find the one that penetrates to the highest NC level. The corresponding value on the NC curve is the NC rating of the noise.

As an example, the measured background noise level of an office is shown on the figure as encircled crosses. This noise would have a rating of NC-38. Since a recommended range of NC-30 to NC-40 has been suggested for an executive office (ASHRAE, 1967, p. 379), it would be considered acceptable for that purpose. But if one were to turn it into a conference room, as is sometimes done with large offices, it would not be as acceptable. Here, the

34

recommended range is NC-25 to NC-35. If one were to try to reduce the noise level to make it more acceptable it is clear from the chart that one should try to find the source of noise in the prominent 250-Hz band and work to reduce that level.

The dashed NCA curves on the figure indicate the direction in which a compromise should be made if economic considerations preclude achieving the normal criterion given by the NC curve.

3.11 NOISE AND NUMBER INDEX.

Another rating for aircraft noise, called NNI, noise and number index, is based on perceived noise levels. It was developed in Great Britain (Committee on the Problem of Noise, 1963) and takes into account the effect of the number of aircraft per day on the annoyance. It is defined by the following relation:

NNI = (Average Peak Perceived Noise Level) + 15 $(\log_{10} N)$ −80

where N is the number of aircraft per day or night. The value 80 is subtracted to bring the index to about 0 for conditions of no annoyance.

The "Average Peak Perceived Noise Level" is obtained in the following way. The maximum perceived noise level that occurs during the passage of each airplane is noted. These maximum levels are then converted into equivalent power and averaged (Section 2.6). This average value is then converted back into a level and used in the equation.

If the perceived noise level is approximated by the use of A-weighted sound levels, the average A-level is obtained in a similar fashion, the 80 is reduced to about 67, and we have

NNI $\simeq$ (Average Peak A-Level) + 15 $(\log_{10} N)$ −67.

3.12 NOISE-POLLUTION LEVEL.

Robinson (1969 and 1971) reviews a number of the measures derived in various countries for rating a composite noise history. He lists the following measures: Noise and number index, Composite noise rating, *Storindex*, Indice de Classification, Aircraft Noise Exposure index, Noisiness index, Aircraft Exposure level, Annoyance index, Traffic Noise index, Equivalent Disturbance level, Office Noise Acceptability Scale, and Noise Imission level. Most of these are closely related.

He generalizes these measures into a new measure called "Noise Pollution Level," which is expressed by the relation

$$L_{np} = L_{eq} + 2.56 \, \sigma$$

where L_{eq} is the noise level over a specified period averaged on an energy basis, and σ is the standard deviation (rms, see paragraph 5.5.1) of the instantaneous level about that average value over the same period. (The coefficient of σ is not as accurate as the precision shown, but it was selected by Robinson from a range of possible values to yield a simple relation for certain noise-level distributions.)

The noise level used in the expression can be the A-weighted level, the loudness level, or some other similar level.

In the calculation of noise-pollution level, the time period is to be one in which similar conditions prevail. Thus, for example, night and day would be treated separately.

35

This noise-pollution level is another way of looking at a noise history and it yields results that are similar to the others. The variety of these measures reflects the considerable activity in this area and the fact that many factors enter into the effects that are to be predicted. Different measures are now standardized and used by different groups. Since it is unlikely that a close correspondence will be found between the effects and a combination of physical measurements (Hazard, 1971), some general agreement on a relatively simple relation is urgently needed.

3.13 MASKING — "I CAN'T HEAR YOU WHEN THE WATER'S RUNNING."

It is common experience to have one sound completely drowned out when another louder noise occurs. For example, during the early evening when a fluorescent light is on, the ballast noise may not be heard, because of the usual background noise level in the evening. But late at night when there is much less activity and correspondingly less noise, the ballast noise may become relatively very loud and annoying. Actually, the noise level produced by the ballast may be the same in the two instances. But psychologically the noise is louder at night, because there is less of the masking noise that reduces its apparent loudness.

Experimenters have found that the masking effect of a sound is greatest upon those sounds close to it in frequency (Egan and Hake, 1950; Fletcher, 1953). At low levels the masking effect covers a relatively narrow region of frequencies. At higher levels, above 60 dB, say, the masking effect spreads out to cover a wide range, mainly for frequencies above the frequencies of the dominating components. In other words, the masking effect is asymmetrical with respect to frequency. Noises that include a wide range of frequencies will correspondingly be effective in masking over a wide-frequency range.

3.13.1 Speech-Interference Level.
Most of us have been in locations where it was impossible to hear over a telephone because the noise level was too high; and, in order to hear, production machinery had to be turned off, resulting in time and money lost. Even direct discussions can be difficult and tiring because of excessive noise. Excessive noise may make it impossible to give danger warnings by shouting or to give directions to workers. Serious problems may occur because of speech interference from noisy machinery while training employees to operate the machinery.

In a large classroom with heavy acoustical treatment, particularly in the ceiling, the attenuation may be so great that the teacher at one end can be but poorly heard through the background noise at the other end, even though the noise is not very great.

Incidentally, other factors also affect speech intelligibility. In a live room, speech syllables are smeared by reflected sound, and the intelligibility is consequently reduced.

Because of the annoyance of interference with speech and also because noise interferes with work where speech communication is necessary, a noise rating based on the speech-interference level is frequently useful. We should know how to improve speech communication in a noisy place. In order to effect this improvement we shall find it useful to evaluate the speech-interference level of a noise. How this can be done will appear from a consideration of how noise interferes with speech.

Noise interference with speech is usually a masking process. The background noise increases our threshold of hearing, and, as a result, we may hear

36

only a few or perhaps none of the sounds necessary for satisfactory intelligibility.

The consonants contain most of the information in speech, but, unfortunately, they are more readily masked than vowels, because they are weaker than vowels. Noise of a certain level may mask some speech sounds and not others, depending on the talking level, the particular sound, and the relative frequency distribution of the sound and of the noise.

The energy of the various speech sounds is distributed over the frequency range from below 100 to above 10,000 Hz. The actual instantaneous distribution depends on the particular speech sound. For example, the "s" sound has its energy broadly distributed in the range from 4000 to beyond 8000 Hz. In contrast, most of the energy in the "ee" sound of "speech" is distributed in fairly definite groups (called "formants") below 4000 Hz. All the frequency range of speech sounds is not necessary, however, for complete intelligibility. A number of experimenters have shown that nearly all the information in speech is contained in the frequency region from 200 to 6000 Hz.

In any frequency subdivision that we may make of this range, the sound-pressure levels vary over a range of about 30 dB, as successive sounds occur. Tests on the intelligibility of speech show that, if we can hear the full 30-dB range in each of the frequency bands into which speech is divided, the contribution to intelligibility by that band will be 100 percent. If, however, noise limits the range that can be heard to only 15 dB, the contribution will be about 50%, and so forth. Furthermore, if the range between 200 to 6000 Hz is divided into a large number of frequency bands of equal importance to speech intelligibility, the total contribution to speech intelligibility is equal to the average of the contributions from the individual bands. This quantity is called the articulation index, because it is a measure of the percentage of the total possible .information that we might have perceived of importance to speech intelligibility (French et al, 1947; Beranek, 1947; Kryter, 1962; ANSI S3.5-1969).

For many noises, the measurement and calculation can be simplified even further by the use of a three-band analysis (Beranek, 1947). The bands chosen are the octave bands centered on 500, 1000, and 2000 Hz.* The arithmetic average of the sound-pressure levels in these three bands gives the quantity called the three-band preferred octave speech-interference level (PSIL). One can use this level for determining when speech communication or telephone use is easy, difficult, or impossible, and one can determine what changes in level are necessary to shift from one order of difficulty to a lower order.

Face-To-Face Communication. For satisfactory intelligibility of difficult speech material, maximum permissible values of speech-interference levels for men with average voice strengths are given in Figure 3-7, which is an extension by Webster of Beranek's work (Webster, 1969).

It is assumed in this chart that there are no reflecting surfaces nearby, that the speaker is facing the listener, and that the spoken material is not already familiar to the listener. For example, the speech-interference level of the factory noise in paragraph 3.5.4 is 80 dB, which is high, and the chart

---

*The bands used before the shift to the currently preferred series were 600-1200, 1200-2400, and 2400-4800 Hz, or those three bands plus the band from 300 to 600 Hz. The results of the two measures are similar, but some shift in the reference values is necessary (Webster, 1965, 1969).

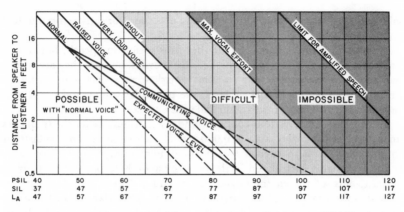

Figure 3-7. Rating chart for determining speech communication capability from speech interference levels. (By permission, Webster, 1969.)

indicates that the two people must ordinarily be no more than two feet apart in order to be understood satisfactorily. If the words spoken are carefully selected and limited in number, intelligible speech will be possible at greater distances.

If a number of conversations are to be held in the same reverberant room, the procedure is more complicated. This chart cannot be used on the basis of the background-noise level before the conversations are in progress, because a given conversation will be subject to interference from the noise produced by all the other conversations. The general procedure for calculating a speech-interference level under those conditions has not been completely worked out.

Telephone Usability in Noisy Areas. The speech-interference level can also be used to predict the expected usability of a telephone under given noise conditions. The following schedule has been found generally satisfactory, when the F-1 Western Electric handset is used for long-distance or suburban calls.

Speech-Interference Level	Telephone Use
less than 60 dB	Satisfactory
60 to 75 dB	Difficult
above 80 dB	Impossible

For calls within a single exchange, the permissible speech-interference levels are 5 dB greater than those shown.

Criteria for Indoor Noise Levels. A suggested rating system for offices, based on a number of psychological and acoustical tests, is shown in Figure 3-8. The curves on this graph relate the measured speech-interference level of the background noise and the subjective rating of the noise ranging from "very quiet" to "intolerably noisy." The two different rating curves illustrate that the environment influences the subjective rating. In order to be rated "noisy" the noise level must be appreciably higher in a large office than in a private office.

It can be expected that the probability of receiving complaints about noise will be high for subjective ratings above "moderately noisy" and low for

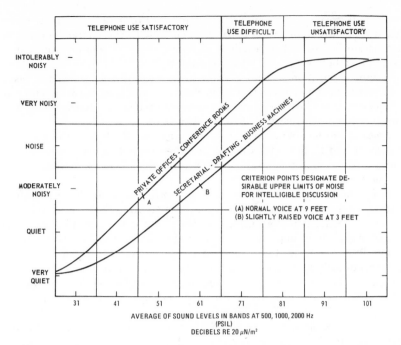

Figure 3-8. Rating chart for office noises. Data were determined by an octave-band analysis and correlated with subjective tests. (Courtesy Beranek and Newman, but modified for preferred bands).

subjective ratings below "moderately noisy." Furthermore, because of direct interference with transferring information, efficiency may be reduced for levels appreciably above the criterion points marked A and B.

Suggested criteria for noise control in terms of maximum permissible speech-interference level (PSIL), measured when the room is not in use, are given in Table 3-5.

The purpose of these criteria will be shown by the following example. Assume that we are to put a small conference room in a factory space. We measure the speech-interference level at that location and find it to be 69 dB, whereas the suggested speech-interference level criterion for a small conference room is 35 dB. The room must then be designed to attenuate the noise

———— **Table 3-5** ————
CRITERIA FOR NOISE CONTROL

Type of Room	Maximum Permissible PSIL (measured when room is not in use)
Small Private Office	45
Conference Room for 20	35
Conference Room for 50	30
Movie Theatre	35
Theatres for Drama (500 seats, no amplification)	30
Coliseum for Sports Only (Amplification)	55
Concert Halls (No amplification)	25
Secretarial Offices (Typing)	60
Homes (Sleeping Areas)	30
Assembly Halls (No amplification)	30
School Rooms	30

39

from the factory space by about 34 dB, in order to have a conference room that will be satisfactory as far as background noise level is concerned (such an attenuation is provided by a double-plastered, three- or four-inch thick stud wall, or by a hollow-tile wall plastered on one side).

A similar but more extensive set of such criteria for noise control, based on A-weighted sound levels, is given in the *Guide and Data Book Systems and Equipment*, 1967, of the American Society of Heating, Refrigerating and Air-Conditioning Engineers. (ASHRAE, 1967).

Privacy. Privacy of conversation is often desired both in the home or apartment and in business. The use of extensive and carefully constructed sound isolation is the safest way to ensure privacy. This approach is expensive, however.

If the noise level outside an executive office is relatively high, only a moderate amount of isolation may be needed to bring the speech level from the office to the point outside the office where it is masked by the background noise. It is important then that the executive office have a background PSIL below 45 dB, in order to avoid encouraging a raised voice level. An exceptionally low background noise level, however, may make it possible for the one in the office to hear those outside, and he will then feel that his office is not private even though it may be so in fact. The inverse may also be true.

If his air conditioner is exceptionally noisy, he may feel that his speech will be covered by the noise. But if the adjacent space is relatively quiet, he may be overheard. In fact, privacy in offices depends on some background noise as well as isolation and distance (Cavanaugh, et al, 1962; Young, 1965), and mutual privacy is often essential. This approach to privacy sometimes requires that noise be introduced, often conveniently by way of turbulent noise from a ventilator grill (Waller, 1969).

3.14 CRITICAL RATIO AND CRITICAL BANDWIDTH.

Early studies of masking led Fletcher (1953) to define a critical bandwidth for hearing. He measured the threshold of pure tones masked by wide bands of noise whose frequency range spread about that of the tone. In the comparison of the levels of the tone and the noise, he used the spectrum level of the noise, which is the level that would be obtained if the noise were filtered through an ideal filter 1-Hz wide (see Chapter 5). He found that, for a wide range of levels, the difference between the threshold level of the masked tone and the spectrum level of the noise was a constant. This constant is now often called a critical ratio. It varies with the frequency of the pure tone, from about 17 dB at 300 Hz to about 28 dB at 8000 Hz (Hawkins et al, 1950). At frequencies below about 500 Hz, the ratio does not change much with frequency.

Fletcher tried narrowing the bandwidth of the noise but with its frequency range centered on the frequency of the tone. He found that above a certain critical bandwidth the critical ratio was reasonably independent of the bandwidth. Below this critical bandwidth the critical ratio decreased, that is, the tone could be more readily heard in the noise. This experiment led to the concept that masking by a noise is mainly a result of the noise energy within a certain frequency band.

The early values quoted for this critical bandwidth are small, being about 50-Hz wide at 250 Hz and 500 Hz, increasing to about 600 Hz at 8000 Hz.

Since then, the results of many experiments have shown large enough variations to cast doubt on the reliability of the critical-band measurement by this technique (de Boer, 1962; Green and Swets, 1966).

Other psychoacoustical measurements have led to specifications of critical bands that are appreciably wider than those quoted above. For example, the loudness of a band of noise is observed as a function of the bandwidth of the noise with constant overall level. The experiments show that up to a certain critical bandwidth the loudness is essentially independent of the bandwidth. Beyond that point the loudness increases with constant over-all sound-pressure level (Zwicker et al, 1957). This critical bandwidth is relatively independent of the level.

This loudness critical band is found to be about 90 Hz wide, centered at 100 Hz, 110 Hz at 500 Hz, and thereafter increasing to about 2300 Hz at 10,000 Hz. Over much of the range it can be reasonably well approximated by a one-third octave. The Zwicker method of loudness calculation is based in part on use of these critical bands (Zwicker, 1960).

3.15 ADDITIONAL HEARING CHARACTERISTICS.

In addition to the characteristics already described, numerous others have been investigated, and a few of these are of interest in noise-measurement problems. Therefore, we shall discuss briefly differential sensitivity for intensity and the pitch scale.

3.15.1 Differential Sensitivity for Intensity.
One question that comes up in quieting a noisy place or device is: "Just how little a change in level is worth bothering with? Is a one-decibel change significant, or does it need to be twenty decibels?" This question is partially answered in the section on loudness, but there is additional help in the following psychoacoustical evidence. Psychologists have devised various experiments to determine what change in level will usually be noticed (Stevens, 1951). When two different levels are presented to the observer under laboratory conditions with little delay between them, the observer can notice as small a difference as 1/4 dB for a 1000-Hz tone at high levels. This sensitivity to change varies with level and the frequency, but over the range of most interest this differential sensitivity is about 1/4 to 1 dB. For a wide-band random noise (a "hishing" sound) a similar test gives a value of about 1/2 dB for sound-pressure levels of 30 to 100 dB (re 20 μN/m^2). Under everyday conditions, a 1-dB change in level is likely to be the minimum detectable by an average observer. On the basis of these tests, we can conclude that 1-dB total change in level is hardly worth much, although 6 is usually significant. It should be remembered, however, that many noise problems are solved by a number of small reductions in level. There is also the importance of a change in character of the noise. For example, the high-frequency level of a noise may be reduced markedly by acoustic treatment, but, because of strong low-frequency components, the over-all level may not change appreciably. Nevertheless, the resultant effect may be very much worthwhile. This example illustrates one reason for making a frequency analysis of a noise before drawing conclusions about the noise.

3.15.2 Pitch and Mels.
Just as they have done for loudness, psychologists have experimentally determined a scale for pitch (Stevens et al, 1937). The unit for this scale is the "mel" (from "melody"), and a 1000-Hz tone at a

level of 40 dB is said to have a pitch of 1000 mels. In terms of frequency, this pitch scale is found to be approximately linear below 1000-Hz and approximately logarithmic above 1000-Hz. Some people have suggested that a frequency analysis with bands of equal width in mels would be more efficient for some types of noise analysis than would one with bands of other widths. At present no commercial analyzers of this type are available, but some work has been done using such an analysis. In addition, the pitch scale has been found useful for some types of charts.

3.16 WEIGHTED SOUND LEVELS.

Rating noise by loudness level, perceived-noise level, perceived level, speech-interference level, or a noise-criterion curve is sufficiently complex that simpler techniques have been sought. Often the simpler approach is to return to the earlier procedures, that is, to use one or two of the presently available weightings on the sound-level meter when rating noises of similar character. The A-weighted sound level has been the most successful of these measures (Young, 1958, 1964; Parkin, 1965; Botsford, 1969).

Another suggested approach is to use a new weighting characteristic, and some of these will be described briefly before reviewing the relative success of weighting networks and their limitations.

3.16.1 Other Weighting Characteristics. Among a number of weighting characteristics that have been suggested recently, N, D or D_1, and D_2 have been proposed for estimating perceived-noise level (Kryter, 1970, Kryter and Pearsons, 1963) E (for Ear) has been suggested for perceived level (Stevens, 1972) and SI is proposed for speech interference (Webster, 1969). These weighting characteristics are shown plotted in Figure 3-9 along with the

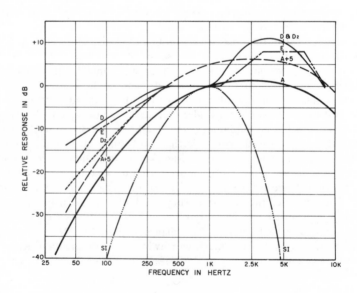

HBNM-9

Figure 3-9. A weighting and other proposed weightings.

42

standard A-weighting. The N weighting is not shown, since it is the same as the D weighting but raised in level by 7 dB (Batchelder, 1968).

The A-weighting raised by 5-dB is also shown for comparison. It is easy to see that the trends of the D, D_2, and E weightings are similar to that of the A. As a result, if we are concerned mainly with rank ordering noises whose energy is widely distributed over the frequency range, we would not expect marked differences in usefulness among these weightings.

3.16.2 Comparison of Calculation Schemes and Weighted Levels. We shall discuss briefly a number of techniques for the following tasks:

1. Predict a subjective effect of any of a variety of noises including a reference tone or narrow band of noise.
2. Rank order any of a variety of common noises for a particular subjective effect.
3. Rank order noises of similar character, for example, automobiles, for their subjective effects.
4. Predict from a weighted level the answer that a calculation scheme gives on a variety of noises.

We must recognize, as discussed earlier, that subjective effects are not consistent to start with, and many factors beyond the physical measurements can enter into the result. Even as far as physical measurements are concerned, however, the effect of the duration of the noise, for example, is an important factor that cannot yet be adequately taken into account.

If we ignore these points and concentrate on the relative behavior of the various weighting and calculation schemes, we find that the calculation schemes tend to be more consistent than a simple weighting for predicting results if they are to be referenced to a tone or a narrow band of noise (Fletcher and Munson, 1933; Churcher and King, 1937; Beranek et al, 1951; Quietzsch, 1955; Stevens, 1956; Kryter, and Pearsons 1963; Bauer et al, 1971; but see Corliss and Winzer, 1965 for an exception). Some relatively large discrepancies in loudness, for example, appear in comparing wide-band noise and a pure tone if a weighted level is used but the loudness predicted from a calculation scheme can be much more nearly in agreement with the subjective effect.

Such errors made in predictions from weighted levels led to many of the studies of loudness summation and to various calculation schemes.

The situation is somewhat different if we merely need to rank order a variety of common noises for their loudness or perceived noise level. Then, if A-weighting or a similar one is used, the consistency is fairly good (Young, 1964; Klumpp et al, 1963). But a C-weighted level almost always appears to be significantly poorer than an A-weighted level in consistency (Wells, 1969). The consistency for interference with speech for a variety of noises (Webster, 1969), for example, is particularly poor for a C-weighted level (standard deviation (σ) = 7.4 dB), better for an A-weighted level (σ = 4.7 dB), and still better for PSIL (σ = 2.8 dB).

Because of the nature of the speech-interference effect, the proposed SI weighting should be better than A-weighting for predicting speech interference, but it should not be as good for predicting other effects, such as loudness.

When we rank order noises of similar character, for example, automobiles or aircraft, we find still less significance in the difference in behavior between the calculation schemes and an A-weighted or similar level (Hillquist, 1967;

Young, 1964; Young and Peterson 1969; Lavender, 1971). But again the C-weighted level is generally poor.

Because the calculation schemes are used for specific effects, a number of studies have been made of how well the various weighted levels can be used to predict the results of the calculation schemes. As a general rule the weightings that are closely related to the calculation scheme tend to predict the related result slightly better than other weightings (e.g. Parkin, 1965; Stevens 1972). Since the A weighting has the same general trend as the weightings used in the calculation schemes, it tends to work reasonably well for any of them (Loye, 1956; Botsford, 1969). It should be recognized that this predictability is only of limited value, since it is removed by one additional variability from the subjective effect.

The relative uniformity of the basic data used for loudness and perceived noise (Stevens, 1972), and the success, however modest, of the A-weighted level in comparison with the C-weighted level leads one to conclude that some improvement could probably be obtained for rating many noises by the use of a weighting that is more like the E or the D_2 weighting (Kryter, 1970; Stevens, 1972).

The speech-interference level appears to be in a different category, however. Because the speech-frequency range is more limited, it is likely that a weighting such as the D_2 or E would be no better, if not less satisfactory, than the A weighting. PSIL is still the approach to use in this application.

3.16.3 A-Weighted Sound Level as a Single-Number Rating.

For simple ratings or screenings of similar devices, the A-weighted sound level at a specified distance is now widely used. This measurement is mainly useful for relatively nondirectional sources that are outdoors and where the effect of the noise also occurs outdoors and nearby. It is also useful in preliminary ratings of similar ambient noises for the human reactions that may occur. Measurement of A-weighted sound-level has been adopted for checking compliance with many ordinances and regulations.

Because of its widespread use, a number of investigators have determined the approximate relation between the A-weighted sound-level of a noise and the calculated loudness level, perceived noise level, and speech-interference level of the noise. Table 3-6 shows the results compiled from various sources (Robinson et al, 1963; Parkin, 1965; Young, 1964, Young and Peterson 1969; Hillquist, 1967; Nakano, 1966; Klumpp and Webster, 1963; ASHRAE, 1967; Jahn, 1965). Because the calculation schemes changed somewhat over the years, complete uniformity in procedures was not maintained; but the effects of the changes were small.

In order to get more consistent results in these relations, Botsford (1969) has used the difference in the C-weighted and A-weighted levels as an additional parameter. He has compiled an extensive set of charts for the various quantities and their relations to the A and C-A level. For the 953 noises he uses, the correlation and standard deviation are relatively good, being poorest for speech-interference level, which had a standard deviation of 2.9 dB (see also Shimizu, 1969).

3.16.4 Some Limitations of a Weighted Sound Level.

When only a single weighted sound level is measured, the usefulness of the measurement is severely restricted. One should almost always try to measure the spectrum also. The spectrum is needed for efficient noise control, because the effects of

Table 3-6

COMPARATIVE NOISE RATINGS

Noise Type		LL-L$_A$ (dB)	PNL-L$_A$ (dB)	L$_A$-PSIL (dB)
Office		13	13	6
Truck		10	13	
Pneumatic Machines		13	14	
Ship Compartment		14	15	
Urban			16	
Aircraft	— Jet	9	12	
	Prop		14	
	Prop (approach)		16	
	Helicopter (piston)		14	
Aircraft	— General			9
	— Flyover			4
Diverse			12	10
Airflow		12		

LL = Loudness level by Stevens Mark VI
PNL = Perceived noise level ~ 1963-65
PSIL = Three-band preferred-octave speech-interference level
L$_A$ = A-weighted sound level

sound isolation, acoustic treatment, vibration reduction and other forms of noise control are frequency dependent. In addition, the reaction to the noise is frequency dependent, and the spectrum can show us the frequency region where the noise energy is most important in determining the effects.

We almost always want to know the reason for the noise rating. The spectrum often provides the most important clues for tracking down and reducing the noise.

If a noisy machine is to be used in a room, we need to know the acoustic characteristics of the room as a function of frequency and the radiated-sound-power level in octave or third-octave bands, in order to estimate the noise level at some distance from the machine.

The spectra help in the long run in providing data for later comparisons when conditions change or if better evaluation techniques are developed.

The limitations of the simple, weighted measurement should be recognized when plans for sound measurements are being made.

3.17 RESIDENTIAL NOISE LEVELS.

Some factories, recreation halls, electrical substations, trucks, and airplanes are so noisy that they annoy people living near them. The reactions of those that are annoyed may range from mild remarks to legal action. Those that are responsible for the noise would naturally like to avoid the expense of court action; in order to maintain the good will of the neighborhood, they are often willing to put considerable effort into controlling the noise, so as to avoid anything but mild annoyance.

In order to put this noise control on a systematic basis, a number of engineering groups have analyzed the experiences obtained in many different situations. They have found that reactions of annoyance cannot be successfully predicted on the basis of a single measurement, or even of computed loudness ratings, but that many factors enter into the problem. In addition to the range of reactions to be expected from different individuals, some other factors are the following: The level and spectrum of the noise; whether or not there are strong, pure-tone components; the time pattern of the noise, including the rate of repetition and the actual time of occurence during the day; and the general background noise level in the residential area affected. So far, the data that is available is limited primarily to the reactions of people in residential areas of single-family houses surrounding industrial plants. We can expect that, because of the conditioning to noises that occur in multiple-family dwellings, the reactions of the people there would be modified.

Studies have also shown that people vary markedly in their susceptibility to noise. In a survey in central London (McKennel and Hunt, 1966), of those interviewed about general factors affecting living, 25% were classified as relatively insusceptible to noise while 10% were regarded as extremely suscep-tible. Since no relation was found between the existing noise environment where they lived and the degree of susceptibility of these adults, one can expect to find some highly susceptible individuals in almost any neighbor-hood.

The work of Rosenblith and Stevens in 1953 (see also Stevens et al, 1955; Beranek, 1954) and Parrack (1957) forms the basis of many of the rating schemes used for residential noise. This work has been modified and verified by others (Kosten and Van Os, 1962). To illustrate the nature of the procedure, here is essentially the techniques developed by those authors but modified to use A-weighted sound levels.

The A-weighted sound level in the residential area can be measured and the corrections applied. (Table 3-7).

Compare the corrected level with Table 3-8 to estimate the average public reaction.

The overlap in these ranges indicate to some extent the variable nature of the reaction.

3.18 EFFECT OF NOISE ON WORK OUTPUT.

Noise can influence work output in many ways; it can interfere with communication (paragraph 3.13.1), and it can cause a decrease in the quality

---

——————————————— Table 3-7 ———————————————

CORRECTIONS REQUIRED FOR VARIOUS
NOISE SUSCEPTIBILITIES

Noise Characteristic	Correction (dB)
Pure tone easily perceptible	+5
Impulsive and/or intermittent character	+5
Noise only during working hours	–5
Noise duration	
continuous	0
⩽ 30 min	–5
⩽ 10 min	–10
⩽ 5 min	–15
⩽ 1 min	–20
⩽ 15 sec	–25
Neighborhood	
Very quiet suburban	+5
Suburban	0
Residential urban	–5
Urban near some industry	–10
Area of heavy industry	–15

46

Table 3-8	
PUBLIC REACTIONS TO CORRECTED NOISE LEVELS	
Corrected Level-dB(A)	Expected Reaction
< 45	No observed reaction
45-55	Sporadic complaints
50-60	Widespread complaints
55-65	Threats of community action
> 65	Vigorous community action

of work output when the background noise level is above 90 dB, but noise is occasionally useful as a means of masking distracting conversations.

Broadbent (1958) and others have found that the effects of noise on work output depend greatly upon the nature of the work; a long-term job requiring constant vigilance is especially susceptible. Noise is more likely to cause a higher rate of errors and accidents than an actual reduction in total output. This result and other findings lead to the interpretation that attention wanders from the work at hand more often as the noise level increases.

From the standpoint of noise reduction, two findings are worth noting: first, noise is more likely to lead to increased errors in susceptible tasks if it is above 90 dB; and second, high-frequency audible noise seems more harmful in this respect than does low-frequency noise.

3.19 NON-AUDITORY EFFECTS OF NOISE ON MAN.

Recently, Glorig (1971) and Kryter (1970) have summarized the present knowledge of nonauditory effects of noise exposure. Very high levels (120 to 150 dB), at certain resonant frequencies of the body structure, can produce noticeable symptomatic reactions. Even moderate noise levels produce temporary changes in the size of some blood vessels, but it is not clear that these effects eventually produce permanent changes. The production of stress and fatigue by noise exposure is difficult to verify in a meaningful way.

Much more research is necessary, and a recent report (Welch and Welch, 1970), of a symposium on the physiological effects of noise, shows that considerable effort is directed toward trying to establish the extent of such effects.

3.20 WHAT VIBRATION DOES.

Vibration related problems can be classified as in Table 3-9.

These problems will be discussed in the following sections on the effects on man, maintenance, vibration specifications, and other effects. The problem of excessive noise has already been reviewed.

3.20.1 Effects of Vibration on Man. The subjective effects of vibration are important to those concerned with passenger or operator comfort in automobiles, planes, boats, trains, and other vehicles. Vibration levels that are structurally safe for a vehicle are often uncomfortable, annoying or even dangerous for the occupant. Some machinery and hand tools vibrate all or parts of the body, and this vibration may affect performance as well as comfort. Sometimes buildings and floors vibrate enough to be alarming or to affect the performance of fine tasks.

Such effects have led to extensive studies, which have been reviewed comprehensively by Goldman and von Gierke (1961) and Guignard (1965). These excellent reviews, which cover the injurious levels of vibration as well

-------------- **Table 3-9** --------------

VIBRATION-RELATED PROBLEMS

Effect on man
    Injury
    Fatigue
    Annoyance
    Interference with performance

Mechanical failure
    Excessive stress
    Fatigue
    Destructive impacts

Other
    Excessive wear
    Excessive noise
    Inadequate performance
    Failure to satisfy vibration specifications

as the subjective aspects, are recommended to those concerned with these problems.

The sensation of vibration is not localized as it is for hearing, since vibration can be felt throughout the body and different mechanisms operate to provide the sensation. Curves that present human responses to vibration cannot, therefore, be as complete as are the equal-loudness curves for simple tones of sound.

As an example of information that is available, Figure 3-10 shows results reported by Parks (1962) for vertical whole-body vibration that was classed by the subjects as "mildly annoying". Another contour is given as the approximate mean threshold at which subjects found the vibration unpleasant (Goldman and von Gierke, 1961). The variability of this determination is large, with a standard deviation of about + 4 dB, −6 dB.

Some comfort criteria and tolerance criteria are now in use (Goldman and von Gierke, 1961; Guignard, 1965). As an example, Janeway (SAE J6a, 1965) has prepared a chart giving recommended limits of vertical vibration for passenger comfort in automobiles. Janeway limited his analysis to data obtained for vertical sinusoidal vibration at a single frequency, with subjects standing or sitting on a hard seat. The recommended characteristic consists of three simple relations, each of which covers a portion of the frequency range. In the low-frequency range from 1 to 6 Hz the recommended limit is a fixed value of jerk. The corresponding maximum comfortable displacement at any frequency between 1 and 6 Hz is 2 divided by the frequency cubed (f^3). Over the frequency range from 6 to 20 Hz the recommended limit is a constant acceleration. The corresponding displacement is $1/3\ f^2$. From 20 to 60 Hz the recommended limit is a constant velocity, and the corresponding displacement is $1/60\ f$. In each instance, the amplitude calculated from these formulas is the maximum displacement from the static positions, expressed in inches. The limits are plotted in Figure 3-11, in terms of the rms acceleration and vibratory-acceleration level in dB re 10^{-5} m/s^2, rms.

Resonance effects of the internal organs and their supports, and the upper torso and the shoulder-girdle structures, probably account for the marked sensitivity to vibration in the range from 4 to 10 Hz (Goldman and von Gierke, 1961; Guignard, 1965). Many other resonances occur, however, because the body structure is so varied (Guignard, 1965). The resonances that

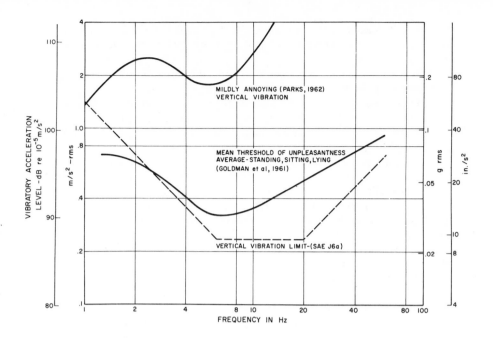

*Figure 3-10. Subjective response of the human body
to vibratory motion as a function of frequency.*

are observed depend on the mode of excitation and the place the vibration is applied.

One of the effects of vibration occurs in some who have worked for two or more years with certain hand-held power tools. They may exhibit Raynaud's phenomenon, in which the fingers become white and numb when the person is chilled. The incidence of this effect seems to be closely related to the vibrational energy in the frequency range from 40 to 125 Hz (Guignard, 1965).

For a visual task, large-amplitude vibration at frequencies between 2 and 20 Hz is particularly disturbing (Guignard, 1966).

3.20.2 Maintenance. It is widely recognized that excessive vibration leads to high costs for machinery maintenance. Conversely, gradual deterioration of machinery, for example, bearings going bad or rotors becoming more unbalanced, leads to increased vibration and noise. Recognition of this latter fact has led some groups to institute periodic vibration measurements of machinery as an important preventive maintenance procedure (Bowen and Graham, 1967; Maten, 1970; Schiff, 1970; Glew and Watson, 1971).

The analysis of vibration permits one to estimate the probable condition of the machine, to schedule downtime for maintenance usually before the condition gets too serious, and to tell what to look at when the machine is shut down.

If a program of this type is pursued, some acceptable limits of vibration must be set to make possible a decision as to when corrective measures must be taken. One approach is to analyze the vibration velocity at all bearing housings, when the machine is newly installed and periodically thereafter.

When an appreciable change in vibration level is noted, the amount of change, the frequency region where it occurred, and the measurement location are used to decide what action if any is necessary.

These early measurements should include the vibration at the various bearing housings in all three directions, vertical and the two horizontal axes. They should be measured for the different operating conditions made possible by the various clutches and speed-changing systems on the machine. Incidentally, these early checks may occasionally reveal a faulty new machine that should be rejected and returned to the manufacturer.

Various degrees of refinement are used in spectrum analysis of these vibrations. A separation of the spectrum into the standard 8- to 10-octave bands (paragraph 5.2.1) is often adequate (Glew and Watson, 1971), but the finer divisions of the 1/3-octave (paragraph 5.2.2) (Bowen and Graham, 1967), and even an analysis into hundreds of bands by an FFT analyzer (see paragraph 5.2.3), are also used.

In addition to a history of the vibration levels for each machine, it is useful to have a type of absolute criterion, of which a number have been proposed. Among those who have proposed criteria, T. C. Rathbone (1939) was a pioneer in synthesizing the available experience in this area. The chart that he prepared in 1939 has been the basis for many subsequent specifications. This chart showed the maximum allowable peak-to-peak displacement as a function of rotation speed, with ratings varying from "Very Smooth" to "Too Rough to Operate."

One of the important points to be gained from such charts is that a simple specification of displacement or even of acceleration is not adequate for a rating, although many have assumed from physical reasoning that one of those parameters should be specified. Actually, velocity happens to be a better parameter to use for a relatively wide range of shaft speeds. For example, Rathbone has recommended some simplified upper limits of vibration that can be specified in terms of velocity for vibration frequencies above 20 Hz (1200 cycles per minute). The limits that he recommended (Rathbone, 1963) are: For power machinery, electric motors, large fans, turbines, pumps, dishwashers, dryers, vacuum cleaners, mixers, etc., the velocity should be less than 0.13 in./s, peak (110 dB re 10^{-8} m/s peak*). For hand tools, small fans, and room air conditioning equipment, the velocity, should be less than 0.1 in./s peak (108 dB re 10^{-8} m/s, peak)**. For precision machinery and business machines, the velocity should be less than .063 in./s, peak (104 dB re 10^{-8} m/s, peak).

These values should be used only as a guide. Considerable variation in significance can be expected for several reasons. For example, the relation between the actual spindle or shaft vibration and the vibration measured on the associated bearing housings is complex and would not necessarily be the same for machines of the same type but of different design.

Furthermore, the vibration at a bearing housing may vary significantly around the housing because of components of different phase being introduced external to the bearing. The nature of the vibration, that is, if it is

---

*For the equivalent rms value (re 10^{-8} m/s, rms) subtract 3 dB; for average values (re 10^{-8} m/s avg), subtract 4 dB.

**The ratings in terms of rms values of sinusoidal vibration, as measured on some vibration meters, will be about 0.7 of these peak values; for average values (actually "average absolute"), use 0.6 of the peak values.

rough or random or of an impact type rather than if it is sinusoidal motion, also affects the value that is significant.

Even if no element of human reaction is involved, different criteria can be set up for the same application. Thus, the manufacturer of a compressor may select a velocity of 0.5 in./s, peak (122 dB re 10^{-8} m/s, peak) measured on the bearing housings, as a safe upper limit, but the user may prefer to have the vibration kept to 0.1 in./s, peak (108 dB re 10^{-8} m/s, peak) or less, for best performance and low maintenance costs (cf. *Power*, Vol 109, May 1965, pp 162-164.)

The manufacturer is influenced by what can be competitively produced and still have a reasonable life, but the user should be willing to pay more for a unit with the reduced maintenance costs that usually accompany lower vibration levels.

It is important to recognize that resilient mounting of a machine will not ordinarily reduce the vibration levels at the machine unless the vibration is coming from the foundation. Resilient mounting may be helpful in preventive maintenance, however, since it can reduce the effects of extraneous vibrations on the machine being measured. The vibration data from any given machine are then more representative of the condition of the machine.

3.20.3 Vibration Specifications. Limits on vibration on many machines have been set for a variety of reasons, generally on the basis of experience. For example, on a good lathe one may find a specification such as:

'Vibration to 1200 rpm (20 Hz) should not exceed 0.0005 in. on bed and 0.0003 in. at spindle.

These are peak-to-peak measurements and the corresponding peak-velocity measurements at 1200 rpm are .03 in./s and .018 in./s. Such a specification should help to insure both high quality of work and low maintenance. But it is strange to find that many manufacturers and users of precision rotating machinery neglect such an important specification.

3.20.4 Other Effects. Many of the useful effects of vibration in chemical, biological, and physical procedures are discussed by Hueter and Bolt (1955), Crawford, (1955), Bergman (1954), Frederick (1965), and Brown and Goodman (1965). The effects of machine-tool vibration have been reviewed by S. A. Tobias (1961), and metallic fatigue has been covered by Harris (1961). Many of the effects of vibration are discussed briefly in books and trade journals for the particular specialty in which the effect occurs. The handbook edited by Harris and Crede (1961) is, however, remarkably comprehensive in its coverage of the many problem areas of shock and vibration.

REFERENCES

Standards

ANSI S3.4-1968, Computation of the Loudness of Noise

ANSI S3.5-1969, Calculation of the Articulation Index

ISO/R131-1959, Expression of the Physical and Subjective Magnitudes of Sound or Noise

ISO/R226-1967, Normal Equal-Loudness Contours for Pure Tones

Other

AIHA (1966), *Industrial Noise Manual*, Second Edition, American Industrial Hygiene Association, 14125 Prevost, Detroit, Michigan 48227.

ASHRAE (1967), *ASHRAE Guide and Data Book, Systems and Equipment for 1967,* American Society of Heating, Refrigerating and Air-Conditioning Engineers, Inc., 345 East 47th St., New York, NY 10017, Chapter 31, pp 377 and 379.

L. Batchelder (1968), "Standards Note: D- and N-Weighted Sound Levels," *J Acoust Soc Am*, Vol 44, #4, October 1968, pp 1159f.

B.B. Bauer, E. L. Torick and R. G. Allen (1971), "The Measurement of Loudness Level," *J Acoust Soc Am*, Vol 50, # 2 (Part 1), August 1971, pp 405-414.

G. von Bekesy *(1960), Experiments in Hearing*, (E.G. Wever, trans and ed), McGraw-Hill, New York.

L. L. Beranek (1947), "The Design of Speech Communication Systems," *Proc IRE*, Vol 35, #9, September 1947, pp 880-890.

L. L. Beranek (1954), *Acoustics*, McGraw-Hill, New York, Part XXXII.

L. L. Beranek (1957), "Revised Criteria for Noise in Buildings," *Noise Control*, Vol 3, #1, pp 19-27.

L. L. Beranek, J. L. Marshall, A. L. Cudworth and A. P. G. Peterson (1951), "The Calculation and Measurement of the Loudness of Sounds," *J Acoust Soc Am*, Vol 23, #3, May 1951, pp 261-269.

L. Bergman (1954), *Der Ultraschall*, S. Hirzel Verlag, Stuttgart, Germany, (Sixth Edition).

E. de Boer (1962), "Note on the Critical Bandwidth," *J Acoust Soc Am*, Vol 34, #7, July 1962, pp 985f.

J. H. Botsford (1969), "Using Sound Levels to Gauge Human Response to Noise," *Sound and Vibration*, Vol 3, #10, October 1969, pp 16-28.

K. A. Bowen and T. S. Graham (1967), "Noise Analysis: A Maintenance Indicator," *Mechanical Engineering*, Vol 89, #10, 1967, pp 31-33.

D. E. Broadbent (1958), *Perception and Communication*, Pergamon Press, New York

B. Brown and J. E. Goodman (1965), *High-Intensity Ultrasonics*, Iliffe Books Ltd., London.

W. Burns (1968), *Noise and Man*, John Murray, London.

N. L. Carter and K. T. Kryter (1962), "Masking of Pure Tones and Speech," *J Auditory Res*, Vol 2, #1, January 1962, pp 66-98.

W. J. Cavanaugh, W. R. Farrell, P. W. Hirtle and B. G. Watters (1962), "Speech Privacy in Buildings," *J Acoust Soc Am*, Vol 34, #4, April 1962, pp 475-492.

J. D. Chalupnik, ed. (1970), *Transportation Noises, A Symposium on Acceptability Criteria*, University of Washington Press, Seattle.

B. G. Churcher and A. J. King (1937), "The Performance of Noise Meters in Terms of the Primary Standard," *JIEE* (London), Vol 84, pp 57-90.

Committee on the Problem of Noise (1963), "Noise—Final Report", Cmnd, 2056, Her Majesty's Stationery Office, London, 1964.

E. L. R. Corliss and G. E. Winzer (1965), "Study of Methods for Estimating Loudness," *J Acoust Soc Am*, Vol 38, #3, September 1965, pp 424-428.

A. E. Crawford (1955), *Ultrasonic Engineering*, Academic Press, New York.

H. Davis and S. R. Silverman (1970), *Hearing and Deafness*, Third Edition, Holt, Rinehart and Winston, Inc., New York.

J. P. Egan and A. W. Hake (1950), "On the Masking Pattern of a Simple Auditory Stimulus," *J Acoust Soc Am*, Vol 22, #5, September 1950, pp 622-630.

J. L. Flanagan (1965), *Speech Analysis Synthesis and Perception*, Academic Press, New York

H. Fletcher (1953), *Speech and Hearing in Communication*, D. Van Nostrand New York.

H. Fletcher and W. A. Munson (1933), "Loudness, Its Definition, Measurement and Calculation," *J Acoust Soc Am*, Vol 5, #2, October 1933, pp 82-108.

H. Fletcher and W. A. Munson (1937), "Relation Between Loudness and Masking," *J Acoust Soc Am*, Vol 9, #1, July 1937, pp 1-10.

J. R. Frederick (1965), *Ultrasonic Engineering*, John Wiley & Sons, Inc., New York.

N. R. French and J. C. Steinberg (1947), "Factors Governing the Intelligibility of Speech Sounds," *J Acoust Soc Am*, Vol 19, #1, January 1947, pp 90-119.

C. A. W. Glew and D. C. Watson (1971), "The Octave Band Vibration Analyzer as a Machinery Defect Indicator," Am Soc Mech Eng Design Engineering Conf Paper, 71-DE-47, April 19-22, 1971.

A. Glorig (1958), *Noise and Your Ear*, Grune & Stratton, New York.

A. Glorig (1971), "Non-Auditory Effects of Noise Exposure," *Sound and Vibration*, Vol 5, #5, May 1971, pp 28f.

D. E. Goldman and H. E. von Gierke (1961), "The Effects of Shock and Vibration on Man," S3-W-39, American National Standards Institute, 1430 Broadway, New York, NY 10018. (Closely parallel to their Chap 44 in Harris and Crede — 1961).

D. M. Green and J. A. Swets (1966), *Signal Detection Theory and Psychophysics*, John Wiley & Sons, Inc., New York.

W. F. Grether (1971), "Vibration and Human Performance," *Human Factors,* Vol. 13, #3, pp. 203-216.

J. C. Guignard (1965), "Vibration," Chapter 29, pp 813-894, in J.A. Gillies, ed., *A Textbook of Aviation Physiology*, Pergamon Press, Oxford.

J. C. Guignard (1966), "Effects of Vibration on Man," *J Env Sci*, Vol 9, #4, August 1966, pp 29-32.

J. C. Guignard (1971), "Human Sensitivity to Vibration" *J Sound and Vib*, Vol 15, #1, 8 March 1971, pp 11-16.

C. M. Harris, ed. (1957), *Handbook of Noise Control*, McGraw-Hill, New York.

C. M. Harris and C. E. Crede (1961), *Shock and Vibration Handbook*, 3 Volumes, McGraw-Hill, New York.

W. J. Harris (1961), *Metallic Fatigue*, Pergamon Press, New York.

J. E. Hawkins, Jr. and S. S. Stevens (1950), "The Masking of Pure Tones and of Speech by White Noise," *J Acoust Soc Am*, Vol 22, #1, January 1950, pp 6-13.

W. R. Hazard (1971), "Predictions of Noise Disturbance Near Large Airports," *J Sound and Vib*, Vol 15, #4, 22 April 1971, pp 425-446.

R. K. Hillquist (1967), "Objective and Subjective Measurement of Truck Noise," *Sound and Vib*, Vol 1, #4, April 1967, pp 8-13.

I. J. Hirsh (1952), "The Measurement of Hearing," McGraw-Hill, New York.

T. F. Hueter and R. H. Bolt (1955),*"Sonics"*, John Wiley & Sons, Inc., New York

M. Jahn (1965), "Subjektive und Objektive Bewertung von Maschinen Gerauschen," *Acustica*, Vol 16, #3, 1965/66, pp 175-186.

R. G. Klumpp and J. C. Webster (1963), "Physical Measurements of Equal Speech-Interfering Navy Noises," *J Acoust Soc Am*, Vol 35, #9, September 1963, pp 1328-1338.

C. W. Kosten and G. J. Van Os (1962), "Community Reaction Criteria for External Noises," National Physical Laboratory Symposium No. 12, *The Control of Noise*, Her Majesty's Stationery Office, London, pp 373-387.

K. D. Kryter (1962), "Methods for the Calculation and Use of the Articulation Index," *J Acoust Soc Am*, Vol 34, #11, November 1962, pp 1689-1697. ("Validation of the Articulation Index," pp 1698-1702.)

K. D. Kryter (1968), "Concepts of Perceived Noisiness, Their Implementation and Application," *J Acoust Soc Am*, Vol 43, #2, Feb 1968, pp 344-361.

K. D. Kryter (1970), *The Effects of Noise on Man*, Academic Press, Inc., New York, Chapter 11 and Part III.

K. D. Kryter and K. S. Pearsons (1963), "Some Effects of Spectral Content and Duration on Perceived Noise Level," *J Acoust Soc Am*, Vol 35, #6, June 1963, pp 866-883.

D. C. Lavender (1971), "Interpretation of Noise Measurements," *J Sound and Vib*, Vol 15, #1, 8 March 1971, pp 1-9.

D. P. Loye (1956), "The Legal Aspects of Noise Control," *Noise Control*, Vol 2, #4, July 1956, pp 56-60.

A. C. McKennel and E. A. Hunt (1966), "Noise Annoyance in Central London," Report S 332. U.K. Government Social Survey, Atlantic House, Holburn Viaduct, London, E.C.1., U.K.

S. Maten (1970), "Program Machine Maintenance by Measuring Vibration Velocity," *Hydrocarbon Processing*, Vol 49, September 1970, pp 291-296.

A. Nakano (1966), "Relation between Noise Rating Number and Objective Measurement of Machine Noise," *J Acoust Soc Ja*, Vol 22, #2, March 1966, pp 62-76.

R. H. Nittinger (1964), "Vibration Analysis Can Keep Your Plant Humming," *Chemical Engineering*, Vol 71, August 17, 1964, pp 152-158.

P. H. Parkin (1965), "On the Accuracy of Simple Weighting Networks for Loudness Estimates of Some Urban Noises," *J Sound and Vib*, Vol 2, #1, pp 86-88.

D. L. Parks (1962), "Defining Human Reaction to Whole-Body Vibration," *Human Factors*, Oct, pp 305-314.

H. O. Parrack (1957), "Community Reaction to Noise," Chapter 36 in Harris (1957).

A. C. Pietrasanta and K. N. Stevens (1958), "Noise Exposure in Communities Near Jet Air Bases," *Noise Control*, Vol 4, #2, March 1958, pp 93-100.

I. Pollack (1952), "The Loudness of Bands of Noise," *J Acoust Soc Am*, Vol 24, #5, September 1952, pp 533-538.

G. Quietzsch (1955), "Objektive und Subjektive Lautstarkemessungen," *Acustica*, Vol 5, *Akustische Beihefte* #1, pp 49-66.

T. C. Rathbone (1939), *Power Plant Engineering*, Vol 43, #11, Nov, pp 721-724.

T. C. Rathbone (1963), "A Proposal for Standard Vibration Limits," *Product Engineering*, Vol 34, Mar 4, pp 68f.

D. W. Robinson (1958), "A New Determination of the Equal-Loudness Contours," *IRE Trans on Audio*, Vol AU-6, January-February 1958, pp 6-13.

D. W. Robinson (1969), "The Concept of Noise Pollution Level," NPL Aero Report AC 38, and "An Outline Guide to Criteria for the Limitation of Urban Noise," NPL Aero Report AC 39, March 1969, National Physical Laboratory, Aerodynamics Division.

D. W. Robinson (1971), "Towards a Unified System of Noise Assessment," *J Sound and Vib*, Vol 14, #3, Feb, pp 279-298.

D. W. Robinson and R. S. Dadson (1956), "A Re-determination of the Equal Loudness Relations for Pure Tones," *Bri J of Appl Phys*, Vol 7, May, pp 166-181.

D. W. Robinson, J. M. Bowsher, and W. C. Copeland (1963), "On Judging the Noise from Aircraft in Flight," *Acustica*, Vol 13, #5, pp 324-336.

D. W. Robinson and L. S. Whittle (1964), "The Loudness of Octave Bands of Noise," *Acustica*, Vol 14, #1, pp 24-35.

W. Rosenblith and K. N. Stevens (1953), "Handbook of Acoustic Noise Control" Vol II, "Noise and Man" WADC Technical Report 52-204, PB111274, June 1953, pp 181-200.

J. Sataloff (1957), *Industrial Deafness* , Blakiston Division, McGraw-Hill, New York.

R. W. Shoenberger and C. S. Harris (1971), "Psychophysical Assessment of Whole-Body Vibration," *Human Factors*, Vol. 13, #1, pp 41-50.

I. Schiff (1970), "Vibration Analysis — Downtime Insurance," *Foundry*, Vol 98, Dec, pp 90f.

T. J. Schultz (1968), "Noise Criterion Curves for Use with the USASI Preferred Frequencies," *J Acoust Soc Am*, Vol 43, #3, Mar, pp 637f.

M. Shimizu (1969), "A Simple Method of Measuring Loudness Level — On Automobile Noises," *J Acoust Soc Jap*, Vol 25, #6, pp 319-324.

S. R. Silverman (1947), "Tolerances for Pure Tones and Speech in Normal and Defective Hearing," *Ann of Otology, Rhinology, and Laryngology*, Vol 56, September 1947, pp 658-677.

L. J. Sivian and S. D. White (1933), "On Minimum Audible Sound Fields," *J Acoust Soc Am*, Vol 4, #4, April 1933, pp 288-321.

SAE J6a (1965), *"Ride and Vibration Data Manual"*, Society of Automotive Engineers, New York.

A. Spoor (1967), "Presbycusis Values in Relation to Noise Induced Hearing Loss," *International Audiology*, Vol 6, #1, July 1967, pp 48-57.

K. N. Stevens, W. A. Rosenblith, and R. H. Bolt (1955), "A Community's Reaction to Noise: Can it Be Forecast?," *Noise Control*, Vol 1, #1, January 1955, pp 63-71.

S. S. Stevens, editor (1951), *Handbook of Experimental Psychology*, John Wiley & Sons, Inc., New York.

S. S. Stevens (1956), "The Calculations of the Loudness of Complex Noise," *J Acoust Soc Am*, Vol 28, #5, September 1956, pp 807-832.

S. S. Stevens (1961), "Procedure for Calculating Loudness: Mark VI," *J Acoust Soc Am*, Vol 33, #11, November 1961, pp 1577-1585.

S. S. Stevens (1972), "Perceived Level of Noise by Mark VII and Decibels (E)", *J Acoust Soc Am*, Vol 51 #2 Part 2, Feb, pp 575-601.

S. S. Stevens, J. Volkmann and E. B. Newman (1937), "A Scale for the Measurement of the Psychological Magnitude Pitch," *J Acoust Soc Am*, Vol 8, #3, Jan, pp 185-190.

S. S. Stevens and H. Davis (1938), *Hearing*, John Wiley & Sons, Inc., New York.

S. S. Stevens and F. Warshofsky (1965), *Sound and Hearing*, Time, Inc., New York.

S. A. Tobias (1961), "Machine-Tool Vibration," Chapter 40 in Harris and Crede (1961).

R. A. Waller (1969), "Office Acoustics—Effect of Background Noise," *Applied Acoustics*, Vol 2, #2, April, pp 121-130.

J. C. Webster (1965), "Speech Communications as Limited by Ambient Noise," *J Acoust Soc Am*, Vol 37, #4, April, pp 692-699.

J. C. Webster (1969), "Effects of Noise on Speech Intelligibility," *Proc Conference Noise as a Public Health Hazard*, Washington, DC, June 13-14, 1968, ASHA Reports 4, The American Speech and Hearing Association, Washington, DC, 1969, pp 49-73.

B. L. Welch and A. S. Welch, ed. (1970), *Physiological Effects of Noise*, Plenum Press, New York.

R. J. Wells (1969), "A New Method for Computing the Annoyance of Steady State Noise versus Perceived Noise Level and Other Subjective Measures," *J Acoust Soc Am*, Vol 46, #1 (Part 1), July, p 85.

R. W. Young (1958), "Don't Forget the Simple Sound-Level Meter," *Noise Control*, Vol 4, #3, May, pp 42f.

R. W. Young (1964), "Single-Number Criteria for Room Noise, *J Acoust Soc Am*, Vol 36, #2, Feb, pp 289-295.

R. W. Young (1965), "Re-Vision of the Speech-Privacy Calculation," *J Acoust Soc Am*, Vol 38, #4, Oct, pp 524-530.

R. W. Young (1968) "Effective Duration of an Aircraft Flyover," Reports of the 6th International Congress on Acoustics, Paper F-3-11, pp F-109-112, Tokyo.

R. W. Young and A. P. G. Peterson (1969), "On Estimating Noisiness of Aircraft Sounds," *J Acoust Soc Am*, Vol 45, #4, April, pp 834-838.

E. Zwicker (1960), "Ein Verfahren zur Berechnung der Lautstarke," *Acustica*, Vol 10, *Akustische Beihefte* #1, pp 304-308.

E. Zwicker, G. Flottorp, and S. S. Stevens (1957), "Critical Bandwidth in Loudness Summation," *J Acoust Soc Am*, Vol 29, #5, May, pp 548-557.

Chapter 4

Hearing-Conservation Programs in Industry

By
Rufus L. Grason and Carol Hetzel

4.1 INTRODUCTION.

Noise has been recognized as a contributing factor in hearing loss for hundreds of years. Chadwick (1963) notes, from about the 12th century, references citing noise-induced hearing losses. Fosbroke (1831), for example, states: "The blacksmiths' deafness is a consequence of their employment; it creeps on them gradually, in general at about forty or fifty years of age. At first the patient is insensible of weak impressions of sound; the deafness increases with a ringing and noise in the ears, ..."

In 1831 it was also recognized that these comments were not new. Fosbroke continues with: "It has been imputed to a paralytic state of the nerve, occasioned by the noise of forging, by certain modern writers, and by the old writers, to permanent over-tension of the membrane, ..." Not until about a century later, however, was this awareness substantiated by data that defined specific characteristics of hazardous noise and indicated how these characteristics might be controlled. The consequence of such careful definition has been twofold:

1. the increasingly common establishment of industrial hearing-conservation programs, and

2. the introduction of federal and state legislation that provides financial compensation for noise-induced occupational deafness.

This chapter defines the hazardous properties of noise, as understood on the basis of current data, their effect on the physiology of the ear, and the manner in which both hearing conservation and legislative programs are working to protect industrial workers.

4.2 THE HUMAN EAR.

4.2.1 Anatomy. Anatomically (Davis and Silverman, 1970), the ear is divided into three sections—the outer, the middle, and the inner ears—through which air-conducted sound waves must travel in order for "hearing" to occur. The outer ear consists of the fleshy appendage attached to the head and the ear canal, both of which serve to channel sound waves toward the elastic tympanic membrane commonly known as the eardrum. The conically shaped tympanic membrane transforms the energy of sound waves into mechanical energy of the middle-ear ossicles, a set of small bones. The ossicle chain, acting as an impedance transformer, transmits the vibrations of the tympanic membrane to the oval window. This window moves in and out, much like a piston, generating pressure waves in the perilymph, a nearly incompressible fluid in the inner ear. The pressure differential that results moves the basilar membrane and the organ of Corti. The hair cells in the organ of Corti transform the mechanical motions into nerve impulses, which are transmitted through the eighth nerve into higher centers in the brain, where they are decoded and interpreted as sound.

4.2.2 Effects of Noise. The description above indicates that sound is transmitted to the brain first by conductive and then by neurological means. Conductive mechanisms—movement of membranes, bones, and fluid—propagate the sound waves from the external through the middle and inner ears. In the inner ear proper, direct conductive stimulation of the tiny nerve receptors translates the previously mechanical activity to an electrical, or neurological, activity.

The importance of making this distinction between conductive and neurological transmission is simply that noise tends principally to damage the neurological auditory mechanisms—the hair cells. Most frequently, noise-induced injury first occurs to the outer- and inner-hair-cell structure; then, if hazardous noise conditions persist, the organ of Corti itself is destroyed. The consequence of such damage is that nerve cells that would have transmitted the auditory signal degenerate; they will never regrow and cannot be replaced. Severe damage from noise exposure, then, is permanent. The one exception to this rule is that short, intense blasts of noise can rupture an eardrum, dislodge a bone in the middle-ear chain, or otherwise damage a conductive mechanism. This acoustic trauma is often temporary and in many cases can be repaired by surgery or, if simple enough, will heal itself in time.

4.3 NOISE-INDUCED HEARING LOSS.

4.3.1 Data Sources.

Field Studies. In recent years, a great deal of research has been carried out defining properties of noise hazardous to human hearing. Many studies have been made in actual industrial environments where the hearing of the workers was assessed over the course of many months and after exposure for many years (Rosenblith, 1942; Ruedi and Furrer, 1946; Cox et al, 1953; ANSI Z24-X-2-1954; Rudmose, 1957; Kylin, 1960; Glorig et al, 1961; Nixon et al, 1961; Schneider et al, 1961; Yaffe and Jones, 1961; Burns et al, 1964; Harris, 1965; Taylor et al, 1965; Baughn, 1966; Atherley et al, 1967; La Benz et al, 1967; Noweir et al, 1968; Botsford, 1969; Cohen et al, 1970; Kronoveter and Somerville, 1970). These studies by their very nature, could not be controlled to yield well-defined statements regarding the exact relations between various noise parameters and hearing loss. What such studies did yield, however, were a series of general principles that laboratory experiments later were to define in detail:

1. Low-frequency noise energy tends to be less damaging to hearing than mid-frequency noise.

2. Beyond certain levels, increased intensity and increased exposure time produce increased hearing loss, and an increased fraction of the exposed group will have significant losses.

3. Individuals show a differential susceptibility to noise-induced hearing loss.

4. Hearing loss due to noise is most pronounced in the region near 4000 Hz, but spreads over the frequency range as exposure time and level increase.

Laboratory Studies. A laboratory-simulated industrial environment, unlike actual industrial situations, has the advantage of permitting the specification and control of noise parameters. The measurement of the effects of noise, however, is potentially difficult, as it would seem to require that a permanent hearing loss be induced in the subject. Fortunately, an alternative procedure has been developed. It is now generally accepted that there are two types of hearing losses—temporary and permanent—both indicated as an increase in an individual's threshold (i.e., the intensity level at which he just detects the presence or absence of an audio signal). When a hearing loss occurs for a relatively brief period of time following exposure to noise, a temporary hearing loss or temporary threshold shift (TTS) is said to have occurred. When the effect of the exposure is to permanently lessen an individual's sensitivity for hearing, a permanent threshold shift (PTS) has occurred. On the basis of recent evidence, many investigators assume certain similarities between TTS and PTS (Glorig, 1967; Kryter et al, 1966). Such an assumption has the practical advantage of permitting laboratory studies to be carried out on various parameters of noise, using TTS as an indication of the long-term effects of noise. Typical experiments set up along these lines commonly involve one parameter of noise—its level, duration, or spectrum, etc—being varied while all other parameters are held constant. The resulting characteristics of the TTS, its duration, extent, rate of growth and rate of recovery, are used as indicators of the character of PTS that would result from prolonged exposure to the same variable.

On the assumption that TTS and PTS are related, a measurement of TTS for any of the varied and complex noises that occur in practice could be a useful guide to the potentially hazardous nature of these noises. Rather than exposing a statistically useful number of subjects to these noises and observe their TTS's, one can simulate TTS behavior by an electrical model that responds in accordance with the experimentally observed TTS behavior (Keeler, 1968). Such devices have been built (Benson et al, 1964; Botsford and Laks, 1970; Moser, 1970) and used on a small scale.

4.3.2 Hazardous Properties of Noise. Using data from studies on PTS and TTS, investigators (see below) have isolated several characteristics of noise as contributors to the destruction of neurological elements in the ear, and consequent loss of hearing. Of these characteristics, at least the following are critical: over-all noise level, the spectrum of the noise, total exposure duration, and the temporal distribution of the noise.

Over-all Sound Level of the Noise Spectrum. Since noise level is only one parameter involved in hearing loss produced by noise exposure, only a preliminary rating of the potential danger is possible with a single noise-level reading. As a general rule, however, it can be stated that noise whose over-all A-weighted sound level is below 80 dB (Ward, 1969) is probably reasonably safe. Since many industrial noise levels are greater than 80 dB (A), additional information about the character of the noise is required before any statement regarding its effects on hearing can be made.

Shape of the Noise Spectrum. Laboratory studies have indicated that TTS is a function of the spectrum of the noise. We indicated earlier that the ear is most sensitive to frequencies above 1 kHz, and that hearing losses occur more readily at these than at other frequencies. Noise containing concentrated energy in the mid-to-high frequency regions (octave bands 600-1200 Hz and above) is more hazardous to hearing than noise containing energy concentrated below 600 Hz (Ward et al, 1959). Evidence also indicates a pure tone at a given level is more damaging to hearing than a band of noise at the same level, centered about that frequency (Cohen and Baumann, 1964; Ward, 1962).

Cumulative Duration of Noise Exposure. PTS data, as well as data gathered in TTS studies, indicate that up to a point, as the total duration of noise exposure increases for any given population, the incidence and magnitude of the resultant hearing loss also increases.

The noise-induced hearing loss may not continue until total deafness is induced. Glorig (1961) found that the permanent hearing loss at 4 kHz stemming from daily noise exposures of 5-8 hours tended to reach a maximum at about twelve years of exposure.

Temporal Distribution of Noise. The relation between intermittent noise and hearing loss is not clearly defined. One simple rule that is approximately correct over a limited range is based on the premise that, regardless of how energy in noise is distributed across time, its net effect upon threshold shift is a function of total energy. This relation is reflected in the recommendations of the American Academy of Ophthalmology and Otolaryngology (AAOO) Committee on Conservation of Hearing (1969).

In their recommendations, the partial noise exposures are related to the equivalent continuous A-weighted noise level by equivalent energy summations. Thus, 90 dB (A) for 12 hours/week, 95 dB (A) for 4 hours/week, and 100 dB (A) for 80 minutes/week are each rated as equivalent to 85 dB (A) for 40 hours/week. This relation can also be expressed as that twice the energy (3 dB (A) increase in level) is permissible for every halving of exposure duration, without increasing the risk.

A number of laboratory studies indicate that the ear can tolerate significantly higher noise levels, when the duration is shortened, than this simple rule allows (Ward et al, 1959). The Department of Labor for example, permits a 5-dB tradeoff in level for each halving of the duration in its Occupational Safety and Health Standards (*Federal Register, 36*, 105, May 29, 1971).

4.4 HEARING-CONSERVATION PROGRAMS.

Industrial hearing-conservation programs are designed to protect workers from the hazardous effects of noise. In order to be effective, a program should include three areas of concentration: noise assessment, noise reduction, and hearing assessment.

4.4.1 Assessment of Noise. A common method of assessing noise involves using a sound-level meter (General Radio Type 1565 or similar) set to A weighting. At this setting, the electrical equivalent of the noise is passed through a weighting network that has a frequency characteristic like that of the human ear at threshold, i.e., both are more sensitive at middle frequencies than at very high or very low frequencies. A single reading on the "A" scale gives an approximate indication of the noise level as it affects the human ear. Under these measurement conditions, an SPL of 80 dB (A) is often regarded as completely acceptable as the level of continuous noise that should not be exceeded in the course of an 8-hour day. For enforcement purposes, however, the Department of Labor has set 90 dB (A) as the limit for 8 hours of exposure per day.

As already noted, however, most industrial noise is not uniform and continuous during the course of an entire day. More commonly, the noise will be intermittent, or fluctuating in level, or both. The regulations of the Department of Labor include rules for determining the equivalent exposure. The present limits are as follows (*Federal Register*, May 29, 1971).

1910.95 Occupational noise exposure.

(a) Protection against the effects of noise exposure shall be provided when the sound levels exceed those shown in Table G-16 when measured on the A scale of a standard sound level meter at a slow response. When noise levels are determined by octave band analysis, the equivalent A-weighted sound level may be determined as follows:

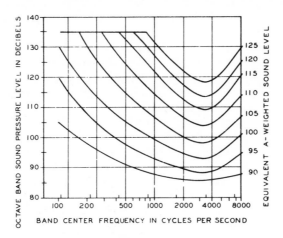

Equivalent sound level contours. Octave band sound pressure levels may be converted to the equivalent A-weighted sound level by plotting them on this graph and noting the A-weighted sound level corresponding to the point of highest penetration into the sound level contours. This equivalent A-weighted sound level which may differ from the actual A-weighted sound level of the noise, is used to determine exposure limits from Table G-16.

——— Table G—16—Permissible Noise Exposures[1] ———

Duration per day, hours	Sound level dBA slow response
8	90
6	92
4	95
3	97
2	100
1½	102
1	105
½	110
¼ or less	115

[1] When the daily noise exposure is composed of two or more periods of noise exposure of different levels, their combined effect should be considered, rather than the individual effect of each. If the sum of the following fractions: $C_1/T_1 + C_2/T_2$ Cn/Tn exceeds unity, then, the mixed exposure should be considered to exceed the limit value, Cn indicates the total time of exposure at a specified noise level, and Tn indicates the total time of exposure permitted at that level.

Exposure to impulsive or impact noise should not exceed 140 dB peak sound pressure level.

(b) (1) When employees are subjected to sound exceeding those listed in Table G-16, feasible administrative or engineering controls shall be utilized. If such controls fail to reduce sound levels within the levels of Table G-16, personal protective equipment shall be provided and used to reduce sound levels within the levels of the table.

(2) If the variations in noise level involve maxima at intervals of 1 second or less, it is to be considered continuous.

(3) In all cases where the sound levels exceed the values shown herein, a continuing, effective hearing conservation program shall be administered.

When the noise level is varying in a simple fashion during the period of exposure, a simple chart record can be prepared to determine the equivalent exposure from the sound-level meter readings. (See *Primer of Plant Noise Measurement and Hearing Testing*, available free from General Radio Company). But if the exposure history is complicated, the GR 1934 Noise-Exposure Monitor, specifically designed to determine the percent of noise exposure automatically, is particularly helpful in checking compliance with the regulations. (See description of monitor in paragraph 6.4).

4.4.2 Noise Reduction. If an analysis of the industrial noise indicates that a hazardous environment exists, a number of steps should immediately be taken to protect the workers in that area. The primary approach is to reduce the sound levels to be less than those allowed.

Modifying the Source (See Chapter 9). Protection commonly begins with an analysis of the environment to locate the source of noise. Once located, the offending device should be modified or replaced with a quieter model. At the very least, specifications for future equipment to be purchased should be written to attenuate the noise production.

Modifying the Path (See Chapter 9). If little can be done to alleviate the noise at its source, then perhaps some modification of the noise path can be effected. Often the distance between the source and the worker can be increased, or the source or the worker can be enclosed in a noise-attenuating barrier.

Protecting the Ear. A third means of implementing noise reduction involves protection of the receptor itself—the human ear. This can be accomplished as indirectly as rotating the worker in and out of the noisy environment, thereby increasing the intermittency of the noise exposure and decreasing the possibility of noise damage. More directly, such protection can—and often does—involve a noise-attenuating device worn over or in the ears of the worker. The particular type of ear protector worn by the worker depends upon a number of factors, among them the individual's ear anatomy and his immediate working environment. In general, there are three types of ear protectors: ear plugs, ear muffs, and helmet.

Ear plugs, made of a nonporous pliable material, are designed to fit into the ear canal. Properly designed, plugs can provide as much as 15-dB attenuation at 125 Hz and 40 dB attenuation at 4 kHz. Dry cotton or similar material is often stuffed into the ear canal as a substitute for well designed plugs. Contrary to popular belief, such material offers virtually no protection from noise, and should not be used as a substitute for plugs, unless the material is well impregnated with wax, a modification which greatly improves its effectiveness.

Ear muffs surround and cover the external ear completely. When designed and fitted properly, the ear muff can meet and, at low frequencies, exceed the attenuation afforded by plugs. However, since these devices surround the ear and adjacent portions of the face, their attenuation is greatly affected by movements of the jaw in chewing, swallowing, and talking.

The helmet, can be as simple as a heavy-duty cloth covering the upper head and ears, or some variation of the hard hat. Generally, the helmet is not an effective protector, having attenuation characteristics less efficient than those of ear plugs.

In summary, we can say that accepted devices, such as ear plugs and muffs, potentially provide virtually the same amount of attenuation. The actual amount of attenuation afforded by these protective devices is primarily dependent upon how well they are fitted, and how consistently they are worn. A recent study (Heffler, 1967) on the effectiveness of ear plugs revealed that, when loosely inserted, plastic plugs provided only 10-dB attenuation at low frequencies, and 35-dB attenuation or better at other test frequencies. It is a fact that the attenuation efficiency of other types of protectors—not merely plugs—falls off as their positioning and fit become poorer. But, even a poorly fitted protective device is better than none at all, and workers in hazardous environments, who use such devices inconsistently or not at all, risk permanent hearing damage.

The percentage of employees misusing protective devices is alarmingly high. Maas (1969), Audiologist and Hearing Consultant for Employers, Mutual of Wausau, indicated at one point that little more than 20% of personal-protection programs could be termed in any way successful. Evidence in support of this statement lies in the fact that, in spite of the institution of protective programs, individual hearing records taken across several years continue to show increasing hearing loss. And the reason protective devices are not working is not that the devices are inadequate, but that they are being used improperly, if at all.

There are a number of steps that can be taken to correct this situation. Most important, the worker must be convinced of the desirability of using these devices. This conviction can be most effectively instilled by a good indoctrination program, which clearly spells out the hazards of unrestricted noise and the utility of personal protective devices worn properly.

Second, the worker should be allowed some choice in the selection of the device he will be wearing. It is essential that for him the device be: comfortable, capable of being worn up to 8 hours per day; non-toxic, causing no irritation or skin reaction when worn; easy to use, store, fit, clean and carry; and durable, capable of surviving for several years of daily use. If these conditions are met, personal-protection programs will have a much higher likelihood of success.

4.5 HEARING MONITORING.

The third and perhaps the most important phase of the hearing-conservation program involves the ongoing monitoring of employees exposed to noisy environments (Hosey and Powell, 1967). If noise is indeed having an adverse effect upon the ear, then a meaningful record of each worker's hearing across time should reflect this change. The measurement of the human hearing function is called "audiometry," and basically requires that the subject make judgments about specified auditory stimuli. These judgments can relate to the least-intense sound that can be detected (absolute threshold), the minimal detectable difference between two sounds (differential threshold), or the matching of one sound characteristic to another. Similarly, the stimuli can be pure tones, white noise, narrow-band noise, or a variety of speech modes. The choice of which judgment is requested and which stimulus is presented is a function of many variables, among them the purpose of the test and the environment in which it is administered.

In industrial situations, the requirements placed upon the audiometric test are, first, that it should be simple to administer and easily understood by the individual taking the test. Second, the test should be a sensitive index of the subject's hearing changes. And finally, the test should be sufficiently well specified and standardized that the comparison of results is possible. All of these requirements are met by the pure-tone absolute-threshold test, which is used extensively in industrial audiometry.

4.5.1 Audiograms. The end result of the administration of a pure-tone threshold test is an audiogram, a permanent record of the subject's hearing sensitivity for each of several pure-tone frequencies presented. Sensitivity is defined in terms of deviation, in dB, from "normal hearing." Normal hearing, in turn is defined both by the International Standards Organization (ISO) and by the American National Standards Institute (ANSI) and is shown by the absolute threshold values in dB SPL shown in Table 4-1. These values, based on 15 different studies of absolute threshold sensitivity in young adults, are representative of an international agreement on the definition of normal hearing. Collectively, these SPL values are referred to as the ISO/ANSI zero reference level, and are used as a basis for uniform calibration of audiometers.

--------------------- **Table 4-1** ---------------------

PURE-TONE REFERENCE THRESHOLD LEVELS *

Frequency (Hz)	dB (re 20 μN/m^2)
125	45
250	25.5
500	11.5
1000	7
1500	6.5
2000	9
3000	10
4000	9.5
6000	15.5
8000	13

*1964 ISO/1969 ANSI, based on measurements made on National Bureau of Standards 9-A Coupler and Telephonics TDH-39 Earphone fitted with MX-41/AR Cushion. Similar values have been developed for other sources.

On the audiogram form shown below, the 0-dB horizontal line represents this zero reference level, which, in turn, is equivalent to the standardized normal threshold values shown in Table 4-1. Deviations from this line are noted as dB Hearing Threshold Level (HTL). A subject, requiring a more intense signal to reach threshold than normal, will show a positive HTL; one requiring a less intense signal than normal will show a negative HTL. (See paragraph 4.7 for a discussion of factors responsible for deviations around the standardized normal value.)

It should be noted that, before the current ISO/ANSI Standards defining normal hearing were accepted, other standards were in effect (Davis and Silverman, 1970, Chapter 7). In 1951, the American Standards Association (ASA) published reference levels that were generally used until 1964 for audiometric calibration. These two sets of scales—1951 ASA and 1964

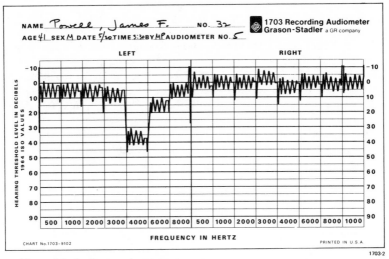

Figure 4-1. Audiogram showing left-ear hearing loss due to acoustic trauma.

ISO/1969 ANSI—differ by about 10 dB across all frequencies, with 0 dB HTL on the ISO/ANSI scale falling at about −10 dB on the ASA scale.

The discrepancy between these two reference levels makes it quite conceivable that an employee tested first on an ASA referenced audiometer and later on an ISO/ANSI referenced audiometer could be assigned a full 10-dB hearing loss when, in fact, his hearing had remained constant from test to retest. Such assumed hearing losses could legally affect the financial compensation awards to the worker (see paragraph 4.8). For this reason, it is extremely important that the appropriate reference level be noted for each audiogram made.

4.5.2 Test Equipment.

Audiometers. As noted in the preceding section, pure-tone threshold tests are most often used in the industrial situation to assess an individual's hearing. The instrument implementing this test is called a pure-tone audiometer, which permits pure tones at specified frequencies and intensities to be presented to the subject. Generally, audiometers used by industry are limited-range units, which commonly provide frequencies of 500, 1000, 2000, 3000, 4000, and 6000 Hz, and earphone output levels of at least 70 dB above the standard threshold reference level. Both parameter ranges are sufficiently wide to permit initial auditory screening/testing of the sort required in industrial situations.

Many requirements are placed on these screening audiometers from users and standards organizations alike. General standards, set up by the American National Standards Institute (ANSI S3.6-1969), for example, specify the purity and accuracy of test frequencies, the accuracy of level in dB SPL, characteristics of the audio switch, and stability, with regard to line voltage and temperature.

Limited-range, pure-tone audiometers can be either manual or automatic. In the manual audiometer, all testing—i.e., the selection and presentation of appropriate frequencies and intensities, and the recording of the subject's responses—is done by hand. The automatic audiometer, a more recent development, administers the test and records the subject's responses with a minimum of operator intervention. Although the particular testing technique employed varies, many automatic audiometers incorporate the Bekesy (1947) technique, which records the subject's threshold estimates continuously, either as a function of frequency (sweep-frequency Bekesy), or as a function of time (fixed-frequency Bekesy). In a typical industrial testing situation, a recording pen is moved along the horizontal axis of the audiogram form, on which several frequencies are located. In the absence of a subject response, an automatic attenuator associated with the subject switch increases the sound level and simultaneously moves the recording pen down along the HTL (vertical) axis of the form. In the presence of a subject response, the attenuator decreases the sound level and moves the recording pen up along the chart's vertical axis. The end result of this procedure is that the subject, instructed to press the switch when he hears the sound and to release when the sound is not heard, adjusts and simultaneously records his threshold continuously across time, for each of several frequencies. In addition to the obvious benefit of operational ease over manually controlled units, automatic audiometers have the advantage of providing increased test-retest reliability by presenting a standard test sequence, free from operator intervention and the consequent likelihood of error. The legal ramifications of such reliability are quite extensive.

Several automatic audiometers of the sort mentioned above are currently available for industrial audiometry. The Grason-Stadler Model 1703 Audiometer (Figure 4-2), for example, is a fully automatic unit that presents a fixed-frequency Bekesy test sequence while providing a record of the subject's responses on an integral X-Y recorder. In addition to standard frequencies, the 1703 tests both ears at 8 kHz, then retests at 1 kHz, the latter used as an indication of test reliability. The 1703 features a unique variable-speed intensity drive that allows the subject to "home in" rapidly on the threshold region, then spend more time precisely defining threshold.

If an audiometer is to provide a true record of an individual's hearing, it must be calibrated in accordance with specified standards. When the unit is first manufactured, its many signal parameters—level, purity, rise/fall time, etc—are all precisely calibrated, often with the aid of wave analyzers and other electronic instrumentation. Once in the field the audiometer should be sent to a calibration laboratory once or twice a year for thorough inspection and testing, to insure this continued calibration.

Typically, unless audible cues indicate a malfunction in the unit's components, a daily field calibration, involving only a check of signal level, provides the needed assurance of accurate operation between such annual or semiannual certifications. To facilitate this field calibration, General Radio offers the Type 1562-Z Audiometer Calibration Set which consists of the Type 1565-B Sound Level Meter and a choice of couplers that connect the meter to the audiometer. To ensure accurate readings from the sound-level meter, a sound-level calibrator is also included. This calibration technique is easy to implement, can be accomplished in a short time, and is extremely reliable. Its frequent use is recommended over alternate methods.

The validity of threshold measurements is affected not only by the calibration of the audiometric instrument, but also the test environment. If there is a high ambient noise level, the test stimuli can be masked, and, as a consequence, the threshold values of the subject can be erroneously elevated (Cox, 1955).

If the audiometric tests are questionable because of high noise levels in the test area, a hearing-conservation program cannot be effectively carried out.

The acceptable levels of background noise for audiometric tests are given in an American Standard (ANSI S3.1-1960).* For the important frequencies used in industrial audiometry these levels are given in Table 4-2, where the center frequency is that of the audiometric test frequency and of the analyzer bands.

Table 4-2

PERMISSIBLE BACKGROUND NOISE LEVELS

Octave Band Center Freq. (Hz)	Test Room Level (dB)		GR 1939 Attenuation (dB)	Level Outside GR 1939 (dB)	
	Max	10 dB Margin		Max	10-dB Margin
500	40	30	46	86	76
1000	40	30	53	93	83
2000	47	37	58	105	95
4000	57	47	61	118	108
8000	67	57	63	130	120

The AAOO (1969) recommends levels that are 10-dB lower than those shown for the octave-band levels, except for the 8000-Hz band, where the recommended level is 52 dB.

In the selection of a location for audiometric testing, the noise environment must, therefore, be considered. It is rarely possible to make the selection on the basis of the noise environment alone, since it is usually desired to make the tests near the medical or personnel departments. Although these areas are usually relatively quiet, they do not often have a low enough low-frequency background-noise level, particularly in a plant that has noise levels high enough to constitute a hazard. In addition, these areas are often variable in level because of the way that personnel movements fluctuate, the occasional doors that slam, the rearrangements of office and factory operations, and the changes in production rate or techniques. One might allow a safety factor for these expected changes, 10 dB is often suggested, in assessing a particular space for suitability and long-term adequacy.

The space set aside for audiometric tests might be in an existing room, if sufficient sound isolation is provided. A more satisfactory procedure is to use a professionally designed and built prefabricated audiometric room (Hirschorn, 1967). Such a room will provide adequate attenuation of noise to permit location in many areas.

The attenuation characteristics of the GR Type 1939 Audiometric Examination Room (manufactured by the Industrial Acoustics Company) are shown in the Table 4-2, along with the permissible background noise levels. If this room is to be used, an octave-band analysis of the noise at the proposed site should show levels that are lower than those shown in the right-hand column.

4.6 PERSONNEL.

There are no firm standards regarding what type of individual is most appropriate to operate the audiometer used in industrial situations. Naturally, since automatic audiometers simplify the testing situation, their use means that less training will be required in order for personnel to administer the test. Regardless of what type instrument is employed, of prime importance is the

---

*The standard uses the older series of octave bands, but the corresponding levels with the new standard series of bands should be essentially the same.

requirement that the person operating the instrument recognize the significance of the test and the need to keep extraneous variables at a minimum. Likewise, instructions to the subject should be consistent and unvarying, since subtle changes in the subject's understanding of his task can effect significant changes in his apparent threshold.

4.7 AUDIOMETRY PROGRAM

In summary, a reliable audiometer, suitable test environment, and conscientious personnel using consistent test routines are all essential to meaningful monitoring of hearing. Once these criteria are met, the audiometry program can and should be implemented in several areas.

4.7.1 Uses. The first application for an industrial audiometric program is often that of pre-employment screening. The results of such tests provide a valuable reference record of the employee's hearing prior to his entering the occupational situation. Since it is probable that 27 out of every 100 workers entering a job have some hearing loss (Maas, 1965), the importance of such a record is great. It can protect the worker already exhibiting susceptibility to hearing loss by causing him to be placed in low-noise work environments. It can also protect him by detecting, at an early stage, a hearing disorder that otherwise might have gone unnoticed. Such pre-employment tests also protect the employer, by providing him with a validated record of the individual's hearing before employment commenced. Without such a reference, legal suits could be initiated by the employee for hearing losses incurred on the job when, in fact, a pre-existing condition was responsible for the loss.

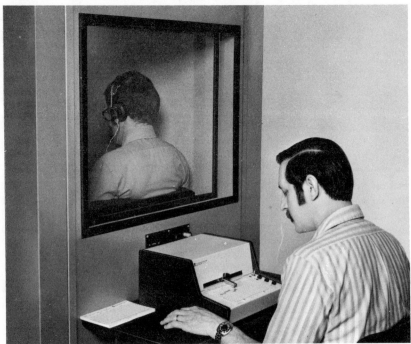

Figure 4-2. Automatic audiometer test showing a freshly recorded audiogram of actual hearing-acuity response. The subject is seated in the GR 1939 Audiometric Examination Room.

A second and equally important use for the audiometry program is the implementation of the follow-up tests of hearing ability. It is imperative that persons stationed in possibly hazardous noise environments have their hearing checked, usually at 9-12 month intervals after job placement, or earlier if they have been regularly exposed to noise levels in excess of 80 dB (A). Retest should not be postponed until speech discrimination problems are noted, since noise can affect hearing in the region of 3, 4, and 6 kHz, even when it does not markedly interfere with hearing for speech. An interval of at least 16 hours after exposure to high noise levels should elapse before measuring hearing. This period provides the ear mechanism sufficient time to recover from the effects of TTS—obviously a prerequisite to making an accurate estimate of threshold.

Follow-up tests should employ standard threshold-testing procedures used in the original examinations. By comparing the current record with the preemployment-threshold audiogram, a qualified tester can estimate what, if any, hearing losses have occurred. Of course, more sophisticated tests may have to be made, to differentiate a real permanent hearing loss from a temporary or false loss—due to inattentiveness or malingering by the sub-ject—and, in the case of the permanent loss, to pinpoint its locus.

4.7.2 Evaluation of Changes. The final—and in many ways the most important—aspect of the hearing program comes from the analysis of em-ployee audiograms. Where hearing losses are indicated, some qualified indivi-dual—in some cases the technician or physician in the plant, in others, an outside audiologist—must determine the cause of the hearing change. There are a host of relevant variables that can be investigated as contributors: physical variables, such as improper earphone placement or high ambient noise level; physiological variables, such as the sex of the subject, his age and general health; psychological variables, such as the subject's motivation and attention fluctuation; and methodical variables, such as the testing technique and instructional set used. Finally, there is the very real possibility that none of these variables can account for the current audiogram and that a perma-nent hearing loss has occurred. From this point on, it is up to the qualified professional, the audiologist and his associates, to ascertain the type of difficulty, its cause and, where possible, its cure. Toward these ends, the data from the industrial monitoring program will be used—the audiogram, informa-tion about the character of the noise, and medical history of the individual. For these reasons, it is essential that this information be kept as current and complete as possible.

4.8 APPROPRIATE LEGISLATION.

Just as the awareness and specification of the hazardous properties of noise has increased in recent years, so also has federal and state legislation to protect employees whose occupation requires that they work in a noisy environment. A number of states have made legislative provisions to compen-sate workers suffering from industry-related hearing losses. Wisconsin, one of the leaders in this area, has had loss of hearing listed as a compensable claim since 1919 (Frederickson, 1967). The first case in the state, however, was filed only in 1951, culminating in a State Supreme Court decision (1953) that allowed the claimant compensation for industrial-noise-induced hearing loss. This case, now a classic, was one of the first instances in which it was agreed that a disability was sustained, even though the employee had not missed work and a wage loss had not been sustained. As a result of this decision, some 500 more claims were filed in a short period of time until, in 1955, the present section of state legislation pertinent to occupational hearing loss was passed (Frederickson, 1967). Briefly, this legislation acknowledges the reality of occupational deafness, defined by permanent partial or total loss of hearing. It further permits the awarding of financial compensation to employees sustaining such a loss, whether partial or total, provided that the loss is verified by hearing tests or medical evaluation. This last phrase emphasizes, once again, the importance of validated audiograms.

The Wisconsin legislation is not unique by any means. AAOO indicates that over 35 of the 50 states acknowledge the existence of occupational hearing loss due to continuous noise exposure, and provide compensation for such loss. In the remaining states, responsibility for hearing loss claims must be determined by a court decision.

In addition, Federal legislation has recently been enacted to protect workers in firms engaged in interstate commerce (see paragraph 4.4.1), and a number of states have similar regulations.*

These regulations, as well as others proposed, underscore the prevalence of high-level noise and its damaging effects on human hearing. It also makes it essential, for the protection of employer and employee alike, that industry-wide hearing conservation programs be implemented immediately to assess, reduce, and monitor the effects of noise.

*Cf. American Conference Governmental Industrial Hygienists, *Threshold Limit Values of Physical Agents Adopted by ACGIH*, (1014 Broadway, Cincinnati, Ohio 45202).

REFERENCES

AAOO (1969), "Guide for Conservation of Hearing in Noise", *Supplement to Trans Amer Acad Ophthalmology and Otolaryngology*, Revised 1969. (Committee on the Conservation of Hearing, c/o Callier Hearing and Speech Center, 1966 Inwood Road, Dallas, Texas 75325).

AIHA (1966), *Industrial Noise Manual*, Second Edition, American Industrial Hygiene Association, 14125 Prevost, Detroit, Michigan 48227.

G.R.C. Atherley, W. G. Noble, and D. B. Sugden (1967), "Foundry Noise and Hearing in Foundrymen," *Ann Occup Hyg*, Vol 10, #3, July 1967, pp 255-261.

W. L. Baughn (1966), "Noise Control-Percent of Population Protected", *International Audiology*, Vol V, #3, Sept 1966, pp 331-338.

G. von Bekesy (1947), "A New Audiometer", *Acta Oto-Laryngol*, Vol 35 1947, pp 411-422.

R. W. Benson, G. Cook, S. H. Pearsall, and J. Woods (1964), "Experimental Investigation of a Prototype Noise Exposure Meter," Aerospace Medical Research Laboratories, WPAFB Tech Doc Rept #AMRL-TDR-64-4.

J. H. Botsford (1969), "Prevalence of Impaired Hearing and Sound Levels at Work", *J Acoust Soc Am*, Vol 45, #1, Jan 1969, pp 79-82.

J. H. Botsford and B. R. Laks (1970), "Noise Hazard Meter", *J Acoust Soc Am*, Vol 47, #1, Jan 1970, p 90.

W. Burns, R. Hinchcliffe, and J. S. Little (1964), "An Exploratory Study of Hearing and Noise Exposure in TextileWorkers", *An of Occup Hyg*, Vol 7, #4, Dec 1964, pp 323-333.

D. L. Chadwick (1963), "Noise-Induced Deafness", *The Practitioner*, Vol 191, #1146, Dec 1963, pp 733-741.

A. Cohen, J. R.Anticaglia, and H. H. Jones (1970), "Noise Induced Hearing Loss, *"Arch Environ Health,"* Vol 20, #5, May 1970, pp 614-623.

A. Cohen and K. C. Baumann (1964), "Temporary Hearing Losses Following Exposure to Pronounced Single Frequency Components in Broad-Band Noise", *J Acoust Soc Am*, Vol 36, #6, June 1964, pp 1167-1175.

J. R. Cox, Jr., R. H. Mansur, and C. R. Williams (1953), "Noise and Audiometric Histories Resulting from Cotton Textile Operations", *AMA Arch Indus Hyg and Occup Med*, Vol 8, July 1953, pp 36-47.

H. Davis, G. T. Morgan, J. E. Hawkins, R. Galambos, and F. W. Smith (1950), "Temporary Deafness Following Exposure to Loud Tones and Noise", *Acta Oto-Laryngol*, Suppl 88, 1950, pp 28ff.

H. Davis and S. R. Silverman (1970), *Hearing and Deafness*, third edition, Holt, Rinehart and Winston, New York.

John Fosbroke, (1831), "Practical Observations on the Pathology and Treatment of Deafness" No. II, *The Lancet*, 1830-31 Vol I, pp 645-648.

A. Glorig (1967), "Some Relations between TTS and PTS," *Fourth Annual Symposium on Noise Effects in Industry*, The East Range Clinic, Dept of Indus Med, Sept, 1967.

A. Glorig, W. D. Ward, and J. Nixon (1961), "Damage Risk Criteria and Noise-Induced Hearing Loss", *Arch Oto-laryngol*, Vol 74, 1961, pp 413-423.

J. D. Harris (1965), "Hearing-Loss Trend Curves and the Damage-Risk Criterion in Diesel-Engine Room Personnel", *J Acoust Soc Am*, Vol 37, #3, March 1965, pp 444-452.

A. J. Heffler (1967), "Personal Protection from Noise", *Fourth Annual Symposium on Noise Effects in Industry*, The East Range Clinic, Dept of Indus Med, Sept 1967, pp VII 1-16.

M. Hirschorn (1967), "Acoustical Environments for Industrial Audiometric Programs" *Sound and Vibration*, Vol 1, #7, July 1967, pp 8-15.

I. J. Hirsh and R. C. Bilger (1955), "Auditory Threshold Recovery After Exposure to Pure Tones," *J Acoust Soc Am*, Vol 27, #6, Nov 1955, pp 1186-1194.

A. D. Hosey and C. H. Powell, eds (1967), "Industrial Noise, A Guide to its Evaluation and Control" U.S. Dept. of Health, Education, and Welfare, Public Health Service Publication #1572, US Govt Printing Office, Washington, D.C. 20402.

J. S. Keeler (1968), "Compatible Exposure and Recovery Functions for Temporary Threshold Shift—Mechanical and Electrical Models," *J Sound and Vib*, Vol 7, #2, March 1968, pp 220-235.

K. J. Kronoveter and G. W. Somerville (1970), "Airplane Cockpit Noise Levels and Pilot Hearing Sensitivity", *Arch of Env Health*, Vol 20, #4, April 1970, pp 495-499.

K. D. Kryter, W. D. Ward, J. D. Miller, and D. H. Eldredge (1966), "Hazardous Exposure to Intermittent and Steady-State Noise", *J Acoust Soc Am*, Vol 39, #3, March 1966, pp 451-464.

B. Kylin (1960), "Temporary Threshold Shift and Auditory Trauma Following Exposure to Steady-State Noise," *Acta Oto-Laryngol,* Supplement 152. (Stockholm).

P. LaBenz, A. Cohen, and B. Pearson (1967), "A Noise and Hearing Survey of Earth Moving Equipment Operators," *Am Ind Hyg Assoc J*, Vol 28, #2, March/April 1967, pp 117-128.

R. M. Maas (1965), "Hearing Conservation—Legislation, Insurance and Compensation Claims", Second Annual Symposium on Noise Effects in Industry, The East Range Clinic, Dept of Ind Med, June 1965, pp I1-12.

R. B. Maas (1969), "Personal Hearing Protection: The Occupational Health Nurses Challenge and Opportunity," *Occup Health Nurs*, May 1969, pp 25-27.

L. M. Moser (1970), "Noise Hazard Meter Based on Temporary Threshold Shift", *J Acoust Soc Am*, Vol 48, #1 (Pt 1), July 1970, pp 105f.

J. C. Nixon and A. Glorig (1961), "Noise-Induced Permanent Threshold Shift at 2000 cps and 4000 cps", *J Acoust Soc Am*, Vol 33, #7, July 1961, pp 904-908.

M. H. Noweir, A-A El-Dakhakhuy and F. Valic (1968), "Exposure to Noise in the Textile Industry of the UAR", *Amer Ind Hyg Assoc J*, Vol 29, #6, Nov-Dec 1968, pp 541-546.

W. A. Rosenblith (1942), "Industrial Noises and Industrial Deafness", *J Acoust Soc Am*, Vol 13, #3, Jan 1942, pp 220-225.

W. A. Rosenblith, Chmn (1954), "The Relations Of Hearing Loss to Noise Exposure", Jan 1954, ANSI Subcommittee Z24-X-2, New York.

W. Rudmose (1957), "Hearing Loss Resulting from Noise Exposure", in C. M. Harris, ed, *Handbook of Noise Control*, McGraw-Hill, New York.

L. Ruedi and W. Furrer (1946), "Physics and Physiology of Acoustic Trauma," *J Acoust Soc Am*, Vol 18, #2, Oct 1946, pp 409-412.

J. T. Sanderson and J. Steel (1967), "Noise Induced Hearing Loss in Bench Glass Blowers," *Ann of Occup Hyg*, Vol 10, #2, April 1967, pp 135-141.

E. J. Schneider, J. E. Peterson, H. R. Hoyle, E. H. Ode, and B. B. Holder (1961), "Correlation of Industrial Noise Exposures with Audiometric Findings," *Amer Ind Hyg Assoc J*, Vol 22, Aug 1961, pp 245-251.

W. Taylor, J. C. G. Pearson, A. Moir, and W. Burns (1965), "Study of Noise and Hearing in Jute Weaving," *J Acoust Soc Am*, Vol 38 #1, July 1965, pp 113-120.

W. Taylor, J. C. G. Pearson, R. Kell and A. Moir (1967), "A Pilot Study of Hearing Loss and Social Handicap in Female Jute Weavers," *Proc of the Royal Soc of Med*, Vol 60, November 1967, pp 1117-1121.

W. D. Ward (1962), "Damage Risk Criteria for Line Spectra," *J Acoust Soc Am*, Vol 34, #10, Oct 1962, pp 1610-1619.

W. D. Ward, A. Glorig, and D. L. Sklar (1958), "Dependence of TTS at 4 kHz on Intensity and Time", *J Acoust Soc Am*, Vol 30, #1, Oct 1958, pp 944-954.

W. D. Ward, A. Glorig and D. L. Sklar (1959), "TTS from Octave-Band Noise-Applications to Damage Risk Criteria", *J Acoust Soc Am*, Vol 31, #4 April 1959, pp 522-528.

C. D. Yaffe and H. H. Jones (1961), "Noise and Hearing: Relationship of Industrial Noise to Hearing Acuity in a Controlled Population," U. S. Dept. of HEW, Pub Health Ser Publication #850 (1961).

Chapter 5

Analysis

5.1 INTRODUCTION.

Electronic techniques can provide more information about sound or vibration signals than merely the over-all levels. We can find out how the energy of a signal is distributed over the range of frequencies of interest, a process that we can describe as analysis in the frequency domain. We can find relations among signals as a function of time by correlation techniques, and we can enhance the appearance of coherent elements in a signal, if a synchronizing trigger is available, by waveform averaging. These two we can class as analysis in the time domain. We can find the amplitude distribution of a signal, which shows how often the signal is at any of a possible range of values, and this process we class as analysis in the amplitude domain.

We shall first discuss analysis in the *frequency domain* in general terms. This type of analysis, which has been called "frequency analysis", "wave analysis", "spectrum analysis", "time-series analysis," and "harmonic analysis", has been widely used for noise measurements. It is invaluable in guiding one to reduce noise and vibration efficiently (see Figure 5-1). It is also helpful

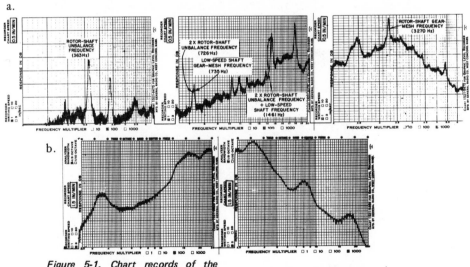

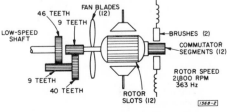

Figure 5-1. Chart records of the vibration acceleration spectrum of a motor and gear-train assembly (see sketch). (a) A 1%-band width analysis, taken with the Type 1568-Wave Analyzer and (b) A 1/3-octave analysis. For diagnostic measurements of this kind, the detail of the spectrum provided by the 1% bandwidth is by far the better.

73

for preventive maintenance. As we have seen in an earlier chapter, it is used in a number of procedures for estimating the probable effects of noise and vibration on man.

The development of electronic digital techniques has made instruments for analysis in the time domain and amplitude domain practical. One aspect of digital techniques, called "sampling", will be described, because it is helpful in understanding the concepts of autocorrelation, crosscorrelation, waveform averaging, and amplitude distribution. After those and some additional processes have been described, the implementation of various forms of analysis and their characteristics will be discussed.

The application of some of these techniques is not so obvious from the earlier discussion as is spectrum analysis, and some references will be given to their use as they are discussed.

5.2 ANALYSIS IN FREQUENCY BANDS.

To make an analysis in the frequency domain, the signal energy is electronically separated into various frequency bands, for example, octave bands, each of which covers a 2-to-1 range of frequencies. The analysis yields a series of levels, one for each band, called "band levels", or for octave bands, "octave-band levels" or "octave-band sound-pressure levels". Here it is apparent that the band in which a reading of level is obtained must be specified if the information is to be of value.

5.2.1 Octave Bands. The preferred series of octave bands for acoustic measurements covers the audible range in ten bands. The center frequencies of these bands are 31.5, 63, 125, 250, 500, 1000, 2000, 4000, 8000, and 16,000 Hz. The actual nominal frequency range of any one of these bands is 2-to-1; for example, the effective band for the 1000-Hz octave band extends from 707 to 1414 Hz.

Another series of octave bands has been widely used in the past. The older bands were a 75-Hz low-pass unit, and the octave bands of 75 to 150, 150 to 300, 300 to 600, 600 to 1200, 1200 to 2400, 2400 to 4800, and 4800 to 9600 Hz, but these are no longer preferred, according to American National Standards. This older series is still specified in a number of test codes, however, and the published data obtained with this series is extensive.*

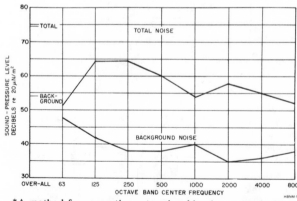

Figure 5-2. A plot of the octave-band analysis of noise from a calculating machine. (Graphic paper for plotting octave band levels is available from Codex Book Co. Inc., Norwood, Mass., as Forms 31464 and 31460 for the preferred octaves and the older series, respectively.)

*A method for converting octave-band levels measured with this older series to levels for the new series is given in Appendix A of ANSI S1.11-1966, American National Standard Specification for Octave, Half-Octave, and Third-Octave Band Filter Sets.

When a graph is made of the results of octave-band pressure level measurements, the frequency scale is commonly divided into equal intervals, between the position designated for each band and the position for the band adjacent to it in frequency. The pressure level in each band is plotted as a point on each of these positions along the other axis. Adjacent points are then connected by straight lines. An example of a plot of this type is given in Figure 5-2. An alternative presentation uses horizontal lines centered on the band at the measured level.

5.2.2 One-Third-Octave Bands. For more detailed analysis of the distribution of sound energy as a function of frequency, still narrower bands are used. The next popular division is a split of the octave into three parts. This choice is based partly on the fact that ten such filters can be arranged effectively to cover a 10-to-1 frequency range. The preferred center frequencies for such a series would be, for example, 100, 125, 160, 200, 250, 315, 400, 500, 630, and 800 Hz. The next 10-to-1 set would start with 1000 Hz as the center frequency and continue by multiplying each number by 10, 100 and so on (1000, 1250, 1600, 2000 . . .). Similarly, lower preferred frequencies are obtained by a division of 10, 100, etc. For practical reasons the usual span of third octaves for acoustic noise analysis runs from 25 to 10,000 Hz.

The actual effective band for a one-third-octave filter at 1000 Hz extends from about 891 to 1122 Hz. That is, the bandwidth is about 23% of the center frequency.

Third-octaves vs. octaves. When we wish to compare a one-third-octave analysis and an octave analysis, it is best to combine the one third octaves, in groups of three to get equivalent octaves. Thus, for example, to find the equivalent 1000-Hz octave-band level, combine the third-octave levels at 800 Hz, 1000 Hz, and 1250 Hz. Suppose the levels are 74.5, 73.0 and 71.0 dB. These levels can be converted to relative power, summed, and then translated back to level. Or we can use the chart of Figure 2-4 to combine them. The combination of 74.5 and 73.0 is 74.5 + 2.3 = 76.8. This result combined with 71.0 is 76.8 + 1.0 = 77.8 dB.

5.2.3 Narrower Bands. Analyzers that use third-octave and octave bandwidths are widely used in acoustics, but still narrower bands are essential for some purposes. One-tenth-octave (6.9%), one-twelfth-octave (5.8%), one fif-

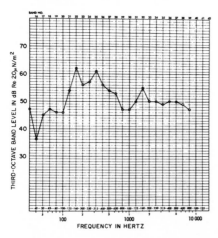

Figure 5-3. Plot of one third-octave analysis of noise from calculating machine. (Codex Book Co., Form 31462.)

75

teenth-octave (4.6%), and one-thirtieth-octave (2.3%), as well as a 1% bandwidth, have been used.

Some systems provide an analysis that effectively divides the spectrum into hundreds or thousands of bands that are a constant number of hertz (e.g. 1-Hz or 10-Hz) wide. These bands are obtained either by resonant filtering, after frequency translation by a technique known as heterodyning, by a correlation technique known as a Fourier transform, or by some combination of techniques.

None of these narrower-band systems is standardized, but they are often essential for use in tracking down sources of noise and vibration and in preventive maintenance.

5.2.4 Spectrum Level. The spectrum level of a noise is the level that would be measured if an analyzer had an ideal response characteristic with a bandwidth of 1 Hz. The main uses of this concept are comparing data taken with analyzers of different bandwidths and checking compliance with specifications given in terms of spectrum level. Charts for converting to this spectrum level from the band levels obtained with octave- and third-octave-band analyzers are given in the accompanying table and in Figure 5-4.

The corrections for spectrum level for a constant-band-width analyzer are independent of the center frequency to which it is tuned but do depend on the bandwidth used. As an example, for a 3-Hz band subtract 4.8 dB (10-Hz, subtract 10 dB, 50-Hz, subtract 17 dB) to obtain the spectrum level.

The conversion to spectrum level has meaning only if the spectrum of the noise is continuous within the measured band and if the noise does not contain prominent pure-tone components. For this reason the results of the conversion should be interpreted with great care to avoid drawing false conclusions.

The sloping characteristic given for the third-octave analyzer in Figure 5-4 results from the fact that the analyzer is a constant-percentage-bandwidth analyzer; that is, its bandwidth increases in direct proportion to the increase in the frequency to which the analyzer is tuned. For that reason a noise that is uniform in spectrum level over the frequency range will give higher-level readings for high frequencies than for lower frequencies, with this analyzer.

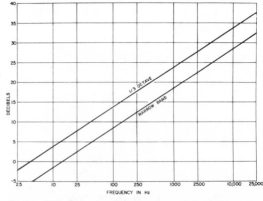

——— **Table 5-1** ———

CONVERSION FROM OCTAVE
BAND TO SPECTRUM LEVELS

Band Center	Decibels*
31.5	13.5
63	16.5
125	19.5
250	22.5
500	25.5
1,000	28.5
2,000	31.5
4,000	34.5
8,000	37.5
16,000	40.5

*To be subtracted from octave-band level readings to obtain spectrum level.

Figure 5-4. Plot showing number of decibels to be subtracted from Type 1564 readings to obtain spectrum level. The "Narrow Band" is about 7% wide. The "1/3 octave" is about 23% wide.

76

5.2.5 Components. The measured value in a band is sometimes called the value of a "component." This term is more commonly used for an analysis that divides the range of interest into a very large number of bands. The center frequency of a band is used to designate the particular component; thus, "the component at 120 Hz," "the 120-Hz component", or "the component whose frequency is 120 Hz." The term "component" is considered particularly appropriate if it is expected that the energy in a particular band is concentrated in a very narrow frequency region, as often occurs at frequencies that are multiples of the power-line frequency or of a rotational frequency of a motor. Then the resultant analysis may be described as showing "lines" at certain frequencies.

5.2.6 Conversion of Octave-Band to A-Weighted Levels. Because A-weighted sound levels are so widely used for noise ratings, some may wish to convert measured octave-band levels to the equivalent A-level when that sound level did not happen to be measured. This conversion is readily accomplished by means of Table 5-2, which is used as follows:

1. Add the correction numbers given in the table to each of the corresponding measured octave-band levels.
2. By means of the table in Appendix I convert these corrected numbers to relative power.
3. Add the relative powers of all the bands.
4. Convert back from power to level in dB.

Note that instead of steps 2, 3, and 4 the summing of the corrected levels can be done in pairs by the chart of Appendix II.

Table 5-2

CORRECTIONS FOR A-WEIGHTED OCTAVE-BAND ANALYSIS

Preferred Series of Octave Bands			Older Series of Octave Bands			
Band Center Frequency (Hz)	Original Flat	Weighting C	Octave Band (Hz)		Original Flat	Weighting C
31.5	−39.4	−36.4	18.75 − 37.5		−43.4	−39.3
63	−26.2	−25.4	37.5 − 75		−29.2	−28.0
125	−16.1	−15.9	75 − 150		−18.3	−18.0
250	− 8.6	− 8.6	150 − 300		−10.3	−10.3
500	− 3.2	− 3.2	300 − 600		− 4.4	− 4.4
1,000	0	0	600 − 1,200		− 0.5	− 0.5
2,000	+ 1.2	+ 1.4	1,200 − 2,400		+ 1.0	+ 1.1
4,000	+ 1.0	+ 1.8	2,400 − 4,800		+ 1.1	+ 1.7
8,000	− 1.1	+ 1.9	4,800 − 9,600		− 0.4	+ 1.9

Table 5-3

EXAMPLE OF CALCULATIONS*

Octave Band Center (Hz)	Band Level (dB)	Correction for A-wtng.	Corrected Level (dB)	Relative Power/10^6
31.5	78	−39	39	.01
63	76	−26	50	1.1
125	78	−16	62	1.6
250	82	− 9	73	20.0
500	81	− 3	78	63.1
1,000	80	0	80	100
2,000	80	+ 1	81	125.9
4,000	73	+ 1	74	25.1
8,000	65	− 1	64	2.5
				338.3[†]

*For the factory noise used previously.

[†]338×10^6 corresponds to 85.3 dB(A)

5.3 TIME SERIES AND SAMPLING.

5.3.1 Time Series. An acoustic signal that is monitored at a point in space can be considered as a variation in pressure as a function of time. This variation is a continuous function that we transform into a similar electrical function by the use of a microphone. We can operate on this electrical signal as a continuous function by electronic circuits, and we call this "using analog techniques."

It is also useful to convert the function into a series of discrete numerical values, which is called a "time series." We can then operate on these discrete values by digital techniques with a computer program. This computer may be one that is easily recognized as such, or it may be built into the system in such a way that its operation is not apparent externally.

♦ **5.3.2 Sampling.** The process of obtaining a series of discrete numerical values from a continuous function is known as sampling. We use electronic circuits to observe the instantaneous voltage of the signal at regular intervals. This instantaneous voltage is then converted into an electrical signal that represents a numerical value proportional to that voltage.

What requirements do we have to put on this time series so that it is an adequate representation of the original continuous function? The answer depends on what information we want from the time series. If we wish to be assured that we can perform a direct spectrum analysis on the time series, we can begin with a specification in the frequency domain. We can see that one factor is how frequently we sample, compared to how rapidly the signal changes. The actual rule is that the sampling rate must be at least twice the highest frequency component in the signal.

The frequency of the signal that corresponds to that minimum sampling rate has been called the "Nyquist frequency," which is then one-half the minimum sampling frequency. The corresponding maximum time between samples, which is the reciprocal of the minimum sampling frequency, is called the "Nyquist interval". As we shall see later we can sample less frequently for operations in the amplitude domain. Sampling less frequently has also been used to transfer information from a limited band at high frequencies to a low-frequency region, but then, care must be taken to ensure that overlapping of information does not confuse the process. The basic point here is that more frequent sampling than at the Nyquist interval is sufficient sampling, but it is not always necessary when we need only a limited amount of information from the signal.

♦ **5.3.3 Quantization.** When the sampled value is converted into an equivalent numerical value by an analog-to-digital converter, each value is represented by a finite number of on-or-off states of electronic elements. The converter has in effect an input-output relation that is a series of steps. The size of the steps depends on the total range to be covered and the number of steps available. Since the equivalent electrical signal is usually coded in binary form, the number of steps is then, say 256, 512, 1024, etc., which is 2 raised to some integer exponent.

The exponent of 2 used is called the number of "bits," and a 10-bit converter would have 1024 discrete values. Since the signal has both positive and negative values, this number may be cited as 512 values plus a sign bit.

Each of the sampled values is now rounded off or quantized to the nearest number of units in the range available. This quantization leads to an error that may be as much as one-half the quantum step or interval in the conversion. On the average, however, it will be less than that, and the equivalent noise contributed by this error has an rms value of about 0.3 times the interval. Furthermore, this noise is distributed in frequency, and when an analysis is made, the equivalent noise level will be correspondingly lower in each band.

An example of small-signal operation is sometimes cited as a limiting feature of the analog-to-digital converter. Assume that the signal applied to the converter has a total voltage excursion that is less than one interval in its range. Then, the output will remain at a zero value, and the signal will not be recognized. This mode sets one limit on a type of dynamic range. But in practice such a situation should not ordinarily occur. The converter should be preceded by electronic amplifiers of sufficient gain so that any signal to be studied can be brought up to the level required for proper utilization of the converter. The dynamic range that is then of interest is the level of the smallest component that can be observed compared to the level of the total signal, which we shall discuss briefly.

In analysis one is often interested in each of a number of small components of a signal, which may contain one or more dominating components. What happens to the small components when the signal is sampled? The answer is that they are preserved but, as described above, quantization noise appears (Sloane, 1968). Since this noise is distributed in frequency, when an analysis into many bands is made, the noise on the average in each band becomes very small. With a high-resolution processor, one can then observe components that need be only somewhat greater than the noise level in the band, which may be appreciably less than the total noise level.

The significant reductions in effective quantization noise that occur in some processing procedures mean that the computing system, used to process the digital data, can advantageously utilize a significantly higher resolution than is used in the analog-to-digital converter. It is for this reason that one can justify the use of a computer with 16-bit resolution for processing data from a 10-bit converter, for example (Korn, 1966, Chapter 6; Widrow, 1961).

♦ **5.3.4 Aliasing and Filtering.** In order to appreciate other effects of this sampling process, it is useful to look at the sampling of some sinusoidal pressure waveforms. "Waveform" is used here to describe the instantaneous amplitude as a function of time. In Figure 5-5 three waveforms are shown

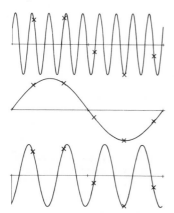

Figure 5-5. Waveforms of three frequencies sampled at the same rates for digital processing.

with sampled points (the crosses) uniformly spaced on the time axis. In the middle example shown, the period of the sampling is one-fifth that of the period of the wave; sampling frequency of 5000 Hz = 5X frequency of the wave (1000). One can see that it is not possible to pass a sinusoid through the points shown that has a lower frequency (longer period) than that shown in the middle.

The lower waveform in the figure is shown sampled at a rate five-fourths the frequency of the waveform, and the upper waveform sampling rate is five-ninths the frequency of the wave. As shown in the figure we can draw another lower-frequency wave through the sample points. The waves have been set up so that all 3 go through equivalent points. If we call the frequency of the middle wave 1000 Hz, and the sampling frequency 5000 Hz, the other frequencies are 4000 Hz and 9000 Hz. We could have shown waves whose frequencies are 6000, 11000, 14000, 16000, 19000, 21000 Hz, etc., all of the same peak amplitude and all going through the same points. Since these cannot be distinguished from one another by the selected set of points, they are called aliases (Blackman and Tukey, 1958, p. 167; Bendat and Piersol, 1966, 278ff). The frequencies of components that are aliases are related by the equation $\pm f_1 = f_2 \pm k f_s$, where f_1 and f_2 are the alias frequencies, k is an integer, and f_s is the sampling frequency.

When these sampled points are treated by digital processing, they are usually assumed to be from a wave of the lowest frequency. If the sampling rate for an incoming signal is not greater than twice the highest frequency of any component in the signal, then some of the high-frequency components of the signal will be effectively translated down to be less than one-half the sampling rate. This translation may cause serious problems with interference of high and low-frequency components.

How are these interference effects avoided? Either we sample at a sufficiently high rate to avoid them, or we put in a low-pass filter to reduce the amplitudes of the higher-frequency components, so that they are no longer large enough to be troublesome.

In order to see what is required here, consider the filter-response characteristic, shown in Figure 5-6, which is for a low-pass filter with a nominal cutoff frequency at 5 kHz. This statement merely means that, in a signal applied to the input of the filter, components with frequencies above 5 kHz are attenuated compared to those components having frequencies below 5 kHz.

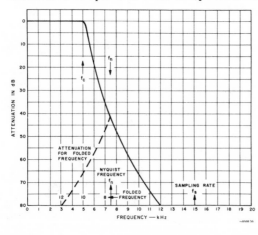

Figure 5-6. Low-pass filter characteristics required to reduce effects of aliasing.

Assume we are interested only in the range below 5 kHz. If we sampled at a 10-kHz rate, and a component at 5.1 kHz was present, it would be equivalent to one at 4.9 kHz and the filter would not adequately reject the component at 5.1 kHz. Our processing would lead us to believe there was a component at 4.9 kHz and we would be misled. Suppose we sampled at a 15-kHz rate as shown on the figure. The 5.1 kHz component would be there, but it is beyond the range of interest, and we would ignore it.

If however, there is a component at 10 kHz, it would appear to be at 5 kHz in the processing, and we might be misled. But now the filter would attenuate this component by some 66 dB, which would probably make it so small that we would not be concerned about it. Any components at a frequency higher than 10 kHz would be attenuated even more and be correspondingly less important. The components originally at frequencies between 5 and 7.5 kHz would appear, but with some attenuation, and they would be ignored, because we assumed interest only up to 5 kHz. Components between 7.5 and 10 kHz would be translated into the range between 5 and 7.5 kHz and also be ignored.

It is sometimes easier to think of the component frequencies as being folded about a frequency equal to one-half the sampling rate. This folding is illustrated on the figure for the attenuation characteristic.

If we wanted to suppress the extraneous components at 10 kHz and beyond even more than 66 dB, we could either use a filter that had more attenuation at those frequencies or go to a higher sampling rate, or both.

In general, it is advantageous to use filters to limit the frequency range of the input data, since we can then use a lower sampling rate and a minimum number of points for a given sample time. These filters when used in this way are often called, "anti-aliasing filters" or, simply, "aliasing filters." If we have to process a signal that lasts for a second and that could have components up to 12,000 Hz, we would have to sample at more than a 24,000-Hz rate. We would then have more than 24,000 values to process. If we are interested only in the range below 1000 Hz, we could use a low-pass filter that starts attenuating at 1000 Hz. We could then sample at a 3000- to 4000-Hz rate, and we would save much time in processing.

◆ **5.3.5 Frame Size.** Some digital operations can be applied in a running fashion to the sampled values as they are produced. But other operations are done in batches, and it is convenient then to think of a set of points or values that are processed as a group, and we shall call such a set a "frame." The word "sample" is also used for such a set, but this usage may lead to confusion, since "sample" is thought by some to be an individual value. "Block" is also used for this set of points, but it is convenient to reserve this word as a more general term for sets of points.

The frame size, which is the number of sampled values in the frame, is most conveniently set up in powers of 2, that is, 64, 128, 256 etc., for many of the operations, but particularly for the calculation of the spectrum values by the fast Fourier transform.

5.4 ANALYSIS IN THE TIME DOMAIN.

5.4.1 Correlation. Correlation is a measure of the similarity of two time series or waveforms, and it is a function of the time displacement between the two (Lathi, 1965, Chapter 12; Anstey, 1966). If a waveform is compared with itself by the correlation process, it is called an autocorrelation. If the waveforms to be compared are distinct, the process is called crosscorrelation.

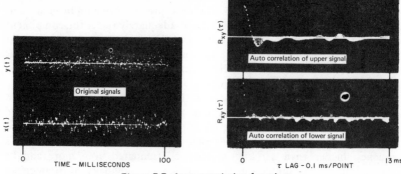

Figure 5-7. Auto correlation functions.

♦ **5.4.2 Autocorrelation.** To obtain the autocorrelation of a waveform or time series we calculate a whole set of averaged products. We multiply point-by-point that waveform with an identical one, and we take the average of these multiplied values, over the full range of the wave. If there is no time displacement, the result is the mean square value, and it is usually termed, power, although it may not be related to physical power. If the two waveforms are shifted in time with respect to each other, another averaged product can be obtained, and so on for many shifts in time. These averaged products as a function of the time displacement, or delay (usually designated by τ and also called "lag"), are the autocorrelation function.

The autocorrelation function is seen to be an extension of the concept of the mean-square value of a wave (more often used, after the square root has been taken, as the root-mean-square value). The autocorrelation function is symetrical about the point of zero delay, and at zero delay it has the maximum value equal to the mean-square value (Figure 5-7).

If the waveform has a periodic component, the autocorrelation function will show a periodic character. This behavior is illustrated by the example shown in Figure 5-8, where a noisy signal contains a periodic component, which is not obvious in the original waveform, but the autocorrelation function shows it clearly (Lee, 1960; Heizman, 1970). Some of the important applications of autocorrelation are based on this property.

♦ **5.4.3 Cross-correlation.** When the cross-correlation function is calculated, we have a measure of the similarity of the two waveforms used in the calculation. Now the maximum value does not always occur with zero delay, but the time at which the maximum value occurs may be significant. As

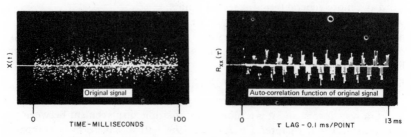

Figure 5-8. Auto correlation analysis of sinewave buried in noise.

82

shown in Figure 5-9 for the two waveforms there correlated, they are most similar when a delay of 0.7 millisecond is used. This time may be an important clue in tracking down the source of a disturbance.

The waves shown are sampled waves. The original waves can be thought of as those shown, with successive points connected by a smooth continuous line.

Applications of Correlation Techniques. Correlation techniques have been applied to determine which among a number of sources is contributing most significantly to the noise at a given point (Goff, 1955); to locate noise sources by direction finding (Faran and Hills, 1952b, Gilbreck and Binder, 1958), to separate aerodynamic noise of turbulent boundary layers from noise radiated by jet engines (Bhat, 1971), to measure panel-transmission loss without requiring that flanking signals be eliminated (Goff, 1955; Burd, 1964; Imai; 1968; Burd, 1968); to reduce the contribution of wind noise to a measurement of noise from a device (Goff, 1955; Burd, 1964); to measure the transient response of rooms (Goff, 1955); to measure the diffuseness of sound in a room (Cook et al, 1955; Balachandran and Robinson, 1967/68), and to measure sound absorption (Goff, 1955; Burd, 1964). The measurements of transmission loss and sound absorption are limited in frequency range by the size of the object and the bandwidth of the applied noise signal. They are also measurements by a particular path and not the averaged random-incidence measurements of the standard methods. They are, therefore, more suited for research studies, for tests of materials in place or for tracking down difficulties rather than for rating procedures.

The application of correlation to signal detection in underwater echo ranging and signal transmission has been extensively investigated (Faran and Hills, 1952a; D. Middleton, 1960; Horton, 1969; Tolstoy and Clay, 1966; and many papers in the *J Acoust Soc Am*).

Correlation has been used to study the vibrations on the two sides of a panel in panel sound-transmission research (Nakamuru and Koyasu, 1968), to study the flow of energy in structures (White, 1969), and to analyze seismic vibrations in geophysical exploration (Anstey, 1966).

♦ **5.4.4 Convolution and Superposition.** A digital operation called "convolution" is sometimes used in the time domain (Lathi, 1965, Chapter 10; Lee, 1960). If one waveform is convolved with another, one of them is reversed in time or folded back. Corresponding ordinates are multiplied and the products added. A whole series of these sums are obtained for different positions of the two waves, and one has a result or output that is a function of the time displacement of the two waves. Except for the reversal in time, the operation is the same as cross-correlation.

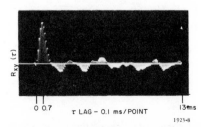

Figure 5-9. Cross-correlation function of the original signals of Figure 5-7.

83

If one of the waveforms is the input signal, the convolution can be used to produce a running average or smoothing of the wave or it can do a differencing operation, depending on the second function used in the convolution.

The operation can also be looked upon as a filtering of the input waveform. In this process the second function is known as the impulse response of the filter. It corresponds to the waveform that results when the filter is stimulated by an idealized impulse of finite energy but zero duration. The filtered output waveform is thus obtained by a convolution of the input waveform with the impulse response of the filter. The relations among the corresponding filter operations in the time domain and the frequency domain are shown in Figure 5-10.

Convolution in this type of operation is also superposition, which is more readily understood. If an input wave is assumed to be a collection of impulses occurring at successive instants of time, we can obtain the output wave by superposition of the individual responses to the impulses.

Each impulse response normally decays as time goes on. Thus, at any one instant the contribution to the output of preceding elements in the input wave is reduced, the farther back in time that we go. The output at any instant is a weighted sum of the past input. The impulse response is the weighting function.

♦ **5.4.5. Waveform Averaging.** Summation Analysis . In the study of noisy signals that include periodic components or that are responses to stimuli, the periodic component of the wave, or the evoked response, can be emphasized with respect to random noise or stray signals by a process known as waveform averaging (Geisler and Rosenblith, 1962; Clark et al, 1961; Nelson and Lassmann, 1968; Rothman, 1970). It is essential in this process that a reference or triggering signal be available.

This process is a simple summing of corresponding ordinates of selected samples of the wave. Because of this summing, waveform averaging is also called summation analysis. Often it is left as a sum, but a division by the number of selected samples is necessary to convert to an average. If we state the operation in sampled terms, it might go like this: We select and store a frame of data as determined by the reference or trigger signal. When the trigger initiates the sampling of another frame, the first of the sampled values of the new frame is added to the first sampled value of the original frame.

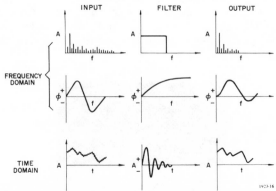

Figure 5-10. Graphical representation of interrelationships between time and frequency functions.

The second sampled value of the new frame is added to the second sampled value of the original frame, and so on. When the third frame is initiated the process is repeated.

If the trigger is synchronized to start a frame at the same point in the period of a repetitive wave, the elements in that wave of that period will sum directly. Noise signals will sum in a random fashion, and the net result is that the ratio of the desired signal to the noise will grow by a factor of the square root of the number of frames summed.

The summing at a periodic rate may be used in vibration studies to emphasize those elements in a vibration waveform that are synchronous with a shaft rotation, for example. It has been used to study the development of small surface defects in bearings (Hannavy, 1967), by summing at a period that corresponds to that of the particular part being studied. A similar procedure has been used to study gear defects (Thompson and Weichbrodt, 1969).

The signal does not have to be periodic if a trigger signal is available that precedes the desired signal by a fixed time. Thus, if a "click" stimulus is used to evoke a brain wave response, there is a reasonably stable delay between the onset of the click and the response. The click signal can be used to trigger the averaging, and the evoked stimulus can be enhanced, or pulled out of the noise, by adding many triggered frames of the response. Because there is some variability in the delay in biological systems, however, only some 10 to 100 frames can be used before the process is no longer helpful. In physical systems, the number of frames that may be useful can be many thousands.

Other methods of averaging are sometimes used. If the data are changing slowly, the averaging may be set up to make earlier data less important in the result than the latest data.

5.5 ANALYSIS IN AMPLITUDE DOMAIN.

♦ **5.5.1 Amplitude Distribution.** Suppose we are observing a noise whose maximum instantaneous sound pressure is 1 N/m^2. We set up a series of timers that record a running total of the times that the instantaneous value is within certain intervals. One of these is for the interval 0 to 0.1 N/m^2, and successive ones go in 0.1 steps in the series: 0.1 to 0.2, 0.2 to 0.3, . . . 0.9 to

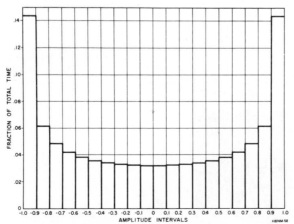

Figure 5-11. Histogram amplitude analysis of a sinewave.

85

1.0 and > 1.0. A similar series is used for the negative values of sound pressure (note that sound pressure is the change in pressure with respect to the ambient average atmospheric pressure).

After these timers have been running for a while, we record the running total for each. We divide each value by the total time for all intervals and plot the results. Suppose we get the plot shown in Figure 5-11. This type of plot is often called a "histogram" or a "frequency distribution" (here "frequency" is used in the sense of "frequency of occurrence" and not "frequency in Hz").

Someone familiar with these plots would guess from Figure 5-11 that the sound-pressure wave that was observed was probably essentially sinusoidal in form. (Actually one cannot be definite about such an observation, since an infinite variety of waveforms could produce the same distribution.) If we refined the interval resolution to the limit, we could obtain the characteristic curve of Figure 5-12 for a sinewave. This plot is an amplitude-density distribution. The area under the wave between any two values is the fraction of the total time that the instantaneous pressure has a value that falls within that interval.

If we measured the amplitude-density distribution for a random noise we might get one of the form shown in Figure 5-13. If we did, we would assume we were dealing with a "Gaussian" noise, which is characterized by the bell-shaped curve. It is also said to have a "normal" distribution. An amplitude-density distribution of this form is commonly observed for acoustic noises.

If a strong sinusoidal component is mixed with random noise, the amplitude-density distribution will be a mixture of the two basic density distributions shown.

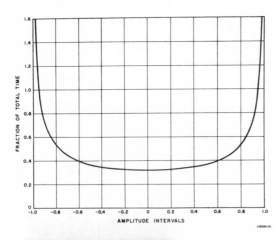

Figure 5-12. Amplitude density distribution of a finely sampled sinewave.

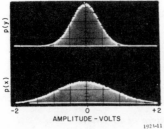

Figure 5-13. Amplitude histograms of random noise.

If we have an amplitude-density distribution, we can calculate certain values that characterize it. For acoustical waves, the mean or average value over a long period is zero. The mean-square value could be obtained by squaring each of the amplitude values, multiplying it by the proportion of the time that it is present, summing these products, and dividing by the total time. This mean-square value is termed the "variance" of the distribution. The square root of this variance is the "standard deviation," usually called "sigma" (σ), and it is also the rms (root-mean-square) amplitude, provided the average is zero, and it is commonly used as a proper measure of the amplitude.

We could calculate other measures of the distribution, but the rms value is the most useful. Most modern acoustic metering systems are designed to indicate this rms value of the signal.

If we measure the amplitude-density distribution again at a later time, we will get a new set of values. We can keep doing this for a number of times and then we can compare the values we get. If they are all essentially alike, we call the noise "stationary," that is, its amplitude-density distribution does not vary significantly with time, at least, say, for the range of times that we are interested in. It is also necessary that the spectrum remains essentially the same for true stationarity.

We have used the terms "essentially" and "significantly" to indicate that absolute equality is not expected for random signals. The meaning of the terms will be described in a statistical sense later, in the discussion of confidence limits and degrees of freedom.

The most important measure of the amplitude distribution of a random signal is the rms value or the standard deviation, and the density plot (Figure 5-14) is given in terms of the rms value. The accumulative value, or amplitude-distribution function, for Gaussian random noise is shown in Figure 5-15.

The amplitude-density distribution is also the probability-density distribution and we can think of it in the following way. Suppose we have a Gaussian noise signal that is stationary. We take one measurement of the instantaneous sound pressure. If we disregard the sign, what is the probability that it will be less than the rms value? For a Gaussian noise this probability is about 68%, which is the area of the amplitude-density distribution curve between the "one-sigma" values (on both sides of the zero level). What is the probability that it will be more than 3 times the rms value? It is about 0.26%.

It is now easy to see that we could have approached this Gaussian characteristic in another way. Suppose we take a whole series of observations of the instantaneous value of a random noise, that is, we sample it. We can now plot a histogram of this set of values. We would expect that the histogram would be similar in shape to the characteristic "bell" or "normal" curve. As we increase the number of observations of the Gaussian noise, the histogram approaches the Gaussian shape more closely.

We can obviously calculate an rms value for the sample. If we do not sample too rapidly in comparison with the time characteristics of the noise, we find that with a set of 100 or more observations we can get a good estimate of the rms value of the noise signal. Note that for this signal we do not require that the sampling be done rapidly, as long as the signal is stationary. In fact the sampling can be done leisurely and not at the Nyquist interval. An interesting laboratory experiment can be based on sampling random noise essentially by hand and, therefore, at a slow rate.

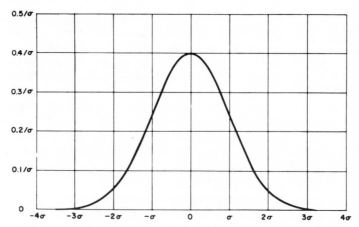

Figure 5-14. The amplitude density distribution p (v) of Gaussian random noise.

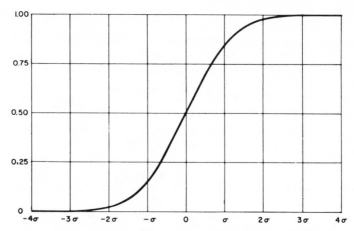

Figure 5-15. The amplitude distribution function P (v) of Gaussian random noise.

If the signal being sampled is a periodic signal, even fewer observations of the signal are required for a good estimate of the rms value. But some unusual sampling situations must be avoided. Thus, the sampling rate must not have the same period as the period of the signal or some integer multiple of that period. When sampling procedures are used in the process of determining the rms value of a wave that may be periodic, these conditions are avoided by one of the following:

1. Sampling at a random rate.

2. Sampling at a rate that changes according to some rule.

3. Sampling with a period less than half the period of the signal.

The measurement of amplitude distribution, in a practical case, is not nearly so useful as a spectrum measurement and it is rarely done (Piersol, 1967). It is helpful, however, to explain it to bring in various ideas and techniques that are used in other applications.

5.5.2 Level Distribution. If the spectrum and the amplitude distribution of a noise remain essentially the same regardless of the time when a set of observations is made, it is stationary. But, actually, we are ordinarily concerned only with a limited time span. If we ignore the startup and shutdown phase of the cycle, the noise of most refrigerators can be regarded as stationary. We can make many measurements while it is running, we can run it again and again, and we can make more measurements that will give consistent results if we duplicate conditions.

Many other noises are not so readily made effectively stationary. Thunder, a sonic boom, a door slam, and an explosion are examples of transient sounds that have to be treated differently. But there are also noises of intermediate types or combinations of noises.

When a machine operator in a shop is setting up his work, the noise from his machine may be at a low level, but there will be some background noise from other machines that are in operation. When he runs his machine, the noise in his vicinity may increase significantly. If we are trying to evaluate the noise he is exposed to, we need to take this variability into account. We can proceed in a fashion similar to that for amplitude distribution to obtain a "level distribution."

We use a sound-level meter to measure the level. (Now it is not the instantaneous value of the wave, but it is the rms value averaged over some time.) We use intervals of level, say 90-92 dB, 92-95 dB, 95-97 dB, etc., with times arranged to indicate the total time that the noise stays within each of the intervals. At the end of the day we could plot a histogram of the result, and we would have a level distribution of his exposure to noise.

5.6 TECHNIQUES AND CHARACTERISTICS OF ANALYSIS.

The basic processes used for spectrum analysis are a filtering, or resonance, technique and a Fourier transform, or correlation, technique. Frequency shifting, or heterodyning, is sometimes used to extend the basic range of these systems, and time compression or scaling is used in some instruments to speed up the filtering process.

As indicated in the earlier sections, the signal can be processed by analog techniques, digitally, or by a combination of the two.

♦ **5.6.1 Direct Filtering.** Many analyzers now use sets of electronic band-pass filters to separate the signal components into the required number of standard bands. When those filters are operating directly at the frequencies of the desired bands, we call the analysis "direct filtering."

Most octave and one-third-octave analyzers use such electronic systems, either combinations of inductors and capacitors, or networks involving resistors, capacitors and amplifiers in feedback circuits, to produce the required resonant effects.

Serial or Parallel Operation. We can classify analyzers by another feature into two types, that is, serial or parallel. In strictly parallel operation, the input signal is passed simultaneously through a set of filters with detectors at the output of each filter (see Figure 5-16). The output level is then available continuously for each filter band.

In serial operation, however, only one detector is used, and the filters are sequentially switched into the circuit or are tuned sequentially to the required frequencies. The level in each band is determined before the next band is measured.

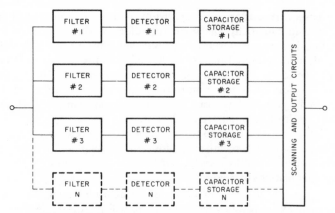

Figure 5-16. Typical parallel-operation analyzer.

The tuning of the filter in serial operation may be continuous through the frequency range or it may proceed in steps. In acoustics, the stepped operation that goes from one standardized preferred center frequency to the next is more widely used than the continuous one, mainly because the spectrum is then characterized by a finite set of numbers.

Serial-type analyzers are usually smaller and less expensive than corresponding parallel types, because they require fewer elements to do the job. The parallel type, on the other hand, can be much faster. Consider the following example. If we dwell for one second to determine the level in each of 30 third-octave bands, the serial analyzer would require 30 seconds, while the parallel analyzer would have the output available after only one second. Some time must be allowed for presenting the data in usable form, but it is obvious that if many spectra with many bands must be measured, much time can be saved by the use of a parallel analyzer.

One can take advantage of the sampling techniques in the amplitude domain, where sampling less often than at the Nyquist interval is generally satisfactory, to make a hybrid type of parallel operation. By the use of sampling, multiplexing, and storage techniques one detector system can be made to act as many.

Digital Filtering. Band-pass filtering can be done digitally on a sampled time series (Gold and Rader, 1969; Oppenheim, 1969; Kuo and Kaiser, 1966; Enochson and Otnes, 1968). An output time series is generated from the input time series by the use of a difference equation, which relates an output value at a particular time to the input values at that time and for some previous times, as well as to one or more previous output values.

By the use of a group of these difference equations, we can simulate a set of one-third-octave filters, for example, that each produce a time series equivalent to a filtered signal. From each of the output time series we can calculate in the computer an rms value to give the one-third-octave levels.

Some of the parameters that affect the dynamic range, the discrimination against interfering signals, and the stability of the output time series are:

1. Accuracy and resolution of conversion to digital form.
2. Length of time series.
3. Actual difference equations used.
4. Accuracy of calculations.

5.6.2 Fast Fourier Transform. Another important spectrum-analysis technique is the basic one of direct application of the Fourier transform. It has only recently become significant in the analysis of actual acoustic and vibration signals as a result of the development of the calculation procedure called the Fast Fourier Transform (FFT) (Bingham et al, 1967; Singleton, 1969; Gold and Rader, 1969). FFT is an efficient way of calculating correlation of a waveform with sinewaves whose frequencies are integer multiples of the frequency corresponding to the time duration of the wave.

In order to apply the FFT to a signal, the signal is transformed into a digital time series as explained previously. A fixed number of consecutive points in the series is selected. Usually, this number is a power of 2, for example, 1024, or 2048. This time series is then transformed into corresponding components in the frequency domain by the use of the FFT calculation in a computer. If the signal is noise, or has the character of noise, a number of transforms must be combined to get statistical stability in the answer.

Some of the parameters that affect the characteristics of the process are the following:
1. Number of samples in selected time period.
2. Accuracy and resolution of the conversion to digital form.
3. Weighting functions used on the sampled values.
4. Number of transforms combined.
5. Accuracy of the calculation procedure.

These parameters determine the frequency resolution, the dynamic range, the discrimination against interfering signals, and the statistical stability of the output spectrum.

The number of output values developed in the analysis is equal to the number of data points in the original frame. But they are in pairs with a real (cosine) value and an imaginary (sine) value for each integer multiple of the fundamental frequency. The two together are then usually described as a frequency component with a real and imaginary part or as a vector with an absolute magnitude and a phase angle. For many acoustical problems, the phase angle is ignored and the magnitude at each integer multiple of the fundamental frequency is the value used as the result of the analysis.

The square of this magnitude is sometimes called an "autospectral value," and the set of squares is the "autospectrum." This set of squared values is also sometimes called the "power spectrum." Since the actual values are hardly ever "power," and since the "cross spectrum" is also used (see paragraph 5.7.1), it is convenient to use the terms "autospectrum" and "cross spectrum" with the similar and related "autocorrelation" and "cross-correlation."

Some simple relations for the frequency transform are as follows:

Number of component lines = 1/2 number of data points in frame.

Frequency range = 1/2 sample rate.

$$\text{Resolution/line} = \frac{\text{Freq. range}}{\text{Number of lines}} = \frac{2 \text{ X Freq range}}{\text{Number of data points}}$$

Frame period = Number of data points/sample rate
= Number of data points x sampling interval

Resolution/line = 1/Frame period

♦ *Windows/Truncation.* When a frame of points is selected and used in an FFT analysis, the time for the initial point becomes the reference for the start of the sine and cosine waves used for the analysis. In addition, the standard transform uses the duration of the frame as the basic period for the analysis. The fundamental component in the analysis has a frequency that is the reciprocal of that basic period, and the frequencies of the other components are integer multiples of that fundamental.

If the actual signal from which the frame is taken is periodic, and if the duration of the frame is an integer multiple of the signal period, then the analysis can give excellent results without modification of the frame. Another way of stating this favorable situation is that the component frequencies of the actual signal are all integer multiples of the fundamental frequency corresponding to the frame period. This situation is unusual, however, and we need to look at the problems of a more general case.

There are a number of ways of looking at what happens in an analysis with a finite duration input. One approach uses the concept of a data or time window. The input signal is regarded as extending indefinitely in time, and the sampled frame can be regarded as the input signal looked at through a finite window in time, or multiplied by a data window that is 0 everywhere except during the sampling period and then it is unity.

When a transform is made, the developed analysis fits the input frame of data correctly, but in doing so, it in effect is analyzing a signal that is the original frame continuously repeated. A simple example of what can happen is shown in Figure 5-17, where a sinewave has been sampled. The discontinuity at the ends leads to an extensive set of components in the analysis that may obscure or interfere with the components of interest. This effect is sometimes called "leakage." If the frame were changed to include more of the original signal, the discontinuity would be different, and the results of the analysis would be different. In this example, if the frame were set to coincide with the period of the sinusoid, there would be no discontinuity, and no difficulty would occur. We cannot, however, adjust the frame to fit any possible signal, because many are not periodic, and even for those that are we would not necessarily know what period to use. With a fixed frame, let us observe the response of the system as we vary the incoming signal frequency. With a rectangular window we will obtain a response of the form shown in Figure 5-18. This response shows the desired peak at f_0 when the applied signal and the frame fit correctly. When the frequency deviates from this optimum value, the response decreases.

Another way of looking at the problem is that the Fourier transform is designed to produce a set of functions that will combine to reproduce the original data. The discrete transform uses only a minimum number of these

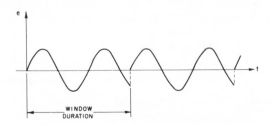

Figure 5-17. A repeated frame of data that shows the discontinuity that can occur when the window duration is not an integer multiple of the basic period of the sampled wave.

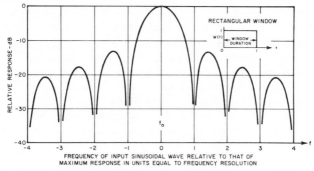

Figure 5-18. Effect of truncation with abrupt rectangular window on the response of the transform.

functions to reproduce these data and the behavior of the combined functions beyond the data window may not be what we would always desire. If we wish to control the behavior beyond the original window, we have to specify more data points outside the original set and thereby enlarge the window.

Several techniques have been developed to reduce the effects of "leakage" or of the finite window. The most commonly used one is a modification of the window to have a smooth transition from zero to the full value, instead of the abruptness of the rectangular window. The simple tapering of the "raised cosine" or the hanning window, shown in Figure 5-19, is the one most widely used, and it is very effective. The response now becomes as shown.

When hanning is used, the data at the ends of the frame are ignored, since they are multiplied by a value near zero. It is important then that the data window be positioned and made wide enough to ensure that the important behavior is centered within the window.

The tapered weighting used in hanning and other windows also broadens the main response of the transform. This broadening can be compensated for by increasing the number of points in the data frame.

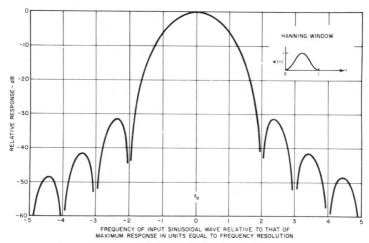

Figure 5-19. Effect of tapered window (hanning) on the response of the transform.

Reducing the effects of interfering components is so important that hanning or some similar tapered weighting should almost always be used.

♦ **5.6.3 Time Compression or Scaling.** When a serial type of analyzer is to be used to analyze a signal that changes with time, the signal is often first recorded on a tape recorder. Sections of the record are then selected, made into tape loops, and played back to the analyzer until the analyzer has had time to go through the desired range of analysis.

If the speed at which the tape loop is reproduced is different from the original recording speed, all the signal components are translated in frequency by the speed ratio, and the repetition period of the loop is changed by the inverse of this ratio. Thus, if we have a one-second loop recorded at 1 7/8 in./s and played back at 15 in./s, the loop will repeat every 1/8th of a second, and a 1000-Hz component will become an 8000-Hz component.

The loop when played back at its original speed repeats every second. The output signal will then have components that are spaced 1 Hz apart. The speeded-up loop will have components with 8-Hz spacing.

If we now analyze this speeded-up loop in third-octave bands, we use the band at 8000 Hz to find the value of the components in the original signal in the 1000-Hz band. The band at 8000 Hz is 8 times as wide as the one at 1000 Hz, and the response of its filter is correspondingly 8 times as fast. Now we can in effect process the signal 8 times as rapidly as at the original speed.

If the signal is converted into digital form, it can be stored in a circulating digital memory rather than in a tape loop. The speed-up that is then possible is many times greater, being 1000-to-1 or even more.

♦ **5.6.4 Frequency Translation or Heterodyning.** Both the serial and parallel types of analyzer can be operated over a wide range of input-signal frequencies by translating the input signal frequencies to be within the range of the analyzer. This technique has been widely used with serial analysis to translate the effective center frequency of a single highly selective filter.

The technique is illustrated in Figure 5-20. Assume we are concerned with the signal components in the vicinity of 1000 Hz. A local oscillator in the device is set to generate a sinewave at 101 kHz. This wave is mixed with the incoming signal, and the resulting components, with frequencies in the immediate vicinity of 100 kHz, pass through the 100-kHz filter and are indicated by the detector system. The component in the original signal at 1000 Hz would be the principal component measured. But components at 100 kHz and at 201 kHz also produce an output at the detector, but they are

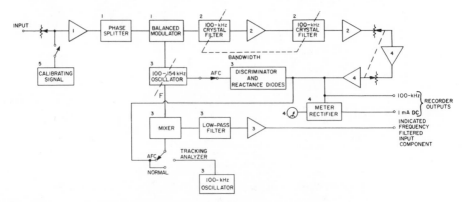

Figure 5-20. Block diagram, a heterodyne analyzer.

94

excluded by filtering or other methods before the frequency translation occurs.

If the frequency of the local oscillator is changed, the input-signal frequencies of the components passed by the filter will also change. In this way, a 10-Hz wide filter at 100 kHz can be made to appear to be a 10-Hz wide filter at any desired frequency.

♦ **5.6.5 Analysis of Random Noise.**

Effective Bandwidth. The actual filter characteristic in any of these systems is not ideal, in the sense of completely rejecting signal components outside the nominal passband. Modern filters can be made sufficiently good, however, that the difference in the results of an analysis, between using a filter with ideal characteristics and using the actual one, are ordinarily negligible for acoustical and vibration signals. In order to attain this behavior they must be designed with the correct effective bandwidth.

To determine the effective bandwidth of a filter, it is driven by a white-noise signal, which is a noise that is uniform in power-per-hertz-bandwidth over a very wide frequency range. The effective bandwidth is then the total output power divided by the output power for 1-Hz bandwidth at the frequency of maximum response. This can also be expressed as the equivalent-ideal-filter bandwidth, where the ideal filter is adjusted to have the same gain as the maximum gain of the actual filter.

The effective bandwidth for an actual filter can be designed to be a third-octave or whatever is required. The shape of the filter, and its actual width in the nominal pass band, are set to pass somewhat less noise to compensate for that passed by the filter outside the nominal band limits. Although this behavior is strictly correct only for white noise, with a good filter characteristic the behavior is also very good for noise spectra that are not uniform.

The effective bandwidth for noise, for a Fourier transform that yields autospectral values, is the sampling frequency divided by twice the number of points in the data frame. If a hanning window is used, however, the elementary bands, represented by the autospectral values, are each broadened by a factor of 1.5, or 1.8 dB. This factor is cancelled out if at least three adjacent bands are summed to provide a broader band, because the maximum response is increased by the same factor.

♦ *Blurring Effect.* Many modern analyzers yield results for practical noises that are essentially those that would be obtained if ideal filters with infinitely steep attenuation characteristics could have been used. But sometimes the results from ideal filters are not ideal, or at least are not easily interpreted. Even an ideal filter "blurs" changes in spectrum level with frequency because of its finite bandwidth. This effect is illustrated by the analysis shown in Figure 5-21. The signal used here was developed by filtering "pink" noise, that is noise with equal energy per octave bandwidth. The pink noise was passed through a combination of low-pass and high-pass filters to give an abrupt transition in spectrum level of about 20 dB. This transition occured at a rate of about 60 dB/octave. This noise was analyzed with 1%, one-tenth-octave, and one-third-octave bandwidths. The recorded levels for each analysis were adjusted at the low frequency end to be alike (Kundert et al, 1969).

Calculations show that these analyzers are performing nearly as well as an ideal set. The analysis with the 1% bandwidth analyzer shows the true nature of the spectrum applied to the analyzers. The others show the effects of the

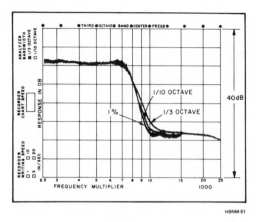

Figure 5-21. Blurring effect and excess level error for various bandwidths (slope = 60 dB/octave).

HBNM-51

wider bandwidths. There is an obvious rounding at the lower corner, and the wider the band used the more the corner is rounded.

The wider bands also show a shift in level, which will occur whenever the spectrum slopes steeply, because the energy passed by the filter, in the region where the level is high, will more than counterbalance the decrease in energy in the opposite region. This shift has sometimes been regarded as an apparent shift in the center frequency of the filter, but when levels are to be specified at preferred frequencies, it may be more convenient to think of it as a shift in level. The extent of the effect can be expressed as an excess in apparent spectrum level, and Figure 5-22 shows the results of calculations for various bandwidths and spectrum slopes. It illustrates the limited resolving power of wide filters even when ideal. This effect is important mainly when comparing results with analyzers of different bandwidths. For most practical noises, the effect is not great except for octave bands. For the one-third-octave band and the extremely steep slope in the example of Figure 5-21, the shift in level in the middle of the slope should be somewhat over 3 dB, which is essentially the shift observed.

A similar effect results in filling in a narrow dip and rounding off the top of a peak in a spectrum. It is merely what is to be expected from the limitations in resolution of a finite bandwidth.

♦ *Degrees of Freedom/Spectrum Averaging.* Assume we analyze successive frames of sampled values of a random-noise signal. The results of a Fourier

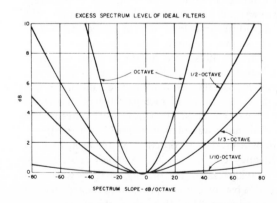

Figure 5-22. Excess level error for various bandwidths.

transform would show a very large variability in the indicated level in any one band, from one frame to the next. This variability is characteristic of a random signal (Bendat and Piersol, 1966; Sloane, 1969).

In order to produce values that have some significance for the band levels of noise, we must combine many samples. We can sum the corresponding squares of the measured spectrum values (autospectra) for a number of frames, which we call averaging. We can sum the squares of the measured spectrum values for a number of adjacent bands, which reduces the resolution but improves the statistical stability. Or we can do both, that is, average and combine bands.

In order to show what needs to be done, we shall describe what happens with a white-noise signal of a given bandwidth, B, in Hz. If this is sampled at the Nyquist interval, we will get all the information available in the signal. If the frame of points is taken over a total time span T, we will have a frame of 2 BT points. This value for bandwidth-limited Gaussian white noise is the number of statistically independent sampled values, which is sometimes called the number of degrees of freedom. It can be used to describe the expected behavior of the variability of the random signal.

If a complete Fourier transform of this frame is now made, each autospectral component (the sum of the squares of the amplitudes of the sine and cosine terms) will have two degrees of freedom. For each independent frame of data that is summed in, two degrees of freedom are added. Thus, if we had 32 autospectral values at 1000 Hz that we had summed (we could normalize by dividing by 32 to get the average), we would have 64 degrees of freedom. From the chart of Figure 5-23 we find that we would have a 95% confidence that the resultant level is not greater than the long-term true value by more than 1.4 dB or less than the true value by more than 1.6 dB.

The results of some measurements on white noise, with a Time/Data 1923-C FFT Analyzer, will illustrate what these statements mean. One

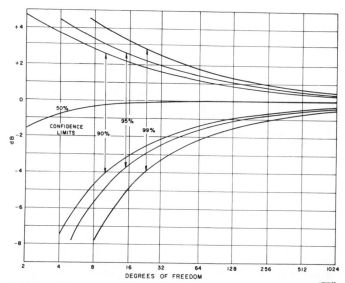

Figure 5-23. Reliability of amplitude analyses as a function of degrees of freedom from the data sample for various confidence limits.

hundred successive levels of the same single band of stationary noise were measured. Each of these 100 levels was a result of 32 averages. (The high-speed processing made it possible to get the 3200 measurements rapidly.) The measured levels were then arranged for plotting on probability paper as shown in Figure 5-24. The expected distributions for 32 and 64 degrees of freedom are also shown and they have been set at the level to give a best fit to the observed data. The results show that any particular averaged level that uses 32 independent frames is very likely to be within a 3-dB span, as predicted. Similar results are shown for a measurement with a hanning window.

The total number of degrees of freedom for a frame of data is reduced by the use of a tapered window, such as hanning. Thus, if a number of adjacent bands are combined by summing the squares of the component values, the number of degrees of freedom will not be twice the number of bands that are combined. If hanning is used, it will approach only about one-half that value. If the noise is not white over the range of the combined bands, or if the noise is not essentially stationary over the time for the frame, the total number of degrees of freedom will be reduced even further.

Thus the chart of Figure 5-23 should be used mainly as a guide.

The summing and averaging that is used here is different from that used in waveform averaging (paragraph 5.4.5). In waveform averaging, the summing is linear and includes the sign, and therefore, random noise, which is random in value, will add up more slowly than a signal that is always of the same wave shape with respect to the starting point of the frame. This type of averaging reduces random noise.

The averaged waveform will have the coherent signal emphasized with respect to the noise by a factor equal to the square root of the number of

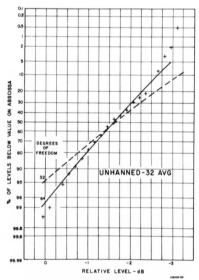

Figure 5-24. Comparison of the statistical stability of experimental measurements with theoretical curves for 32 and 64 degrees of freedom.

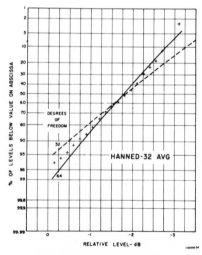

Figure 5-25. Comparison of the statistical stability of experimental measurements with theoretical curves for 32 and 64 degrees of freedom — hanning was used.

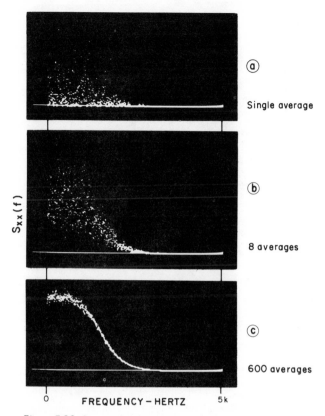

Figure 5-26. Averaged auto spectrum of band-limited noise.

sums. This technique "pulls" a signal out of noise. If one were interested in the spectrum of the coherent signal only, waveform averaging before transforming to obtain a spectrum would be a good approach when it is possible.

The spectrum-averaging procedure used in this section sums the squares of the magnitudes of the components, and the sign does not enter, since the squared value is always positive. This spectrum averaging gives a more stable, that is, less variable, value for the spectrum levels of a random-noise signal, provided the noisy signal is stationary over the averaging period. When measurement of the noise level is important, as is often the case in acoustics, spectrum averaging makes possible a more reliable measurement of the level, as shown in Figure 5-26.

It is also interesting to note that spectrum averaging sometimes makes it possible to find a periodic signal that may otherwise be obscured by noise, provided the noise is stationary. The point involved here concerns the fact that a transform of a single frame yields spectrum levels for the noise that have only two degrees of freedom. The variability of level is then very large. A pure-tone component that is of the same order as the band level of the noise will appear as just another noise component among many in its vicinity that are similar in amplitude.

If many frames are averaged as shown in Figure 5-27, the noise-spectral values are more uniform in level. Then the effect of an added periodic component will be apparent by its projection beyond the relatively uniform

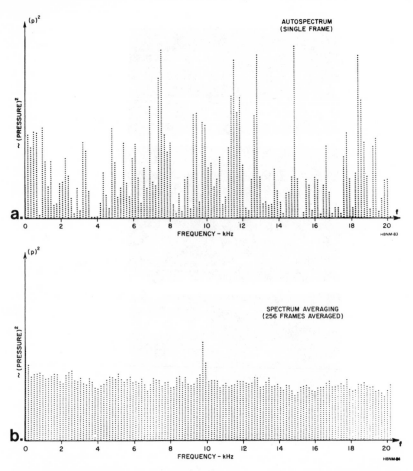

Figure 5-27. Autospectra of a signal that contains a sinewave buried in random noise. The autospectrum for a single frame is shown at (a), and the normalized average of the autospectra for 256 frames is shown at (b).

amplitude of the average noise-spectral values in its vicinity. This averaging procedure is particularly appropriate when both periodic and random signals are important.

♦ *Statistical Stability in Analog Systems.* The measurement of random noise on an analog system involves essentially the same concepts as in a digital system. Now, however, the metering circuit provides some averaging, and two meter speeds are often provided in acoustic measuring instruments. These two speeds are designated fast and slow, with the slow condition yielding the longer averaging time.

The fact than an averaging time is used leads to a dependence of the statistical stability on bandwidth. That is, if a random noise is analyzed with an analog system, the extent of the meter fluctuations depends on the bandwidth. The narrower the band, the greater are the fluctuations and the longer is the averaging time required for a satisfactory estimate of the level.

A relatively simple principle is involved here. A narrow band is used to get fineness of detail. The finer the detail that is desired, the more time is needed to obtain the result to a certain degree of confidence.

♦ *Example of Random-Noise Measurement.* To illustrate by an actual numerical example the type of behavior that occurs, some measurements were made of an arbitrary level of a random-noise generator in the octave band from 150 to 300 Hz. With the fast meter speed, the average of the fluctuating levels indicated on the meter was estimated to be about +5 dB, where in a period of 30 seconds the level fluctuated from a minimum of +3.3 dB to a maximum of +6.5 dB, a range of 3.2 dB. In the slow position the estimated level was +4.7 dB, and the level fluctuated over a three-minute period from a minimum of +3.8 to a maximum of +5.7, a range of 1.9 dB. Some sample readings were as follows: fast position: 4.8, 4.1, 5.3, 3.7, 5.8, 4.9, 5.3, 5.2, 6.2, 4.6; slow position: 4.4, 5.1, 3.9, 4.9, 4.2, 5.0, 4.7, 4.1, 4.3, 4.9. (These sample readings were taken with the help of a stroboscope, to avoid observer bias in selecting readings and to make it possible to take definite readings on the rapidly moving pointer in the fast position.) One hundred samples were taken for each position. The average value on an energy basis for slow was +4.72, with the lowest reading +3.8 and the highest +5.8. The average for fast was +4.74, with a low reading of +3.1 and a high reading of +6.2.

Taking such a set of readings is not the usual way to obtain the indicated level; rather, one estimates a value by observing the pointer fluctuations. But these discrete samples permit one to describe statistically the behavior that can be expected.

For the fast position one would expect only 1 in 1000 readings to differ from the average by more than about −3 dB or +2.4 dB, a range of 5.4 dB. The corresponding extremes for one chance in 100 is about −2.3 dB or +1.9 dB, a range of 4.2 dB; for 1 in 10, about −1.4 to +1.2, a range of 2.6 dB. Note that the range is not symmetrical.

These statements about variability can be expressed in another way, which is the converse of that above. If any reading is taken in the fast position, the chances are only 1 in 100 that the long-time average value of the noise is below the observed value by more than 1.9 dB or above the observed value by more than 2.3 dB. These limits are called the 99% confidence limits.

Confidence Limits for Octave Bands. A chart of the 99% confidence limits for octave bands for random noise measurement is given in Table 5-4.

These ranges of uncertainty can be reduced by the use of the average of a number of independent readings. The reduction in the range is approximately inversely proportional to the square root of the number of independent observations. Thus, the average of four observations would reduce the uncertainty to about one-half that shown.

─────────────── Table 5-4 ───────────────

CONFIDENCE LIMITS FOR RANDOM
NOISE IN OCTAVE BANDS

Center Freq (Hz)	99% Confidence Limits (dB) Meter Speed	
	Fast	Slow
31.5	-4.2, +7.0	-2.5, +3.3
63	-3.2, +4.7	-1.8, +2.2
125	-2.4, +3.1	-1.3, +1.5
250	-1.7, +2.1	-1.0, +1.1
500	-1.2, +1.4	-0.7, +0.7
1,000	-0.9, +1.0	-0.5, +0.5
2,000	-0.6, +0.7	-0.3, +0.3
4,000	-0.5, +0.5	-0.2, +0.2
8,000	-0,3, +0.3	-0.2, +0.2
16,000	-0.2, +0.2	-0.1, +0.1

The range of uncertainty is sometimes called the statistical error.

Averaging By Observation. When one observes the fluctuations of a meter for a time and estimates an average, the extent of the reduction of the uncertainty is limited by the fact that all the observations are not independent, and one can remember and use only a small portion of the total observed behavior. The observations are not independent because of the finite time required for the pointer to assume a new value. In the fast position of the meter, one should allow about one-half second between observations; in the slow position, an interval of one to two seconds is desirable.

◆ *Averaging By Circuit Time Constants.* The smoothing or reduction in fluctuations achieved by the electrical circuit is often characterized by an equivalent time constant. The averaging time constant required to reduce fluctuations of a rectified noise signal to a desired amount for a given band width of noise is approximately:

$$T \approx \frac{1250}{\Delta f \sigma^2} \text{ seconds}$$

where T is the averaging time
Δf is the bandwidth of the noise in Hz.
σ is the standard deviation of the fluctuations at the output of a linear detector in percent.

Duration of a Sample. The uncertainty that results from the limited observation time, in comparison with the detail desired in the frequency domain, occurs for other time limitations as well. Moreover, some of these may not be under the control of the operator. Thus, the sound source may not perform uniformly over an extended period of time; for example, a rocket may run for only a fraction of a minute. During launch, the time available for observing a rocket may be only a few seconds or less.

When a noise signal, recorded on a magnetic-tape recorder, is to be studied, it is customary to take short samples for analysis. These samples are cut from the full recording and formed into loops that can be run continuously in the recorder. This procedure directly limits the fineness of detail possible in the analysis and also limits the accuracy with which one can determine the actual level in a band.

This limitation of accuracy results from the fact that the maximum time during which independent information can be obtained is the sample duration. If the noise is sufficiently uniform with time, a longer sample can be used to obtain increased accuracy, or measurements on a number of samples can be averaged.

Because of the inherent variability of random noise, analyses of distinct samples of the same noise will not yield identical results. The expected spread in values predicted by statistical theory can be used as a guide in judging whether the results of such analyses agree well enough to be useful. Unless this inherent variability is appreciated, one can be led into rejecting useful data, rejecting a useful analysis system, or placing too much reliance on a particular measurement.

Fluctuations Produced in Practice. The table of values shown for the octave bands is based on the analysis of noise that is uniform in energy per hertz throughout the band. In the wider bands, the values shown are misleading for acoustical signals, because the energy is not uniformly distributed. One should expect from such values that, when the full range of a sound-level meter is used, the fluctuations would be a small fraction of a decibel. As a matter of fact, one can find many examples of an over-all sound level that fluctuates over many decibels.

One example is the background noise of private offices. Here, for C weighting in the slow meter position, one can commonly find fluctuations of three or more decibels. The fluctuation corresponds to a band that is only tens of hertz wide rather than 8000 to 10,000 hertz wide, such as that of the response of the sound-level meter. This is because the energy in the sound is concentrated in the low frequencies over a relatively narrow band. The fluctuations reflect only the relation between the equivalent frequency band of the signal applied to the metering circuit and the averaging time of the circuit. Whether the energy is concentrated in a narrow band by means of an electrical analyzer or by the source and the path to the microphone is immaterial.

Interpretation of Fluctuations. One can conclude, then, that if the observed fluctuations are significantly greater than would be expected, an important part of the random-noise energy is concentrated in a band or bands that are narrower than the pass band of the measuring system. (Another possibility is that the type of noise is sufficiently different from normal that the fluctuations for a given bandwidth are inherently excessive. This behavior is possible for a tone whose frequency varies in a region where the response of the measuring system varies markedly with frequency.) It is also clear that if the fluctuations are significantly smaller than would be expected, the noise very likely includes some discrete tones that have significant amounts of energy.

5.6.6 Speed of Processing — "Real Time." If an analyzer can operate to process the input signal continuously, it is often called a "real-time" analyzer. This type of operation usually requires a parallel type of analyzer or some storage system. The accuracy and frequency range over which it may operate in real time is usually significant, particularly with digital equipment, and the cost usually increases with the speed and accuracy.

In an FFT system, which operates on discrete frames of data, real-time operation requires what is called "buffered-mode" operation. Here one frame of data is being stored while another is being processed. Then, if the processing can be done within the time taken to acquire a frame of input data, real-time operation is possible. Since many noise analyzers require that a number of spectra be summed, the real-time operation with the buffered mode can make it possible to utilize the full data available in a given time.

The real-time feature is particularly important for signals that vary in character with time, for example, the sounds from aircraft, missiles, speech, music, and many machinery operations, and when it is unproductive to tape record the sounds for later analysis.

Other definitions of real time have been used, and the basic requirement seems to be that the operation must be completed quickly enough to suit the application at hand. The user must recognize this time factor as another element in his choice of analysis equipment. To illustrate the range of times involved, consider the problems of analysis with a 10-Hz band over the range from 20 Hz to 20000 Hz. A serial analyzer will take about 1000 to 2000 times the time required for a very fast FFT system to do the basic processing.

5.6.7 Dynamic Range. The dynamic range of an analyzer is set by an upper limit of distortion and a lower limit of internal noise, selectivity, or arithmetic processing errors. If a signal that is too high in level is applied to an analyzer, the analyzer will be overloaded. As a result of the overload, the indicated spectrum will be different from the actual spectrum. How seriously the spectrum is distorted depends on the way in which the overload occurs. But, ordinarily one can avoid overloading by the use of reasonable care in following the procedures given in the instructions for the analyzer.

Internal noise of an analyzer is often a lower limiting factor in the analysis range possible. Unless this internal noise is significantly less than the applied signal, it can affect the indicated spectrum. The selectivity characteristic of the analyzer also limits the range, particularly close in frequency to strong components. In addition, some analyzers, particularly older designs, have ultimate rejection of components outside the passbands of only 30 to 40 dB.

Other factors that enter into the dynamic range of digital systems are aliasing and quantization, which are discussed in paragraph 5.3.4. A factor that is related to the quantization is the detail of arithmetic processing. For example, in additions, subtractions or multiplications, it is frequently necessary to maintain a constant number of bits in the results. If this is done by simple truncation or dissymmetrical rounding, the noise introduced is usually greater than for symmetrical rounding. An even more important effect can occur in squaring the amplitudes of components, as is done for autospectral values. Sometimes the squared values are limited to the same number of bits as the basic values, in order to save storage space. This procedure can result in the loss of all information for low-level components and effectively reduce the dynamic range by a factor of two.

5.7 TWO-SIGNAL FUNCTIONS.

♦ **5.7.1 Cross Spectrum and Cross-Correlation.** A number of functions show relations between two signals. We have already briefly described cross-correlation which expresses the similarity of two signals as a function of time. A related function is cross spectrum, which is the Fourier transform of the cross-correlation and expresses the similarity as a function of frequency.

The cross-spectral function can also be calculated from the Fourier transforms of the two time series by a conjugate multiplication. This type of multiplication gives the products of the magnitude and the differences of the

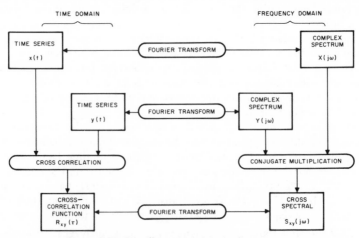

Figure 5-28. Time/frequency-domain diagram.

phases of the two signals. The alternative routes to the cross-spectral function are shown in Figure 5-28 (Heizman, 1970). One of the important applications of the cross spectrum is in the calculation of the transfer function.

Just as for autocorrelation and cross-correlation, the autospectrum and the cross spectrum are related in that the autospectrum is the cross spectrum with both signals being the same.

However, it would be wasteful to calculate the auto spectrum by either process shown in Figure 5-28, since the only output is the square of the magnitude of the components and only one transform is necessary for the autospectrum.

5.7.2 Transfer Functions and Coherence. The transfer function of a device or a system is the ratio of the output to the input. This function, which is ordinarily defined in the frequency domain, can be useful for studying noise and vibration problems. If we have the frequency analysis of both the input and the output signals, we can then have the transfer function by taking the ratio of the output to the input at each corresponding frequency component.

It is easy to see that we can select many different points in a system to be the output. Assume we have an electrically driven hydraulic pump that is in an enclosure. We are concerned about the noise and vibration that it produces. What do we regard as the output? It could be the acoustic noise at various places outside the enclosure, or inside the enclosure. It could be the vibration at the pump housing or the vibration of the pipes.

We can look at the input in a similar way. If we are interested in the noise outside the enclosure, it is hardly useful to regard the electrical-power-line terminals as the input. The vibration at various points on the pump or on the pipes could be useful as an input, for the noise outside the enclosure as the output.

In most practical acoustical and vibration problems, enough extraneous noises are present to make the simple measurement of the transfer function unreliable. By the use of an alternative form of the transfer function, these extraneous effects can be reduced. The transfer function is also the ratio of the cross spectrum of the input and output to the autospectrum of the input (Sloane, 1970; Roth, 1971). The use of the cross spectrum, which includes those components that are common to both input and output, eliminates any extraneous components that do not appear in both.

Another function that is related to the transfer function is the coherence function. It is normalized by including the input and output in both numerator and denominator, as opposed to the transfer function, which has only the input in the denominator. The coherence function is the ratio of the square of the magnitude of the cross spectrum to the product of the input and output auto spectrums. The coherence function covers a range of magnitudes from 0 to 1 as a function of frequency, and the value depends on how well the input and output values at each frequency are related. It provides a useful further parameter to help in interpreting the transfer function.

The combination of transfer and coherence functions provides a powerful technique in the study of noise sources and transmission paths.

5.8 ANALOG VS DIGITAL.

In an analog filter system, each filter band is essentially a separate element or is achieved by individual tuning. This technique is well suited for processing of, say, 8 octave bands or 30 third-octave bands or for serial analysis.

Analog equipment for these tasks is available with excellent characteristics and at lower cost than for digital equipment.

In a digital system that uses the Fast Fourier Transform, a whole series of filter bands is achieved by the one transform. The difference then between 32 or 2048 filter bands is mainly a matter of memory size. Accordingly, digital techniques become preferred as the desired number of filter bands increases.

In addition, many types of operations on the data are often easy to include once the data is in digital form. Examples of these are averaging, addition of corrections, combining bands in different ways to give both narrow bands and third-octave bands, use of weightings of various kinds either in the time domain or the frequency domain, and calculation of noise ratings. In other words digital equipment is more flexible than analog equipment.

Digital processing can have very high resolution, has unlimited repeatability, can handle vast amounts of data, and is almost insensitive to environmental factors such as ambient temperature and pressure.

Since the original signal is in analog form, some processing is often conveniently done by analog techniques before sampling and conversion to a digital form. The system is then a hybrid one and may combine some of the desirable features of both techniques.

REFERENCES

Standards
ANSI S1.11-1966, Specification for Octave, Half-Octave, and Third-Octave Band Filter Sets.
ANSI S2.10-1971, Methods for Analysis and Presentation of Shock and Vibration Data.
IEC 225-1966, Octave, half-octave and third-octave band filters intended for the analysis of sounds and vibrations.

Other
W. B. Allen and E. C. Westerfield (1964), "Digital Compressed-Time Correlators and Matched Filters for Active Sonar", *J Acoust Soc Am*, Vol 36, #1, Jan, pp 121-139.

N. A. Anstey (1966), "Correlation Techniques — A Review", *J. Can Soc Explor Geophys*, Vol 2, #1, Dec 1966, pp 1-28 and *Geophys Prospecting*, Vol 12, #4, 1964.

P. K. Baade (1966), "Instrumentation Trends for Noise Reduction, as Seen by a Mechanical Engineer", *J Audio Eng Soc*, Vol 14, #4, Oct, pp 302-306.

C. G. Balachandran and D. W. Robinson (1967/68), "Diffusion of the Decaying Sound Field", *Acustica*, Vol 19, #5, pp 245-257.

J. S. Bendat and A. G. Piersol (1966), *Measurement and Analysis of Random Data*, John Wiley and Sons, New York.

W. V. Bhat (1971), "Use of Correlation Technique for Estimating In-flight Noise Radiated by Wing-mounted Jet Engines on a Fuselage", *J. Sound and Vib*, Vol 17, #3, pp 349-355.

C. Bingham, M. D. Godfrey and J. W. Tukey (1967), "Modern Techniques of Power Spectrum Estimation", *IEEE Trans on Audio Electroacoust*, Vol AU-15, #2, June, pp 56-66.

R. B. Blackman and J. W. Tukey (1958), *The Measurement of Power Spectra*, Dover Publications, Inc., New York.

R. Bracewell (1965), *The Fourier Transform and Its Applications*, McGraw-Hill, New York.

A. N. Burd (1964), "Correlation Techniques in Studio Testing", *Radio and Elec Engineer*, Vol 27, #5, May, pp 387-395.

A. N. Burd (1968), "The Measurement of Sound Insulation in the Presence of Flanking Paths," *J Sound and Vib*, Vol 7, #1, January 1968, pp 13-26.

L. J. Chamberlain (1971), "A Simple Discussion of Time-Series Analysis", *Sound and Vibration*, Vol 5, #4, April 1971, pp 18-25.

W. A. Clark, R. M. Brown, M. H. Goldstein, Jr., C. E. Molnar, D. F. O'Brien, and H. E. Zieman (1961), "The Average Response Computer (ARC): A Digital Device for Computing Averages and Amplitude and Time Histograms of Electrophysiological Response", *IRE Trans on Bio-Medical Electronics*, Vol BME-8, #1, Jan, pp 46-51.

R. K. Cook, R. V. Waterhouse, R. D. Berendt, S. Edelman, and M. C. Thompson, Jr. (1955), "Measurement of Correlation Co-efficients in Reverberant Sound Fields", *J Acoust Soc Am*, Vol 27, #6, Nov, pp 1072-1077.

G. R. Cooper and D. C. McGillem (1967), *Methods of Signal and System Analysis*, Holt, Rinehart and Winston, Inc., New York.

P. W. Cooper (1964), "Correlation Detection in a Duovelocity Medium with Application to Seismic Disturbances", *J Acoust Soc Am*, Vol 36, #7, July, pp 1378-1382.

L. D. Enochson and R. K. Otnes (1968), *Programming and Analysis for Digital Time Series Data*, Navy Publication and Printing Service Office, Washington, D.C. 20390.

J. J. Faran, Jr. (1968), "Random-Noise Generators", *General Radio Experimenter*, Vol 42, #1, Jan, pp 3-13.

J. J. Faran, Jr., and R. Hills (1952a), "Correlators for Signal Reception", Tech Memo 27, Sept, Acoustics Res Lab Div. App Sci, Harvard Un, Cambridge Mass.

J. J. Faran, Jr. and R. Hills (1952b), "The Application of Correlation Techniques to Acoustic Receiving Systems", Tech. Memo #28, Nov., Acoustics Res Lab, Div. Appl Sci, Harvard Un, Cambridge, Mass.

C. D. Geisler and W. A. Rosenblith (1962), "Average Responses to Clicks Recorded from the Human Scalp", *J Acoust Soc Am*, Vol 34, #1, Jan, pp 125-127.

D. A. Gilbrech and R. C. Binder (1958), "Portable Instrument for Locating Noise Sources in Mechanical Equipment", *J Acoust Soc Am*, Vol 30, #9, Sept, pp 842-846.

K. W. Goff (1955), "Application of Correlation Techniques to Some Acoustic Measurements", *J Acoust Soc Am*, Vol 27, #2, Mar, pp 236-246.

B. Gold and C. M. Rader (1969), *Digital Processing of Signals*, McGraw-Hill, New York.

A. Hannavy (1967), "New Detection Devices Help Predict Potential Failure", *Prod Engineering*, Mar 27, pp 37-44.

C. L. Heizman (1970), "Signal Analysis with Digital Time Series Analyzers", *General Radio Experimenter*, Vol 44, #7-9, July-Sept, pp 3-7.

C. W. Horton, Sr. (1969), *Signal Processing of Underwater Acoustic Waves*, U.S. Gov't Printing Office, Washington, D.C. 20402.

S. Imai (1968), "On a Simplified Hybrid Analog-Digital Correlator for Sound Measurements," Reports of the 6th Inter Cong on Acoust, Tokyo, Aug, pp E-13-16.

T. C. Kincaid (1968), "Optimum Waveforms for Correlation Detection in the Sonar Environment: Noise-Limited Conditions," *J Acoust Soc Am*, Vol 43, #2, Feb, pp 258-268.

G. A. Korn (1966), *Random-Process Simulation and Measurements*, McGraw-Hill, New York.

W. R. Kundert and A. P. G. Peterson (1969), "Spectrum Analysis of Stationary Noise Signals", *Sound and Vibration*, Vol 3, #6 June, pp 16-24.

F. F. Kuo and J. F. Kaiser (1966), *System Analysis by Digital Computer*, John Wiley & Sons, Inc., New York.

H. F. H. Lange (1967), *Correlation Techniques*, Iliffe Books Ltd, London, and D. Van Nostrand Company, New York.

B. P. Lathi (1965), *Signals, Systems and Communication*, John Wiley & Sons, Inc., New York.

Y. W. Lee (1960) *Statistical Theory of Communication*, John Wiley & Sons, Inc., New York, 1960.

G. C. Maling, Jr., W. T. Morrey and W. W. Lang (1967), "Digital Determination of Third-Octave and Full-Octave Spectra of Acoustical Noise", *IEEE Trans Audio Electroacous*, Vol AU-15, #2, June, pp 98-104.

D. Middleton (1960), *An Introduction to Statistical Communication Theory*, McGraw-Hill, New York.

S. Nakamuru and M. Koyasu (1968), "Measurements of the Vibration Correlation between Both Surfaces of a Multi-Layer Panel," *Reports of the 6th International Congress on Acoustics,* Tokyo, Aug, pp E-125-128.

D. A. Nelson and F. M. Lassman (1968), "Effects of Intersignal Interval on the Human Auditory Evoked Response," *J Acoust Soc Am*, Vol 44, #6, Dec, pp 1529-1532.

A. V. Oppenheim, ed (1969), *Papers on Digital Signal Processing*, The M.I.T. Press, Cambridge, Mass.

107

A. G. Piersol (1967), "Practical Interpretations of Unusual Characteristics in Reduced Vibration Data", *J Env Sci*, Vol 10, #1, Feb, pp 17-21.

P. R. Roth (1971), "Effective Measurements Using Digital Signal Analysis", *IEEE Spectrum*, Vol 8, #4, April, pp 62-70.

H. H. Rothman (1970), "Effects of High Frequencies and Intersubject Variability on the Auditory-Evoked Critical Response", *J Acoustical Soc Am*, Vol 47, #2 (Part 2), February 1970, pp 569-573.

R. C. Singleton (1969), "A Short Bibliography on the Fast Fourier Transform", *IEEE Trans Audio Electroacous*, Vol AU-17, #2, June, pp 166-169.

E. A. Sloane (1966), "An Introduction to Time-Series Analysis", Monographs I, II, and III, Time/Data Corporation, Palo Alto, Calif.

E. A. Sloane (1968), "The Effects of Quantization on Small Signals", Technical Bulletin No. 1, Time/Data Corporation, Palo Alto, Calif.

E. A. Sloane (1969), "Comparison of Linearly and Quadratically Modified Spectral Estimates of Gaussian Signals", *IEEE Trans Audio Electroacous*, Vol AU-17, #2, June, pp 133-137.

E. A. Sloane (1970), "Measurement of Transfer Function and Impedance", *General Radio Experimenter*, Vol 44, #7-9, July-Sept, pp 8-13.

M. W. Smith and R. F. Lambert (1960), "Acoustical Signal Detection in Turbulent Airflow", *J Acoust Soc Am*, Vol 32, #7, July pp 858-866.

R. A. Thompson and B. Weichbrodt (1969), "Gear Diagnostics and Wear Detection", ASME Vibration Conference Paper #69-VIBR-10, and *Machine Design*, Vol 41, May 15, pp 181-183.

I. Tolstoy and C. S. Clay (1966), *Ocean Acoustics*, McGraw-Hill, New York, 1966.

P. H. White (1969), "Cross Correlation in Structural Systems: Dispersion and Nondispersion Waves", *J Acoust Soc Am* Vol 45, #5, May, pp 1118-1128.

B. Widrow (1961), "Statistical Analysis of Amplitude-Quantized Sampled Data Systems", *AIEE Trans*, Vol 79, Part II, *Applications and Industry, 1960*, Jan, pp 555-568.

J. F. Wilby and F. L. Gloyna (1970), "Correlation Measurements of Airplane Fuselage Vibrations", *J Acoust Soc Am*, Vol 48, #1 (Part 1), July, p 80.

Chapter 6

Instrumentation for Noise and Vibration Measurement

6.1 GENERAL.

Sound measuring systems use a microphone (or, as a more general term, a transducer) to transform the sound-pressure variations into a corresponding electrical signal. This signal is amplified, measured and analyzed by electronic instruments.

Although some nonelectronic instruments have been used in the past for sound measurements, hardly any are used at present. The dominance of electronic techniques is a result of their versatility and extensive development and the need in acoustics for operation over a wide range of frequencies for which those techniques are well suited.

Many vibration measurements, however, are still made with nonelectronic techniques. When the vibratory motion is slow and large, the measurement can sometimes be made visually, with a scale. If the motion is slow but small, a measuring microscope may be used. For rapid motion, a stroboscope can be used to produce an apparent slow-motion replica of the rapid motion for optical measurement. This technique is discussed in more detail later in this handbook.

Table 6-1

GENERAL RADIO SOUND- AND VIBRATION-MEASURING INSTRUMENTS

	Calibration	Transducers & Accessories	Preamplifier	Sound & Vibration Meters, Tape Recorder, Impact Meter	Analyzers/ Filters	Graphic Recorders & Display Units
Acoustics	Sound-Level Calibrator	Ceramic Microphones (1", ½")		Precision Sound-Level Meter and Analyzer (Octave)		
		Electret Microphones (1", ½", ¼")	Preamplifier (Optional)	Sound-Level Meter	Level Recorder and 1/3-Octave Band Analyzer	
		Condenser Microphones (1/2", 1/4" 1/8")	Preamplifier with Bias Supply	Noise Exposure Meter	Sound & Vibration Analyzer (1/3 & 1/10 octave)	Graphic Level Recorder
		Couplers	Multichannel Amplifier	Impact Noise Analyzer	Wave Analyzer (1% Bandwidth)	
		Cables		Cassette Data Recorder	Real-Time Analyzer (1/1, 1/3, or 1/10 Oct)	DC Recorder
		Windscreens			FFT Analyzer	Storage Display Unit
		Tripod				
Vibration	Vibration Calibrator	Accelerometers (Pickups)	Preamplifier (Optional)	Vibration Meter		
		Cables Magnet Clamp	Multichannel Amplifier	Cassette Data Recorder	Universal Filter	
		Control Boxes to use with SLM or Analyzers				

The measuring system may be entirely mechanical or a mixture of mechanical, electrical, and optical elements. Many of these systems have been described in the literature (Ormondroyd et al, 1950; Harris and Crede, 1961). Of the many possible systems, the one particularly adaptable to a broad range of applications uses a vibration pickup (also called a transducer) to transform the mechanical motion into a corresponding electrical signal. As for sound measurements, this signal is amplified, measured, and analyzed by electronic instruments.

We shall describe the two types of transducers, microphones and vibration pickups, and then the electronic equipment. A listing of the transducers and the various instruments is shown in Table 6-1.

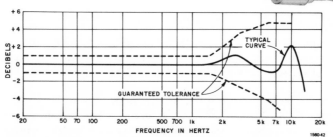

Figure 6-1. Random incidence response for a General Radio 1-in. Ceramic Microphone on 10-in. gooseneck mount.

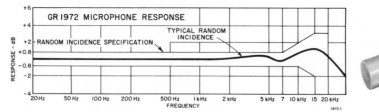

Figure 6-2. General Radio 1/2-in. Ceramic Microphone.

6.2 TRANSDUCERS — TRANSDUCER SYSTEMS.

Two different types of microphones are widely used for sound measurements. They are the piezoelectric-ceramic type and the condenser type.

6.2.1 Ceramic Microphones. The ceramic microphone uses a piezoelectric ceramic (lead-titanate, lead-zirconate) as the voltage-generating element. (The term piezoelectric indicates that the material produces a voltage when it is strained.) A diaphragm fastened to the ceramic transfers the sound-pressure variations into a corresponding varying force that bends the ceramic element (Bauer, 1957; Bonk, 1967).

This stable and rugged microphone has a smooth frequency response and is relatively unaffected by normal temperature and humidity changes. It is regularly supplied with the latest sound-level meters and is available for use with other measuring instruments. It can be mounted directly on the instrument or separately, with connection by extension cable when it is necessary to avoid the effects of the observer and the instrument case on the acoustical measurement. Because of its good characteristics and ease of use, this type of microphone is generally preferred for most sound-measurement applications.

The 1-in. size (actually 0.936 in. or 23.77 mm in diameter) is the most commonly used microphone, because it has an acceptable combination of characteristics with regard to sensitivity, frequency response, and omnidirectionality. The 1/2-in. size (12.7 mm in diameter) has a better high-frequency response and is less directional but these improvements are obtained at the expense of sensitivity.

Typical responses for the two sizes of ceramic microphones are shown as a function of frequency in Figures 6-1 and 6-2. The responses are usually given for particular values of incidence of the sound on the microphone. For a cylindrically symmetrical microphone with the diaphragm mounted perpendicular to the axis of symmetry, sound propagation along the axis toward the microphone is called "$0°$ incidence" and sometimes "perpendicular incidence." Propagation perpendicular to the axis is "$90°$ incidence" or "grazing incidence."

When the angle of incidence of sound is equally likely to be any value, as is essentially the situation in a highly reverberant room, an averaged value of response is calculated from the total directivity characteristic. This averaged response is called the "random-incidence response." It is the one used for rating response in the American National Standard for sound-level meters.

For low frequencies, as would be expected, the microphone is essentially omnidirectional. As the frequency of the sound increases, its wavelength becomes more nearly comparable with the dimensions of the microphone and directional effects are noticeable. At a given frequency the directional effect for the smaller microphone is correspondingly less than for the larger one.

6.2.2 Condenser Microphones. Another type of microphone, known as the condenser, electrostatic or capacitor microphone, is used for measurement purposes (Hawley, 1955; Rasmussen, 1960/1963). Again a diaphragm is used and it is set in motion by the sound pressure. Here, the variation of an electrical capacitance, formed between the thin, stretched diaphragm and a backplate, is used to develop an electrical signal when a high polarizing voltage is applied to the capacitor.

Responses as a function of frequency for such microphones are shown in Figure 6-3. These small microphones have excellent response to high frequencies and are used for wide-frequency-range acoustical investigations.

6.2.3 Electret Microphones. Another microphone of the condenser type uses a thin, plastic sheet, which has a conductive coating on one side. The other side of the sheet rests on a perforated, metallic backplate with many small, supporting raised points. The sound pressure is applied to the plastic surface, which moves with respect to the backplate, thus varying the capacitance between the conductive coating and the backplate. By the use of a suitable plastic and proper treatment, the microphone maintains its own polarization, and the capacitance change generates a corresponding electrical voltage. When the microphone is self polarized in this way, it is called an "electret microphone" (Sessler and West, 1966; Djuric, 1972). This microphone can also be built to have an excellent combination of characteristics.

6.2.4 Hydrophones. Microphones used for underwater sound measurements are called hydrophones (Figure 6-4). They also generally use piezoelectric ceramics as the sensitive element (Tucker and Gazey, 1966). Various types of hydrophones are available from such companies as Atlantic Re-

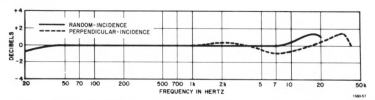

Figure 6-3. Frequency characteristics of two different half in. condenser microphones. They optimize response for specified sound incidence.

search, Chesepeake Instrument Corporation, Clevite Ordnance, Gulton Industries, Scientific-Atlanta, and Wilcoxon Research.

6.2.5 Vibration Pickups. The vibration pickups supplied by General Radio, as shown in Figure 6-5, are all inertia-operated, lead-zirconate, lead-titanate, piezoelectric devices that generate a voltage proportional to the acceleration of the pickup (Dranetz and Orlacchio, 1961; Mason, 1961, Carlson, 1952). Voltages proportional to velocity and displacement of the vibrating body are

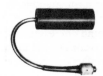

Figure 6-4. A typical hydrophone.

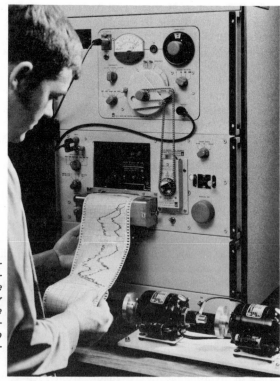

Figure 6-5. Typical application of a vibration pickup. It is mounted on the end bell of the left motor in the foreground and the vibration signal is being analyzed by a General Radio automatic-recording 1/3-octave-band analyzer.

112

also obtainable by the use of electronic integrating networks to convert the voltage generated by the pickup. This type of pickup has the advantage of small size, light weight, and wide frequency range, and it does not require a fixed frame of reference for the measurement.

6.2.6 Transducer Sensitivity. Microphone sensitivity is now rated in terms of the reference sensitivity of 1-volt output for a pressure of 1 newton/(meter)^2 or in terms of the older reference, 1 V/μbar. The apparent sensitivity levels for these two ratings differ by 20 dB; a pressure of 1 N/m^2 corresponds to 94 dB re 20 μN/m^2, whereas 1 μbar corresponds to 74 dB re 20 μN/m^2. A typical microphone open-circuit (unloaded) sensitivity level is −40 dB re 1 V/(N/m^2). If the sound-pressure level were 134 dB re 20 μN/m^2, the open-circuit output from this microphone would be 1 V (see Figure 6-6).

The sensitivity of an accelerometer is commonly rated in terms of open-circuit (unloaded) output in millivolts (.001 V) for an acceleration that corresponds to that of gravity (g). Since the acceleration of gravity (9.80665

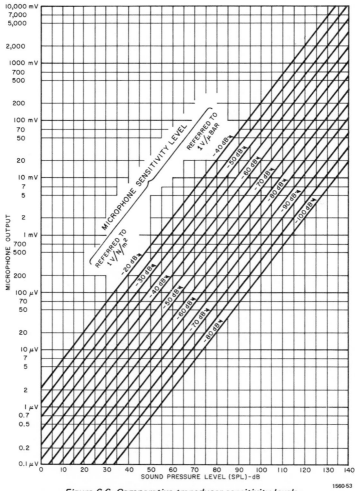

1560-53

Figure 6-6. Comparative transducer sensitivity levels.

m/s² or 386.09 in./s²) is always directed toward the center of the earth, an alternating acceleration rated in terms of "g" units is to be interpreted as a use of the numerical value only. As such, it is sometimes used for the peak value of a sinusoidal acceleration or the rms value (0.707 times the peak for a sinusoidal vibration). As long as it is recognized that the electrical output and the acceleration are to be measured in the same way, rms and rms, or peak and peak, it is not necessary to specify in the sensitivity statement which is meant; the numerical sensitivity should be the same for both.

The relations among velocity, displacement, and acceleration depend on the frequency as well as the amplitude (Appendix IV). To find the transducer output for a given frequency and velocity or displacement, convert the vibration to the equivalent acceleration (Appendix IV, Figure IV-1 and IV-2), and then the chart of Figure 6-7 can be used.

6.2.7 Preamplifier. The preamplifier shown in Figure 6-8 is a high-input-impedance, low-noise amplifier (Marteney, 1970). It is particularly well suited for amplification of the output of capacitive sources, such as ceramic and condenser microphones and piezoelectric vibration pickups, and for use with sound-level meters and analyzers when a long cable must be used between the microphone and the instrument. A gain of 20 dB (10:1) is available for increasing the ultimate sensitivity of analyzers for low-level measurements.

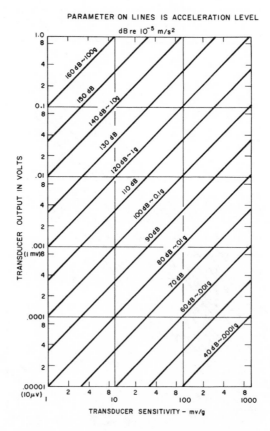

Figure 6-7. Chart to determine transducer output for various acceleration parameters.

Figure 6-8. A typical field installation for microphone use. The tripod mount is shown supporting a Type 1560-P42 Preamplifier, into which a 1/2-inch microphone has been plugged. The foam sphere at the top is a windscreen that fits over the microphone to permit accurate measurements outdoors.

The preamplifier shown can also provide a 200-V polarizing voltage for a condenser microphone. It obtains its own power from another instrument or a separate supply.

6.2.8 Wind Screen. In order to reduce the wind noise produced when a microphone is placed in a wind, a wind screen, shown in Figure 6-8, should almost always be used outdoors.

6.2.9 Tripod. A microphone and preamplifier is often best suspended in position by its connecting cable. When this arrangement is not possible, a tripod with suitable adaptor devices can be used to hold the microphone in the desired position (see Figure 6-8).

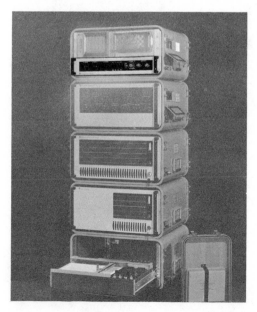

Figure 6-9. The Type 1566 Multichannel Amplifier shown mounted in a field transportable automatic sound analysis system in which it scans the inputs of up to 16 remote microphones.

6.2.10 Multichannel Amplifier. Many sound and vibration measurements can be simplified by use of a scanner that connects, in sequence or in any arbitrary order, the outputs from a number of transducers to a single metering or analyzer system. The unit shown in Figure 6-9 scans up to 16 channels and amplifies each.

6.3 SOUND-LEVEL METERS.

The basic instrument of a sound-measuring system is the sound-level meter. It is a portable meter for reading in terms of a standard reference pressure (20 μN/m^2) the sound level at its microphone. Fundamentally, the instrument consists of an omnidirectional microphone, a calibrated attenuator, a stabilized amplifier, an indicating meter, and weighting networks. The networks provide the three common sound-level meter responses, A, B, and C (see Figure 2-3).

Four types of sound-level meters are specified in the latest American National Standard Specification for Sound-Level Meters, S1.4-1971. These are called Types 1, 2, 3, and S or "Precision," "General Purpose," "Survey" and "Special Purpose," respectively. The first three types differ in their

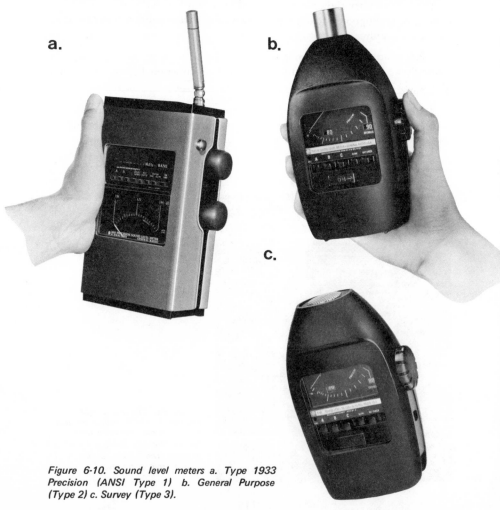

Figure 6-10. Sound level meters a. Type 1933 Precision (ANSI Type 1) b. General Purpose (Type 2) c. Survey (Type 3).

116

performance requirements, with the requirements being most strict for the Type 1 or Precision Sound Level Meter and progressively less strict for the types 2 and 3. The special-purpose sound-level meter is one that meets the requirements of one of the other types, but does not contain all three weighting networks.

The three basic types are available and are shown in Figures 6-10. They are all small, light in weight, and easy to use. They can be mounted on a tripod, held in the hand or placed on table or bench with equal facility. Readings and settings are easily made with the microphone in a vertical or horizontal position.

The units shown also include an output for driving analyzers, recorders, oscilloscopes, and earphones.

The Type 1933 Precision Sound-Level Meter and Analyzer (Kundert and Marteney, 1971) also includes a special detector circuit for measuring impulse sounds (paragraph 6.9) and it has a set of octave-band filters (paragraph 6.6.1). This instrument is the key one in the 1933 Sound Analysis System. This system permits one to make a wide variety of measurements in the field, and its versatility is a result of the features included in the 1933.

In the precision sound-level meter shown, the microphones fit atop a telescoping 18-in. extension to reduce the effects of the instrument and operator on the source field. When the operator and instrument must be removed even farther from the microphone, a cable can be used, and a 10-ft cable is included. The measurements are not affected by the use of the cable

Figure 6-11. The Type 1934 Noise Exposure Monitor, shown in an industrial application.

117

because the preamplifier in the 1933 is detachable and connects to the cable at the microphone end to prevent loss in signal level.

6.4 NOISE-EXPOSURE METER.

An instrument for evaluation of noise exposure according to the regulations of the U.S. Department of Labor (OSHA, 1970) is shown in Figure 6-11 (Partridge, 1971). It is a special-purpose sound-level meter, which includes a calculator to do the measuring, accumulation, exposure calculation, and even impact detection automatically. The result is read out on a digital display and is also available as digital and analog electrical signals for use with recorders or printers. The recorded time of occurrence of high exposure levels is helpful in determining how to reduce the noise-exposure level.

Pushbuttons permit the user to select the appropriate length of working day for the exposure calculation. At the end of this measurement period, the instrument holds the noise-exposure percentage until it is reset. At any intermediate time one can flip a switch to read the percentage of allowable noise exposure accumulated to that instant.

A security case is also available to reduce the possibility of tampering with the instrument or measurement.

6.5 VIBRATION METER.

The instrument for vibration measurements that corresponds to the sound-level meter is the vibration meter, shown in Figure 6-12. It takes advantage of the wide frequency range of the piezoelectric type of pickup with a response for the measurement of acceleration extending smoothly from 2 to 20,000 Hz. The meter is calibrated directly in terms of peak,

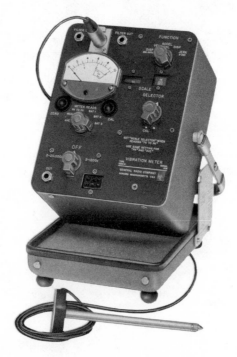

Figure 6-12. Type 1553 Vibration Meter shown with pickup connected.

118

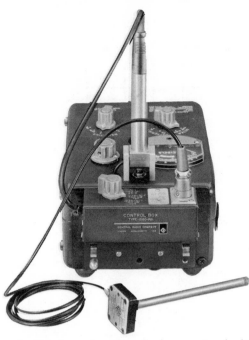

Figure 6-13. The 1560-P11B Vibration Pickup System with the 1551-C Sound-Level Meter.

peak-to-peak, and average displacement, velocity, acceleration, and jerk; these are indicated in mils, in./s, in./s^2, and in./s^3, respectively. Another model of this instrument indicates the same quantities in metric units, i.e., mm, m/s, m/s^2, and m/s^3, respectively.

Since the vibration pickup used with this meter is of the acceleration type, two stages of electrical integration and one of differentiation are necessary to provide the various types of response. The integrating and differentiating circuits are built in as part of the amplifier.

The instrument is direct-reading for acceleration, velocity, and displacement from 2 to 2000 Hz, and direct-reading for jerk over the frequency range of 1 to 20 Hz, when used with the Type 1560-P52 pickup normally supplied. When used with the Type 1560-P53 pickup, the direct-reading range starts at about 25 Hz and extends to 20 kHz for acceleration measurements. For velocity and displacement measurements, the high-frequency range is limited to about 2000 Hz by the internal noise level in the instrument.

6.5.1 Vibration Pickup System With The SLM Vibration measurements can be made with a sound-level meter when a vibration pickup is substituted for the microphone as shown in Figure 6-13. An auxiliary control box, which is connected between the meter and the pickup, converts the response so that the meter indicates velocity and displacement as well as acceleration. The combination of pickup and control box, called a vibration pickup system, provides a convenient and inexpensive way for owners of sound-level meters to make vibration measurements within the audio-frequency range. However, the sound-level meter circuits respond down to only 20 Hz, consequently the combination is not suitable for measuring lower-frequency vibrations. The vibration meter must be used where low frequencies are important.

The sound-level meter is calibrated in decibels, which must be converted to vibration amplitude, velocity, or acceleration. The calibration chart supplied

119

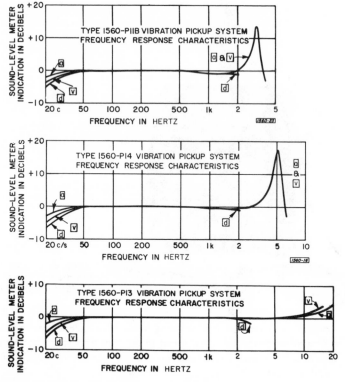

Figure 6-14. Over-all frequency response of Type 1560-P11B, 1560-P13, and 1560-P14 Vibration Pickup Systems and sound-level meter for constant applied acceleration, displacement, and velocity.

with each vibration pickup system gives the proper conversion factors for that system when it is used with a sound-level meter. By means of these data, plus the decibel table in the Appendix, the readings can be readily converted to in. (displacement), in./s (velocity), or in./s/s (acceleration), or to the proper metric units.

Three such pickup systems are available. The Type 1560-P11B Vibration Pickup System is a low-cost unit for general use, the Type 1560-P13 is for high-frequency measurements, and the Type 1560-P14 is for very low-vibration-level measurements. Typical over-all frequency response characteristics for these systems used with a sound-level meter are shown in Figure 6-14.

6.6 ANALYZERS.

Even if a sound-level meter were perfect (i.e. fit with no tolerance all the design objectives of the ANSI or IEC Standards), the reading obtained by it in any given noise field is inadequate for a complete understanding of the problem. The number of decibels indicated by a sound-level meter tells nothing about the frequency distribution of the noise. It is true that by judicious use of the weighting networks in a sound-level meter one can learn something about the frequencies present, but this knowledge is only qualitative. For most important problems it is necessary to use some type of frequency analyzer to determine the noise spectrum, as described in Chapter

5. It is also often helpful to measure the correlation of two noise signals, the transfer and coherence functions, and the other measures described in Chapter 5.

The vibration meter measures the displacement, velocity, acceleration, or jerk of a vibration. Unless the waveform is substantially sinusoidal, however, the vibration meter by itself gives little information about the frequencies of the individual vibration components. An analyzer, therefore, is desirable and often is a necessity. As with noise, the analysis of vibration provides clues to the sources of the vibration components and information necessary in the suppression of the vibration.

A number of analyzers are available for use with the sound-level meter or the vibration meter or for use with microphones and vibration pickups directly or with preamplifiers. These analyzers vary in cost, complexity, and ease of operation. Choice among them is generally determined by the amount of detailed information needed, the speed of processing required, the nature of the output format, and the auxiliary processing that may be required.

The simple, serial analyzers will be described first. These analyzers can be hand operated, and the band levels can be read from an attenuator setting and a meter reading. Some of them can also be coupled to recorders to yield a descriptive plot of the band levels as a function of frequency.

The analyzing systems that can provide detailed data rapidly will then be described.

6.6.1 Octave-Band Analyzers. The Type 1933 Precision Sound Level Meter and Analyzer, shown in Figure 6-10, includes an octave-band filter set that makes possible the simple and rapid analysis of noises having complex spectra (Kundert and Marteney, 1971). As described in Chapter 8, it is widely used for frequency analysis of noise, particularly for product rating, production-line testing, preventive maintenance, checking for compliance with some ordinances, and for estimating some subjective effects.

This portable, battery-operated instrument is a complete sound-level meter with a microphone, a preamplifier, an attenuator, weighting networks, an amplifier (which drives the filters), an indicating meter, and monitoring outputs. The set of octave-band-pass filters, selected by means of a rotary switch, range in center frequency from 31.5 to 16,000 Hz. The direct-reading level range with the microphones supplied is 10 to 150 dB re 20 μN/m^2. The filters meet the requirements of ANSI S1.11-1966, Class II, Type E.

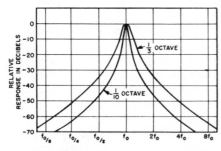

Figure 6-15. The Type 1564 Sound and Vibration Analyzer shown with selectivity characteristics.

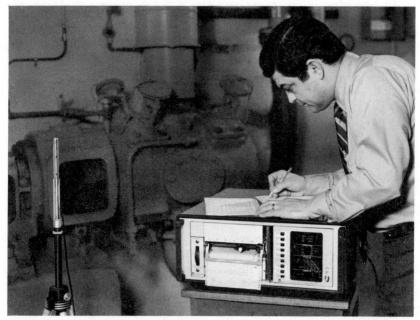

Figure 6-16. Type 1523 Graphic Level Recorder being operated with the Type 1523-P3 plug-in to make automatic stepped 1/3-octave-band analyses of compressor noise.

6.6.2 Third-Octave-Bandwidth Analyzer. For more detailed analysis of noise, a third-octave-band analyzer, such as that shown in Figure 6-15, is often used (Kundert, 1963). In addition to the third-octave band, this instrument also has a one-tenth-octave band. A typical selectivity characteristic for these two bands is also shown. This instrument can be tuned to any center frequency between 2.5 and 25,000 Hz, and the shape of the selectivity curve is constant in terms of percentage of the resonant frequency over the entire range.

The meter scale is calibrated in decibels for use in sound measurements and in linear units for vibration measurements. The direct-reading range for sound-pressure levels with a microphone attached is 44 to 150 dB. With the Type 1560-P40 or P42 Preamplifier, the minimum is extended to 24 dB and long cables can be used without loss in sensitivity.

This analyzer can be operated from the power line or from a rechargeable battery.

The filter characteristics meet the requirements of ANSI S1.11-1966, Class II, Type E.

Third-octave analysis is now widely used, particularly for checking compliance with noise and vibration specifications. It is most often used with a graphic-level recorder to give a graph of the energy distribution of the noise and vibration as a function of frequency (see paragraph 6.7).

The analysis of a noise is made more automatic with the stepped 1/3-octave-band analyzer system shown in Figure 6-16. Here, the analyzer is part of a level-recorder system, and successive, preferred, 1/3-octave bands are selected as the recorder chart moves and the pen records the band level. The range of 1/3-octave-band center frequencies is from 1 Hz to 500 kHz, and the beginning and final frequencies are selectable within that range.

122

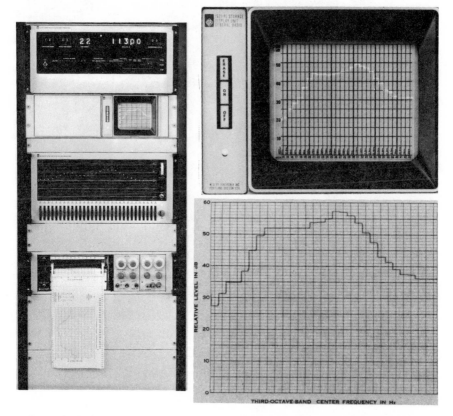

Figure 6-17. Type 1921 Real Time Analyzer (left) with Type 1921-P1 Display Scope and Type 1522 Recorder shown recording a measurement. Enlarged displays at right.

A wide choice of averaging time is selectable. In addition, the averaging can also be automatically programmed to decrease with increasing frequency in such a fashion that essentially a constant confidence level is achieved.

In order to achieve the most rapid 1/3-octave analysis, a complete set of filters must be driven in parallel. This technique is used in the Type 1925 Multifilter, (Kundert, 1968a). It can include up to 30 such filters anywhere in the frequency range from 3.15 Hz to 80,000 Hz. Full octave or 1/10-octave filters in that range are also available. These filters meet the requirements of IEC 225-1966 and the highest applicable requirements of ANSI S1.11-1966.

Attenuators for each filter channel are also available. These can be set to compensate for irregularities in frequency response of other parts of a system, or to weight the band level in any desired way.

The detector system for this multifilter is the 1926 Multichannel RMS Detector (Lapointe, 1969). It combines with the multifilter to form the Type 1921 Real-Time Analyzer, shown in Figure 6-17. This system has a 70-dB dynamic range with integration times selectable from 1/8 s to 32 s. The band numbers and measured band levels can be displayed on high-intensity neon-readout tubes, or the complete results of a spectrum analysis can be displayed on the 1921-P1 Storage Display Unit.

Figure 6-18. The Type 1921 Real-Time Analysis System operating under computer control. The computer and peripherals are shown at left.

```
CLEAR

ID: FLYOVER TEST 3

DURATION IN SECS: 12

OUTPUT: EPNL, PNL, TPNL

START


EPNL =  109.0

 TIME   PNL    PNLT
   .5   97.1    99.0  *******************
  1.0   98.4   100.0  ********************
  1.5  100.6   101.9  **********************
  2.0  102.8   104.2  ************************
  2.5  104.8   106.1  **************************
  3.0  107.1   108.3  ***************************
  3.5  110.2   111.3  *****************************
  4.0  113.3   113.3  *******************************
  4.5  114.4   115.6  **********************************
  5.0  111.2   111.2  *****************************
  5.5  113.0   113.6  *******************************
  6.0  112.7   112.7  ******************************
  6.5  111.0   111.6  *****************************
  7.0  108.3   109.9  ****************************
  7.5  105.1   105.1  **************************
  8.0  100.9   102.0  **********************
  8.5   98.1    99.2  *******************
  9.0   96.9    97.9  *****************
  9.5   95.8    96.5  ****************
 10.0   95.9    97.2  *****************
 10.5   92.9    94.3  ***************
 11.0   92.2    93.5  **************
 11.5   90.9    92.8  *************
 12.0   84.4    86.8  *******
```

Figure 6-19. Typical teletype printout of an EPNL analysis of airport noise generated by a computer-controlled Type 1921 system.

The results of the analysis can also be recorded on the 1522 Dc Recorder, also shown in Figure 6-17 and described in paragraph 6.7. A sample of such a recording is shown as well.

Since the 1921 Real-Time Analyzer is programmable by digital signals and the spectrum is available in digital form, it can be combined with a computer to provide on-line calculations of effective perceived noise level (EPNL) according to FAA specifications, or ASHRAE, ARI, AMCA, and SAE ratings of a noise, make vibration signature comparisons for preventive maintenance, etc. Such a system is shown in Figure 6-18, and a teletype printout of an EPNL calculation from the system is shown in Figure 6-19.

6.6.3 One-Percent-Bandwidth Wave Analyzer. When still finer detail of analysis is desired, the Type 1568 One-Percent-Bandwidth Wave Analyzer, shown in Figure 6-20, may be used (Kundert, 1966). It has a very selective tunable filter covering the frequency range of 20 to 20,000 Hz. The shape of the selectivity curve is constant in terms of the percentage of the resonant frequency over the entire range. The meter scale is calibrated in linear units for vibration measurements and in dB for sound measurements.

When a Type 1560-9531 1-in. ceramic microphone set, (for which the analyzer supplies the power), is connected to the analyzer, component levels from 24 to 128 dB sound-pressure level can be measured. The output of the analyzer will drive a graphic-level recorder so that an automatic recording of a noise or vibration spectrum is readily obtained.

6.6.4 Wave Analyzer. The Type 1900 Wave Analyzer uses a fixed-frequency filter in a tunable heterodyne system similar in principle to the common superheterodyne radio receiver (Peterson, 1964). It is continuously tunable from below 20 Hz throughout the audio band in a single sweep of the main tuning dial. The resulting filter characteristic is constant in response, with respect to the number of hertz deviation from the center frequency, over the entire tuning range.

This characteristic is convenient for analyzing random noise, because the spectrum level is obtained by a constant correction of the indicated level. Most such analyzers are narrow in bandwidth, however, and an analysis of noise must then proceed slowly because of the long averaging time required. A significantly wider band, such as 50 Hz, which is available on the Type 1900 is very much faster and relatively easy to use for noise analysis. Narrow bands of 3 and 10 Hz are also provided.

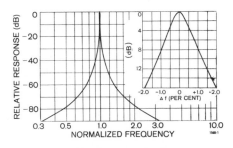

Figure 6-20. The Type 1568 Wave Analyzer shown with attenuation characteristics of the filter.

This analyzer has an output for recording and a linear frequency scale. When an analysis that is linear in frequency scale is made, one can readily track down harmonic relations, since successive integral harmonics are spaced uniformly. Thus, the analysis of rotating or reciprocating machinery, including gear trains, electric motors, and turbines, by a wave analyzer is often to be preferred to other types of analysis.

The analyzer has an electrical output arranged so that the system is a continuously tunable filter. Thus, one can listen by means of earphones to the component or band selected by the analyzer. Furthermore, if one applies a broad-band noise signal to the input, one can obtain at the output a narrow band of noise, preferably 50-Hz wide for most acoustic measurements, whose center frequency is continuously tunable over the full range of the analyzer. This signal is desirable for some acoustic tests of rooms, walls, and hearing.

Another mode of operation of the analyzer yields a sine-wave signal at the output that is always at the frequency to which the analyzer is tuned. This is then a convenient source (to drive an amplifier and speaker) and detector for over-all electrical or acoustical response measurements.

6.6.5 Fast Fourier Transform Analyzers. As explained in Chapter 5, digital techniques of time-series analysis are providing another versatile approach to the study of acoustic and vibration signals, including not only spectrum analysis, but also transfer functions, coherence functions, cross spectra, and auto and cross correlation. The T/D 1923 Analyzer, shown in Figure 6-21, is a pushbutton-controlled, programmed system of this type (Chamberlain, 1971). It has been built to be exceptionally versatile and yet easy to use. The basic functions are selectable by pushbuttons, and the various stages in the process can be viewed on the storage display oscilloscope. The signal can be viewed initially as a function of time. When a frame of input points is selected for analysis, they can be displayed to ensure that the desired section was selected. The frame can be transformed, and the result displayed to show the analysis.

Spectrum averaging for noise signals, and rectangular or hanning weighting of the input data, are also provided for improving processing. The buffered-mode of operation permits real-time continuous processing of noise signals, up to a certain frequency range, for processing all the data for maximum statistical accuracy. The upper frequency limit for this real-time mode depends on the function performed. For auto-spectral calculations, the 1923-C can operate in real time to about 500 Hz and the 1923-A to about 25,000 Hz.

Although the basic analysis provided by the FFT is one with uniform resolution in Hz, the results can be transformed into an equivalent 1/3-octave analysis for comparison with such data. This operation is not as efficient for the third octaves as the parallel processing of the 1921 system, but it does permit use of the same processor for detailed analysis with a frequency resolution of as fine as .025% of the desired maximum frequency to 50 kHz, as well as in 1/3-octaves or octaves, depending on the programming specified.

The FFT can also provide phase information, which may be useful in transfer-function studies or in tracking down troubles in repetitive systems, where the time of occurrence of related events is significant.

An alphanumeric display of the selected function and control settings is furnished. The output can be preserved on a printer or a recorder.

Since the analysis results are in the proper form for computer use, additional processing of the data can readily be done in the computer by the

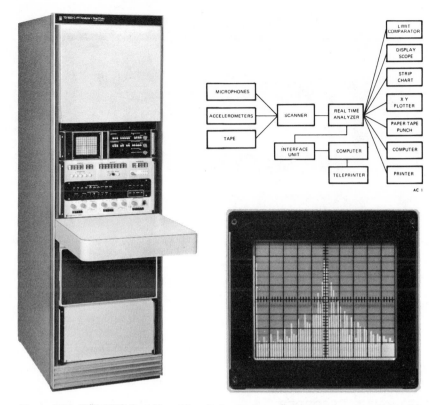

Figure 6-21. T/D 1923 Real-Time Time-Series Analyzer (left). Diagram suggests possible expansions towards complete on-line systems. Scope detail, lower right.

use of additional programming. For example, the spectrum signature can be compared with stored criteria, or with previous signatures, to determine if action or further study is necessary. The spectrum can be modified by a calculation routine to yield a rating of the noise.

The scope of applications for these versatile processors can be seen from comments about some specific applications. In noise and vibration control, there is noise and vibration source, path, and direction identification. In addition, for preventive maintenance, the spectrum is sometimes used to identify incipient troubles. This technique is sometimes called signature analysis. The processing techniques used for these purposes are not only the straightforward spectrum analysis, but also the transfer and coherence function to identify probable cause-and-effect relations, the cross-correlation function to relate two or more signal pick-up points in time, waveform averaging and spectrum analysis to dig a repetitive signal out of noise to find its waveform or spectrum, and spectrum averaging to obtain a statistically stable spectrum of a stationary noise signal.

The processing capabilities of such devices are so broad in frequency range, time span, and function that these techniques are being applied in many other areas beyond the scope of this book. Examples can be found in medicine, biophysics, economics and business analysis and forecasting, physics, communications, and geophysics.

127

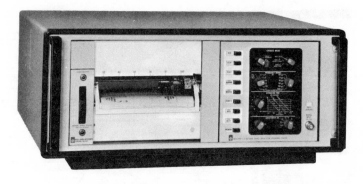

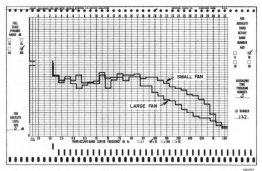

Figure 6-22. Type 1523 Graphic Level Recorder with -P3 1/3 Octave Band Analyzer plug-in accessory at right. Typical chart record shown below.

6.7 GRAPHIC RECORDER.

Graphic recorders of various types are used to produce a permanent, reproducible record of the results of a measurement. As an accessory to sound and vibration instruments, they can be used to record over periods of time the sound level near highways, airports, residences, or the vibration levels of building floors or walls, bridges, or airframes and to measure reverberation time. The resulting information is much more extensive than that obtainable from a few readings of a meter, and when observations over a long period are desired, the recorder can be unattended.

Some recorders can be used with an analyzer to plot the frequency spectrum of a noise source or of a vibrating object. The combination of a recorder with a tunable oscillator and other accessories can produce records of the acoustic-transfer characteristics of rooms, walls, microphones and loudspeakers, the electrical response of analyzers, networks, and amplifiers, and the vibration transfer characteristics of shakers, vibration pickups, and structures.

The 1523 Level Recorder shown in Figure 6-22, is the basic element in a system to do these many different operations. It is a servo-type strip-chart, pen recorder that uses a disposable cartridge. It has a wide range of speeds for the chart drive, of averaging times for the detector system, and of level ranges for recording. The maximum level range is 100 dB. Limit comparators are included for use in production test systems.

When this recorder is used with the appropriate plug-in, it forms a level-recorder system, and it can be used for the applications of recording as a function of time mentioned above. When the recorder is used with the 1523-P3 Stepped 1/3-Octave-Band Analyzer plug-in, it becomes a recording analyzer as described in paragraph 6.6.2. When it is used with the 1523-P2 Sweep Oscillator plug-in and other accessories, it can record responses and transfer characteristics as a function of frequency.

This sweep oscillator covers the frequency range from 1 to 500,000 Hz and the upper and lower limits of the sweep can be selected in the range of 5 to 200,000 sec/10:1 frequency change. The time/decade can be maintained constant, or it can be set to decrease (increase speed) with increasing frequency. This decreasing sweep time is usually satisfactory for measurements on most physical systems, and it saves measurement time compared with maintaining the slow rate required for the low-frequency end of the range.

The 1522 Dc Recorder shown in Figure 6-17, is a versatile, programmable strip-chart recorder that is particularly well suited for recording the results of an analysis on the 1921 Real-Time Analyzer, which it will do much faster than the conventional X-Y plotters (Basch, 1969).

A number of the manually operated analyzers can be driven mechanically from the 1521-B Graphic Level Recorder and the results of the analysis can be automatically plotted (Basch, 1964). Figure 6-5 shows the 1911 Recording Sound and Vibration Analyzer for producing continuous frequency plots of the 1/3 or 1/10-octave spectrum of sound and vibration signals. Figure 6-23 shows the chart output of the 1913 Recording Wave Analyzer for 1%-bandwidth plots of the spectrum of acoustic and vibration signals.

A d-c output is available from the 1933 Precision Sound-Level Meter and Analyzer that is directly proportional to the indicated level in decibels over a 40-dB range. It can be used to drive a simple recorder, when the sound level or vibration level is to be recorded as a function of time.

6.8 MAGNETIC-TAPE RECORDER.

The magnetic-tape recorder has become a useful tool for the acoustical engineer both in research and in development, (Kamperman, 1958; Tall, 1958; Mee, 1964; Peterson, 1967). It stores a signal as variations in the magnetic state of the particles on the tape. The time scale then becomes a length scale on the tape.

The signal to be stored must be supplied to the recorder as an electrical signal; and, for recording noise as a function of time, this electrical signal is usually obtained from a high-quality microphone. When measurements are to be made on the stored signal, the recorded tape is played back on the recorder and measurements are made on the electrical output signal.

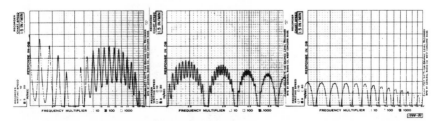

Figure 6-23. Frequency spectrum analysis of a 1.0 ms pulse at a 70 Hz repetition rate. The 1% bandwidth yields high resolution at low frequencies, shows the envelope at high frequencies.

The magnetic tape recorder is being used to perform the following functions in the field of noise measurements:

1. To keep reproducible records of progressive changes in a sound. These changes may be a result of the application of successive noise-control procedures, for example.

2. To record a noise for analysis by a number of techniques, when the particular approach to be used is not at first obvious and it is not convenient to use the original source repeatedly.

3. To record a noise in the field for detailed study in the laboratory, where more complex instrumentation systems can be used.

4. To record a sound that varies with time. Samples can then be selected from the recording for analysis to obtain the change in spectrum as a function of time.

5. To record a short-duration sound, which can then be played back repetitively to simplify analysis.

6. To monitor over long periods to catch intermittent sounds, which can then be separated out for analysis.

7. To record noises that are erratic or intermittent, possibly by binaural techniques, to aid in tracking down sources.

8. To record a noise to permit a frequency translation for convenience in analysis.

9. To record a transient noise in order to change the time scale or to invert the time scale for ease of graphic recording.

10. To permit subjective or objective comparison among sounds recorded at different times. The subjective judgment can then be made by groups listening under similar conditions.

11. To permit observation of the subjective effects of altering a signal, for example, by filtering, clipping, or adding noise.

12. As a measurement system with a recorded signal as the source and a recording channel as the detector, for example, in the measurement of reverberation characteristics.

Figure 6-24. Type 1935 Cassette Data Recorder storing inputs from a GR 1933 SLM.

These applications have been stated for acoustical signals, but most of them apply to vibration signals as well.

The small, portable, cassette, data recorder, shown in Figure 6-24, is specially designed for noise recording. When used with the 1933 Precision Sound-Level Meter and Analyzer, the 1935 Cassette Data Recorder records the signal on one channel and the setting of the sound-level meter range control on the other channel. On playback, the signal on the main channel is reproduced, and the range information from the other channel is shown on a digital display. Voice notes can also be recorded by breaking into the range code on the second channel.

Alternatively, the second channel can record the signal from a second sound-level meter in place of the range data. The normal recording speed is 1-7/8-in./s, but a speed of one-fourth normal is also provided. The signal gain from record to playback is normally set to unity (0 dB).

6.9 IMPULSE-NOISE MEASURING INSTRUMENTS.

Impulse-type noises, such as those produced by punch presses or drop hammers, cannot be properly measured by the simpler sound-level meters. The Type 1933 Precision Sound-Level Meter and Analyzer (Figure 6-10), however, includes an impulse detector response with a fast rise time and slow decay to give a more useful indication of the level of such noises. This type of detector response has been standardized in some countries. It has the useful characteristic that, in addition to providing a measure that can specify the impulse, it will give the same answer on steady sounds as the normal detector system. Thus, it is easy to compare readings on repetitive sounds to check on the impulse nature of the sound.

For some measurements the actual peak value of the impulse sound is desired. Such a measurement response is obtained on the 1933 Precision Sound-Level Meter and Analyzer in the peak response mode. Otherwise, the 1556-B Impact Noise Analyzer, shown in Figure 6-25, can be used as an accessory to any of the sound-level meters to measure the peak value of the sound.

6.10 RANDOM-NOISE GENERATORS.

The random-noise generators (Faran, 1968), shown in Figure 6-26, are sources of high-level, broad-band electrical noise, which can be converted to

Figure 6-25. The Type 1565 Sound-Level Meter can be combined with a Type 1556 Impact Noise Analyzer to give direct readings on impulse-type noise.

131

Figure 6-26. General Radio random noise generator; spectrum characteristics of output of 1381 shown(left) and 1382 (right).

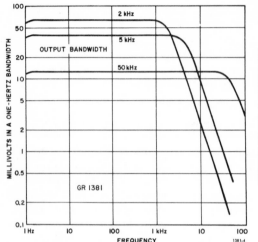

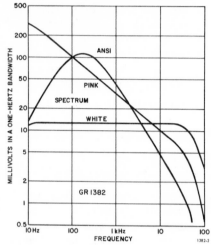

acoustic noise by means of an earphone or a power amplifier and a loudspeaker. Such acoustic noise is useful in psychoacoustic experiments. in the measurement of reverberation time and noise transmission, in loudspeaker- and microphone-response measurements, in microphone testing, and for calibration procedures.

The output of a random-noise generator can be filtered by one of the analyzers or by the 1952 Universal Filter (Figure 6-27) to provide a band of noise anywhere in the audio range. This type of signal is often preferred to the broadband-noise signal for the measurements mentioned above.

The output of a random-noise generator can also be converted to a random mechanical motion by an electromechanical shaker for mechanical testing of components and structures. The 1381 Random-Noise Generator is most suitable for this application because it includes electrical filtering to limit the bandwidth to 2, 5, and 50 kHz, and adjustable clipping of the noise signal limits the excursion of the electrical voltage. The 2 and 5-kHz bands are often used in vibration testing.

The 1382 Random-Noise Generator is more suitable for acoustic testing, since it provides white noise (constant-energy-per-hertz-bandwidth), pink noise (constant-energy-per-octave-bandwidth), and the noise specified in ANSI Standard S1.4-1961, paragraph 3.2.2. The pink noise is often preferred for tests with analyzers having a constant-percentage bandwidth, for example, octave or 1/3-octave. These different spectra are shown in Figure 6-26.

6.11 CONTINUOUSLY ADJUSTABLE FILTER.

Some vibration measurements require that high-frequency portions of the frequency spectrum be eliminated from the observation. Sometimes the

132

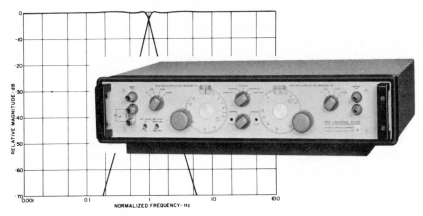

Figure 6-27. Type 1952 Universal Filter; at left are low-pass and high-pass filter characteristics.

system bandwidth can be reduced to decrease the relative intensity of extraneous signals without affecting the important part of the signal to be studied, or the effect on the signal of limiting the bandwidth needs to be studied. Such applications are often handled by adding the 1952 Universal Filter, shown in Figure 6-27, to a system. It will perform as a continuously adjustable low-pass, high-pass, band-pass or band-reject filter over the frequency range of 4 to 60,000 Hz (Kundert, 1968a).

Controlled bands of noise can be generated by the use of this filter with a random-noise source. Such bands are often useful for psychoacoustic tests, room-acoustics tests, and vibration tests.

6.12 TONE-BURST GENERATOR.

The combination of an oscillator and a tone-burst generator (Skilling, 1968) is a source of electrical tone-burst waveforms that can be converted to acoustical tone bursts by means of an earphone or a power amplifier and loudspeaker. Such an acoustical signal is useful in room-acoustic measurements, in psychoacoustic experiments, in studies on transducers and acousti-

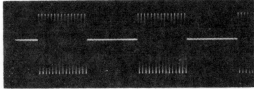

Figure 6-28. Tone-burst pattern from 1396-B Tone Burst Generator. Input, 3 kHz; 16 cycles on; 16 cycles off.

133

cal material properties, and in amplifier tests. It is particularly helpful in locating stray reflections in anechoic chambers and in tracing sound-transmission paths.

The 1396-B Tone-Burst Generator, shown in Figure 6-28, produces an abrupt on-off transition and is particularly useful for measurements of physical systems. The on and off times can be set in terms of the number of cycles of the input wave or a separate wave or in terms of time.

The G/S Model 929E Electronic Switch and Model 471 Interval Timer in combination constitute a flexible means of controlling an audio signal, including an abrupt tone burst or one with rise and decay times of 1 to 500 msec. The signal, with a gradual rise and decay time, is more suitable for psychoacoustic testing than one that is abrupt.

6.13 AUTOMATIC-LEVEL REGULATOR.

In the testing of response or transmission-loss characteristics in room and building acoustics, it is often helpful to control or regulate the level of the test signal to keep it constant. The 1569 Automatic Level Regulator (Kundert and Woodward, 1968), shown in Figure 6-29, is an important element in such a system. It can, for example, reduce a level variation of 25 dB to a variation of only 1 dB, when it is supplied with the proper reference signal and it is inserted as part of the signal-supply loop. Such large initial variations can occur because of the marked frequency irregularity of rooms and many loudspeakers.

6.14 OSCILLOSCOPE.

A cathode-ray oscilloscope is a useful means of observing the waveform of a sound or vibration signal from a sound-level meter or a vibration meter. It can be used to measure the peak amplitude of a wave and, after some experience, the observer can, by adjusting the sweep frequency, tell something about frequency components by looking at the wave. In addition, the oscilloscope makes possible the study of the instantaneous values of a vibration motion. In contrast to the vibration analyzer and other wave analyzers that present information in terms of frequency, the oscilloscope presents information as a function of time. This representation is often of great assistance in the solution of vibration problems. Because the oscilloscope presents information instantly and continuously, and because its frequency response is not a limiting factor, it is useful in the study of any vibration waveform.

For sound and vibration measurements an oscilloscope with slow sweep rates, long-persistence screen, and dc amplifier is recommended. Many oscillo-

Figure 6-29. Type 1569 Automatic Level Regulator.

134

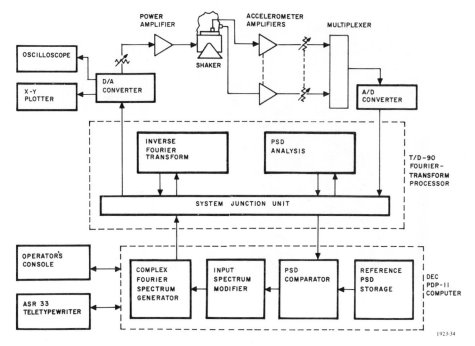

Figure 6-30. System configuration for signal analysis and control of shaker system.

scopes have provision for the addition of a camera, which makes possible a permanent record of the wave shape being studied.

6.15 VIBRATION SHAKERS.

Several types of vibration shakers are widely used (Booth, 1963). One of the most versatile is the electrodynamic shaker. These shakers, produced in a wide range of sizes, are used by vibration engineers in many ways to help evaluate performance of instruments, components, and structures. Typical uses are: endurance or fatigue testing of electrical and mechanical structures, testing of resilient or shock mounts, shake testing of electrical components such as switches, relays, or amplifiers, determination of damping characteristics of materials, and calibration of vibration pickups.

Some tests use sinewave motion, with the frequency either set to a resonance of the device under test or swept over a specified band. Random motion is becoming widely accepted in vibration testing, with a random-noise generator used as the signal source (see paragraph 6.10), and an adjustable band-pass filter used to shape the noise spectrum.

Since the motion of the shaker is affected by the structure fastened to it, the drive system cannot always be readily preset to produce a required motion of the device being tested. The motion at the fastening points of the device may be monitored with vibration pickups and analyzed to check the spectrum. This information can then be used to set the shaker drive signal to the proper spectrum shape and level. The ultimate approach is to arrange the system to monitor and control the level automatically. This approach becomes very involved for random vibration and requires a control system of the complexity shown in Figure 6-30.

Figure 6-31. Type 1562 Sound Level Calibrator installed on a sound level meter (left). A Type 1557 Vibration Calibrator is shown at right.

6.16 CALIBRATORS.

Much is to be gained from the use of an accurately calibrated acoustical- or vibration-measurement system. When an accurate calibration is made, the consistency of comparison measurements can be improved, a closer approach to an allowed performance specification is possible, and careful attention to measurement techniques will be repaid by more accurate measurements.

6.16.1 Sound-Level Calibrator.
When an over-all acoustical check of a system at several frequencies is desired, the sound-level calibrator can be used (Gross, 1967a). It comprises a small, stabilized, and rugged loudspeaker mounted in an enclosure that fits over the microphone of the sound-level meter. The chamber is so designed that the acoustic coupling between loudspeaker and microphone is fixed and can readily be repeated. The level is high enough so that readings are unaffected by normal background noises.

The calibrator in Figure 6-31 includes its own battery-operated oscillator to drive the transducer, which supplies a known level at 125, 250, 500, 1000, and 2000 Hz to the microphone. This device permits a quick check of the performance of an acoustic measurement system over the most important frequency range for acoustical measurements. It is also invaluable for calibrating a measurement tape recorder and for supplying calibrating signals for recording.

6.16.2 Audiometer Calibrators.
Audiometry is one of the fields of measurement where it is particularly important to have equipment in proper operating condition and well calibrated. Comprehensive calibrations should be done at least every 6 months, by the manufacturer or at some other laboratory qualified to certify such calibrations. In addition, a daily monitoring check on the audiometer and earphones can be done quickly and easily with the 1562-Z Audiometer Calibration Set. If the audiometer is not used daily, the monitoring check can be done before use of the audiometer.

The basic instrument in the 1562-Z is the 1565-B sound-level meter, which, of course, is essential to a hearing-conservation program for checking

136

Figure 6-32. The GR 1562-Z Audiometer Calibrator shown measuring the output of a 1703 Audiometer earphone.

noise levels in the plant. It is coupled to the earphone of the audiometer by an earphone coupler, which is included (Gross, 1966, 1967b, 1968). The sound level produced in the audiometer earphones can then be checked by the sound-level meter in accordance with the expected level as given in the instructions. For an independent check on level a 1562 Sound-Level Calibrator is also part of the set.

6.16.3 Vibration Calibrator. The vibration calibrator shown in Figure 6-31 is a small, single-frequency calibrator useful for checking the over-all operation of a vibration-measuring system (Gross, 1960). The calibrator consists of a resiliently supported cylindrical mass, driven by a small, transistorized, electromechanical oscillator mounted within the cylinder. Small accelerometers may be mounted on either of two disk-shaped platforms attached to the shaker. Large accelerometers may be mounted in place of the disk-shaped platforms. To calibrate an accelerometer, the level control is adjusted for a meter reading corresponding to the mass added to the moving system of the calibrator. The accelerometer is then being driven at an acceleration of 1 g at 100 Hz. The excursion of the calibrator can be adjusted for 1-g acceleration with any pickup weighing up to 300 grams.

6.17 STROBOSCOPES.

The stroboscope is valuable in many vibration studies and therefore in noise control work, because it permits rotating or reciprocating objects to be viewed intermittently and produces the optical effect of slowing down or stopping motion. For instance, an electric fan revolving at 1800 rpm will apparently stand still, if viewed under a light that flashes uniformly 1800 times per minute. At 1799 flashes per minute the fan will appear to rotate at 1 rpm, and at 1801 flashes per minute it will appear to rotate backwards at 1 rpm.

Because the eye retains images for an appreciable fraction of a second, no flicker is seen except at very low speeds. The apparent slow motion is an exact replica of the higher-speed motion, so that the motion of the high-speed

137

Figure 6-33. Type 1531 Strobotac® electronic stroboscope (left), Type 1531-P2 Flash Delay (attached to stroboscope), and Type 1536-A Photoelectric Pickoff.

machine can be analyzed with the stroboscope under normal operating conditions.

This type of instrument can be used to measure the speeds at which vibrations occur in most rotating or reciprocating machines. Displacements in vibrating parts can often be measured accurately with the aid of a microscope, if a fine reference line is scribed on the part. This technique has been used to confirm the calibration of vibration calibrators, and automotive engineers have used it to measure crankshaft whip and vibration.

6.17.1 Strobotac® Electronic Stroboscope. The Strobotac® electronic stroboscope, shown in Figure 6-33, is a small, portable stroboscope calibrated to read speed directly in revolutions per minute (Holtje, 1966). The light source is a strobotron tube, mounted in a parabolic reflector. The frequency of an internal electronic pulse generator determines the flashing speed, which can be adjusted by means of a direct-reading dial. Normal flashing range is from 110 to 25,000 per minute. Another model of the Strobotac® is available for flashing rates up to 150,000 per minute, and that model can be operated from a rechargeable battery. Speeds above and below this range can be measured by use of flashing rates that are simple multiples or submultiples of the speed to be measured. As the flashing rate of the Strobotac is decreased below 600 per minute, the flicker becomes pronounced due to the inability of the human eye to retain successive images long enough to give the illusion of continuous motion.

Of especial use in vibration measurements is the provision for connecting an external synchronizing signal to the Strobotac. Thus the light flashes can be triggered directly by a 1536-A Photoelectric Pickoff, which uses a photocell to synchronize the stroboscope with repetitive mechanical motion. It requires no attachment to the device being observed, and thus can be used effectively with low-torque devices. The output of the photoelectric pickoff requires amplification to trigger the stroboscope; this is provided by the Type 1531-P2 Flash Delay Unit, which also permits observation of the vibration at any point in its cycle.

The stroboscope can also be flashed by the output from one of the vibration-pickup systems described in paragraph 6.5.1. For instance, a vibration pickup can be used with a sound-level meter or vibration meter to send triggering impulses to the stroboscope. Filtering is necessary between the measuring instrument and the stroboscope. An octave-band or a narrow-band analyzer can be used for such filtering.

6.17.2 Strobolume   The 1540 Strobolume® electronic stroboscope provides a very bright light over a large area (Miller, 1969). The maximum beam width is 40° x 65°. It can be controlled by an accurate oscillator for the range of 110 to 25,000 flashes per minute, by an oscillator/delay unit, or by a control unit to respond to external signals. The light output and versatility of the 1540 make it well suited for TV applications, such as video recordings of rapidly-moving parts in mechanical devices.

6.17.3 Motion Analysis Set.   The Type 1539-A Motion Analysis and Photography set is arranged for visual analysis of a repetitive motion or inspection of a process where the independent flashing-rate setting of the Strobotac is not required and for high-speed photography with conventional cameras. The major application areas for the motion analysis are in machinery and metal working, including packaging, printing, textile, earthmoving machinery, metal products, shipbuilding, automotive manufacturing, ordnance, chemical processing and aerospace.

6.17.4 Stroboscopic Applications.   Stroboscopic techniques are widely used for visual observation of vibration. The high-speed performance of fans, propellers, and other rotating devices can be studied by means of the slow-motion effect of the stroboscope, and sources of vibration and noise due to misadjustments, misalignment, and wear can be readily detected. The vibratory modes of turbine blades are checked as they are driven electromagnetically, and the mode shapes are observed with the aid of an optical magnifier under stroboscopic illumination. Similarly, the flapping of the blades of a model helicopter rotor has been observed in slow motion by stroboscopic illumination.

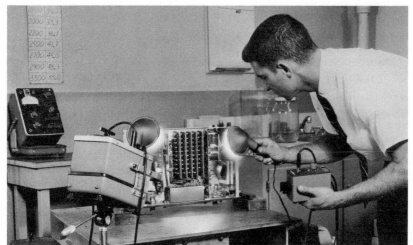

Figure 6-34. Combination of instrumentation forces to solve a vibration problem. Shown are the Types 1538 and 1539 Stroboscopes, paired with a Type 1553 Vibration Meter, to study the motion of parts on an electronic assembly being exercised on a shake table.

The stroboscope can also be used to observe the motion of apparatus being tested on a shaker, as in Figure 6-34. If the flashing rate is just slightly offset from the frequency of the shaker, a slow-motion replica of the high-speed vibration will result, so that the displacement can readily be observed. The form of the motion can be seen, and one can often tell what section needs to be strengthened and how damping material and damping devices can best be applied.

When a rotating or reciprocating machine is brought up to speed or is a variable-speed device, there may be resonant vibration modes of various parts at certain speeds, known as critical speeds. If these parts are visible and can be illuminated by a stroboscope, it is often possible to use the slow-motion feature to check on the actual behavior of the part at resonance. One can see if it is a fundamental resonance or a multiple resonance with various sections going in phase and others in phase opposition. This type of observation can be of great assistance in the determination of the proper treatment to reduce the resonant vibration.

TV cameras and receivers and video recording techniques offer a greater degree of flexibility in the use of stroboscopic techniques, particularly for remote observation.

Photographic recording of the stroboscopically illuminated motion makes possible accurate measurements of the motion. The accurately timed, very-short-duration light flashes provide the time scale and the almost instantaneous sampling of the motion.

For further details on the stroboscope and its uses consult F. T. Van Veen, *Handbook of Stroboscopy*, General Radio Company, Concord, Mass., 1966, and Charles E. Miller, *Handbook of High-Speed Photography*, General Radio Company, Concord, Mass., 1967.

6.18 SYSTEMS, COMPUTERS, AND PERIPHERAL EQUIPMENT.

When a number of instruments and devices are arranged to work together to solve a measurement problem, the combination is often called a measurement system. Engineering such a system requires the planning of the over-all design to yield the required output information from the selected inputs, the selection of the individual parts of the system, the design and development of the interconnection means (often called "interfacing"), and the testing and debugging of the completed system.

Most of the items described in this chapter can be integrated into such measurement systems. The block diagrams of Figure 6-35 and 6-36 illustrate this statement. The source of the signal is often a transducer or a bank of transducers, or it may be a recorded signal. If there is more than one input source, they will need to be selected or scanned. This signal is then measured or analyzed, and the result is transferred to an output device or to a computer for further processing before it is sent to an output device.

Sometimes the interconnection of the various parts is simple, because they have been designed to work together. But often careful attention to many details is necessary in order to make the system as a whole work well, and the development of electronic circuits to modify the output of one device to satisfy the needs at the input of the cascaded device may be necessary. For example, when an output is in analog form and it is to drive a device that

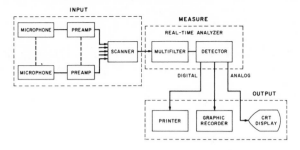

Figure 6-35. System for acoustic power measurements.

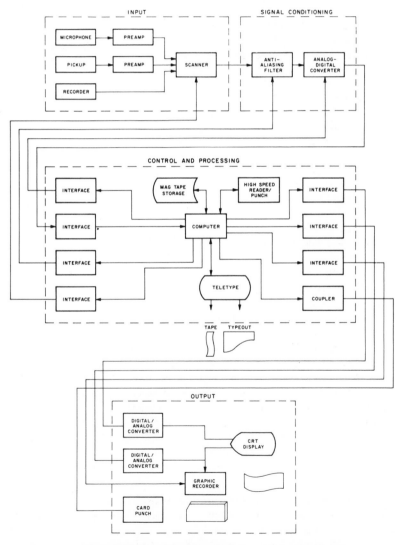

Figure 6-36. Computer controlled system for measurement
and analysis by digital techniques.

141

requires a digital form of input, it is obvious that some significant interfacing electronics is necessary.

To illustrate the nature of the problems here is a list of some of the input and output characteristics that need to be considered in the connection of two devices.

Analog-to-analog connection
> Impedance
> Signal levels
> Frequency response
> Interaction
> Grounding
> Stray pickup
> Dc levels
> Power requirements
> Connectors

Digital-to-digital connection
> Logic levels
> Polarity
> Code
> Number of bits
> Parallel or serial
> Clock rate
> Pulse durations
> Logic load
> Interrupt logic
> Noise immunity
> Connectors
> Buffer storage

Analog-to-digital connection
> Those above plus
> Analog-to-digital (A/D) converter characteristics

Digital-to-analog connection
> Those above plus
> Digital-to-analog (D/A) converter characteristics

In addition to the equipment already described in this chapter that may be used in systems, as already implied, a digital computer is often included in larger systems because of the versatility it gives to the system (Fichtenbaum, 1969; McAleer, 1971; Peterson and Fichtenbaum, 1969). It will be described briefly. Other devices that are mainly used in systems and are often called "peripheral equipment" will also be described briefly.

When a computer is part of a system, the program for the computer ("software") must fit the particular devices used in a given system, and the interconnecting hardware that permits the computer to control the devices and to receive data from them or send data to them must also be included (DEC, 1968, 1970).

6.18.1 The Computer in Acoustical Systems. We shall discuss the role of a computer in a measurement system in two parts, as a programmed calculator and as a system controller.

Computer as Calculator. Most engineers regard a computer as a high-speed programmable calculator. In this role it can play a useful part in acoustics, because many of the results that we want are not given directly by the values measured by acoustic instruments but are derived from them by various calculations.

Here are some of the measures and effects we may wish to calculate or predict from acoustical measurements.

1. **Human reactions**
   Loudness and loudness level
   Perceived-noise level
   Articulation index
   Speech-interference level
   Hearing-damage risk
   Noise criteria
2. **Speech**
   Spectrum vs time
   Formant tracking
3. **Source characteristics**
   Spectrum vs time
   Sound power
   Directivity
   Loudness efficiency rating of loudspeakers
4. **Room acoustics and materials testing**
   Reverberation
   Transmission loss
   Absorption
5. **Statistical measures — searching and sorting**
   Signature analysis and comparisons
   Averaging or integrating multiple runs
   Maxima of a series of spectra
   Amplitude distribution
   Correlations
6. **Miscellaneous**
   Microphone corrections
   Weighted levels

In the past, most of the above have been calculated from analog measurements without the use of an electronic computer, or in some instances special analog devices have been designed to permit the direct measurement of the desired result. Computer systems will be increasingly used for these acoustic-measurement problems because of the benefits that such systems can provide.

It takes 3 or 4 minutes to calculate loudness level or perceived noise level with a desk calculator from 25 third-octave band levels, and it may take even longer to calculate the discrete-tone corrections for perceived noise level. Furthermore, there aren't many who can do a number of these calculations, even with a desk calculator, without making mistakes.

If an electronic computer is programmed to do this calculation, the calculation time is insignificant. It may take a second or so for the teletypewriter to print out the answer, however.

Accurate and rapid calculation of the desired end result is only one of the benefits of a computer system. We shall describe others in the role of the computer as a system controller.

Computer as System Controller. As a controller, the computer makes the various elements operate together as a complete, versatile system. The computer stores the parameters required for one or more tests, accepts particular parameters or directions from the operator for each test, sets up the required functions on the measuring instruments, sequences the measuring instruments through the test procedures, stores the measured results, processes the data, and presents the computed output to the operator.

The program can be arranged to set up the particular test sequence desired from very simple commands typed by the operator.

The output, which consists of the measured and computed results, can be presented by the computer system in many different forms. For example, it may be printed with the units and other explanatory information for easier interpretation by the operator.

The system program can include a search for unreasonable data or overload conditions. A measured value that is far from the expected may be a result of a defect in the measuring system, incorrect operating procedure, or a fault in the device under test. When such an unusual value occurs, the computer can be programmed to shut down the system and wait for operator intervention, or to perform other special procedures, as well as to print the unexpected result with a warning comment.

The computer can sequence the system through special tests designed to find faults in any part of the system or to effect an initial reference calibration, which may be used later in the measurement sequence. In extensive systems, periodic use of fault-finding tests can be an important aid in finding and correcting defects, in order to avoid collecting useless data.

The test sequence of the calculated parameters can be controlled by the computer program to depend on the results of the measurements. For example, if various noise signals are being processed to give the loudness level, the speech-interference level and the hearing-damage-risk criterion could also be checked by the program to print an output warning when critical levels are exceeded.

In general, the physical equipment required to carry out computer instructions is versatile. Once the computer and associated measurement system are set up to make certain basic measurements, we can often add extra features by the preparation and storage of a new program. When the computer has a large memory, many different programs can be stored at the same time in the computer.

Requirements for an Instrumentation Computer. Some of the important requirements for a computer that is to be used in an instrumentation-control capacity are:

1. The computer must have a flexible input-output arrangement. It must be easy to transfer large amounts of data and control information, from the measuring instruments to the computer, and between the computer and other input and output devices.

2. The computer should have an adequate storage capacity for the task at hand. It must be sufficiently fast in terms of what can be accomplished in a given time interval to meet the needs of the instrumentation system.

3. The computer should be small and comparatively low in cost to warrant inclusion of the computer in the system.

4. The computer must function dependably in an industrial environment. It must be relatively easy and straightforward to maintain and should be capable of some form of self-testing.

The program for the Computer (Software). The program for an instrumentation system may include such widely varying functions as control of measuring instruments, calculation of various predictors of human reactions, comparisons with stored criteria, calculation of statistical measures of the measured results, and the printout of a summary. In order to prepare this program, the programmer must be familiar with the measurement task, the characteristics of the equipment comprising the system, and the characteristics of the computer. The function of the programmer/engineer is then one of designing a program rather than designing instrumentation hardware.

Large-vs-Small Computers. For most instrumentation systems, a small computer is adequate for the job. A small computer should then almost always be used. But if a large computer is already available in an organization, it is often proposed that it be tied into the instrumentation system to do the job. This procedure is usually impractical for one or more of the following reasons:

1. In an instrumentation system, the timing of responses to events in the system may be crucial. If the large computer is run on a batch-processing basis, the use in instrumentation and control becomes impractical. Either the instrumentation system must have top priority and complete availability of the necessary computer facilities when the measurement is in process or a fast time-sharing system should be used.
2. Connection of an instrumentation system to a large computer is difficult and expensive, particularly if the computer is remote, as in a time-sharing system. The task of programming may be difficult, because the instrumentation manufacturer may not be familiar with the particular large computer and the measurement task at hand, and the user's engineers may not know how to program the system. The expense of the special interconnection, the cabling, and the more involved programming may exceed the cost of the small computer.
3. If the instrumentation system is tied to a large computer, it fails when the computer fails. With a small computer in the system, the user can do his own maintenance or even keep a spare system, if it is essential that the down time be minimized.
4. With a small computer as part of the system, it is under the complete control of the user and not subject to limitation or regulation by the department controlling the large computer.

When Should a Computer Be Used? Factors that affect the decision to include a computer in a measurement system:

1. Quantity of data to be processed.
2. Rate at which data must be processed.
3. Complexity of the measurement function, for example, involved sequencing of instruments.
4. Calculations needed on the directly measured data to obtain required output results, e.g., corrections, calculation of loudness, mean and standard deviations of sets of data.
5. Use of system to perform different measurement tasks. When the basic instruments can be programmed through the computer to perform the required measurement tasks, the cost of the computer with several programs may be less than the alternative instrument systems, or at

*Figure 6-37. Typical computer-
controlled system built around
the 1921 Real-Time Analyzer.*

least the possibility of using the computer for several tasks may contribute to justifying its cost.

6. The versatility of the computer system. It may permit one to avoid the expensive development of specialized instrumentation for a particular job.

An Acoustical Measurement System. The particular system shown in Figure 6-37 uses a small computer with the 1921 system. It is programmed to take a series of measurement samples of an input noise signal. The third-octave levels for each noise sample are stored in the computer memory. The program permits the calculation of the octave-band levels, the loudness level by the method given in ANSI S3.4, and the speech-interference level. It can also select the maximum loudness of any of the loudnesses calculated for the noise samples.

The computer program for the test system is kept on a punched paper tape and is loaded through a tape reader on the teletypewriter into the computer memory. In normal operation, the program is stored in the memory indefinitely and is ready to run whenever the power switch is turned on. All transfer of data and instruction between the operator and the computer occurs through the teletypewriter.

The computer is connected to the 1921 system by cables and circuits called "interface circuits." These circuits interpret the computer commands to control the instruments, they perform any required shifting of voltage levels, they accomplish intermediate storage of data, and they transfer the measured data from the 1921 system to the computer.

Figure 6-38. Type 1923-C FFT Analyzer for high-speed computer-controlled signal analysis.

To begin a test, the operator connects his noise signal — from a microphone preamplifier, vibration pick-up, or a tape recorder, for example — to the input of the 1921 system. With the power switch turned on and the controls on the 1921 system set properly, the operator types on the teletypewriter the instructions for the test he wants.

The computer program then controls the operation and prints out the desired measurement results.

The T/D 1923C FFT Analyzer, shown in Figure 6-38, is another computer-controlled system. It uses A/D converters to change the analog input signals (from transducers) into time series. These series are then processed, as described in Chapter 5, by the computer to yield the Fourier transform, the autospectrum, the crosscorrelation, the transfer function, or a number of other functions. The output is displayed on a storage scope or it can be put on a recorder, printer, or other peripheral equipment.

This sytem can also be used with a special keyboard that permits simplified programming to transform and modify the data in many ways.

6.18.2 Peripheral Equipment. A wide variety of peripheral equipment is used with modern instrumentation and data-processing systems (McAleer, 1971; Arnold et al, 1969), and a few of the more commonly used accessories will be described briefly.

Teletypewriter (teletype). A teletype is commonly connected to a computer. It is used to type-in information to the computer or to print-out information from the computer at a rate up to 10 characters/second.

It often has an accessory mounted on it for reading and punching paper tape at up to 10 characters/second. The program for a computer is often stored on paper tape in the form of a series of punched holes. When the proper loading program is in the computer, the program tapes can be read on the teletype reader, interpreted, and stored as a program in the computer memory. It is also possible to punch a paper tape, by means of a proper program in the computer, to store data or a program for future use.

147

Paper-Tape High-Speed Reader/Punch. When computer programs are stored on paper tape, they are usually so long that they take 15 minutes or more to read in on the tape reader attachment for the teletypewriter. If a number of programs are to be run on the computer, it is usually worthwhile to use a high-speed tape reader to read in tapes.

If data are to be stored on paper tape, or if the computer setup is to be used in the development of programs, a high-speed punch may be worthwhile.

Digital Printers. Often a printed record of the measured results is desired. Various forms of printers are available. They range from the teletype, through high-speed column printers and line printers.

Magnetic Digital Storage. Programs or data in digital form can also be stored on magnetic tape. The transfer of digital signals between the magnetic tape and the computer is much faster than for paper tape. The ordinary audio tape recorder cannot be used for this purpose, however, since the requirements are quite different, particularly with respect to the drive mechanism, the heads, the electronic systems and the tape. In order to ensure accuracy in the transfer of the digital signals, the tape must be of exceptionally high quality. Some redundancy is added to the digital signals when they are stored, and this redundancy is used to check that the transfers are correct.

The magnetic-storage medium can also be in the form of a metal disk that has a thin magnetic-oxide coating on both sides. When it is in this form, any stored program can be located more quickly than for storage on tape. But for a large storage capacity, disk storage is more expensive than tape storage.

Do not Fold, Staple, or Mutilate. Almost everyone closely associates the computer with the punched-card form of storage of digital information. The punched card has the important advantage that readily readable information can be printed on it, and for that reason it appears almost indispensable for some applications. The devices for punching and reading cards are more expensive than those for paper tape, however, and for most of the acoustical data-processing applications the cards are not needed.

REFERENCES

Standards
ANSI S1.4-1971 Sound-Level Meters
ANSI S1.11-1966 Octave, Half-Octave, and Third-Octave Band Filter Sets
IEC/123 (1961) General Purpose Sound-Level Meters
IEC/179 (1965) Precision Sound Level Meters
IEC/225 (1966) Octave, Half-Octave, and Third-Octave Band Filters

Other
R. R. Arnold, H. C. Hill, and A. V. Nichols (1969), *Modern Data Processing*, John Wiley & Sons, Inc., New York.
M. W. Basch (1964), "New Talents for the Graphic Level Recorder," *General Radio Experimenter*, Vol. 38, #9, Sept, pp 15-24.
M. W. Basch (1969), "A Programmable High-Speed Dc Recorder," *General Radio Experimenter*, Vol. 43, #5/6, May/June, pp. 16-21.
B. B. Bauer (1957), "Microphones for Sound-Level Meters," *J Acoust Soc Am*, Vol. 29, #12, Dec, pp. 1333 f.
L. L. Beranek (1949), *Acoustic Measurements*, John Wiley & Sons, Inc., New York.
B. A. Bonk (1967), "The New General Radio Microphone," *General Radio Experimenter*, Vol. 41, #5/6, May/June, pp. 3-8.
G. B. Booth (1963), "Vibration Generation," Chapter 9 in Crandall, 1963.
K. A. Bowen and T. S. Graham (1967), "Noise Analysis, A Maintenance Indicator," *Mech Engineering* Vol. 89, #10, pp. 31-33.

E. V. Carlson (1952), "A Ceramic Vibration Pickup," *Trans IRE Prof Group on Audio*, PSA-10, Nov-Dec, pp. 2-8.

L. J. Chamberlain (1971), "A Simple Discussion of Time-Series Analysis," *Sound and Vibration*, Vol. 5, #4, April, pp. 18-25.

S. H. Crandall, ed. (1963), *Random Vibration*, Vol. 2, The MIT Press, Cambridge, Mass.

D. Davis (1965), *Acoustical Tests and Measurements*, H. W. Sams, Indianapolis.

A. Dranetz and A. W. Orlacchio (1961), "Pickup Characteristics," Chapter 16, Part I in Harris and Crede, 1961.

DEC (1968), *Introduction to Programming 1969*, Digital Equipment Corporation, Maynard, Mass.

DEC (1970), *PDP8/E Small Computer Handbook 1971*, Digital Equipment Corporation, Maynard, Mass.

S. V. Djuric (1972), "Electret Condenser Microphones For Measurement," *J Acoust Soc Am*, Vol 51, #1, Part 1, Jan, p 129.

FAA (1969), *Federal Aviation Regulations, Part 36 — Noise Standards: Aircraft Type Certification*, Federal Aviation Administration, Department of Transportation.

J. J. Faran, Jr. (1968), "Random Noise Generators," *General Radio Experimenter*, Vol. 42, #1, Jan, pp. 3-14.

Federal Coal Mine Health and Safety Act (1969), Public Law 91-173, 91st Congress, S.2917, December 30, 1969.

M. L. Fichtenbaum (1969), "Computers in Instrument Systems," General Radio Automatic-Impedance-Measurement Seminars (unpublished).

C. A. W. Glew and D. C. Watson (1971), "The Octave Band Vibration Analyzer as a Machinery Defect Indicator," Am. Soc. of Mech. Engineers, Paper 71-DE-47, April.

R. L. Grason (1970), "Audiometric Measurement: 150 Years of Applied Research," *General Radio Experimenter*, Vol. 44, #10-12, Oct/Dec, pp. 3-7.

E. E. Gross, Jr. (1960), "Little Dithers," *General Radio Experimenter*, Vol. 34, #11/12, Nov/Dec, pp. 3-5.

E. E. Gross, Jr. (1966), "A Standard Earphone Coupler for Field Calibration of Audiometers," *General Radio Experimenter*, Vol. 40, #10, Oct, pp. 15-20.

E. E. Gross, Jr. (1967a), "New Five-Frequency Sound-Level Calibrator," *General Radio Experimenter*, Vol. 41, #5/6, May/June, pp. 9-13.

E. E. Gross, Jr. (1967b), "Field Calibration of Audiometers," *General Radio Noise Measurement*, Vol 1, #1, March, pp. 3-5.

E. E. Gross, Jr. (1968), "New Audiometer Calibration Set," *General Radio Experimenter*, Vol 42, #4, April, pp. 20-22.

C. M. Harris and C. E. Crede (1961), *Shock and Vibration Handbook*, McGraw-Hill, New York, Vol. I, Chapters 12 through 17.

M. S. Hawley (1955), "The Condenser Microphone as an Acoustic Standard," *Bell Laboratories Record*, Vol. 33, #1, Jan, pp. 6-10.

M. C. Holtje (1966), "Flash—A New Strobotac Electronic Stroboscope," *General Radio Experimenter*, Vol. 40, #4, April, pp. 3-9.

G. W. Kamperman (1958), "A Portable Magnetic Tape Recorder for Acoustical Measurements," *Noise Control*, Vol. 4, #1, Jan, pp. 23-27.

W. R. Kundert (1963), "New Performance, New Convenience with the New Sound and Vibration Analyzer," *General Radio Experimenter*, Vol. 37, #9/10, Sept/Oct, pp. 1-9.

W. R. Kundert (1966), "A One-Percent-Bandwidth Wave Analyzer," *General Radio Experimenter*, Vol. 40, #9, Sept, pp. 10-18.

W. R. Kundert (1968a), "A Universal Filter for Low-Frequency Work," *General Radio Experimenter*, Vol. 42, #4, April, pp. 14-19.

W. R. Kundert (1968b), "A Calibrated Spectrum Synthesizer," *General Radio Experimenter*, Vol. 42, #10, Oct, pp. 5-10.

W. R. Kundert and C. A. Woodward (1968), "A Versatile Level Regulator for Swept-Frequency Sound and Vibration Testing," *General Radio Experimenter*, Vol. 42, #4, April, pp. 10-13.

W. R. Kundert and E. R. Marteney (1971), "A Modern Portable Sound Analysis System," 7th ICA, Budapest.

W. R. Kundert, J. A. Lapointe, and G. R. Partridge (1969), "New Generation Acoustical Analyzers," *General Radio Experimenter*, Vol. 43, #5/6. May/June, pp. 3-11.

J. A. Lapointe (1969), "Some Notes on Digital Detection," *General Radio Experimenter*, Vol. 43, #5/6, May/June, p 12 f.

H. T. McAleer (1971), "A Look at Automatic Testing," *IEEE Spectrum*, Vol 8, #5, May, pp 63-78.

E. R. Marteney (1970), "A Big Little-Brother Preamplifier," *General Radio Experimenter*, Vol. 44, #10-12, Oct/Dec, p. 8.

W. P. Mason (1961), "Properties of Piezoelectric and Piezoresistive Materials," Chapter 16, Part 2 in Harris and Crede.

E. Meyer and H. Kuttruff (1962), "Progress in Architectural Acoustics," in Richardson and Meyer, pp. 222-277.

C. D. Mee (1964), *The Physics of Magnetic Recording*, North Holland, Amsterdam.

C. E. Miller (1969), "Detailed Viewing in Ambient Brightness," *General Radio Experimenter*, Vol. 43, #9/10, September/October 1969, pp. 3-6.

C. E. Miller (1970), "Using Stroboscopy," *Machine Design*, Vol. 42, 30 April 1970, 14 May, 1970. (two parts).

J. Ormondroyd, R. B. Allnutt, F. Mintz, and R. D. Specht (1950), "Motion Measurements," *Handbook of Experimental Stress Analysis*, M. Hetenyi, ed., John Wiley & Sons, Inc., New York, Chapter 8, pp. 301-389.

OSHA (1970), Williams-Steiger Occupational Safety and Health Act of 1970 (84 Stat 1593, 1600; 29 U.S.C. 655, 657) Occupational Safety and Health Administration, Part 1910 — Occupational Safety and Health Standards-*Federal Register*, May 29, 1971, Washington, D.C., Vol. 36, #105, Part II.

G. R. Partridge (1971), "A Noise Exposure Meter," *J Acoust Soc Am*, Vol. 41, #1 (part 1), Jan, p. 129.

A. P. G. Peterson (1967), "The Tape Recorder in Acoustical Measurements," *Sound and Vibration*, Vol. 1, #10, Oct, pp. 14-20.

A. P. G. Peterson and M. L. Fichtenbaum (1969), "The Computer in Acoustical Measurement Systems," General Radio Real-Time Sound and Vibration Measurement Seminar (unpublished).

G. Rasmussen (1960), "Pressure Equalization of Condenser Microphones and Performance at Varying Altitudes," *B & K Technical Review*, #1, pp. 3-23.

G. Rasmussen (1963), "Miniature Pressure Microphones," *B & K Technical Review*, #1, pp. 3-10.

E. G. Richardson and E. Meyer, eds. (1962), *Technical Aspects of Sound* Vol. III, Elsevier Publishing Company, Amsterdam.

G. M. Sessler and J. E. West (1966), "Foil-Electret Microphones," *J Acoust Soc Am*, Vol. 40, #6, Dec, pp. 1433-1440.

T. J. Schultz and B. G. Watters (1964), "Propagation of Sound Across Audience Seating," *J Acoust Soc Am*, Vol 35, #5, May, pp. 885-896.

J. K. Skilling (1968), "Redesigned Tone-Burst Generator Has Customer-Suggested Features," *General Radio Experimenter*, Vol. 42, #10, Oct, pp. 14f.

WHPCA (1969), Occupational noise-exposure regulations under Section 50-204.10 of the Walsh-Healey Public Contracts Act — Safety and Health Standards, *Federal Register*, Vol. 34, #96, May 20, 1969, amended July 1, 1969.

J. Tall (1958), *Techniques of Magnetic Recording*, MacMillan, New York.

D. G. Tucker and B. K. Gazey (1966), *Applied Underwater Acoustics*, Pergamon Press, Oxford, Chapter 5.

F. T. Van Veen, (1966), *Handbook of Stroboscopy*, General Radio Company, Concord, Mass.

C. A. Woodward (1965), "A New, Low-Noise Preamplifier," *General Radio Experimenter*, Vol. 30, #6, June, pp. 1-6.

C. A. Woodward and E. E. Gross, Jr. (1968), "A Precision Sound-Level Meter," *General Radio Experimenter* Vol. 42, #4, April, pp. 3-6.

Chapter 7

What Noise and Vibration Measurements Should be Made

7.1 INTRODUCTION.

A wide variety of noise and vibration measurements can be made. They range from a simple measurement of sound level to a detailed vibration analysis showing hundreds of components of a complex vibration. Confronted with so many possible choices, one might well ask, "What measurements should we make, and what instruments do we need for our job?"

The answer to this question depends of course on what the job is. If the problem is one of checking compliance with a certain noise or vibration specification, the specification is usually set up so that the particular measurement required is reasonably clear and only some guidance as to choice of instruments and their use is needed. But if we are trying to reduce the noise produced by an appliance, the situation is more complex and extensive discussion is necessary.

In all these applications careful attention to the acoustic environment is essential. That is, if the background noise is serious or if reflected sound is significant, a significant penalty may result because the measured noise is higher than it would be under ideal conditions. These problems are discussed in the next chapter.

In order to organize the many possible answers to the basic question in a manner that will make the information readily usable, this chapter is arranged on the basis of the application. The next step is to find the field that fits the job in the following list and then to look up the referenced section.

Devices that are Noisy or Vibrate Excessively (7.2)
    Product Noise and Test Codes (7.2.1)
    Production-Line Testing (7.2.2)
    Product Noise and Vibration Reduction (7.2.3)
    Machinery Preventive Maintenance (7.2.4)
Environmental (Community) Noise (7.3)
    Hearing Damage Risk from Noise Exposure (7.3.1)
    Local Noise Ordinances (7.3.2)
    Motor Vehicle Noise (7.3.3)
    Powered Equipment Used Outdoors (7.3.4)
    Airport Noise (7.3.5)
Architectural Acoustics (7.4)
    Sound Absorption (7.4.1)
    Sound Transmission Loss (7.4.2)
    Reverberation Time or Decay Rate (7.4.3)
    Response Testing (7.4.4)
    Tone-Burst Testing for Echoes (7.4.5)
    Site Selection (7.4.6)

7.2 DEVICES THAT ARE NOISY OR VIBRATE EXCESSIVELY.

7.2.1 Product Noise and Test Codes. Specifications of acceptable noise limits for products are becoming relatively common. These specifications are usually given as maximum sound levels or maximum octave-band levels or sometimes third-octave band levels at certain measuring points. Some specifications also include the measurement of radiated acoustic power.

Various engineering groups and trade associations have standardized test codes for measuring the noise from certain devices, for example, transformers, cooling towers, electric motors, fans and blowers, etc. These codes are often referenced as a part of a specification in order to standardize the measurement procedure to be used in checking for compliance to a maximum noise requirement. A representative list of test codes is given in the standards section of the Appendix.

A-Weighted Sound Levels. A simple example of noise testing is the check for compliance by a manufacturer for a customer who requires that the A-weighted sound level at 3 feet from any major surface of a motor be less than say 55 dB. He may also specify that the motor be mounted on a hard reflecting surface in an essentially anechoic space. Here, the A-weighted sound level needs to be measured and a sound-level meter with a microphone will do the job.

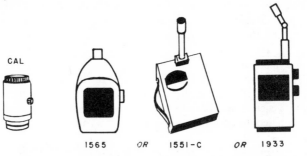

Figure 7-1. System to measure "A"-weighted sound levels.

The 1565 Sound-Level Meter may be adequate for this test, and it is generally wise to include a 1562 Sound-Level Calibrator as part of the measurement system. If measurements below 40 dB may be required, the 1551-C Sound Level Meter should be substituted.

In many instances, however, it can be worthwhile to use a 1933 Precision Sound-Level Meter even for this simple measurement, because of the improved accuracy for the A-weighted measurement.

Octave-Band Analysis. Some customers may specify the maximum allowable octave-band levels under certain measurement conditions. The 1933 Precision Sound Level Meter and Analyzer is the appropriate instrument to use, because it provides the octave-band analysis at high accuracy and a wide range of sensitivity levels.

Again, a 1562 Calibrator should be included as a check on the accuracy of the measurement.

For estimates of probable customer reaction to the noise of a product, an octave-band analysis of the noise is the most widely used measurement. The band levels are used to calculate loudness level or perceived noise level. If competitors' products are measured in the same way, either procedure should permit one to rank the units in order of acceptability with good reliability.

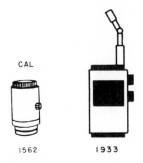

Figure 7-2. Octave-band analysis.

Acoustic Power Output. The use of acoustic-power output for rating noisy devices is widely recognized as the best approach for certain measurements. Acoustic power is calculated from the results of a number of sound-pressure level measurements, usually octave or 1/3-octave-band levels. The procedure requires a controlled environment, usually an anechoic room, a reflecting floor in an anechoic room, or a reverberation room. Under certain conditions the requirements on the environment may be relaxed. The instrumentation used here covers a wide range.

For example: It can be a group of microphones scanned with a 1566 Multichannel Amplifier and analyzed with a 1921 Real-Time Analyzer. The 1921 may be adjusted to read the sound power level in each 1/3-octave band directly. If the calculation of directivity factor or other data reduction is required, a small computer may be connected to the 1921. Calculated results can be printed out on a Teletype. In place of a group of microphones, it can be a moving microphone that scans a given area as its output is analyzed on a 1921 Real Time Analyzer, with the averaged output plotted on a 1522 Dc Recorder. It can be a 1933 Precision Sound Level Meter and Analyzer with its microphone on a tripod. An analysis at each of a number of microphone positions is made. Here, the results are recorded and calculated by hand.

Product Noise and Test Codes. In order to be more specific, some examples of instrumentation for certain test codes will be given.

The American Society of Heating, Refrigerating, and Air-Conditioning Engineers (ASHRAE) has prepared a set of standards* for measuring the noise radiated by heating, refrigerating, and air-conditioning equipment. These standards are used by the Air-Conditioning and Refrigeration Institute (ARI) to obtain the basic data in their standards for rating the equipment.

The preferred basic instrument for this use is the 1921 Real-Time Analyzer. It provides the highly selective third-octave filters and the long averaging times required by the standards.

A group of microphones scanned with a 1566 Multichannel Amplifier, or a microphone that moves over a long path as the sound-pressure-squared is integrated in the 1921, may be appropriate.

The Compressed Air and Gas Institute (CAGI) and the European Committee of Manufacturers of Compressed Air Equipment (PNEUROP) have prepared a "CAGI-PNEUROP Test Code for the Measurement of Sound from

---

*See Appendix VII for list of standards and codes.

153

Pneumatic Equipment," ANSI S5.1-1971. It specifies procedures and operating conditions for the equipment, and it requires octave-band analysis of the noise at a number of points near the equipment.

A precision sound-level meter and a calibrator are required, and the observer and measuring instrument are to be at least one meter away from the microphone. These requirements lead to the use of the 1933 Precision Sound-Level Meter and Analyzer with 10-feet of cable, a tripod, and a 1562 Sound-Level Calibrator, which are all a part of the Sound Analysis System.

If the measurements are to be part of a production test, various degrees of sophistication can be used in the instrumentation, procedures, and setup to speed up the measurement. Since 5 or 10 measurement locations are specified, fixed supports and microphones at each location could be used. These could connect into the 1566 Multichannel Amplifier, which can scan the outputs of the microphones manually or automatically. The octave-band analysis could be done with a 1921 Real-Time Analyzer, with the measured equipment noise levels and background noise levels plotted on a 1522 Dc Recorder.

The noise-certification tests for aircraft, as prescribed in Part 36 of the Regulations of the Federal Aviation Administration (FAA, 1969) require extensive instrumentation and calculations. The noise at a number of points must be recorded on magnetic tape, during specified landing and takeoff procedures. The recording must also include a calibration signal. The response characteristics of the recorder must be exceptionally good, since they must meet the requirements of IEC-R179 (Precision Sound Level Meters).

The recorded noise is then analyzed every half second, into 1/3-octave bands, by a 1921 Real Time Analyzer. These band levels are processed successively by an associated small computer, by a simple recursive arithmetic process, to produce the required dynamic response. Each 0.5 second set is then stored in the computer. The levels are corrected for the calibration results and the effective perceived noise level is calculated. This result is then corrected for departures from the standard flight path and standard atmospheric conditions.

The standard prepared by the Institute of Electrical and Electronic Engineers for Airborne Noise Measurements on Rotating Electric Machinery, IEEE No. 85, Feb. 1965, covers a variety of measurement procedures. These include sound-level measurements and sound analysis in octave or third-octave bands, at a point or at a number of points in the vicinity of the machinery. When the sound-power level is required, it is calculated from the band levels measured at certain specified points.

For sound-level and octave-band level measurements, the 1933 Precision Sound-Level Meter and Analyzer would be preferred. Since measurements are to be made at a number of points, the measurement procedure can be speeded by the use of a number of microphones and a 1566 Multichannel Amplifier. It can be automated still further by the use of a 1921 Real Time Analyzer and a 1522 Dc Recorder to plot the results of the analysis.

If 1/3-octave analyses are desired, the convenient combination of a 1523 Level Recorder, with the 1523-P3 Stepped 1/3 Octave-band Analyzer plug-in, is suggested. When it is used with a 1560-P42 Preamplifier and a 1560-P5 Microphone, band levels as low as about 34 dB re 20 μN/m^2 can be recorded. If lower-level recordings are needed, the recorder can be driven from a 1551-C Sound Level Meter or a 1933 Precision Sound-Level Meter and Analyzer.

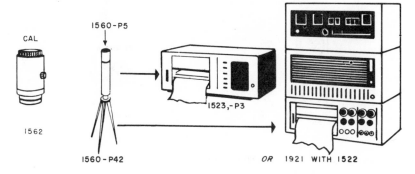

Figure 7-3. Production-line testing instrumentation.

7.2.2 Production-Line Testing. Ideally, many devices should be tested for noise output on the production line. Noise measurements on the production line are often possible, but hardly ever in an ideal manner. That is, precision acoustical testing usually requires a large, isolated, echo-free space, which would not ordinarily be considered for inclusion as part of a production line. Nevertheless, useful noise measurements can often be made with relatively simple procedures, although the accuracy of rating may be significantly reduced compared with that possible with an ideal measurement.

In this discussion we shall consider briefly several possible solutions to this problem, ranging from the elaborate to the simple. For some expensive devices where the noise level is exceptionally important, for example, large power transformers, the required very large, isolated, echo-free chambers have been used to test each unit as it is produced. When the device is not so large and low frequencies are not important, a reasonable-size anechoic chamber with refrigerator type doors can be used.

Although the acoustic environment is an important consideration for all the noise measurements discussed in this chapter, the requirements of production testing make the control of the environment a more difficult problem than it is in a research and development laboratory.

A massive, tight, resiliently mounted enclosure is necessary to avoid pickup of ambient stray noise that will affect the measurement. For the same reason the access door must be one that seals exceptionally well. Then, in order to get the required echo-free behavior, extensive treatment of the inside is necessary.*

An enclosure with hard walls can also be used in some instances. Here the design should be such as to make it a reverberation room.

A much simpler technique is sometimes satisfactory for production-line screening of noisy devices. This approach depends on a vibration measurement that has been correlated with the acoustic noise. For example, acoustic measurements of a number of samples may show that the noisy ones are invariably noisy in one or two octave bands, say the bands at 500 and 1000 Hz. Then a measurement of the vibration of these samples may show what vibration levels are acceptable in these bands. Some exploration of the vibration of the various surfaces of the device will be necessary to find the critical

---

*Anechoic chambers of various sizes are manufactured by, for example, the Eckel Corporation, 155 Fawcett Street, Cambridge, Mass.

155

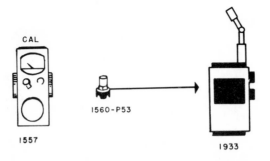

Figure 7-4. Alternate production-line testing instrumentation.

areas. Usually, the major surfaces should be tried first. In production, the tests should be made with the device resting on a very thick, resilient pad or mounted in soft mounts that help isolate against ambient vibration.

The high-speed 1/3-octave analysis that is possible with the 1921 Real Time Analyzer makes it particularly suitable for production testing. When it is used with a 1522 Recorder, one can have a permanent record of the noise analysis. If the 1921-P1 Storage Display Unit is used as an accessory, one can obtain a display of the spectrum for a rapid check. The attenuator bank, which is part of the 1921 Analyzer, can sometimes be used to adjust the display band levels on the 1921-P1 for a flat go-no-go limit.

The 1921 Real-Time Analyzer can be made a part of a computer-controlled system that is exceptionally versatile. It can compare the measured spectra with stored spectra or criteria, to determine the acceptability of the device under test. It can transform the spectra into calculated loudness, or perceived noise level, or the ARI 270 Sound Rating, and print out the calculated result. It can print out certain stored messages that depend on the value measured. It can have a set of operator-controlled programs for different tasks.

The T/D 1923 FFT Analyzer can provide even more flexibility because of the detailed analysis that is possible over a wide range of audio frequencies.

7.2.3 Product Noise and Vibration Reduction. In a program for the reduction of noise and vibration, the tape recorder is a key instrument. It permits one to store in reproducible form a record of the results of successive noise- and vibration-control measures. Such a series of records may be particularly useful for demonstrating to a consultant's client, or to the management of a plant, what has been accomplished in reducing noise. From an engineering viewpoint, these recordings are also valuable when a change in plans requires a change in analysis procedure.

Some sounds vary significantly in level and character with time. Appliances that go through a cycle of different operations (dishwashers and clothes washers, for example) produce such sounds. Although an appliance can be programmed to stay in the same phase of the cycle for long periods, it is usually more convenient to make a recording of each phase. These recordings can then be played back repeatedly for detailed analysis.

Some devices, for example a gas engine, drift slowly but significantly in speed. As a result, the basic noise pattern changes, and the drift is often serious enough to preclude direct, detailed analysis of the noise spectrum at a

156

variety of speeds, with the usual slow-scan techniques. One can, however, run the engine for a reasonable period at each of a number of selected nominal speeds and record short samples, say five seconds, at each of these speeds to form a series of tape loops. Each loop is played back and is analyzed. Since the inertia of the rotating system is often so large that serious fluctuations in speed do not occur in the short interval of the tape loop, the engineer obtains a series of frequency spectra that can be related to shaft speed. He may then be able to deduce much about the noise producing mechanisms from the relations between amplitude, frequency, and shaft speed.

The analysis of intermittent sounds or signals can be a helpful step in tracking down the sound sources. By means of tape recording, one can monitor the noise from a device for long periods, to catch these intermittent sounds, which can then be separated out for analysis.

Background noise may make noise studies of machines impractical when acoustically isolated rooms are not available. Often, however, the background noise is much less during lunch periods or outside normal working hours, particularly early in the morning, and measurements may then be practical. Even during such periods a complete study of the noise may be awkward or inconvenient, but, if tape recordings can be made during the quiet periods, the recorded signal can be analyzed at any convenient time.

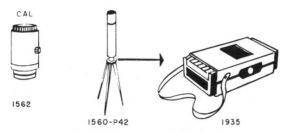

Figure 7-5. Noise recording assembly.

The full range of analysis equipment is helpful in the product-development phase. The detailed analyses, and the wide variety of techniques available, make the 1923 FFT Analyzers invaluable in tracking down the cause and sources of troublesome components of the noise. The other analyzers provide varying degrees of detail in the analysis, and often one can select the one that is most suitable for a particular job from among the 1568, 1564, 1523 with -P3 plug-in, 1921, 1923, and 1933.

For any of these studies, the 1933 Precision Sound Level Meter and Analyzer is helpful for making the basic reference measurements of overall level, A-weighted level, and even octave-band analysis for checks on ratings as the noise-control procedures are instituted. It also provides the impulse mode for measuring noise from typewriters, trippers, chain drives, riveters, and the like.

If vibration reduction is the prime goal, vibration pickups should, of course, be used to supply the signals to the analyzers. But even if noise reduction is the desired goal, the reduction is often accomplished by reducing the vibration of various parts of the device. Here vibration pickups should be used, or the motion should be studied with stroboscopic observation of the moving parts. This procedure is described in Chapter 9.

157

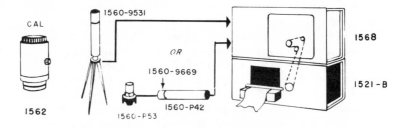

Figure 7-6. Narrow-band sound or vibration analysis.

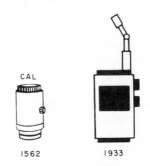

Figure 7-7. Impact-noise analysis in octave bands.

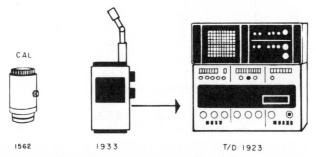

Figure 7-8. Narrow-band high-speed vibration analysis, including correlation, transfer function, and summation analysis as well as spectrum analysis.

7.2.4 Machinery Preventive Maintenance. Only one aspect of machinery maintenance is considered here, namely, the relation of the vibration level of a machine to its condition. That is, vibration measurements can guide in predicting incipient failure of a machine, in deciding when cleaning, parts replacements, and other maintenance procedures are necessary, and in determining the relation between vibration and the performance of the machine.

The best general measurement for this purpose is velocity, and it is usually measured at the bearing housings. The 1553 Vibration Meter provides for velocity measurements, and it can be used for quick surveys. But since analysis of the vibration signal is almost always desirable, the 1933 Precision Sound-Level Meter and Analyzer with a vibration pickup and a control box is a choice that reduces the total number of instruments required.

158

One basic technique in this form of preventive maintenance is to compile a history of the analyzed vibration levels at each bearing housing. When the levels change noticeably, the situation is reviewed to see if it is reasonable or if it is likely that deterioration of some structure has occurred. It can then be used as one guide in deciding when and how machinery is to be overhauled. Octave-band analyses have been found helpful here (Glew and Watson, 1971), but 1/3-octave analyses are also used (Bowen and Graham, 1967). Here, the history is conveniently compiled in the form of a series of recorded vibration levels taken on a 1523 Level Recorder with a 1523-P3 Stepped 1/3-Octave-Band Analyzer plug in. The remarkable range of that analyzer, 1 Hz to 80,000 Hz, means that the full range of the vibration meter, including the important low-frequency range, is nicely covered.

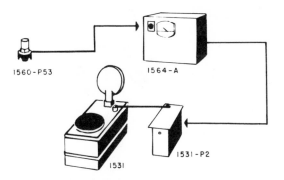

Figure 7-9. Tenth octave-band vibration analysis with stroboscopic observation.

When many machines are being monitored, so that many analyses need to be made and recorded, the combination of a 1921 Real Time Analyzer and a 1522 Dc Recorder provides a rapid way of producing the data to be studied for maintenance procedures.

Fine detail of analysis may be helpful in investigating certain faults of rotating machinery, and the narrower-band analyzers, including the T/D 1923 FFT Analyzers, are then appropriate instruments to use. These FFT Analyzers also provide correlation measurements and waveform averaging (summation analysis), which are useful investigational tools in machinery maintenance (see paragraphs 5.4.1 and 5.4.5).

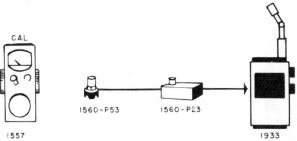

Figure 7-10. Velocity measurement and analysis sytem.

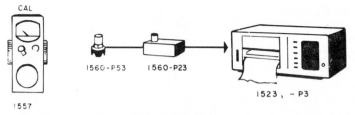

Figure 7-11. Recording system for compiling history of 1/3 octave vibration velocity levels for continuing machinery preventive maintenance program.

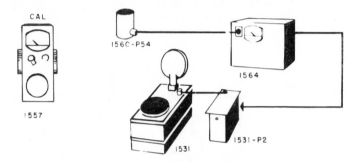

Figure 7-12. In-place balancing assembly.

One common source of trouble in machinery is rotational unbalance. A measurement system to help in-place balancing consists of a Type 1560-P54 Vibration Pickup, the Type 1564 Sound and Vibration Analyzer, Type 1531-P2 Flash Delay, and the Type 1531 Strobotac.

7.3 ENVIRONMENTAL (COMMUNITY) NOISE.

7.3.1 Hearing Damage Risk from Noise Exposure. As described in Chapter 4, the noise near some machines is intense enough to cause permanent hearing damage, if the exposure continues for long periods. As explained, the main technique for checking potentially dangerous areas is to measure the A-weighted sound level with a standard sound-level meter. If the sound is impulsive, the sound-level reading should include a peak reading taken on a 1933 Precision Sound-Level Meter and Analyzer. Alternatively, a 1556-B Impact Noise Analyzer connected to the 1565 sound-level meter is available to measure this peak value.

A more convenient and satisfactory measurement of the noise exposure is possible with a 1934 Noise Exposure Monitor, which combines the observed levels according to the current regulations and also monitors the peak level.

These measurement procedures are the ones currently used under the regulations of the Williams-Steiger Occupational Safety and Health Act of 1970 (OSHA, 1970), the Walsh-Healey Public Contracts Act, as amended, and the Federal Coal Mine Health and Safety Act of 1969.

As pointed out in Chapter 4, if potentially hazardous noise exists in a plant, audiometric examinations of exposed personnel and work to control the noise are necessary. The audiometric examinations can be contracted out, or with the use of a 1703 Automatic Recording Audiometer, they can be done at the plant, as described in Chapter 4. Other instrumentation is useful in noise control, which is discussed in Chapter 9 and Section 7.2.

7.3.2 Local Noise Ordinances — Area Noise. Some cities and towns regulate the maximum noise levels permitted at lot boundaries, with the limits set according to the district. Most of these ordinances now use the A-weighted sound level measured on a sound-level meter although some specify octave-band levels.

In the 1971 Chicago Noise Ordinance, for example, the noise level in business and commercial districts at the lot boundary is not to exceed 62 dB (A). In residential areas the noise level coming from a residence is not to exceed 55 dB (A) at the lot boundary. In manufacturing, districts the noise is measured at the district boundaries and the limits range from 55 to 66 dB (A).

The sound-level meter should be used with a windscreen for this monitoring. Since the operations in a factory can vary considerably during the day and night cycle, some plants may require monitoring with a recorder on the output of a sound-level meter for long periods of time. A 1565 Sound-Level Meter and a 1523 Level Recorder with a 1523-P1 Amplifier plug-in or a 1933 Precision Sound Level Meter and Analyzer and a simple, dc strip chart recorder can be used.

The extensive use of air-conditioning units, particularly those with outdoor heat exchangers, has made noise monitoring more important in residential areas. Air conditioners can be particularly bothersome at night when some wish to have their bedroom windows open, and monitoring the noise on a hot night is particularly appropriate.

7.3.3 Motor-Vehicle Noise. Some states and some cities and towns in the USA and many other countries have ordinances or laws that set permissible limits on noise from motor vehicles. These are also generally specified in terms of the A-weighted sound level at some distance from the vehicle. Chicago sets limits on the vehicles as sold, as well as in operation.

7.3.4. Powered Equipment Used Outdoors. Much construction and industrial equipment is used outdoors, and many power tools, power lawnmowers, riding tractors, etc. are used in residential areas. These are also being regulated in an attempt to reduce the noise nuisance, again mainly by the specification of maximum A-weighted sound levels.

7.3.5 Airport Noise. Noise of busy airports is of great concern to those living nearby. In some areas vigorous community action has resulted, and much effort is now being devoted to studies of how to control and reduce this noise impact. Some airports have extensive noise-monitoring systems. By imposing maximum limits on the noise level permitted for the aircraft that use the airport, the airport operator can bring the noise problem under better control. By gradually lowering those limits as quieter aircraft are developed, he can effect further improvements.

California is requiring noise monitoring with maximum noise level limits for all airports that have a noise problem. A-weighted sound levels, as determined with the slow dynamic characteristic, are used. The A-weighted levels are summed over time on an energy basis to obtain a noise-exposure level (NEL), referenced to 20 $\mu N/m^2$ and one-second duration. This noise-exposure level is used in different ways to obtain limits on the allowable levels, either as a single event or as a daily community noise equivalent level (CNEL). The accumulation for CNEL is adjusted to give more weight to the noise occurring between 1900 and 2200 hours and most weight to noise occurring between 2200 and 0700 hours. The annual CNEL at different locations is used to determine the noise impact area according to the boundary at which the annual CNEL is equal to a set value and according to the land use. The criterion value set for the CNEL is to be lowered in subsequent years.

These requirements on the noise monitoring systems show that something appreciably more complex than a sound-level meter and recorder is required, and specialized systems have been developed for this purpose. A noise-monitoring terminal for this use should contain a microphone, an A-weighting network, squaring, averaging, integrating, conversion and timing circuits, and an output recording or logging device. This terminal can be used as a separate monitoring device, or, similar terminals with the addition of conversion circuits and transmission lines can be tied in as part of a computer-controlled system to monitor the noise over a wide area surrounding an airport.

7.4 ARCHITECTURAL ACOUSTICS.

A wide variety of measurements are made in the field of architectural acoustics (Meyer and Kuttruff, 1962). Some of these are formalized by standards, and others require individual judgment in deciding what needs to be measured and how it needs to be measured. Detailed analysis of all these measurements is beyond the scope of this book, but useful references will be cited in the brief summaries given here. In particular, Davis (1965) gives helpful discussions of instrumentation and details of measurement.

7.4.1 Sound Absorption. A method of test for the sound absorption of acoustical material in reverberation rooms is described in the American Society for Testing and Materials C423-66 (also ANSI S1.7-1970). This standard specifies the requirements for the reverberation room, the test signal at test frequencies of 125, 250, 500, 1000, 2000, and 4000 Hz, the mounting of the test specimen, and the measurement procedure. One possible arrangement of instruments is a noise generator supplying an octave-band analyzer,

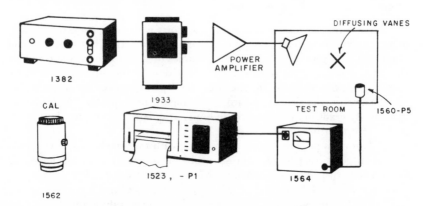

Figure 7-13. A system for sound absorption measurements.

followed by a power amplifier, which drives some loudspeakers that can be switched on and off. A microphone is connected by means of a cable to a 1/3-octave analyzer, which drives a graphic level recorder.

The particular instruments chosen may depend on other measurements to be made. Thus, the 1521-B recorder could be substituted for the 1523 recorder with the 1523-P1 preamplifier plug-in. The octave-band filter is not essential; it helps in overriding background noise.

The basic procedure is to measure the decay rate of sound, which is a band of noise, with and without the acoustical material in the room. These two measurements permit one to calculate the sound absorption of the specimen.

7.4.2 Sound Transmission Loss. The American Society for Testing and Materials E90-70 gives the recommended practice for the Laboratory Measurement of Airborne Sound Transmission Loss of Building Partitions. Here, two reverberant rooms with a common wall, the wall under test, are required. A diffuse noise field is set up and measured in one room and is also measured in the other. From these two measurements and a measurement of the sound absorption in the second room (see paragraph 7.4.1) the transmission loss can be calculated.

One possible arrangement of instruments is a noise generator followed by a power amplifier, which drives loudspeakers in the first room. A microphone in each room is connected by means of cables to a 1/3-octave analyzer, so that the level in each room can be monitored. A sound-level calibrator is essential in order to compare the sensitivities of the two microphone systems.

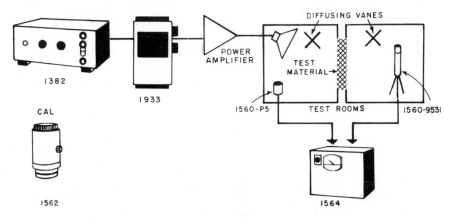

Figure 7-14. A system for sound transmission measurements.

Since a good space average of the sound-pressure in each room is desired, a number of microphone positions may be needed in each room. Rather than moving a microphone from one position to another, a group of microphones can be scanned by a 1566 Multichannel Amplifier. One 1566 can be used for both rooms. With the 1562 Sound-Level Calibrator as a source, the sensitivity of each transducer can be equalized by the individual-channel gain adjustments in the 1566. If a 1921 Real-Time Analyzer is used for the 1/3-octave measurements, the squared outputs of the microphones can be combined in the detector system as they are scanned. The set of microphones in one room would be scanned and then the set in the second room.

Another standard, ASTM E336-67T, Tentative Recommended Practice for Measurement of Airborne Sound Insulation in Buildings, specifies how similar measurements should be made in the field. Since the conditions of the measurement cannot be as well controlled as in the laboratory situation, the results may be quite different. The measurement techniques are similar, although not necessarily identical, but the instrumentation required is generally the same as outlined above.

7.4.3 Reverberation Time or Decay Rate. The rate at which sound decays in an auditorium has been found to be a useful quantity in rating an auditorium. If sound decays too rapidly, the room sounds "dead," and an organ, for example, played in a dead hall loses much of its appeal. A very live room, that is, one in which the sound decays slowly, may be useless as a lecture hall, because the individual syllables of speech are obscured by the persisting sounds of previous syllables.

The more common name for the characteristic that rates sound decay is "reverberation time," which is the time taken for the sound to decay 60 dB after the source has stopped. This time is usually measured by exciting the room with a band of noise, which requires a noise generator and a power amplifier driving one or more loudspeakers (see Figure 7-15). In an auditorium or theater, the power amplifier and loudspeaker system for sound reinforcement can usually be used as part of this measurement system.

This sound is then picked up by a microphone feeding another 1/3-octave filter, which drives a graphic level recorder with a 40 or 50 dB potentiometer. The pickup system is adjusted so that the level on the recorder is near full scale. The sound is then suddenly turned off and the graphic level recorder plots the decay. A straight line is drawn on the chart to fit the average slope of the curve. From this slope, one can calculate the rate of decay and the reverberation time. A number of refinements are often introduced into this process, and these are discussed in the book by Davis and in papers in the Journal of the Acoustical Society of America. These measurements are made over a wide frequency range and in a number of representative places in the hall.

A tape recorder can be of great help in this measurement (Schultz, 1963). (See Figure 7-16.)

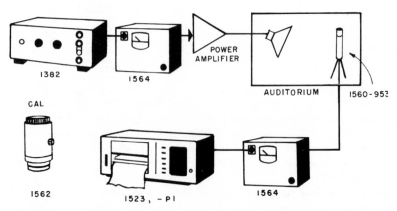

Figure 7-15. Decay-rate and reverberation measurements for 1523 system.

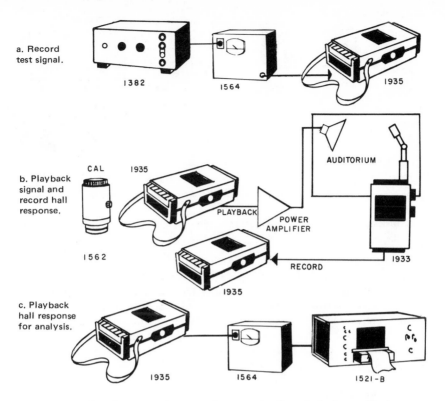

Figure 7-16. Use of tape recorders to perform an acoustic analysis of an auditorium.

When it is necessary to simplify the testing procedure at a hall (if, for example, an audience is present), an alternative procedure may give useful information with relatively short testing time. The hall is excited by means of a broad-band of "pink" noise (noise whose spectrum level decreases with increasing frequency to yield constant energy per octave of bandwidth). The sound in the hall is recorded on a tape recorder with the noise on and during the decay period when the noise is suddenly switched off. Later, in the laboratory, this recorded signal is played back through a 1/3-octave analyzer and a graphic level recorder. This recording is repeated for the full range of the desired settings of frequency of the analyzer. In this way, a complete picture of the decay rate as a function of frequency can be obtained with only one "exposure" at the hall. Some of the detail, particularly at lower levels, may be obscured, however, by the background noise in the hall.

7.4.4 Response Testing. The equalization of a sound system, to obtain good uniformity of response with frequency, can improve the performance of the system. The suggested procedure for measuring the response is as follows: The sound system is driven by broadband pink noise. The sound produced is then analyzed by a recording 1/3-octave analyzer (Figure 7-17). This analysis is carried out for a number of representative places in the area to be covered by the sound system.

The adjustments in the frequency response are then made on the basis of a study of the response curves. The fine details of the curves are ignored, and the broader trends are used to decide how best to adjust the frequency-re-

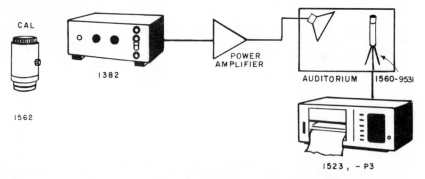

Figure 7-17. Response testing system using "pink" noise.

sponse controls. Sometimes the measurements may show up defects or errors in the system.

7.4.5 Tone-Burst Testing for Echoes. Because of the serious effects of echoes on speech intelligibility, testing for the amplitude and time of arrival of direct and reflected sounds is an important tool in evaluating a hall (Schultz and Watters, 1964). One suggested procedure is to excite the hall with a tone burst of about 16 milliseconds duration (Figure 7-18). The resulting sound is then picked up and displayed on an oscilloscope as a function of time. The pattern on the oscilloscope can often be interpreted in terms of the principal reflections that occur, and it may point the way to significant improvements in the hall. Ideally, this study should be made over the audio-frequency range.

7.4.6 Site Selection. Noise and vibration are obvious factors to consider in the selection of a building site. Buildings for certain purposes (for example, concert halls and sound studios) may be much more expensive to design and build if they must be placed in a noisy environment and at the same time have low background noise. A careful study of the sound and vibration conditions at a site is essential for a proper estimate of a suitable design for such buildings. Some useful information can be obtained with a sound-level meter and with a vibration meter. But an octave-band analysis of the sound and vibration is much more useful, because the cost of isolating against low

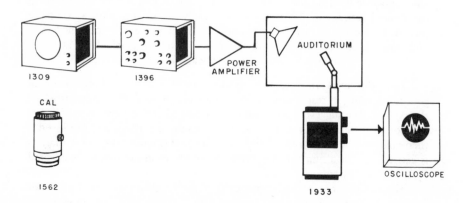

Figure 7-18. Tone-burst testing system for echoes.

166

frequency noise is much greater than that of isolating high-frequency noise, and the knowledge of the level of low-frequency sounds and vibrations may be an essential element in cost studies.

A related problem is that of locating a studio within an existing building. Here, a careful survey of possible locations may lead to a significant saving in construction costs.

REFERENCES

L. L. Beranek (1949), *Acoustic Measurements*, John Wiley & Sons, Inc., New York.

K. A. Bowen and J. S. Graham (1967), "Noise Analysis: A Maintenance Indicator," *Mechanical Engineering*, Vol. 89, #10, 1967, pp. 31-33.

D. Davis (1965), *Acoustical Tests and Measurements*, H. W. Sams, Indianapolis.

FAA (1969), Federal Aviation Regulations, Part 36-Noise Standards: Aircraft Type Certification, Federal Aviation Administration, Department of Transportation.

Federal Coal Mine Health and Safety Act (1969), Public Law 91-173, 91st Congress, S.2917, December 30, 1969.

C. A. W. Glew and D. C. Watson (1971), "The Octave Band Vibration Analyzer as a Machinery Defect Indicator," Am Soc of Mech Engineers, Paper 71-DE-47, April 1971.

E. Meyer and H. Kuttruff (1962), "Progress in Architectural Acoustics," in Richardson and Meyer, 1962, pp. 222-277.

OSHA (1970), "Part 1910—Occupational Safety and Health Standards," under authority of Williams-Steiger Occupational Safety and Health Act of 1970 (P.L. 91-596) (84 Stat. 1593, 1600; 29 U.S.C. 655, 657) Federal Register Vol. 36, #105, May 29, 1971, Washington, D.C.

E. G. Richardson and E. Meyer, eds. (1962), *Technical Aspects of Sound Vol III*, Elsevier Publishing Company, Amsterdam.

T. J. Schultz, "Problems in the Measurement of Reverberation Time," *Journal of the Audio Engineering Society*, Vol. 11, #4, October 1963, pp. 307-317.

T. J. Schultz and B. G. Watters (1964), "Propagation of Sound Across Audience Seating", *J Acoustical Society Am*, Vol. 36, #5, May 1964, pp. 885-896.

WHPCA (1969), Occupational noise-exposure regulations under Section 50-204.10 of the Walsh-Healey Public Contracts Act — Safety and Health Standards, *Federal Register*, Vol. 34, #96, May 20, 1969, ammended July 1, 1969.

Chapter 8

Techniques, Precautions, and Calibrations

8.1 INTRODUCTION.

The previous chapter was designed to help in deciding what measurements need to be made for a given acoustic or vibration problem. This chapter discusses how to make the measurements. Other chapters provide help in interpreting the results of the measurements.

The goal is to make valid measurements (Stein, 1962). In order to achieve this goal, it is helpful to recognize that the results of a measurement are determined by a number of factors, among which are the following:

1. The phenomenon being measured.
2. The effect of the measurement process on the phenomenon being measured.
3. The environmental conditions.
4. The characteristics of the transducers and instruments being used at the time they are used.
5. The way the transducers and instruments are used.
6. The observer.

Although many useful measurements are made by those with little background in acoustics, the chances of making valid measurements are increased as the understanding of these factors becomes more thorough. Thus a good knowledge of vibration and acoustics, of transducers, of instruments, and of measurement techniques, is helpful in making noise measurements. In this chapter we shall, therefore, provide information that is particularly pertinent for measuring noise.

Even when one does not need to measure noise according to a standard procedure, it is often wise to try to do so if an appropriate standard can be found. The standards have been prepared to help obtain valid data. They are useful guides for the inexperienced, and they help the experienced to keep in mind the required steps in a measurement procedure. They help to make comparisons of measured results more meaningful.

Those who prepare the standards try to recognize as many of the problem areas as they can and they attempt to set the requirements and procedures to bring them under control. But, often significant compromises have to be made because not enough is known to resolve the problem, or the available instrumentation may be inadequate. As the state of the art advances, the standards can be improved correspondingly. It is, therefore, important to use the most recent standards.

The general standard ANSI S1.13-1971, "Standard Methods for the Measurement of Sound Pressure Levels," is particularly recommended.

A thorough study of the instruction books supplied with the instruments to be used will often make it clear how to make the most effective use of the instruments. Practice in their use on familiar sounds is also helpful, and acoustical calibrating signals are particularly good for this purpose.

As implied in the listing of factors that determine the measurement results, the use of a precision instrument does not guarantee that a measurement will be valid or accurate. When measurements are done properly, however, a precision instrument will help to yield more consistent results than is possible with a less precise instrument. Better measurement techniques then will be less limited by instruments, and improved results can be obtained more readily.

An obvious but important rule in any measurement task is to review the results to see if they are reasonable. If they are not, try to track down possible sources of trouble, particularly simple things like poor connections, plugs in the wrong places, no power, low batteries, controls set incorrectly, damaged equipment, stray grounds and pickup. If nothing can be found that can be corrected to bring the data into line, perhaps the data only seem unreasonable because of limited understanding of the phenomena or of the measurement process.

The results of a noise measurement may be a key factor in resolving a noise problem. In addition, the experience and data often help in doing a better job on another noise problem. Careful records of noise measurements can be valuable for future reference on subsequent problems, and this possibility should be kept in mind in tackling a noise problem.

A recognition of the accuracy limitations of acoustic and vibration measurements is important, in order to be reasonable in the approach to a measurement problem. Thus, consistency to 0.1 dB or better is attainable in only a few laboratory calibration procedures in acoustics and not in general acoustical measurements. Field calibrations of sound-level meters at one frequency with a calibrator may be consistent to 0.5 dB or slightly better. A consistency of 1 dB is difficult in general measurements, even under carefully controlled conditions, but it is a more reasonable goal than 0.1 dB.

8.2 SOUND MEASUREMENTS.

Most of the applications discussed in the previous chapter require a measurement of either sound-pressure level as a function of frequency or of sound level. These quantities are measured at a single point or at a number of points that are determined by the conditions of the application.

The basic procedure for measuring the sound level or the sound-pressure level at a given point is to locate the sound-level-meter microphone at that point and to note the reading of the sound-level meter. Some preliminary exploration of the sound field is usually necessary to determine that the point selected is the correct one, and this exploration is discussed later in this chapter. Other practical details regarding this measurement are also given in this chapter, but the actual manipulation of the individual instrument controls is discussed in the instruction books that are furnished with the instruments.

We shall discuss the choice of microphone and auxiliary apparatus, the effects of extraneous influences, the recording of adequate data, the calibration of the instruments, and the interpretation of the data. Much of this discussion is necessary because no ideal instrument or combination of instruments and accessories is available that would be suitable for all conditions.

8.2.1 Choice and Use of Microphone. The microphones supplied with modern sound-level meters are suitable for most sound measurements. For very high sound levels and for high-temperature applications, special microphones need to be used. The performance characteristics of these modern microphones, as well as their limitations, are reviewed here. In addition, some of the problems encountered with the use of microphones supplied on earlier instruments are discussed briefly.

Low Sound Levels. A microphone used to measure low sound levels must have low "self-noise," and it must produce an output voltage sufficient to override the circuit noise of the amplifier in the sound-level meter. The type of microphone supplied with the sound-level meter is very good in this respect, and sound levels down to about 24 dB can be measured with it. The smaller microphones are less suitable.

When a sound is analyzed, the minimum measurable sound-pressure band level is even lower than 24 dB with the Type 1560-P5 microphone, because the equivalent internal noise in a selected band is less than the over-all noise.

When microphone cables are used, a preamplifier must be placed at the microphone if one must preserve the ability to measure low sound-pressure levels. (See paragraph 6.2.7.)

High Sound Levels. The sound-level meter microphone is well suited for the measurement of sound-pressure levels up to 150 dB. The 1/2-in. ceramic microphone can be used up to 165 dB. Certain blast microphones (such as those made by Atlantic Research Corporation, Alexandria, Va.; Chesapeake Instrument Corporation, Shadyside, Md., and Massa Laboratories, Hingham, Mass.) can be used directly with the sound-level meter for sound-pressure levels up to about 190 dB.

Low-Frequency Noise. The ceramic- and condenser-type microphones are well suited for measuring low-frequency noise. In fact, measurements may be made down to 5 Hz with a 1933 Precision Sound-Level Meter and Analyzer. The 1551-C Sound-Level Meter is designed to cover the frequency range down to 20 Hz and even at 10 Hz the response is down only 10 dB. This 20-Hz limit is adequate for most ordinary noises.

High-Frequency Noise. The primary requirements on the microphone for accurate measurement of high-frequency sounds are small size and uniform frequency response at high frequencies. For measuring over-all sound levels, the high-frequency characteristic is not so important because most machinery noises do not include strong high-frequency components. Even for those sounds that do include significant energy at the high-frequency end, the decrease in response required at high frequencies for the standard weightings, means that the important noise energy is generally well within the range of the regular microphone furnished on the sound-level meter.

If the noises are to be analyzed, and accurate measurement of band-pressure levels at high frequencies is important, the 1/2-in. ceramic, electret, or condenser microphones should be used. If good response beyond the audible range is required, the 1/4-in. electret or condenser, or 1/8-in. condenser microphones can be used, provided the sound-pressure levels are high enough to be adequately beyond the background noise of the system.

Humidity. Long exposure of any microphone to very high humidity should be avoided. The ceramic microphones are not damaged by extremes of humidity. The chemical Rochelle salt, which was used in microphones furnished with the earlier Types 1551-A, 1551-B, and 759-B Sound Level Meters, and in the Type 1555-A Sound-Survey Meter, however, gradually dissolves if the humidity is too high (above about 84%). The Rochelle-salt crystal unit in the microphone, however, is protected by a coating, so that it is relatively unaffected by high humidity. Nevertheless, it is wise to avoid unnecessary exposure. A Rochelle-salt microphone should not be stored for long periods in a very dry atmosphere, since it can dry out.

NOTE

Rochelle-salt-crystal microphones are no longer supplied by General Radio Company.

A condenser microphone is not damaged by exposure to high humidity, but its operation can be seriously affected unless proper precautions are taken. For proper operation it is essential that very little electrical leakage occur across the microphone. The exposed insulating surface in the microphone has been specially treated to maintain this low leakage, even under conditions of high humidity. In spite of the precaution, the leakage may become excessive under some conditions. Then it may be advisable to keep the microphone at a temperature higher than the ambient temperature to reduce the leakage. In climates where the humidity is normally high, it is recommended that the microphone itself be stored at a temperature above ambient to avoid condensation.

An electret microphone can stand for long periods the normal variations in temperature and humidity without significant change in sensitivity. But, if the humidity is normally high, an electret microphone should be stored in a small jar containing silica gel. A relative humidity of 90% is the maximum recommended for the electret.

High or Varying Temperature. Although most noise measurements are made indoors at average room temperatures, some measurement conditions expose the microphone to much higher or lower temperatures. When these conditions are encountered, it is essential to know the temperature limitations of the equipment.

The microphones supplied with the 1565 and 1551-C Sound-Level Meters will withstand temperatures of -40° to $+60^\circ$C without damage. Even at 95°C, a permanent sensitivity loss of only about 0.5 dB may occur. In contrast, the maximum safe operating temperature for Rochelle-salt crystal microphones, formerly furnished with some sound-level meters, is about 45°C (113°F). At 55.6°C (132°F), the Rochelle-salt crystal is permanently changed. It is, therefore, not safe to put a Rochelle-salt microphone in the trunk or back of a car that is to be left standing in the sun.

The normal operating temperature range for the condenser microphone systems is from -30° to $+65^\circ$C. They will withstand higher temperatures without damage, but a limit of 80°C is recommended for the preamplifiers. The electret condenser microphone should be limited to -25° to $+55^\circ$C (131°F).

Fortunately, it is usually possible to keep the sound-level meter itself at more reasonable temperatures. Its behavior at extreme temperatures is limited by the batteries. Temperatures of even 55°C (130°F) will result in much-shortened battery life. Operation below -10°F is not ordinarily possible without special low-temperature batteries.

Microphones are usually calibrated at normal room temperatures. If a microphone is operated at other temperatures, its sensitivity will be somewhat different and a correction should be applied. The correction for sensitivity for the ceramic microphone is only about $-.01$ dB per degree Celsius, so that for most purposes the correction can be neglected.

Hum Pickup. Dynamic microphones are sometimes used for measurement purposes because they are readily used with long cables. The development of modern preamplifiers, such as the 1560-P42 Preamplifier, makes the use of dynamic microphones unnecessary. But if they are used, care must be taken to avoid hum pickup, which is the induction of undesired electrical signals from the external magnetic field of equipment such as transformers, motors, and generators. Ceramic and condenser microphones are relatively free from this undesirable effect.

Long Cables. For the most accurate sound measurements, only the microphone should be put into the sound field, and the measuring instruments and the observers should not be near the point where the sound-pressure is to be measured. For this reason, and also for the situations when it is impossible or impractical for the observer to be near the microphone, an extension cable is ordinarily used to connect the microphone to the instruments. If the microphone is attached directly to a preamplifier, long cables can be used without any deleterious effects. Condenser and electret microphones should almost always be used directly on a preamplifier.

When a microphone is used directly with an extension cable, a correction for loss in sensitivity is necessary. This correction is readily determined by the use of a Type 1562 Sound-Level Calibrator. (See paragraph 8.2.3.) The correction is about 7 dB when a 25-ft cable (650 pF) is used between a 1-in. ceramic microphone and the instrument, so that 7 dB should be added to the indicated level to obtain the level at the microphone. For longer cables the correction is greater. For Rochelle-salt microphones, the correction is a function of the temperature of the microphone; values are given in the instruction manuals for instruments using such microphones.

Wind Effects. The microphone should also be kept out of any appreciable wind, if possible. Wind on the microphone produces a noise, which is mainly of low frequency as shown in Figure 8-1. This added noise may seriously upset the measurement, particularly for high wind speeds, since the noise increases with wind speed. If it is not possible to avoid wind on the microphone, a wind screen should be used. The 1560-9521 Wind Screen reduces the wind noise significantly, as shown in Figure 8-1, without a serious effect on the frequency response.

Since the wind noise is mainly of low-frequency, the use of A-weighting reduces the over-all wind-induced noise level markedly. It is, therefore, possible that a useful A-weighted level can be measured, even though a flat or C-weighted level of the noise source is obscured by wind noise. But even here the wind screen is a desirable addition.

Direction of Arrival of Sound at the Microphone. Some microphones are designed to be directional at all frequencies. That is, the response of the microphone depends on the direction of arrival of the sound wave. Most of the microphones used for sound measurements, however, are essentially omnidirectional at low frequencies (below about 1 kHz). At frequencies so high that the size of the microphone is comparable to the wavelength of the sound in air, even these microphones will show directional effects. This

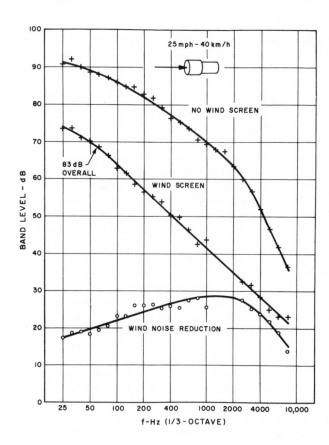

Figure 8-1a. Wind noise spectrum-flat weighting.

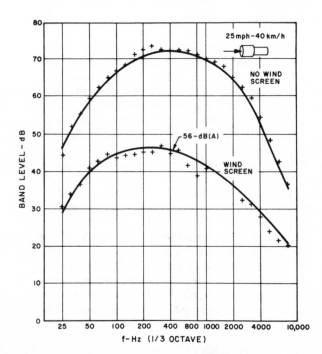

Figure 8-1b. Wind-noise spectrum-A weighting.

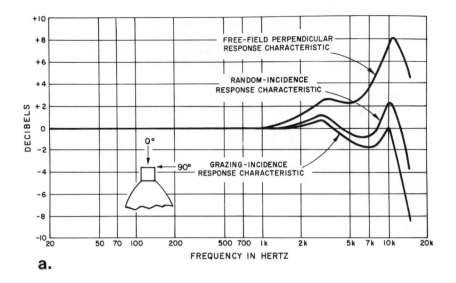

a.

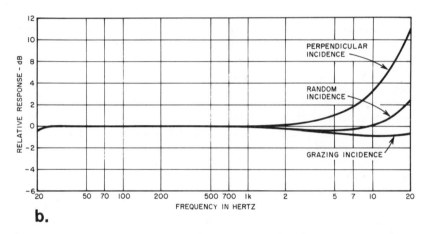

b.

Figure 8-2. Typical response characteristics for
the ceramic microphones, (a) 1-in., (b) ½-in.

change in response with direction should be considered in positioning the
microphone for a measurement. The extent of these variations is shown by
the frequency response characteristics of the different microphones (see
Figure 8-2). The microphone is usually positioned so that the response to the
incident sound is as uniform as possible.

When sound-pressure level is measured in a reverberant room at a point
that is not close to a noise source, the sound arrives at the microphone from
many different directions. Then the orientation of the microphone is not
critical, and the response is assumed to be that labeled "random incidence."
Under these conditions, nevertheless, it is usually desirable to avoid having
the microphone pointing at a nearby hard surface, from which high-frequency
sounds could be reflected to arrive perpendicular (0° incidence) to the plane
of the diaphragm. (For all the microphones used in the General Radio Sound

175

Measurement System this perpendicular incidence is along the axis of cylindrical symmetry of the microphone. This axis is used as the 0° reference line.) If this condition cannot be avoided, the possibility for errors from this effect can be reduced by some acoustic absorbing material placed on the reflecting surface.

When measurements are made in a reverberant room at varying distances from a noise source, the microphone should generally be oriented so that a line joining the microphone and the source is at an angle of about 70° from the axis of the microphone. When the microphone is near the source, most of the sound comes directly from the source and a 70° incidence response applies. On the other hand, near the boundaries of the room the incidence is more nearly random and the random-incidence response applies. These two response curves are nearly the same, so that there is little change in the effective response characteristic as the microphone is moved about the room. This desirable result would not be obtained if the microphone were pointed at the noise source.

If, however, a source is to be measured in a nearly anechoic or free-field space, the use of a microphone with a uniform response for perpendicular incidence may be preferred. Then the microphone can be pointed at the source, and the directional behavior will help to reduce the effects of extraneous noises. Although this type of microphone is acceptable for international standards on sound-level meters, it is not acceptable for ANSI S1.4-1971.

Position of Microphone. In previous sections of this chapter some comments have been made on various aspects of the problem of placing the microphone in the most satisfactory position for making the noise measurement. In general, the location is determined by the type of measurement to be made. For example, the noise of a machine is usually measured with the microphone placed near the machine according to the rules of a test code, or if its characteristics as a noise are desired, a comparatively large number of measurements are made according to the methods and the placement given in paragraph 8.3.5.

It is important to explore the noise field before deciding on a definite location (paragraph 8.3.4) for the microphone.

Many measurement locations may be necessary for specifying the noise field, particularly if the apparatus produces a noise that is highly directional. Further discussion of directionality is given in 8.3.2.

If the noise level is measured for calculation of the speech-interference level or loudness level or for determination of deafness risk, it is important to explore the noise field to make sure that the measurement made is representative. The possible effects of obstacles in upsetting the distribution of sound, particularly at high frequencies, should be kept in mind during this exploration.

At first thought, it seems logical, when measurements regarding noise exposure are made, to mount the microphone at the operator's ear. Actually, because of the variables introduced by the effect of the operator's head being close to the microphone, this technique is not used, except in certain scientific tests with special probe microphones. All ratings of speech-interference, loudness, and deafness risk are based on a measurement with no person in the immediate vicinity of the microphone. The microphone should, however, be about where the operator's ear would normally be.

8.2.2 Effects of Room and Nearby Objects.

Effect of Observer and Meter Case. As mentioned in the previous section, the observer can affect the measured data if he is close to the microphone. When measurements are made in a live room and not close to a source, the effect is usually not important. But if measurements are made near a source, it is advisable for the observer to stand well to the side of the direct path between the source and the microphone. *For precise measurements in a very dead room, such as an anechoic chamber, the instruments and the observer should be in another room with only the source, the microphone, the extension cable, and a minimum of supporting structure in the dead room.*

For many measurements, however, it is most convenient to be able to carry the sound-level meter around. When held in the hand, the sound-level

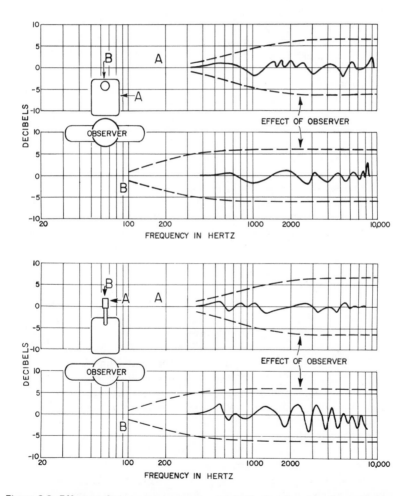

Figure 8-3. Effect on frequency response as a result of using the microphone directly on the swivel post of the instrument (in two positions) without an observer present, and the extent of the effect with an observer present. A single-frequency, plane, acoustic wave was used in an anechoic chamber, and the decibel values are the differences between the response under the conditions noted and the response of the microphone alone.

177

meter should be held in front of the observer with the sound coming in from the side. The magnitude of the error that can be caused by the way the instrument is held can be evaluated from the data shown in Figure 8-3. These data show the difference between the readings of the meter with and without the observer present, as a function of frequency. Two locations are shown: (1) the sound-level meter is between the observer and the noise source, (2) the noise source is located to one side of the observer, and the sound-level meter is held in front of the observer. It is apparent that, if the instrument is held properly, little error in reading of the over-all level will occur for most noises. For additional information on this subject, refer to R. W. Young (1962).

The meter case itself may also disturb the sound field at the microphone as shown by the other characteristic curves in Figure 8-3. There is practically no effect below 1000 Hz, and, again, on most noises, little error in measuring over-all level will result if the microphone is left on the instrument. When an analyzer is used with the sound-level meter, however, it is advisable to separate the microphone from the instruments and to use an extension cable. This refinement is not necessary, however, if the only data that are of interest are below 1000 Hz.

Room Design and Effect of Nearby Objects. When a noisy device is to be tested for its acoustic output, the space in which it is tested can have a significant effect on the results. Unless a reverberation room (paragraph 8.3.4) is used, the measurement room used for evaluating a noise source should be sufficiently well treated so that no appreciable standing wave exists. Ideally the room should be anechoic. If any small standing-wave pattern remains, the average of the maximum and minimum decibel readings should be taken. If the differences are more than 6 dB, the level should be taken as 3 dB below the maximum readings that occur frequently. This standing-wave pattern, however, should not be confused with the normal decrease in level with distance from the source or with the directivity pattern of the source.

Objects in the room reflect the sound waves just as do the walls of the room. Consequently, all unnecessary objects should be removed from the measurement room. In general, no objects, including the observer, should be close to the microphone. If it is impractical to follow this principle, the objects should usually be treated with absorbing material.

One troublesome but not frequent effect of nearby objects results from sympathetic vibrations. A large, thin metal panel if undamped can readily be set into vibration at certain frequencies. If one of these frequency components is present in the noise, this panel can be set into motion either by airborne sound or by vibration transmitted through the structure. This panel vibration can seriously upset the noise field in its vicinity. One way of checking that this effect is not present to any important degree is to measure the sound field as a function of the radial distance from the source. The sound should decrease, when not very close to the source, about 6 dB as the distance is doubled. This procedure also checks for reflections in general.

When the acoustical environment is being measured, no change should be made in the usual location of equipment, but the sound field should be carefully explored to make sure that the selected location for the microphone is not in an acoustic shadow cast by a nearby object or is not in a minimum of the directivity pattern of the noise source.

Effect of Background Noise. Ideally, when a noise source is measured, the measurement should determine only the direct air-borne sound from the source, without any appreciable contribution from noise produced by other sources. In order to ensure isolation from other sources, the measurement room may need to be isolated from external noise and vibration. As a test to determine that this requirement has been met, the American National Standard Method for the Physical Measurement of Sound, S1.2, specifies the following:

"If the increase in the sound pressure level in any given band, with the sound source operating, compared to the ambient sound pressure level alone, is 10 dB or more, the sound pressure level due to both the sound source and ambient sound is essentially the sound pressure level due to the sound source. This is the preferred criterion."

If the background noise level and the apparatus noise level are steady, a correction can be applied to the measured data according to the graph of Figure 8-4. The procedure is as follows: After the test position has been selected according to the test code and after exploration of the field as outlined in paragraph 8.2.1, the background noise level is measured in the test position. Then the sound level is measured with the apparatus operating. The difference between the sound level with the apparatus operating and the background level determines the correction to be used. If this difference is

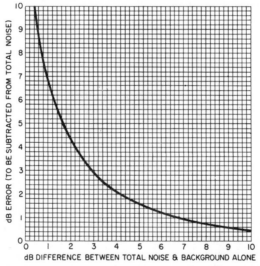

Figure 8-4. Background noise correction for sound-level measurements.

less than 3 dB, the apparatus noise is less than the background noise; and the level obtained by use of the correction should be regarded as only indicative of the true level and not as an accurate measurement. If the difference is greater than 10 dB, the background noise has virtually no effect, and the reading with the apparatus operating is the desired level. An example of a situation intermediate between these two is as follows: The background noise level is 77.5 dB, and the total noise with the machine under test operating is 83.5 dB. The correction, from the graph of Figure 8-4, for a 6.0-dB difference, is 1.2 dB, so that the corrected level is 82.3 dB.

When apparatus noise is analyzed, the background noise level in each band should also be analyzed to determine if the correction for the level in each band is necessary and possible. The spectrum of the background noise is usually different from that of the noise to be measured, and the corrections in each band will be different.

If this difference between background level and total noise level is small, an attempt should be made to lower the background level. Usually the first step is to work on the source or sources of this background noise to reduce the noise directly. The second step is to work on the transmission path between the source and the point of measurement. This step may mean simply closing doors and windows, if the source is external to the room, or it may mean erecting barriers, applying acoustical treatment to the room, and opening doors and windows, if the source is in the room. The third step is to improve the difference by the method of measurement. It may be possible to select a point closer to the apparatus, or an exploration of the background noise field may show that the measuring position can be shifted to a minimum of this noise. The latter possibility is more likely when an analysis is being made and the background level in a particular band is unusually high. It may also be possible to point the microphone at the apparatus to obtain an improvement at high frequencies (see Figure 8-2); it may be necessary to use a directional microphone; or it may be desirable to use a vibration pickup.

8.2.3 Instrument Precautions.

♦ *Low Noise Levels — Effect of Circuit Noise.* When low noise levels are to be measured, the inherent circuit noise may contribute to the measured level. This effect is usually noticeable in the range below 40 dB when a small microphone is used or a ceramic microphone is used on the end of a very long cable. If the microphone is directly on the sound-level meter, the level at which this effect may be important is below 30 dB, if the C weighting is used or even lower if the A or B weighting is used. To measure the circuit noise the microphone may be replaced by a well-shielded capacitor with a capacitance equal to that of the microphone. A correction can then be made for this noise, if necessary, by the same procedure as outlined for background noise in paragraph 8.2.2. If the circuit noise is comparable to the noise being measured, some improvement in the measurement can usually be obtained by use of an octave-band analyzer. The circuit noise in each band should be checked also to see if correction is necessary.

Whenever low noise levels must be measured and extension cables are used, the Type 1560-P42 or P40 Preamplifier should be used at the microphone.

Hum Pickup. When noise is measured near electrical equipment, a check should be made that there is no appreciable pickup of electro-magnetic field in the sound-measuring system. The procedure depends on the directional character of the field. The orientation of the instruments should be changed to see if there is any significant change in level. If an analyzer is used, it should be tuned to the power-supply frequency, usually 60 Hz, which would be the 63-Hz band for the octave-band analyzer, when this test is made. If no analyzer is included, the C-weighting should be used in this test to make the effect of hum most noticeable, and a good-quality pair of earphones, with tight-fitting ear cushions, should be used to listen to the output of the sound-level meter.

If a dynamic microphone is used, tests should be made with different orientations of the microphone, with the microphone disconnected, and with the sound-level meter disconnected from the analyzer. If there is pickup in the microphone, proper orientation may be adequate to make a measurement possible, or electromagnetic shielding may be necessary.

If the hum pickup is in the instruments, they can usually be moved away from the source of the electromagnetic field, or, alternatively, a proper orientation is usually sufficient to reduce the pickup to a negligible value.

When ac-operated instruments are used as part of the measuring setup, a check should be made for 120-Hz as well as 60-Hz hum. This hum may be in the instruments, or it may appear as a result of the interconnection of different instruments. These two possibilities may be distinguished by a check of the instruments individually. If each is separately essentially free from hum, different methods of grounding, balancing, or shielding should be tried. Sometimes reversal of the power-plug connection to the line helps to reduce the hum.

High Sound Levels — Microphonics. All vacuum tubes and some transistors are affected by mechanical vibration. Those used in the sound-measuring equipment have been selected to be less sensitive to vibration than the usual types. But at sufficiently high sound levels, even these can be vibrated to such an extent that they contribute an undesired signal to the output. Trouble from this effect, which is called microphonics, is not usually experienced until the sound levels are well above 100 dB, unless the instruments are placed on supports that carry vibrations directly to the instruments.

The usual test for microphonics is to disconnect the microphone and observe whether or not the residual signal is appreciably lower than the signal with the microphone connected. For the octave-band analyzer, the input cord can be disconnected to see if the indicated level comes from the input signal or if it is generated within the instrument. The instruments can also be lifted up from the support on which they have been placed to see whether or not the vibrations are transmitted through the supports or if it is the airborne sound that is causing the vibration.

Possible remedies for microphonic troubles are as follows:
1. Place the instruments on soft rubber pads.
2. Remove the instruments from the strong field to another room and interconnect with long cables.
3. Put in deadened sound barriers between the instruments and the sound source.

Mechanical vibration also affects the microphone itself, in that the output of the microphone is dependent on the airborne and solid-borne vibrations that are impressed upon it. The effects of the solid-borne vibrations are not usually important in the standard, sensitive microphones because of the type of construction used; but these vibrations are usually of great importance for the low-sensitivity microphones used in the measurement of high sound levels. A mechanically soft mounting should generally be used for such a microphone, in order to avoid trouble from these vibrations. Often merely suspending the microphone by means of its connecting cable is adequate.

♦ *Interpretation of the Meter Pointer.* Two ballistic characteristics are provided for the meter on the sound-level meter: The "FAST" position is normally used. It will be noticed, however, that most sounds do not give a constant level reading. The reading fluctuates often over a range of a few decibels and sometimes over a range of many decibels, particularly in analysis at low frequencies. The maximum and minimum readings should usually be noted. These levels can be entered on the data sheet as, say, 85-91 dB or 88 ± 3 dB.

When an average sound-pressure level is desired and the fluctuations are less than 6 dB, a simple average of the maximum and minimum levels is usually taken. If the range of fluctuation is greater than 6 dB, the average sound-pressure level is usually taken to be 3 dB below the maximum level. In selecting this maximum level, it is also customary to ignore any unusually high levels that occur infrequently.

The "SLOW" meter speed should be used to obtain an average reading when the fluctuations on the "FAST" position are more than 3 or 4 dB. On steady sounds the reading of the meter will be the same for either the "SLOW" or "FAST" position, while on fluctuating sounds the "SLOW" position provides a long-time average reading.

A more detailed discussion of this problem is given in succeeding paragraphs.

Tones and Beats. The indicated sound level of a constant-amplitude pure tone is steady, and so is that of a mixture of tones, unless at least two components are close together in frequency. Examples of sounds that have a constant indicated sound level are transformer hum and noise from some rotating electrical machinery. When the combined noise of several machines is measured, the indicated level is also constant, unless the speed of the machines is such that some of the major noise components are only a few cycles apart in frequency. In this situation an audible beat, a periodic rise and fall in amplitude, occurs, and the indicated level also rises and falls.

Varying-Speed Sources. Machinery that operates at a varying speed usually produces a noise that fluctuates in level. If the speed varies periodically, the level will also vary periodically. This variation results because the noise produced by the machine varies with speed, because the response of the room in which the measurement is made varies with frequency, and, if an analyzer is used, because the response of the measurement system varies with frequency.

If the machine speed varies erratically, the noise level will also vary erratically, and the behavior may be similar to that of random noise.

Random Noise. The indicated sound level of a random noise, such as that produced by jets, blowers, combustion chambers, ventilating systems, etc., is not steady. In fact, all sounds contain some random noise energy, and most have enough so that the indicated level fluctuates noticeably. The extent of the fluctuation is a clue to the nature of the sound.

The fluctuations in level are ordinarily not a result of erratic behavior of the measuring equipment, but rather reflect the irregularities in the process of noise production. This process can often be considered as a combination of many sources that produce sound at random time intervals. The measurement of such noises can be treated on a simplified statistical basis that is satisfactory for almost all sounds.

Average Energy Level of a Random Noise. When a random noise is measured, the first important result that is desired is the long-time average energy level. This concept leads to taking the average of the fluctuating pointer reading. If the fluctuations are less than about 2 dB, this average can be easily and confidently estimated to a fraction of a decibel. If the fluctuations cover a range of 10 dB or more, the average is much less certain.

The extent of the meter fluctuation depends on the meter characteristic. The slower the movement, the smaller are the fluctuations. Thus, if the fluctuations exceed 3 or 4 dB for the "FAST" meter position, the "SLOW" meter position should be used.

When the fluctuations are large, the nature of the source or sources should be considered. If the noise-generating mechanism shifts from one mode to another, it may be desirable to characterize the noise level by more than one average value. This choice is obvious for a dishwasher, for example, where the wash, rinse, and dry cycles differ significantly. But this choice may also be useful in machines where the mode shifts more rapidly.

If the noise is random and the fluctuations are large only because the effective noise bandwidth is small (see paragraph 5.6.5) the average value should be obtained on an energy basis.

Calibration and Corrections. Satisfactory noise measurements depend on the use of measuring equipment that is kept in proper operating condition. Although the instruments are reliable and stable, in time the performance of the instruments may change. In order to ensure that any important changes will be discovered and corrected, certain simple checks have been provided for the General Radio line of sound-level equipment, and these will be discussed in this section. These checks can be made as routine maintenance checks, and some of them should usually be made before and after any set of noise measurements.

In addition to these routine checks, more complete calibration of the system may be desirable for accurate measurements, particularly above 1000 Hz. These calibrations are also discussed in this section.

Electrical Circuit Calibration. The Type 1933 and 1551-C sound-level meters and the analyzers have built-in calibration circuits for checking amplifier gain. In each case the gain of the amplifier is compared with the attenuation of a stable, resistive attenuator.

This test does not check the sensitivity of the microphone and the indicating instrument; these tests are discussed in the next section. The indicating instrument is rugged and relatively unaffected by temperature changes. Its temperature coefficient is about -0.02 dB/°F (-0.036 dB/°C).

Acoustical Calibration at Preferred Frequencies. The Type 1562 Sound-Level Calibrator provides an over-all system calibration at 125, 250, 500, 1000, and 2000 Hz. If a record is kept of the calibration of a microphone as a function of frequency, any significant change in the relative calibration is readily noticed. If such a change occurs, the microphone and the calibrator should be checked as soon as possible. Here, it is useful to have more than one microphone on hand, so that a second microphone can be used if the first is damaged; at the same time, a consistency check on its calibration can help to ensure that the calibrator has not been damaged.

In the interests of maintaining accuracy in sound measurements, another calibration service is provided for owners of General Radio instruments. If these instruments are brought in to one of the General Radio offices, the level will be checked by means of an acoustic calibrator. This calibration will usually show if the instrument is operating correctly. If there is a serious discrepancy, the situation will have to be handled as a regular service problem.

The calibrator can also be used to measure the microphone cable correction. The procedure is as follows:

    a. After the noise measurement has been made, the calibrator is put on the microphone, with the microphone at the end of the cable, and a level reading is taken on the sound-level meter.

b. The microphone is removed from the end of the cable and put directly on the sound-level meter. The calibrator is put on the microphone at the sound-level meter and a second level reading is taken.

c. The difference between these two level readings is the cable correction.

For high accuracy, it is usually essential to have a calibration of the microphone response characteristic as a function of frequency. When this calibration is available and an analysis of a noise is made, correction can be made for the microphone frequency-response characteristic. This correction can be applied only if the noise is analyzed or if the sound is dominated by a component of known frequency, as, for example, in the measurement of loudspeaker response. Otherwise, one must check the uniformity of response of a system to be sure that the measured level of a noise is correct.

Calibration At High Frequencies. The accurate calibration of a microphone at high frequencies in terms of sensitivity vs frequency requires elaborate facilities. Only a few laboratories (e.g., The National Bureau of Standards) offer such calibration as a regular service. General Radio Company will calibrate response vs frequency only for those microphones that it supplies. Such calibration is supplied with all microphones manufactured by General Radio Co.

At General Radio, a free-field perpendicular-incidence calibration is made by comparison with laboratory-standard condenser microphones (ANSI S1.12-1967 Specifications for Laboratory Standard Microphones), according to the methods given in S1.10-1966, Calibration of Microphones. The working-standard microphones are periodically compared with a condenser microphone that has been calibrated at the National Bureau of Standards. They are also periodically calibrated on an absolute basis by the reciprocity method.

Since the sound-level meter standard is based on a random-incidence specification, the perpendicular incidence calibration is automatically converted to the random incidence calibration in the plotting procedure, so that calibrations supplied by General Radio are for random-incidence response and data for converting to perpendicular-incidence or grazing-incidence calibrations are included.

Correction For Frequency-Response Characteristic. It is customary to set the calibration of an acoustical measurement system to indicate the correct level at 400 or 500 Hz. At other frequencies, the differences between true and indicated levels, as determined from a calibration curve, can be applied as corrections to the results of a noise measurement. At frequencies above 1000 Hz, the directional characteristic of the microphone should be taken into account, and the particular curve that corresponds to the actual angle of incidence used should be used for the corrections.

Comparison Tests Among Different Sound-Level Meters. When measurements are made on the same noise with two different sound-level meters, it is commonly found that the readings differ by a significant amount. The preceding material in this chapter should indicate most of the possible sources of discrepancy between the two. Differences in the microphone characteristics are usually the chief cause of this discrepancy. For example, if one sound-level meter uses a dynamic microphone and the other uses a ceramic microphone, and if the noise contains strong-low frequency components, large differences can occur because of the generally poorer low-frequency response of the dynamic microphone. When these effects are understood, most of the discrepancies are readily explained.

———————————Table 8-1———————————

ANSI* SLM CALIBRATION TOLERANCE—C-WEIGHTING

Tolerance —dB

Frequency Hz	Type I Precision	Type II General Purpose	Type III Survey
10	±2.5		
12.5	±2		
16	±2		
20	±2	+3,—∞	+4,—∞
25	±1.5	+2,—2.5	+3,—4.5
31.5	±1.5	+1.5,—2	+2.5,—3
40	±1	+1,—1.5	+2,—2.5
50 to 630	±1	±1	±2
800	±1	±1	±2.5
1000	±1	±1.5	±2.5
1250	±1	±1.5	±2.5
1600	±1	±2	±3
2000	±1	±2.5	±3.5
2500	±1	+3.5,—3.0	±4
3150	±1	+4.5,—3.5	±4.5
4000	±1	+5,—4	±5
5000	+1.5,—2	+5.5,—4.5	±6
6300	+1.5,—2	+6,—5	±7
8000	+1.5,—3	±6	±7
10000	+2,—4	+6,—∞	+7,—∞
12500	+3,—6		
16000	+3,—∞		

*ANSI S1.4-1971.

Another factor that can contribute to this discrepancy concerns the average level. For purposes of meeting certain tolerances, the average level of an instrument made by one manufacturer may be set slightly differently from that made by another.

If the instruments are not operating properly, or if standing waves are not averaged out, serious discrepancies can, of course, be expected.

In order to set an upper limit to these differences among sound-level meters, the American National Standard Specifications for Sound-Level Meters, S1.4-1971, sets certain tolerances on the prescribed frequency characteristics. Representative values for C weighting are shown in Table 8-1.

Incidentally, when a sound-level meter is calibrated with a 1562 Sound-Level Calibrator, these tolerances should be considered in comparing the actual sound-level meter reading with the expected calibration level.

Effect of C Weighting on Band Levels. In principle, the response of the equipment supplying an analyzer should be as uniform as possible to obtain true pressure levels. Sometimes the "C" weighting is used for octave-band measurements. If this is done for instruments meeting the latest ANSI and International standards, there will be small differences in level at the low- and high-frequency ends, compared with the levels that would be obtained with a more nearly uniform response, because of the specified roll-offs in response for the C weighting. Thus, the C-weighted octave-band level is less, by about 3 dB for the bands centered at 31.5 and 8000 Hz, and by 0.8 dB for the bands at 63 and 4000 Hz, than with the uniform response weighting (flat). The shifts in level for the bands in between are too small to be significant.

Check On Over-All Level. When an octave-band analysis has been made, it is good practice to check that the sum of the individual band levels on an energy basis (see Appendix II) is equal within 1 or 2 dB to the over-all level. If this result is not obtained, an error exists, either in the summing or the measurement procedure, because of faulty or incorrectly used equipment, or because the noise is of an impact type. Impact-type noises sometimes give over-all levels appreciably less than the sum of the levels in the individual bands, even when the fast position of the meter switch is used. This result is obtained because of the inability of the meter to indicate the instantaneous levels occurring in very short intervals. The narrow-band levels at low frequencies tend to be nearer the peak value in those bands, while the over-all and high-frequency bands are significantly less than the peak value. When this type of discrepancy is noted, the impulse mode of the 1933 Precision Sound-Level Meter and Analyzer should be used.

Earphones and Stethoscope. A pair of high-quality earphones with tight-fitting earphone cushions is a useful accessory for noise measurements, and high-impedance dynamic or crystal-type phones are recommended. Good earphone cushions are essential to improve the low-frequency response and to help reduce the leakage of external noise under the earphone.

When a measurement system is being set up, the earphones should be plugged into the output of the sound-level meter. Then a listening test should be made to determine that the noise heard in the earphones is the same type of noise heard without the earphones. It is possible to detect trouble from microphonics (usually a ringing sound) or stray pickup in this fashion.

When the noise level is high, say, 90 dB or higher, the leakage of external noise under the earphone may be sufficient to mask the sound from the earphones. Then the earphone cushions should be checked for tightness of fit. In addition, the signal from the earphones can be increased by use of an attenuator setting on the sound-level meter 10 dB lower than that required for a satisfactory reading on the meter. This change of 10 dB is usually not enough to overload the output, but a large change should be avoided. It may also be desirable to have a long cord available, so that it is possible to listen to the output of the earphones far from the noise source.

The earphones can also be used on the output of an analyzer to detect troubles from stray pickup. In addition, a listening test may help one to determine which frequency bands contain the noise that is most objectionable in a given situation.

When the noise level is very high, the earphones on the sound-level meter may be useful in improving speech communication between observers during a measurement run. One observer wears the earphones then the other observer shouts into the sound-level meter microphone. A definite improvement in speech communication results.

A similar procedure using a nonelectrical, medical stethoscope is also possible. One observer has the ear tips in place, and the other speaks in to the receiver of the stethoscope.

8.2.4 Mounting of the Device Under Test.
It is often noticed that the noise level produced by a machine is highly dependent on its mounting. A loose mounting may lead to loud rattles and buzzes, and contact to large resonant surfaces of wood or sheet metal may lead to a sounding-board emphasis of various noise components. For these reasons particular care should be given to the method of mounting. In general, the mounting should be as close to the method of final use as possible. If the machine is to be securely bolted to a heavy concrete floor, it should be tested that way. If the actual conditions

of use cannot be duplicated, the noise measurements may not be sufficient to predict the expected behavior, because of the difference in transmission of noise energy through the supports. The usual alternative is to use a very resilient mounting, so that the transmission of energy to the support is negligible.

8.2.5 Effects of Atmospheric Pressure. Some acoustical measurements are affected by atmospheric pressure and temperature. The output of the 1562 Calibrator, for instance, varies somewhat with pressure, and the rated reference level occurs at a standard atmospheric pressure of 1013 millibars. If the pressure when the calibrator is used is significantly different from 1013 millibars, a correction should be made. The altitude where the calibrator is used is usually the most significant factor in determining the average atmospheric pressure, and a chart for correcting for this effect is included in the calibrator instruction book. Since the output of most other sound sources is affected by the pressure, a chart relating height to average pressure is included here (Figure 8-5). The actual variation in output with pressure for practical sources is usually between that shown by the corresponding decibel scale on the right and one-half that value. Thus, for altitudes up to 2 km (6560 ft), the change in output with altitude is generally less than 2 dB.

The variation of atmospheric pressure at a given location from day to day is usually less important, but for careful measurements where fractions of a decibel are being considered, the actual atmospheric pressure should be

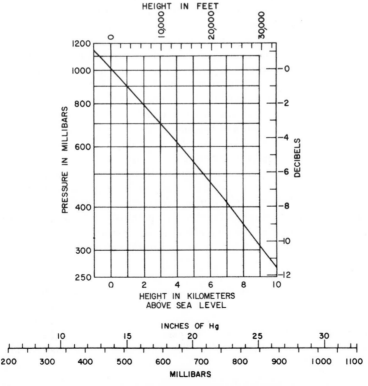

Figure 8-5. Corrections for sound pressure level for atmospheric pressure at various altitudes.

187

noted. The pressure can be obtained from the local weather bureau, and a correction for the difference in altitude between the point where the acoustical measurements are made and the weather bureau may be necessary. This correction is readily estimated from the chart.

8.3 SOUND FIELDS.

The behavior of sound in various environments has been described briefly at various places in this book. We shall now discuss it in more detail in order to explain how sound-power measurements are made.

We shall begin with a discussion of a simple source under idealized conditions. Then we shall point out various factors that alter the idealized conditions and discuss in general what the important effects are.

8.3.1 Simple Source in Free Field.

Point Source. Any vibrating object will radiate sound into the air. The amount of sound radiated depends on the amplitude of vibration of each vibrating part, the area of each part, and the time pattern of the vibrations, including the relative time pattern compared with that of the other parts.

The simplest form of source is a sphere that vibrates uniformly over its entire surface. We can think of this source as a round balloon with air in it. We periodically pump some more air into it and then let the same amount of air out. If the surface of the balloon then expanded and contracted uniformly, the balloon would be a simple, spherical source. This source radiates sound equally in all directions from an apparent center, which is the center of the balloon. It then is a "point" source, insofar as sound radiation is concerned.

Free Field. If such a point (or spherical) source is in the air far from any other objects, including the ground, the sound pressure produced by the source is the same in every direction at equal distances from the point source. Furthermore, the sound pressure is halved for each doubling of distance from the point. This change is usually expressed as a decrease in sound-pressure level of 6 dB. The sound field produced under these idealized conditions is called a free sound field or, simply a free field because it is uniform, it is free from all bounding surfaces, and it is undisturbed by other sources of sound.

Power Level in Free Field. Under free-field conditions, a single measurement* of the sound-pressure level at a known distance from a point source is enough to tell us all about the sound field radiated by the source. For example, we can then predict the level at any other point, since the sound pressure varies inversely as the distance from the source. We can also compute the total sound power radiated by the point source. This calculation is usually made in terms of the power level re 10^{-12} watt (PWL) of the source (paragraph 2.3). Then the required relation to the sound-pressure level (SPL) is:

$$PWL = SPL + 20 \log r + 0.5 \text{ dB}$$

where r is the distance in feet from the point source to the point where the sound-pressure level is measured. This relation is correct for a point source in a free field at normal room temperature and barometric pressure, that is, 20°C and 1013 millibars. At other temperatures and pressures, the correction shown in the graph of Figure 8-6 applies. This correction is usually unimportant.

---

*The concept of a point source is an idealized one. It is not reasonable to assume that an actual source is a true point source, so that one should never be content with a single measurement.

188

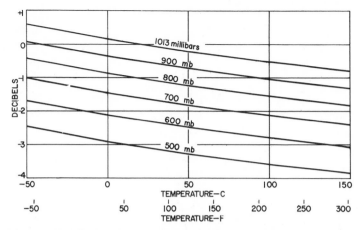

Figure 8-6. Corrections for temperature and barometric pressure to be applied when the equations relating power level (PWL) and sound-pressure level (SPL) are used. The correction is to be added to, if positive, or subtracted from, if negative, the sound-pressure level computed by the equation from the power level. If the power level is to be computed from a given sound-pressure level, the correction should be subtracted from, if positive, or added to, if negative, the given sound-pressure level before the numerical value is substituted in the equation.

As an example, suppose that we measure a sound-pressure level of 73.5 dB re 20 μN/m^2 at a distance of 20 ft from a point source. Then

PWL = 73.5 + 20 log 20 + 0.5 = 100 dB re 10^{-12} W.

The value for 20 log r can be found from a table of logarithms or from the decibel tables in the Appendix, where the columns labeled as pressure ratios should be used for this distance.

The power level can be converted to actual acoustic power in watts as explained in paragraph 2.3. For the example above, the 100 dB corresponds to an acoustic power of .01 W.

We can also use the equation to predict sound-pressure levels at any distance in the free field if we know the acoustic power radiated. Thus, this point source radiating .01 W, corresponding to a power level of 100 dB re 10^{-12}, produces a sound-pressure level of 100 −20.5 = 79.5 dB re 20 μN/m^2 at 10 ft from the source.

8.3.2 Directional Source in Free Field.

Directional Source. In actual practice, noise sources are not as simple as point sources. The sound is not radiated uniformly in all directions, either because the shape of the sound source is not spherical, or because the amplitude and time phase of the vibrations of the different parts are not uniform, or both. The net result is that more sound is radiated in some directions than in others.

Sound-Pressure Contours. In other words, the sound-pressure level for a given distance is different in different directions. As an example, let us observe the sound field surrounding a large 60-cycle power-distribution transformer, as shown in Figure 8-7. The contours around the transformer correspond to the indicated values of sound-pressure level. This source is obviously directional, since the contours are not circular.

189

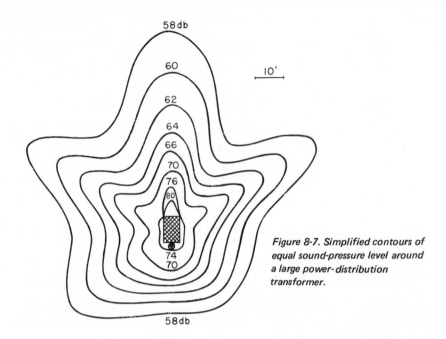

58 db

60

10'

62

64

66

70

76

80

74

70

58 db

Figure 8-7. Simplified contours of equal sound-pressure level around a large power-distribution transformer.

When such a directional sound source is far from any other objects, however, it behaves in some ways like a point source. For example, the sound-pressure level decreases 6 dB for each doubling of distance, provided we start our measurements at a distance away from the source that is several times the largest dimension of the source, and provided we move directly away from the source. From the example of the transformer in Figure 8-7, we see that, at distances greater than several times the length of the transformer, the contours are similar in shape and the levels decrease approximately 6 dB for each doubling of distance. In actual practice this idealized behavior is upset by the effects of variation in terrain, atmospheric conditions, and the interference of nearby objects.

Near Field and Far Field. We can also see that at locations close to the transformer the sound-level contours are different in shape from those at a distance. Furthermore, there is no apparent center from which one finds the 6-dB drop for each doubling of distance. Consequently, this "near-field" behavior cannot readily be used to predict the behavior at a distance. The differences between the near field and "far field" can be described in part as follows: Assume we have a source in which one part moves outwardly while another moves inwardly and vice versa. The air pushed away by one part will then tend to move over to compensate for the decrease in air pressure at the inward moving part. If the air can move over quickly enough, there will be considerable motion of air between the two parts, without contributing much to radiation of sound away from the source. The time factor in this motion of air can be expressed as a relation between the distance to be covered and the wavelength of the sound in air. The wavelength, λ, at normal temperature is as follows:

$$\lambda \simeq \frac{1130}{f} \text{ ft} \simeq \frac{344}{f} \text{ meters}$$

where f is the frequency in hertz and 1130 f/s is the speed of sound. Then, in

190

order that the near field effect should not be very important, one should be at least one wavelength away from the source. This dimension should be determined on the basis of the lowest frequency of interest. For the example of the 60-Hz transformer, the lowest frequency of sound is 120 Hz, which corresponds to a wavelength of about 10 ft.

Another factor that enters into the differences between the near field and far field behavior is the way the sound waves spread out from a source. The sound waves from a large source vary with distance differently from waves produced by a small source. But at a distance of several (3 to 4) times the largest dimension of the radiating source, "spherical spreading" is said to exist, and the behavior is then nearly independent of the size of the source.

♦ *Directivity Factor.* When we are interested in sound-pressure levels beyond the immediate vicinity of the source, any sound can be treated as a point source, provided we introduce a directivity factor. This factor takes into account the variation in sound-pressure level with direction to the source. This directivity factor, which is a function of direction and frequency, is usually labeled Q. It can be expressed as the ratio of two acoustic powers. One of these powers is that which would be radiated by a point source, in order to produce the observed sound-pressure level in the specified direction. The other power is the total acoustic power radiated by the actual source.

♦ *Sound-Pressure Level for a Directional Source.* When we know this directivity factor for the direction of interest, we can use it, in the earlier equation for a point source, as a multiplying factor on the power. Expressed in terms of level the new equation is as follows:

$$\text{SPL} = \text{PWL} + 10 \log Q - 20 \log r - 0.5 \text{ dB.}$$

This equation relates the power level of the source, the sound-pressure level in a given direction at a distance r feet from the source, and the directivity factor for that direction. (This equation is also subject to the minor corrections for temperature and pressure shown in Figure 8-6).

For example, let us assume that an auto horn whose measured power level is 104 dB is sounded. We are interested in the sound-pressure level at a distance of 20 ft in the horizontal plane of the horn, but at an angle of 20° from the principle axis of the horn. Along this direction of 20° from the axis the directivity factor is 5, say. Then we have

$$\text{SPL} = 104 + 10 \log 5 - 20 \log 20 - 0.5 = 84.5 \text{ dB}$$

at 20 ft in the required direction.

8.3.3 Simulated Free Field. The free-field condition does not occur in practice, because of the effects of sound reflected from the ground or floor, from nearby objects, and from walls and ceiling. The result of these reflections is that the sound-pressure level measured at a distance from the source is different from that predicted by the free-field equations. The reflections can be reduced by acoustic absorbing materials applied to the reflecting surfaces. By the proper design and application of this treatment, one can produce in a room a limited space having the essential characteristics of a free field over a wide frequency range. Many such rooms, called "anechoic" or "free-field" rooms, have been built and are described in the literature. When accurate measurements of the radiated sound power and directivity are required, the measurements should be made in such an environment.

191

8.3.4 Effect of Reflections in a Room.

The sound that a noise source radiates in a room is reflected by the walls, floor, and ceiling. The reflected sound will again be reflected when it strikes another boundary, with some absorption of energy at each reflection. The net result is that the intensity of the sound is different from what it would be if these reflecting surfaces were not there.

Close to the source of sound there is little effect from these reflections, since the direct sound dominates. But far from the source, unless the boundaries are very absorbing, the reflected sound dominates, and this region is called the reverberant field. The sound-pressure level in this region depends on the acoustic power radiated, the size of the room, and the acoustic absorption characteristics of the materials in the room. These factors and the directivity characteristics of the source also determine the region over which the transition between reverberant and direct sound occurs.

A second effect of reflected sound is that measured sound does not necessarily decrease steadily as the measuring position is moved away from the source. At certain frequencies in a room with hard walls, marked patterns of variations of sound pressure with position can be observed. Variations of up to 10 dB are common and, in particular situations, much more can be found. These variations are usually of the following form: As the measuring microphone is moved away from the source, the measured sound pressure decreases to a minimum, rises again to a maximum, decreases to a minimum again, etc. These patterns are called standing waves. They are noticeable mainly when the sound source has strong frequency components in the vicinity of one of the very many possible resonances of the room. They also are more likely to be observed when a frequency analysis is made; and the narrower the bandwidth of the analyzer, the more marked these variations will be.

In a room, the spacing from one minimum in sound pressure to another is on the average greater than one-half wavelength.

Reverberation Room. If a room has very little sound absorption, the room is said to be "live" or reverberant. Sound from a source in such a room will be reflected many times, as it bounces back and forth on the surfaces of the room. At any one point in this room the sound will have arrived there from many directions because of the many reflections. If the room dimensions are properly proportioned and certain other design features are included, the flow of sound energy in all directions can be made nearly equally probable, and the field is then said to be diffuse. This type of room is called a reverberation room, and it is widely used for the measurement of the sound-absorption of materials, as well as for sound-power measurements, when the directivity characteristics are not required.

Ordinary rooms. The sound field in an ordinary room cannot be described in detail. The acoustical boundary conditions of ordinary rooms are extraordinarily complicated, and most sound sources are also complicated. The result of this complexity is that one can attempt only an average-type of description. Even a rough approximation can be useful, however, and we shall review briefly some of the work on room characteristics as it applies to the sound produced by a source in a room.

◆ *Room Constant.* In order to simplify the analysis of the effect of the room, it is assumed that enough measurements are made so that any standing-wave patterns can be averaged out. A number of other assumptions are made, and then a relation of the form shown can be developed (Beranek, 1954; Hopkins and Stryker, 1948). Thus,

$$SPL = PWL + 10 \log \left[\frac{Q}{4\pi r^2} + \frac{4}{R} \right] + 10.5$$

where the new symbol R is the room constant, and the dimensions are in ft and ft^2. The corresponding equation in metric units is

$$SPL = PWL + 10 \log \left[\frac{Q}{4\pi r^2} + \frac{4}{R} \right] + 0.2$$

The room constant is defined by the equation:

$$R = \frac{\alpha S}{1-\alpha}$$

where S is the total area of the bounding surfaces of the room and α is the average absorption coefficient of the surfaces of the room at a given frequency.*

Since most rooms are not uniform in surface conditions, the value for αS is obtained by adding the absorptions for the individual areas. Thus, for a simple example, we have most of the wall area and all of the ceiling treated with 900 square feet of acoustical material of a particular type that has a coefficient of absorption of 0.70 at 500 Hz (one of the standard test frequencies). The rest of the walls are 300 square feet of 1/2-inch gypsum board on 2x4's ($\alpha = .05$). The floor is 400 square feet of concrete ($\alpha = .016$). The total absorption is then as follows: $\alpha S = 0.70$ x 900 + .05 x 300 + .016 x 400 = 651 absorption units at 500 Hz. If people and furniture are also present, the appropriate absorption units should be added to the room absorption to obtain the total absorption. The average value for the absorption coefficient is then obtained by dividing the total absorption by the total surface area. In the above example we have:

$$\alpha = \frac{\alpha S}{S} = \frac{651}{1600} = 0.41$$

The corresponding room constant is

$$R = \frac{\alpha S}{1-\alpha} = \frac{651}{1-0.41} = 1100 \text{ ft.}^2$$

At frequencies above about 2000 Hz, the sound absorption in the air in a very large room is often enough to affect the room constant appreciably. This absorption increases with frequency, and it varies markedly with humidity and temperature. The absorption at normal room temperatures is a maximum at relative humidities in the range of 10 to 30%. As an example of the extent of the effect, assume we have a room having a volume of 250,000 cubic feet. Then at 6000 Hz, air absorption alone could produce a room constant of up to about 10,000 square feet. Since the effective room constant thus produced

---

*Tables of values of absorption coefficients are given by the Acoustical and Insulating Materials Association (1971) and in books on architectural acoustics (Knudsen and Harris, 1950; Parkins and Humphreys, 1963).

varies approximately as the volume of the room, the effect in small, treated rooms is usually negligible.

The relation given above is shown graphically in Figures 8-8 and 8-9, where Figure 8-8 applies to the nondirectional or simple source or to a directional source in the direction having a directivity factor of 1 (Q=1), and Figure 8-9 applies to the directions having the labeled values of directivity factor.

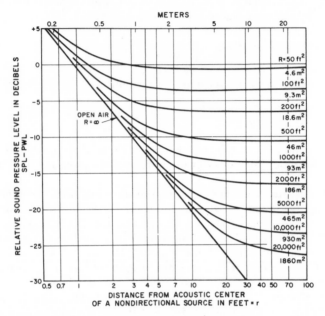

Figure 8-8. Chart showing the sound-pressure level, SPL, relative to the power level, PWL, for a nondirectional source for different values of the room constant, R, as a function of the distance from the source.

♦ *Reverberant Field.* The graphs of Figure 8-8 and 8-9 show that close to the source the sound-pressure level tends to vary with the distance from the source as it does under free-field conditions (R = ∞). But far from the source the sound-pressure level becomes independent of the directivity and the distance to the source. This region is called the reverberant field. Here, the level is determined by the acoustic power radiated by the source and the acoustic characteristics of the room. The region over which the transition between the free-field behavior and the reverberant field occurs is determined by the directivity factor and the room constant.

Actual Room Behavior. In a well-designed reverberation room, the behavior on the average is similar to that shown in the figures. Most other rooms have characteristics that on the average fall between that reverberant behavior and the free-field sound-pressure level decrease of 6 dB for each doubling of the distance (Ogawa, 1965; Gober and Lubcke, 1966; Yamamoto, 1961; Peutz, 1968).

In flat rooms (i.e., rooms whose ceilings are low relative to room length and width), the sound-pressure level at a distance from the source tends to decrease a fixed amount, but less than 6 dB, for each doubling of distance. The decrease depends on the sound absorption in the room. In very long rooms or halls, the sound-pressure level tends to decrease a fixed number of

194

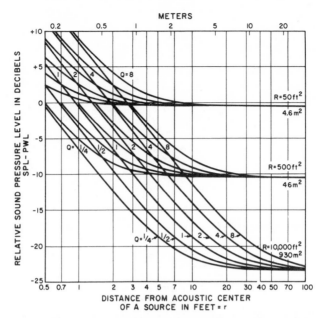

Figure 8-9. Chart showing the sound-pressure level, SPL, relative to the power level, PWL, for a directional source as a function of the distance from the source. The relation is shown for three different values of the room constant, R, and for six different values of the directivity factor Q.

decibels for a constant increment in the distance from the source.

In the vicinity of local obstructions and other areas with marked changes in acoustic characteristics, the sound-pressure level can change markedly.

In order to illustrate one of these effects, we shall reproduce a set of measurements made on a rectangular studio with an acoustic noise source covering the range from 300 to 600 Hz (Ogawa, 1965). The studio was 13.5 m by 24 m by 4.2 m and the average absorption coefficient at 500 Hz was 0.25. The room constant is then about 320 m^2 or about 3400 ft^2. Figure 8-10 shows the results of measurements in this room. The crosses are the observed sound-pressure levels and the smooth curve is plotted to correspond with the room-constant.

The calculations from the simple formula tend to overestimate the level at a considerable distance from the source. The average trend of the sound-pressure level is a drop of about 3.5 dB for a doubling of the distance. The marked departure from the behavior expected, on the basis of the simple formula, is a result of the fact that the average absorption was relatively high and the height was relatively low compared to the other dimensions, but it is similar in shape to that of many large, general, office areas.

Much more complicated formulas can yield values in closer agreement with the measurements, but the calculations become impractically tedious unless they are programmed on a computer. The simple formula is still useful for a preliminary estimate of the expected behavior, particularly if the absorption is small and if no one room dimension is markedly different from the others.

8.3.5 Measurement of Acoustic Power. A noise rating is often intended to make possible the prediction of the noise level that the apparatus will

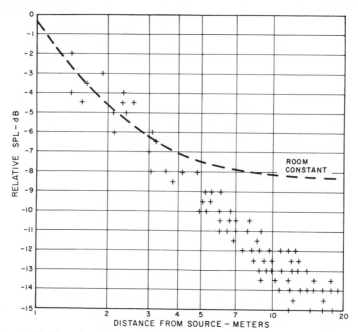

Figure 8-10. Plot of actual measurements made in a room with an absorption coefficient of 0.25 vs calculated performance (dashed line). (Ogawa, 1965.)

produce when installed. In order for the rating to be adequate for this purpose, the total acoustic power radiated by the source and the acoustic directivity pattern of the source should be included as part of the rating. We shall explain in this section how the power and directivity can be determined, but first we shall discuss the limitations of the usual method of noise rating.

For example, an air compressor may be rated by the manufacturer as producing a noise level of 85 dB at a distance of 5 ft. This level may have been calculated by an averaging of a few sound-level readings 5 ft from the compressor. When it is installed and the level is measured, the new level may be, say, 90 dB at 5 ft. Naturally, the purchaser feels that he should complain because the machine was incorrectly rated; perhaps he returns the compressor, or he decides that he can no longer trust the manufacturer. Actually, the manufacturer may have been entirely correct in his noise measurements, but the rating was inadequate. The difference of 5 dB may have been caused by incorrect installation, but usually such a difference is a result of the acoustical characteristics of the factory space. By the use of an adequate rating system and a knowledge of acoustical room characteristics, it would have been possible to predict this effect.

Another part of this problem is the prediction of levels at places in the factory other than at the measurement distance. For example, the nearest worker may be 20 ft away, and the level at a distance of 20 ft is then more important than at 5 ft. Again, a knowledge of the acoustic power radiated and the acoustical characteristics of the factory space will be needed to predict the probable level at this distance.

The procedure suggested here for determining the power and directivity is based on measurements of the sound-pressure level at a number of points around the noise source. The measurement of sound-pressure level has already been discussed. We shall discuss here the selection of the points at which to measure the sound-pressure levels, the method of calculating acoustic power, and the requirements on the characteristics of the space in which the measurement is to be made.

Four different types of environment are considered in the discussion of sound-power measurements, that is, free field or anechoic, free-field above a reflecting plane, reverberation room, and a semireverberant field. The choice among these is determined by many factors, most of which will become evident from the descriptions that follow. The influence of development in instrumentation are not described in the procedures, but they need to be considered also. In particular, the fewer microphone positions required for the reverberant room measurement is no longer as significant a factor as it was. The techniques for scanning a number of microphone outputs and summing on a pressure-squared basis, as provided by the 1566 Multichannel Amplifier and the 1921 Real-Time Analyzer, now simplify the anechoic measurement or the free-field measurement above a reflecting plane to the point that their other advantages make them more attractive than formerly.

♦ *Measurement Procedures.* The source characteristics are obtained by use of the principles discussed earlier in this chapter.* Generally, the following characteristics must be determined:

1. The total sound power radiated by the source, as expressed by the power level, as a function of frequency.
2. The directional characteristics of the source, as expressed by the directivity factor, as a function of direction and frequency.

♦ *Measurements Around the Source.* If free-field conditions can be closely approximated, the power level and directivity can be calculated from the sound-pressure levels measured at a number of points. These measurements are made at points at equal distances from the source and all around the source. The points can be considered as being on the surface of a hypothetical sphere surrounding the source. The radius of this sphere should be at least twice the largest dimension of the source but not less than 2 ft (0.6 m).

If the equivalent of a free field is produced by extensive treatment of the surfaces of a room, the hypothetical measurement sphere should not be closer to the absorbent surfaces than 1/4 wavelength corresponding to the center frequency of the lowest frequency band of interest. Since anechoic chambers built with wedges have the wedges about one-fourth wavelength long at the lowest frequency of interest, one can readily estimate the minimum dimensions for an anechoic chamber. For a noise source less than a foot in maximum dimension, the wall-to-wall inside distance should then be at least one wavelength plus 4 ft (1.2 m). The following table gives this value for some limiting frequencies.

f (Hz)	λ+4 (ft)	λ+1.2 (m)
100	15.3	4.6
125	13.0	4
160	11.1	3.4
200	9.6	2.9

Theoretically, the sound-pressure levels over the entire surface of the sphere should be measured. The practical procedure for approximating this

---

*The procedures outlined here and in subsequent sections are similar to those given in ANSI S1.2-1962, "Standard Method for the Physical Measurement of Sound," and that should be consulted for specific details on the standard method.

exploration is to select a number of points at which measurements will be made. Areas on the sphere are then associated with these points. These areas have the measurement points as their centers, and the extent of each area is determined by the nearness of the other measuring points. In the process of making the basic measurements, the microphone should be moved around to determine the variation in sound-pressure level within each area. If the variations in sound-pressure level within any one area are greater than 2 dB, it is advisable to select additional measuring points in that area. However, if no attempt is being made to obtain an accurate picture of the directivity pattern, the extent of the variation can be noted. Then, provided the variation is less than 6 dB, the average level can be used as a representative value for the area.

Uniformly Distributed Measuring Points. The calculations for the radiated power are simplified if the measuring points are uniformly distributed on the surface of the sphere. Because of the nature of the geometric pattern, only six such sets of points are possible. These six sets have 2, 4, 6, 8, 12, and 20 uniformly distributed points. The locations for the sets of 8, 12, and 20 points are shown in Figures 8-11 through 8-13. These are now generally used, although a different orientation with respect to the ground plane may be found desirable for some particular applications. The areas associated with the sets of 8, 12, and 20 points are regular spherical triangles, regular spherical pentagons, and regular spherical triangles, respectively.

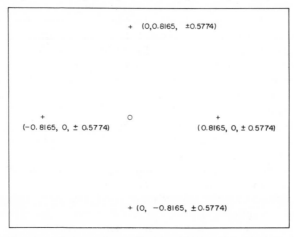

Figure 8-11. Plan view of eight points uniformly distributed on a sphere of unit radius. Coordinates are given in terms of distances from center along three mutually perpendicular axes (x, y, z). The "±" refers to the existence of two points, one above the x-y reference plane and one below. When measurements are to be made on a hemisphere, only the four points above the plane are used.

Other sets of points that may be useful are those that correspond to the vertices of an Archimedean semiregular polyhedron. The most interesting of these have 24 (R. M. Robinson, 1961), 48, and 60 points. Although these points are not uniformly distributed, they are all of equal importance, because the distribution of points around any one point is the same for all points.

◆ *Hemispherical Measurements.* When the device to be tested is normally mounted on a concrete foundation, on the ground, or on a wall, it is often desirable to test it while it is so mounted. The environment that approximates

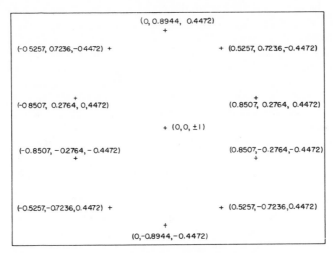

Figure 8-12. Plan view of 12 points uniformly distributed on a sphere of unit radius. Coordinates are given as in the previous figure. When measurements are to be made on a hemisphere, only the six points above the x-y reference plane (positive values of z) are used.

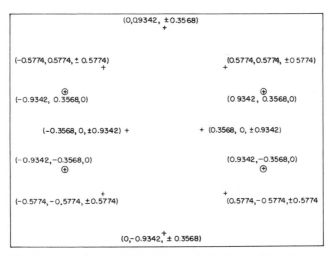

Figure 8-13. Plan view of 20 points uniformly distributed on a sphere of unit radius. Coordinates are given as in Figure 8-11. When measurements are to be made on a hemisphere, 12 points are used, eight above the reference plane and four in plane (z = 0, shown encircled). The four in the plane are weighted by a factor of 1/2 in power (see text).

this is a free field above a flat, hard reflecting plane. This can be an open paved area outdoors that is far from any other obstructions, or it can be an otherwise anechoic chamber with a hard floor or wall.

The sound-pressure level measurements should be made at points on a hypothetical hemisphere surrounding the source. The sets of points that lead to simple calculations of power level are now modified. A set of 4 points (half the set of 8) can be properly used, and a set of 6 points (half the set of 12) can be used even though the distribution is not exactly uniformly. A set of 12 can also be used, but then 4 of the set must be weighted by a factor of one-half (or, 3 dB is subtracted from the levels at these four points). See Figure 8-13.

The reflecting plane affects the sound-radiation characteristics of the source (ANSI S1.2-1962; Baade, 1964; Ellison et al, 1969). The near-field conditions are extended and the directivity pattern is more complex, compared with the conditions of the same source in a free field. Because of these effects, the hypothetical test hemisphere centered about the source should have a radius at least twice the average distance of the source from the reflecting plane, but not less than twice the maximum dimension of the source of 2 ft (0.6 meter).

The reflecting plane should extend beyond the farthest microphone position a distance at least one wavelength that corresponds to the center frequency of the lowest frequency band to be used. The effects of other obstacles and reflecting surfaces should be minimized by keeping them away from the source and the microphone positions.

Because the reflecting plane introduces a plane of symmetry, the measuring points that are at equal heights above that plane have some redundancy. This redundancy makes them less useful for providing a good space-average sound-pressure level than for the same number of points with no two of them at the same height. A double rotation of the set of 20 points of Figure 8-13 makes it possible to produce such a set of 10 for the hemisphere, and a representative set of coordinates is given in Figure 8-14. This set of points is not included in the standard.

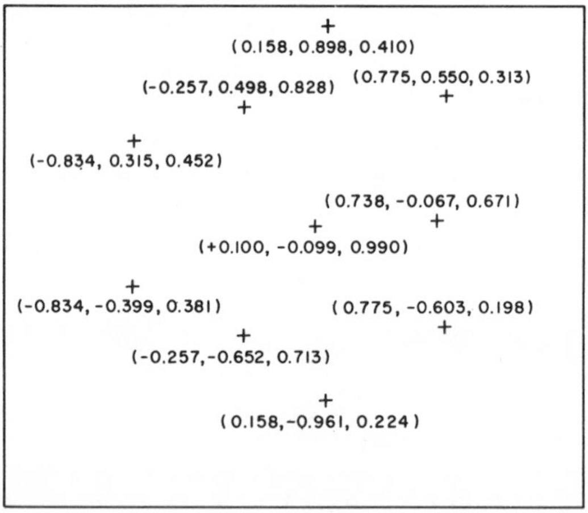

Figure 8-14. Plan view of 10 points distributed on a hemisphere of unit radius.

When the hemisphere is used, the procedure for calculating power is the same as that described for the sphere. But 3 dB should be subtracted from the power level finally obtained, because the area of the hemisphere is just one-half that of the sphere.

♦ *Rotation of Source.* Another way of simplifying the calculations is to rotate the source, with the microphones placed on the surface of a hypothetical sphere surrounding the source, so that the projections of their positions on the axis of rotation are uniformly distributed. A variation of this method, practiced by the Bell Telephone Laboratories (Jenkins, 1954), calls for the rotation of a set of microphones about a stationary source.

♦ *Calculation of Power Level.* If exploration shows that the basic set of points yields representative data, the calculations of the power level and directivity factor can be made. For a uniformly distributed set of points, first calculate the average level on a power basis. If the total range of sound-pressure levels is less than 6 dB, a simple arithmetical average is usually adequate. The accurate method for any situation is as follows: Convert the decibel readings at each of the points of measurement to power ratios by using the tables in the Appendix, add these power ratios, and convert back to a decibel level. Then, subtract the decibel value corresponding to a power ratio numerically equal to the number of levels used (for 8, 12, and 20 readings subtract 9, 10.8, and 13 dB, respectively). The result is then the average level, which we shall call $\overline{SPL}$. Provided free-field conditions exist, the power level is then calculated from the equation:

$$PWL = \overline{SPL} + 20 \log r + 0.5 \text{ dB}$$

where r is the radius of the measuring sphere, in feet. When the rotating source or rotating microphones are used, the average energy during a complete rotation as well as for all the microphone positions should be taken, and the corresponding average sound-pressure level used in the above formula.

♦ *Calculation of Directivity Factor.* After the average sound-pressure level, $\overline{SPL}$, has been determined, the directivity factor can also be calculated. If it is desired for a particular direction, the sound-pressure level on the measuring sphere corresponding to that direction, SPL_1, is measured. The difference between this level and the average level is called the directional gain, DG_1. Thus,

$$DG_1 = SPL_1 - \overline{SPL} \text{ dB}$$

To determine the directivity factor, Q, convert the DG_1 value in decibels into a power ratio by using the decibel tables in the Appendix. Thus, a directional gain of -2 dB corresponds to a directivity factor of 0.63.

Effect of Room on Measurements. The space in which power level and directivity are to be determined must be carefully considered. As explained previously, the measurement should ordinarily be made in an anechoic chamber. Sometimes the measurement can be made outdoors, far from other objects. If the device under test is normally mounted on the ground, this outdoor measurement may be ideal, provided that the location is free from interfering objects and the background noise level is low enough.

♦ *Requirements on Room Characteristics.* If the measurement is to be made in a room, it should be a large room, with extensive acoustic treatment. Large acoustic absorption is particularly important if the directivity characteristics must be accurately determined. In order to obtain satisfactory results in moderate-sized rooms, extraordinarily good acoustic treatment must be used. Many of these special anechoic chambers have been built.*

♦ *Sound Source in a Reverberant Room.* All sources that radiate sound as discrete tones, or as very narrow-band components, and all sources whose directivity must be determined, should be measured by the above free-field procedure. The total power radiated by a source, whose sound energy is distributed over a wide band of frequencies, can, however, be determined in a reverberant room — that is, a room with hard walls, floor, and ceiling.

---

*Anechoic chambers of various sizes are manufactured by, for example, the Eckel Corporation, 155 Fawcett Street, Cambridge, Mass.

♦ *Measurements in a Reverberant Room.* In a reverberant room, sound power can be determined from measurements of average sound pressure in the room and of the total absorption. The absorption is determined from a measurement of the rate at which a transient sound in the room decays. The procedure is as follows: The sound source in the room is turned on and the sound is allowed to reach a steady value. The sound is picked up by the microphone of a sound-level meter whose output is recorded on a graphic-level recorder. The sound source is abruptly turned off, the sound in the room decays, and this decay is plotted by the graphic level recorder. The slope of the decay curve, in dB per second, is the rate of decay, D.

For a highly reverberant room, that is, where D is small (say 50 dB/s or less), the sound power level of the source is then given by the following expression.*

$$PWL = \overline{SPL} + 10 \log V + 10 \log D - 47.3$$

where V is the volume of the room in cubic feet and $\overline{SPL}$ is the average sound-pressure level in the reverberant field. The numerical value of 47.3 in the above formula varies with atmospheric pressure, as shown in Figure 8-15. For most measurements at sea level the value of 47.3 can be used.

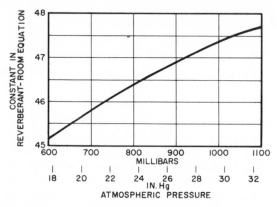

Figure 8-15. Variation of numerical constant in the equation relating power level and sound-pressure level for a reverberant room.

♦ *Room Requirements.* In order for the measurement to be accurate, the room must satisfy the following conditions:

1. If the source has a broad spectrum and the measurements are made in octave bands, the smallest dimension of the room should be at least equal to a wavelength at the center frequency of the lowest octave band of interest.
2. No two dimensions of the room should be alike or have a ratio that is an integer. A ratio of $1 : \sqrt[3]{2} : \sqrt[3]{4}$ for the height, width, and length is often recommended.
3. The walls of the room should be hard and smooth. Large, hard objects should be near the boundaries of the room to help diffuse the sound.
4. The average absorption coefficient of the room should not be greater than .06. This requirement will lead to a decay rate that is less than

*The procedures given are essentially those of ANSI S1.2-1962, "Physical Measurement of Sound," but the standard gives it in more detail. The standard gives the expression in terms of the reverberation time. (See also Young, 1959; Hardy, 1959; and Wells and Wiener, 1961).

202

about 50 dB/sec for a room of 1000 cubic ft (28 m^3), and less than about 30 dB/sec for a room of 10,000 cubic ft (280 m^3). For the lowest octave-frequency band the average absorption coefficient may be as much as 0.15.

5. The source should be mounted on the floor or other surface if normally used that way, but at least 1/4-wavelength from the other surfaces with which it is not normally associated. Otherwise, it may be suspended in the room, but not in the center, at least 1/4-wavelength from the walls. No large surface of the source should be parallel to any nearby surface unless it is ordinarily installed that way.

♦ *Sampling and Averaging Procedure.* The desired sound-pressure level is an average taken at several positions about the source, but at a distance from the source at least equal to the largest dimension of the source and yet not closer to any wall than 1/4 wavelength. The measurement positions should also be at least 1/2 wavelength apart. The average sound-pressure level should be determined on an energy basis.

In order to measure the room characteristics, the decay rates at the same set of measurement positions should be averaged for each measured band. If the ultimate measurements are to be in octave bands, an octave-band noise source should be used; for instance, a random-noise generator, filtered by an octave-band analyzer, driving an amplifier and loudspeaker may be used as the source. The decay rate for a given set of room conditions will remain constant over a considerable time, except at the high audio frequencies where air absorption is critically dependent on relative humidity.

In a well-designed reverberation room, fewer measurement points are needed than for the free-field measurement. If the source is not highly directional, and if large rotating vanes are used to alter the standing-wave pattern during the measurement, two or three microphone positions may be adequate for the measurement. This procedure in effect averages the sound-pressure level over a large area. So few microphone positions are not recommended, however, unless extensive experience has shown that the results are the same as those obtained with many microphone positions. (Lubman, 1968)

Another method of exploring the sound field to obtain an average is to swing the microphone around a wide area, but it is not as efficient as discrete widely spaced microphones (Waterhouse and Lubman, 1970). Still another method is to rotate the source.

The 1921 Real-Time Analyzer with its true mean-square integrating detector is ideal in providing the average level in this application.

Comparison Method. The procedures given above require special rooms for the measurement of radiated power. When such measurements must be made in an ordinary room, a different technique has been proposed by Hardy, Wiener, Wells, and others. This is a comparison method, in which a standard source similar to that to be measured is used as a reference. The radiated power of this standard source must have been determined by one of the preceding techniques.

Measurement Procedure. The measurement procedure is as follows:
a. The standard source is turned on in the room. Sound-pressure level is measured at several places around the source at a distance from the source equal to at least the maximum dimension of the source. The

measurements are usually made in octave bands. The measured levels are averaged on an energy basis for each band.

b. The unknown source is operated in place of the standard source. The sound-pressure levels are measured at the same points as before and averaged for each octave band.

c. For each octave band the difference in average level, between the standard and the unknown, is applied to the known power level of the standard source.

Requirements for Standard Source. The standard source should produce a stable and reproducible sound. Such sources have been developed for the Compressed Air and Gas Institute and for the fan and blower industry (Hardy, 1959).

Requirements for Room. The measurement room should be large and its characteristics should approach those of a reverberant room. No obstructing object should be in the immediate vicinity of the source or the microphone positions.

♦ **8.3.6 Predicting Noise Levels.** When the acoustic power output and the directivity pattern of a device are known, the noise levels that it will produce under a variety of conditions can be predicted (on the average) with fair accuracy. These predictions are based on the principles discussed earlier in this chapter.

If a noisy device is placed in a room that is not anechoic, it is desirable to measure the decay rate of sound, D, in the room; and then the following formula, adapted from one by Young, can be used to predict the average level of sound in that part of the room where the reverberant field dominates:

$$\overline{SPL} = PWL - 10 \log V - 10 \log D + 47.8$$

where V is the volume of the room in cubic ft. PWL is the source power level and the constant 47.8 varies with atmospheric pressure (to determine the variation add 0.5 dB to the values shown in Figure 8-15).

Close to the source, the level is almost as if free-field conditions existed. The level decreases with increasing distance from the source and the average approaches the reverberant field level. Here, standing waves will exist and it is only the average level that can ordinarily be predicted. At points less than 1/4 wavelength from a hard wall, the level will be higher than the average in the reverberant field. Very near a hard wall the increase may be as much as 3 dB; very close to an edge, 6 dB; and right at the vertex of a corner, 9 dB.

When the decay rate in the room cannot be measured, it can be estimated from a detailed knowledge of the room and its surface conditions. The procedures are given in books on architectural acoustics. There the calculation procedure is normally given for reverberation time, T. The decay rate, D, is then easily obtained as follows:

$$D = \frac{60}{T}$$

A related procedure is to calculate the room constant, from the characteristics of the room. Then the equation given there can be used to estimate the sound-pressure level. The discussion in paragraph 8.3.4 should also be considered in order to modify the prediction to fit the actual conditions.

As described earlier, the near-field behavior of a source may not be closely related to the far-field behavior that constitutes the radiated sound power. As a result, a knowledge of the radiated sound power does not ensure that one can estimate reliably the level near a machine. When it is important to know the sound level very close to a machine, as is often the situation for noise-exposure measurements, the actual sound level should be measured at the desired point. As explained earlier, exploration is desirable here, because close to the machine the sound level may vary markedly with position.

The sound-pressure level produced by the source is also affected by its position in the room — that is, if it is suspended in the middle of the room, or mounted on the floor, wall, or ceiling, or in a corner. It is often very difficult to predict the exact effect, however (Waterhouse and Cook, 1965). Ordinarily the level is higher when the source is very near a hard surface than when it is in the middle of the room. And, as explained earlier, if the source is generally mounted on a hard surface it should be measured that way, so that the effect on the source is taken into account. Then the levels in another room can be predicted with better accuracy.

8.3.7 Record of Measurements. One important part of any measurement problem is obtaining sufficient data. The use of data sheets designed specifically for a noise problem helps to make sure that the desired data will be taken and recorded; a sample data sheet is shown in Figure 8-16. The following list of important items may be found helpful in preparing data sheets of this type:
1. Description of space in which measurements were made. Nature and dimensions of floor, walls, and ceiling. Description and location of nearby objects and personnel.
2. Description of device under test (primary noise source). Dimensions, name-plate data and other pertinent facts including speed and power rating. Kinds of operations and operating conditions. Location of device and type of mounting.
3. Description of secondary noise sources. Location and types. Kinds of operations.
4. Type and serial numbers on all microphones, sound-level meters and analyzers used. Length and type of microphone cable.
5. Positions of observer.
6. Positions of microphone. Direction of arrival of sound with respect to microphone orientation. Tests of standing-wave patterns and decay of sound level with distance.
7. Temperature of microphone.
8. Results of maintenance and calibration tests.
9. Weighting network and meter speed used.
10. Measured over-all and band levels at each microphone position. Extent of meter fluctuation.
11. Background over-all and band levels at each microphone position. Device under test not operating.
12. Cable and microphone corrections.
13. Date and time.
14. Name of observer.

When the measurement is being made to determine the extent of noise exposure of personnel, the following items are also of interest:
1. Personnel exposed — directly and indirectly.

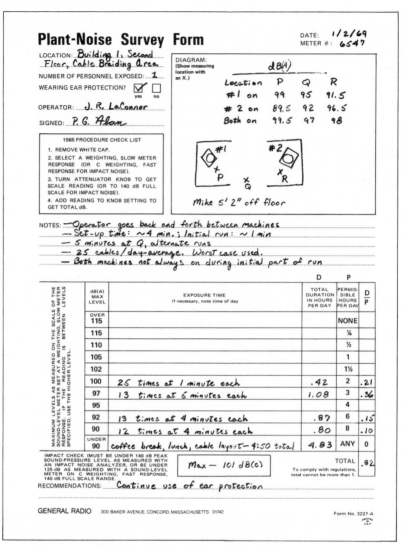

Figure 8-16. A sound-survey data sheet.

2. Time pattern of the exposure.

3. Attempts at noise control and personnel protection.

4. Audiometric examinations. Method of making examinations. Keeping of records.

The sample form shown in Figure 8-16 is appropriate for a noise survey for noise exposure calculations under the Occupational Safety and Health Act of 1970 (84 Stat. 1593) (See Chapter 4 and *"Primer of Plant-Noise Measurement and Hearing Testing,"* General Radio Company, 1971).

8.4 VIBRATION MEASUREMENT TECHNIQUES.

8.4.1 Introduction. The reason for measuring vibration usually determines both the quantity to be measured and the point or points at which the vibration pickup should be placed. Sometimes, however, the correct pickup location is not obvious and some exploration of the vibration pattern of the device being studied is necessary. Furthermore, the pickup must be correctly oriented, and this too sometimes requires exploration.

Fastening a pickup to a device is usually a simple task, if the device is much larger than the pickup and if the important vibration frequencies are below 1000 Hz. Otherwise, difficulties may arise because of the mechanical problem of fastening the pickup at the desired point, because the pickup seriously affects the motion to be measured, or because the method of attachment affects the performance of the pickup.

8.4.2 Choice and Use of Pickup.

Range of Levels. A very wide range of vibration levels can be covered by the pickups available. The most sensitive pickup can be used with the vibration meter or the control box and sound-level meter to measure down to .01 in/s^2 or .0003 m/s^2. At the other extreme, the Type 1560-P53 pickup can be used up to 1000 g. Special pickups are manufactured for even higher accelerations.

Frequency Range. The Type 1560-P52 Pickup is particularly well suited for low-frequency vibration measurements. When connected to the Type 1553 Vibration Meter, this pickup can be used at frequencies down to 1 Hz; with the Type 1564 Sound and Vibration Analyzer it can be used down to 2.5 Hz. The other pickups can also be used down to 2.5 Hz, if they are connected to a Type 1560-P42 or 1560-P40 Preamplifier.

The Type 1560-P53 Pickup has a resonance at about 28,000 Hz, which imposes a practical upper frequency limit of about 20,000 Hz. The other pickups in the General Radio line are limited to a maximum frequency of about 2000 Hz.

Orientation of Pickup. The piezoelectric accelerometers used in General Radio vibration-measuring instruments are most sensitive to vibrations in the direction perpendicular to the largest flat surface on the pickup. This direction is the one for which the rated sensitivity applies. The sensitivity in other directions varies approximately as the cosine of the angle with respect to this rated direction, with a minimum of about 5% (or less) of rated sensitivity, when vibrated in a direction perpendicular to the rated one.

For accurate results, the pickup must be properly oriented with respect to the direction of motion. In practice, this orientation is usually not critical, however, because sensitivity changes slowly with direction, there being a drop of only about 2% for a 10-degree change in orientation.

The direction of maximum vibration at a point is often obvious from the structure that is vibrating. That is, it is usually in the direction of least stiffness. But this rule is sometimes misleading, because of the many possible resonant modes of vibration, some of which are perpendicular to the obvious direction of least stiffness. Such a mode can be strongly excited if close to the frequency of a component of the driving force. Furthermore, the nature of the motion may favor one mode of vibration rather than another.

When it is important to be certain of the direction of motion, one can measure the motion along three mutually perpendicular axes. Often one can select these so that only one of these components of motion is significant, and that will determine the choice of direction. Otherwise, they must be combined vectorially to yield a resultant total; then, one needs to know the relative phase of the components. To determine phase, sums and differences can be measured with two pickups, as explained later, or another set of three measurements can be made along mutually perpendicular axes that are rotated from the first step. With two sets of measurements, one can sort out the possible combinations and calculate the direction of the total motion. Often it is simple to obtain the direction of the maximum motion by experiment.

Except for simple harmonic motions, this resultant direction is of significance only as a function of frequency. Then an analyzer is essential so that one can determine the motion for the individual components.

When one attempts to measure vibration in a direction that is not the direction of the total vibration at the point of measurement, the orientation is more critical, because the vibration in the other directions will provide some signal in the output. It is often impractical to measure a directional component that is less than 5% of the total vibration at a point.

The above procedure does not lead to a measurement of the rotational vibration about a point. This type of measurement can be made with a torsional vibration pickup or by the technique discussed in paragraph 8.4.5.

Hand-Held Pickup. When one must explore a vibration pattern or make a quick check of the vibration amplitude, one is tempted to hand hold the pickup against the device being measured. If the device is massive and is vibrating with a significant amplitude, this technique can be useful for frequencies below about 1000 Hz. There are enough serious limitations to this technique, however, so that it should not generally be expected to yield accurate or highly reproducible results (Gross, 1965).

When the pickup is held by hand, a test probe, a pointed metal rod, is fastened to the pickup to facilitate applying the probe to the desired point. The motion is transmitted along the rod to the pickup, and the motion in the direction of the rod actuates the pickup.

Because the test probe adds another element to the pickup, the response is different from that of the pickup alone. Typical relative frequency response characteristics are shown for two types of probe in Figures 8-17 and 8-18. More than one response run is shown to indicate the variability that can occur. Note resonance in the range from 1400 to 2000 Hz introduced by the long (6 3/8-in.) probe, and the one above 2000 Hz for the probe with the short conical tip.

Unless the device being tested is massive, the force, mass, resilience, and damping introduced by the hand may seriously alter the motion, and another method of applying the pickup should be tried.

Some vibration is applied to the pickup by tremor of the hand. This vibration is made up chiefly of components below 20 Hz, and the peak-to-peak order of magnitude is 5 in./s^2 acceleration, 0.2 in./s velocity, and 10 mils displacement, when the pickup is held against a relatively stationary surface. These values will be appreciably attenuated by a low-frequency cutoff at 20 Hz, such as is obtained on the "DISP-20 CUTOFF" position of the vibration meter. Then the observed peak-to-peak displacement is of the order of 0.2 mil.

This tremor sets a lower limit to the vibration that can be observed when the pickup is hand-held against the vibrating device. One should not attempt to use a hand-held pickup down to the levels quoted above unless some filtering is introduced to reduce the low-frequency response.

208

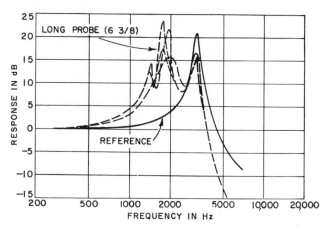

Figure 8-17. Frequency response of vibration pickup mounted on hand-held long (6 3/8-in.) probe. Several sample responses are shown. The curve labeled REFERENCE is the frequency response of the pickup without the probe.

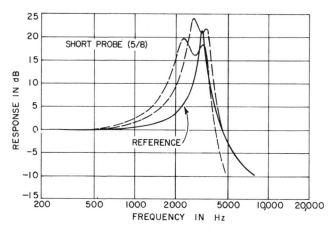

Figure 8-18. Frequency response of vibration pickup mounted on hand-held short (5/8-in.) probe. Several Sample responses are shown.

Pickup Fastening Methods. Pickups are fastened to a vibrating surface by many different methods. For greatest accuracy the fastening should be as direct and as rigid as possible (Rasanen and Wigle, 1967; Gross, 1965). But if the acceleration is less than gravity, if only a temporary fastening is desired, and if only low frequencies are present, simple fastenings are adequate. These may be plasticene or double-sided adhesive tape placed between the base of the pickup and a flat surface at the point desired. If the surface is horizontal, flat, and smooth, the pickup may be wrung to the surface with a thin film of petroleum jelly. Another simple technique, useful on magnetic materials, is to fasten a magnet to the pickup and then attach the magnet to the surface to be measured.

At high accelerations, these simple fastenings are not satisfactory, and a stud or bolt must be used to hold the pickup directly against the surface being measured.

The performance of some pickups is affected by any attachment to the pickup body other than to the reference surface, so that a pickup should not be attached by clamps to the body of the pickup.

When the pickup is to be permanently installed, the use of an adhesive, such as a dental cement, Eastman 910, or an epoxy cement, is often advisable. For best results, one should be careful to use only a thin layer, so that the elastic characteristics of the bonding cement will not affect the behavior of the pickup.

For maintenance tests, it is often convenient to fasten a very smooth flat iron disk to bearing housings with a very hard epoxy cement. The disk should be pressed as tight as possible against the housing. Then a magnetic attachment can be used, again with a thin film of silicone grease or petroleum jelly to ensure good contact.

The fastening should be rigid, so that the pickup does not move significantly with respect to the surface to which it is fastened. Any rocking motion, or looseness that might lead to chattering, should be prevented. If the fastening alone is not adequate to prevent this looseness, the use of some plasticene in addition may be helpful. When fastening, even by bolts, the use of a lubricant or petroluem jelly is advisable to ensure close contact between the pickup and the fastening surface, without putting undue strain on the pickup.

When the surface is not smooth or flat, the pickup is sometimes mounted on a bracket. For low vibration frequencies (below a few hundred hertz), the bracket can readily be made stiff enough so that it does not seriously affect the behavior of the pickup.

The procedure for obtaining a good connection between the pickup and the vibrating surface is illustrated by the specifications of MIL-STD-740B (SHIPS).

Transducers shall be attached as follows:

(a) Transducers shall be attached to blocks, which are to be brazed or welded to equipment, or subbase, as close as possible to the mounting points of the equipment to be tested.

(b) The blocks shall be made of steel and shall be as small as possible. The block surfaces on which transducers are mounted shall be plane and shall have a surface finish of 125 micro-inches rms or better and be mutually perpendicular within one degree.

(c) Three holes in the mounting blocks shall be drilled and tapped to a depth of at least 1/4 inch with 10-32 NF threads to accommodate triaxial arrays of transducers which shall be attached to the blocks with insulated steel studs. The holes shall be perpendicular to the finished surfaces within plus or minus 1 degree.

(d) Just before transducers are mounted on a block, all mating surfaces shall be cleaned of all dirt, grease, and other foreign matter in preparation for mounting. The surfaces of the attachment area and the studs shall be lightly covered with clean oil or grease.

(e) The mounting blocks shall not be removed and shall be preserved with a rust inhibiting coating after completion of testing.

(f) If brazing or welding cannot be accomplished, the mounting blocks shall be attached to the location with a thin layer of epoxy resin cement. Blocks attached by cement shall be removed upon completion of test. The

transducers may be attached directly to the equipment being tested only where there is insufficient space to accommodate the mounting block.

The pickup is calibrated in terms of the motion of the flat contacting surface of the pickup. Because of the resilience of the fastener and the mass of the pickup, this surface of the pickup will not move exactly as the surface being measured moves. At low frequencies this difference is easily made insignificant by the relatively simple techniques discussed. But at high frequencies care must be used in fastening to keep this effect small.

The mass of the Type 1560-P52 Vibration Pickup is sufficiently small that simple temporary fastenings are adequate even to frequencies beyond the normal resonance at about 3200 Hz. This fact is illustrated by the response-vs-frequency characteristics shown in Figure 8-19 and 8-20. In each instance, the pickup was driven at a constant acceleration. The reference condition is the response for the vibration pickup wrung to the smooth, flat surface of the driver with petroleum jelly lubricant. The acceleration was .002 g.

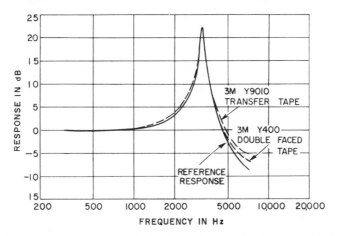

Figure 8-19. Frequency response of vibration pickup attached by means of Minnesota Mining Y9010 and Y400.

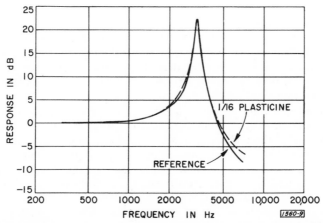

Figure 8-20. Frequency response of vibration pickup attached by means of 1/16-in. thick layer of plasticene.

The effect of fastening by means of double-sided tape was generally less than 10% deviation from the reference condition at all frequencies up to the resonance at 3200 Hz. In some instances, the deviation over the range to 3200 Hz was only about 2%. The variability was probably a result of changes in contact adhesion obtained with different samples of the tape.

Plasticene as a fastening means, even as thick as 1/16-in. showed very good reproduction of the reference performance, being within 2 to 5% up to 4000 Hz. In one instance, a marked departure from the reference performance was found even at 500 Hz, and this was quickly traced to the fact that the pickup had come loose from the plasticene. This example illustrates the importance of careful inspection of the fastening during a test, particularly when one cannot check the performance independently.

The response of the pickup when held to a smooth, flat, steel plate by means of the Type 1560-P35 Permanent Magnet Clamp is shown in Figure 8-21. Up to 5 kHz, the response is very similar to the reference response. One should fasten the pickup carefully to the magnet so that no rocking motion is possible, and the magnet itself should be placed on a smooth surface so that it, too, will not rock; otherwise, serious errors may result.

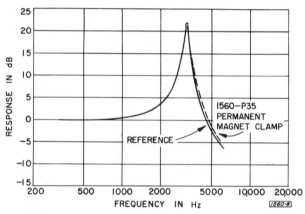

Figure 8-21. Frequency response of vibration pickup attached by Type 1560-P35 Permanent-Magnet Clamp.

8.4.3 Stray Effects.

Effect of the Pickup on the Vibration. The mass added by the pickup to the vibrating surface being measured changes the motion of that surface. If the added mass is much smaller than that of the vibrating surface and is closely coupled to it, the effect is small except near resonant modes. Thus, it is important to have a lightweight pickup.

One can often judge the effect of adding the mass of a pickup by noting the difference in behavior with the pickup fastened and with another mass equal to that of the pickup, in addition to the pickup. If the difference is negligible for these two conditions, the effect of the pickup is usually unimportant. Under certain conditions near the resonant vibration frequency of the device under test, even a small mass can shift the resonance enough to affect the motion at the original resonant frequency by a large amount.

When it is possible to change the excitation rate or frequency so that resonance with the pickup in place is re-established, the behavior at the new resonant point will often be sufficiently similar to the resonance behavior without the pickup that the resonant condition can be satisfactorily measured.

When stroboscopic observation of the motion is possible, the effect of the mass of a pickup on the motion can often be judged by direct observation of the behavior with and without the pickup present.

Mounting of the Device Under Test. The actual vibration that a device experiences will depend on the way in which it is mounted. If it is rigidly mounted to a massive concrete structure, the vibration may be much less than if it is mounted with a very resilient mount. For many tests the very resilient mounting is preferred in order to obtain the maximum motion. But often the proper procedure is to mount the device for a vibration test just as it will be mounted in actual use.

Background Vibration. Some background vibration is always present. If a motor is put on a factory floor for a vibration test, it will be possible to measure motor vibration even when it isn't running. This background vibration must be considered as a lower limit to the vibration that can be measured. But, of course, one can do something about this lower limit. Often placing the device on a thick felt or foam pad will isolate it sufficiently from the background, but then the mounting is no longer rigid. Another approach is to use a separate, massive concrete block as a table on which to mount the device in any way desired. The block is suspended by resilient mounts. The natural vibration frequency of the block on its mounts should be made significantly lower than any frequency of interest in the test.

Peak Versus rms or Average. Although a few applications of vibration measurements require the use of the peak or peak-to-peak amplitude, most experimenters specify these values only because they are traditional. When vibration signals are analyzed to find the individual components, however, the rms or rectified average values are more useful. This usefulness depends on two facts. First, rms component values can be summed on an energy basis to give the over-all rms value. For many wave shapes this result is also essentially true for the rectified average values. But the result of combinations of peak values of components can be misleading and confusing, particularly for coherent periodic signals, which are relatively common in vibration work. The second fact is that if the signal is random in amplitude distribution, there is an additional inconsistency among peak values. As a result, if you measure a peak value of a vibration signal, it is also wise to note the rms or average value.

8.4.4 Calibration of Vibration Measurement Systems. In order to ensure that one can make satisfactory vibration measurements, the instruments used must be kept in proper operating condition. The vibration meter itself can be checked electrically very simply by the built-in calibration system, and the instrument should be checked at the start of a test, after the instrument has been on and allowed to stabilize for a few minutes.

The vibration calibrator should also be used regularly to check the complete measurement system. If the acceleration produced by the calibrator reads between 340 and 430 rms (or 950 to 1220, peak-to-peak) in./s^2 on an electrically calibrated vibration meter, there is reasonable assurance that the pickup and the meter are operating correctly. If the agreement is not satisfactory, one should first check that the correct pickup for the vibration meter is being used, and that the internal reference dial in the meter is set to the correct pickup sensitivity. If these are all checked and agreement is still unsatisfactory, another pickup should be tried (with the internal reference dial set to its nominal sensitivity). The next step would be to have the pickup and the calibrator checked at the General Radio Company.

Vibration pickups are rugged and stable, but they can be damaged. Although a damaged pickup will ordinarily be detected by the check at 100 Hz provided by the vibration calibrator, it is possible, but most unusual, for the sensitivity at other frequencies far from 100 Hz to be affected when that at 100 Hz is not. Therefore, the frequency response of pickups should be verified periodically by calibration at the National Bureau of Standards or at the General Radio Company.

♦ **8.4.5 Simple Method To Determine Rotational Vibration.*** When analysis of rotational vibration must be made on an existing installation and a torsional pickup cannot readily be used, the following technique may be useful. Two vibration pickups and a summing network are required in addition to the vibration meter. One must assume that the engine behaves like a rigid mass and that its center of gravity is equidistant from all four mounting posts.

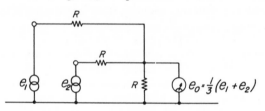

Figure 8-22. A simple resistive summing circuit.

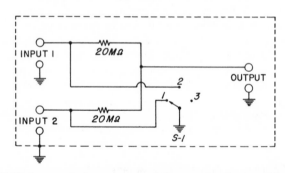

Figure 8-23. A convenient arrangement of the summing circuits of Figure 8-22.

A simple summing circuit is shown in Figure 8-22. The voltages e_1 and e_2 represent the output signals of two vibration pickups, and the voltage e_o represents the signal fed into the input of the vibration meter. If the three resistors R are equal, e_o will be $1/3$ ($e_1 + e_2$). A practical arrangement of this circuit is shown in Figure 8-23. Only two resistors are shown, since the third resistor is in the input circuit of the vibration meter. One pickup is connected to input No. 1 and the other pickup is connected to input No. 2. The output of the summing circuit is connected to the input of the vibration meter. When

---

*This method was suggested by Mr. George Kamperman of Kamperman Associates, Downers Grove, Ill. He has used this technique on numerous occasions with gratifying results.

switch S-1 is at position 1, one third of the output of pickup No. 1 is applied to the input of the vibration meter. When S-1 is set at position 2, one third of the output of pickup No. 2 is applied to the input of the vibration meter. When S-1 is at position 3, one third of the sum of the outputs from the two pickups is applied to the input of the vibration meter.

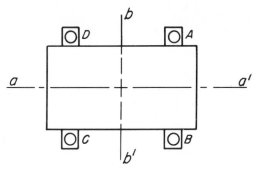

Figure 8-24. Outline of engine and mounting (top view).

The top view of a typical engine and its mounting is outlined in Figure 8-24. A and B represent the forward engine mounts while C and D represent the rear engine mounts. With the two pickups (oriented for vertical-displacement measurement) mounted on the two forward engine mounting brackets, the translational or vertical amplitude is indicated on the vibration meter when the output signals of the two pickups are summed. The rotational mode of vibration is canceled out. When the outputs of the two pickups are summed 180° out of phase or subtracted, the rotational amplitude of vibration is indicated on the vibration meter and the translational mode of vibration is canceled out. The pickup can be mounted upside down to shift the output 180° to perform the subtraction of outputs, or, the pickup can be left in its normal mounting position and the 180° shift in the phase of its output can be achieved with an electronic phase inverter. By making the set of measurements outlined above on all pairs of mounting brackets (A,B-A,D-C,D-B,C) the amplitude of any rotational or rocking motion about the axes a-a' or b-b' can easily be sorted out from the direct vertical or translational motion of the engine.

REFERENCES

Acoustical and Insulating Materials Association (1971), *Performance Data: Architectural Acoustical Materials,* Acoustical and Insulating Materials Association, 205 West Touhy Avenue, Park Ridge, Illinois 60068.

P. K. Baade (1964), "Sound Radiation of Air-Conditioning Equipment; Measurement in the Free-Field Above a Reflecting Plane," *ASHRAE Trans,* Vol. 70, pp. 217-227.

L. L. Beranek (1954), *Acoustics,* McGraw-Hill, New York, Part XXIV.

A. J. Ellison, C. G. Moore, and S. J. Yang (1969), "Methods of Measurement of Acoustic Noise Radiated by an Electric Machine," *Proc Inst Electrical Eng.,* Vol. 116, #8, August, pp. 1419-1430.

H. J. Gober and E. Lubcke (1966), "Sound Field in Very Wide and Long Rooms," *J Acoust Soc Am,* Vol. 39, #6, June, p. 1266.

E. E. Gross, Jr. (1965), "Vibration Measurements with the Sound-Level Meter," *General Radio Experimenter,* Vol. 39, #7, July, pp. 3-9.

H. C. Hardy (1959), "Standard Mechanical Noise Sources," *Noise Control,* Vol. 5, #3, May, pp. 22-25.

H. F. Hopkins and N. R. Stryker (1948), "A Proposed Loudness-Efficiency Rating for Loudspeakers and the Determination of System Power Requirements for Enclosures," *Proc IRE.*, Vol 36, #3, March, pp. 315-335.

R. T. Jenkins (1954), "A New Sound Integrator," *Bell Labs Record*, Vol. 32, September, pp. 331-335.

V. O. Knudsen and C. M. Harris (1950), *Acoustical Designing in Architecture*, John Wiley & Sons, Inc., New York.

D. Lubman (1968), "Fluctuations of Sound with Position in a Reverberant Room," *J Acoust Soc Am*, Vol 44, #6, December, pp. 1491-1502.

Y. Ogawa (1965), "The Applicable Limit of Beranek's Formula and Ishii's Formula of Sound Pressure Level Distribution in a Room," *J Acoust Soc Jap*, Vol 21, #3, May, pp. 137-140.

V. M. A. Peutz (1968), "The Sound Energy Density Distribution in a Room," *Reports 6th Intl Cong. on Acoustics*, August, Paper E-5-2, pp. E-165-168.

G. K. Rasanen and B. M. Wigle (1967), "Accelerometer Mounting and Data Integrity," *Sound and Vibration*, Vol. 1, #11, November, pp. 8-15.

R. M. Robinson (1961), "Arrangement of 24 Points on a Sphere," *Math Annalen*, Vol 144, pp. 17-48.

P. K. Stein (1962), *Measurement Engineering*, Stein Engineering Services, Tempe, Arizona.

R. V. Waterhouse and R. K. Cook (1965), "Interference Patterns in Reverberant Sound Fields II," *J Acoust Soc Am*, Vol 37, #3, March, pp. 424-428.

R. Waterhouse and D. Lubman (1970), "Discrete versus Continuous Space Averaging in a Reverberant Sound Field," *J Acoust Soc Am*, Vol. 48, #1 (Part 1), July, pp. 1-5.

R. J. Wells and F. M. Wiener (1961), "On the Determination of the Acoustic Power of a Source of Sound in Semi-Reverberant Spaces," *Noise Control*, Vol. 7, #1, January-February, pp. 21-29.

T. Yamamoto (1961), "On Distribution of Sound Energy Along a Corridor," *J Acoust Soc Jap*, Vol. 17, #4, December, pp. 286-292.

R. W. Young (1959), "Sabine Reverberation Equation and Sound Power Calculations," *J Acoust Soc Am*, Vol. 31, #7, July, pp. 912-921.

R. W. Young (1962), "Can Accurate Measurements be Made with a Sound-Level Meter Held in Hand?" *Sound*, Vol. 1, #1, January-February, pp. 17-24.

Chapter 9

Noise and Vibration Control

9.1 INTRODUCTION

When we want to reduce noise or vibration, we usually begin by measuring the spectrum of the noise or vibration to obtain the quantitative information that is helpful in doing something about the problem. We compare the measured levels with the acceptable levels, which are often estimated by use of one of the criteria given in Chapter 3. The difference between these two levels is then the reduction necessary.

The next step is to find out how this reduction can be achieved most satisfactorily. A complete discussion of this problem is not possible in this handbook. But since many of those using this book are just beginning to work on noise and vibration problems, a few introductory statements on the subject will be made. Useful information on this subject will be found in books on noise control and architectural acoustics, in books on mechanical vibrations, in some books on acoustics in general, and in articles in various journals. (See references for Chapter 9 and the list of journals in Appendix VII). We shall discuss noise control first.

The general approach to noise reduction can be divided into two major parts as follows:
1. Reduction of noise at its source.
2. Reduction of noise level at the ear of the listener by changes in the path from the source.

9.2 NOISE CONTROL AT THE SOURCE.

It is usually wise to see first if the noise can be reduced at the source. A different type of source might be selected. For example, a process might be changed so that parts are welded instead of riveted together. A source of different basic construction but of a similar type might be used. For example, a slower fan of many blades can sometimes be substituted for a high-speed two-bladed fan. Or, the construction of the particular source at hand might be modified, and this procedure will be discussed briefly.

When modification of a source is attempted, a decrease in the radiated power is usually the most important change that can be made. This usually means a reduction of vibration amplitudes and of the radiation of sound produced by the vibration. We can separate this problem into three sections:
1. Decrease the energy available for driving the vibrating system.
2. Change the coupling between this energy and the acoustical radiating system.
3. Change the structure that radiates the sound so that less is radiated.

In each of these sections it is usually helpful to track down the important sources of noise and the path of transmission by using frequency analysis of the sound and vibration. The effects of changes in the source (for example, speed, structure, and mounting) on the spectrum should also help in finding the important elements. The reduction of the vibration that produces noise is discussed later in this chapter. Change in the coupling system frequently means the use of vibration isolation mounts. It may also mean decreased or even increased stiffness in some members transmitting the vibration. Or it may mean better fastening of some parts to massive, rigid members. Resonant structures are often troublesome coupling members. The resonance may be in the mechanical structure or in an air chamber. In either situation it is usually possible to shift the resonance by changes in the structure or to damp the resonance by adding absorbing material. Mufflers may be needed on exhaust or intake systems. Changing the radiating structure often means nothing more than reducing the external surface areas of the vibrating parts as much as possible. It may be possible to put holes in the radiating member to reduce the efficiency of radiation. Less stiffness of the part may help to reduce radiated sound by permitting sections to vibrate in different time patterns. Large surfaces near the vibrating parts should also be avoided, since these surfaces may increase the radiating efficiency of the vibrating parts.

Another possible way of modifying the source to improve the noise situation is to change the directivity pattern of the radiated sound. When streams of air or other gases come out of an opening, they radiate sound that may be highly directional at high frequencies. Changing the direction of flow can shift this pattern. It may be possible to direct it in such a way that noise in certain directions is considerably reduced.

9.3 CONTROL OF THE PATH OF SOUND.

The control of the noise by changes in the path of the sound can be analyzed into three sections:
1. Change in relative position of source and listener.
2. Change in acoustic environment.
3. Introduction of attenuating structures between source and listener.

9.3.1 Changes in Position.
Increasing the distance between the noise source and the listener is often a practical method of noise control. Furthermore, merely rotating the source of noise may permit one to decrease the level if a change to a direction of low directivity factor is achieved. Both these procedures are effective only in the region where approximately free-field conditions exist.

9.3.2 Change in Environment.
The most obvious change that can be made in a room to reduce the noise level is to add acoustical absorbing material. A wide variety of commercial acoustical materials is available. These materials are often of great value in a noise reduction program, but the limitations of this treatment should be realized. These materials are mainly useful in the room where the noise originates, and there they help mainly to reduce the noise level at some distance from the source. But at the same time not much reduction is obtained at a distance of 2 ft, say, which is a common distance between a machine and the operator's ear.

9.3.3 Attenuating Structures.
A number of different types of attenuating structures are used for reducing the noise level for the listener. One of these is an ear defender, which may be an ear plug, waxed cotton, or earmuffs. Others

are walls, barriers, and total enclosures. Almost any degree of reduction of airborne sound can be achieved by a total enclosure or a combination of several enclosures. But as the required attenuation increases so does the complexity, weight, and cost. In addition, great care must be taken that the attenuation gained by the enclosure is not lost by sound transmission through a ventilating duct or by solid-borne vibration. Because of this possible flanking transmission in ventilating systems, total enclosures frequently require carefully designed ventilating systems with ducts lined with absorbing material. These lined ducts are essentially mufflers for the air stream.

When a door is required in a total enclosure, it should be built with air-tight seals at all joints. A refrigerator-type door is usually satisfactory when it can be used. A total enclosure should also be lined at least on part of the inside walls with absorbing material. This lining helps to keep the noise at the walls of the enclosure at the lowest practical level.

A barrier is not as effective as a total enclosure, but it does help to shield high-frequency sound. Little attenuation of low-frequency sound is obtained unless the barriers are very large, and the attenuation of high-frequency sound is usually only a few decibels unless the opening that remains is relatively small. Here, too, absorbing material should cover the barrier to avoid exaggerating the level by reflections from the barrier.

9.3.4 Illustrative Example. In order to illustrate the possible noise reduction achieved by use of vibration isolation, barriers, enclosures, and acoustic treatment, an example made up for the purpose is shown in a series of figures, Figures 9-1 and 9-2. We intend to show here only the general nature of the noise reduction obtainable as given by changes in the octave-band spectrum and the speech-interference level. Actual results will vary in detail, and situations do occur where the results differ materially from those shown because of factors not considered here. But, in general, the noise reduction shown in the figures can be considered typical.

Figure 9-1a shows the octave-band analysis of the noise from the assumed machine. The speech-interference level is also shown. This machine is a noisy one with a spectrum that shows appreciable noise energy all over the audible range. All the noise measurements are assumed to be made in the relative position shown for the microphone, designated M on the figures.

The use of vibration isolation mounts may be an important step in noise control. As shown in Figure 9-1b, the initial result, however, is often only a moderate reduction of the low-frequency noise. The machine itself usually radiates most of the high-frequency noise directly to the air, and the amount radiated by the floor is small. A reduction in the vibration level at the floor only is then not important at high frequencies. At low frequencies, however, the machine may be too small to be effective in radiating sound, and then the floor may act as a sounding board to contribute materially to low-frequency sound radiation.

It is even possible to increase the noise as a result of the use of vibration mounts. This result is usually found when the stiffness of the mounting is of such a value that some vibration mode is exaggerated by resonance, but resonance can be avoided by proper design of the mounting. In the illustrative example it is assumed that the mounting is sufficiently soft that the basic vibration resonance of the machine on the mounting system is below 20 Hz. In this particular example no significant change in the speech-interference level is shown as a result of the use of vibration isolation mounts alone.

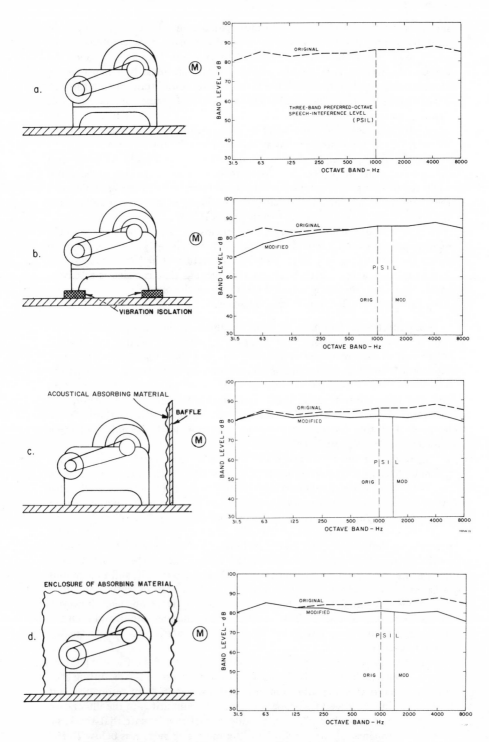

Figure 9-1. Examples to illustrate the possible noise reduction effects of some noise control measures; (M) is microphone position.

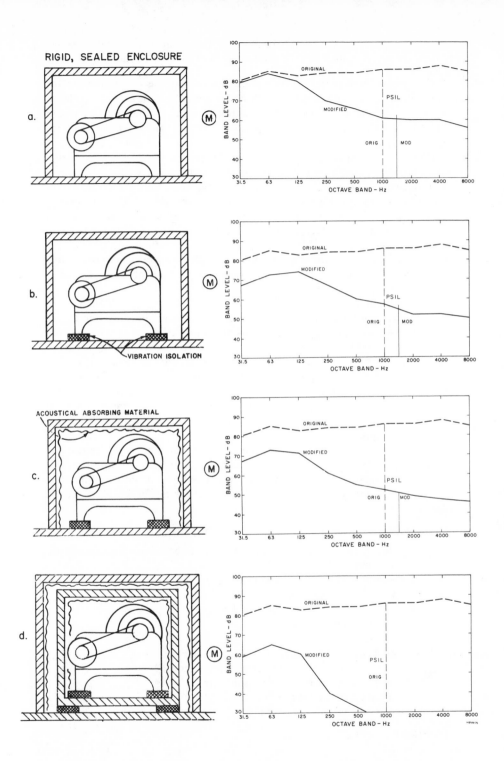

Figure 9-2. Examples to illustrate the noise reduction possible by the use of enclosures.

The results shown in Figure 9-1c illustrate that a barrier is mainly effective at high frequencies, and there it produces only a moderate reduction in noise level.

The novice in this field sometimes assumes that the materials used for sound absorption can also be used alone for sound isolation. If we build an enclosure solely of these materials mounted on a light framework, we would typically find the result shown in Figure 9-1d. Only at high frequencies do we have a noticeable reduction in level, and even there it is a small reduction.

A more satisfactory enclosure is built of more massive and rigid constructional materials. Assume that we enclose the machine by a well-sealed, heavy, plasterboard structure. Then we might observe the result shown in Figure 9-2a. Here an appreciable reduction is obtained over the middle- and high-frequency range. The enclosure is not as effective as it might be, however, because two important factors limit the reduction obtained. First, the vibration of the machine is carried by the supports to the floor and then to the whole enclosure. This vibration then may result in appreciable noise radiation. Second, the side walls of the enclosure absorb only a small percentage of the sound energy.

The addition of a suitable vibration isolation mounting will reduce the noise transmitted by solid-borne vibration. This effect is illustrated in Figure 9-2b. Here we see a noticeable improvement over most of the audio spectrum.

When the sound absorption within an enclosure is small, the noise energy from the machine produces a high level within the enclosure. Then the attenuation of the enclosure operates from this initial high level. The level within the enclosure can usually be reduced by the addition of some sound-absorbing material within the enclosure, with the result that the level outside the enclosure is also reduced. This effect is shown in Figure 9-2c, which should be compared with Figure 9-2b.

If even more noise reduction is required than that obtained by the one enclosure, a second, lined, well-sealed enclosure can be built around the first. The first enclosure is supported within the second on soft vibration mounts. Then a noise reduction of the magnitude shown in Figure 9-2d can be obtained.

9.4 SUMMARY OF NOISE REDUCTION PROCEDURES.

The approach to a noise reduction problem can be summed up as follows:
1. Consider the source.
>   Can a quieter machine by substituted?
>   Can the noise energy be reduced?
>   Can a useful change be made in the directivity pattern?
>   Are resilient mounts of any use here?
>   Can a muffler be used?
2. Consider the path from the source to the listener.
>   Can the source or the listener be readily moved?
>   Is acoustic treatment a useful solution?
>   Should barriers be erected?
>   Is a total enclosure required?

9.5 VIBRATION REDUCTION.

The basic procedure for vibration reduction will be described briefly. Many specialized techniques have been developed also, and a complete summary of these is impractical here. More extensive information on vibration reduction will be found in the references.

The first step is usually a careful inspection to see if a common-sense, simple, quick solution is available. A part may be loose or broken, and fastening it or replacing it may cure the trouble. If a solution is not obvious, a systematic approach to the problem is suggested.

The approach to reducing vibration is summarized as follows:

1. Change source or coupling to vibrational driving force.
   Reduce its strength.
   Eliminate it by substitution, or otherwise.
   Isolate it.
   Change its character, frequency (speed).
2. Reduce response to driving force.
   Insert isolating members.
   Damp vibrating elements.
   Detune resonant systems.
   Change mass. Increase mass of stationary elements or reduce mass of moving elements.
   Change stiffness.
   Add auxiliary mass damping or resonant absorbers.

9.5.1 Changing the Driving Force. In order to see how the driving force can be changed, it is useful to review the many ways that a vibratory force is developed. Here there are two basic processes involved. Either mechanical energy of some type is coupled into mechanical vibratory energy by one or more methods, or energy in some other form is transformed into mechanical vibratory energy, as outlined below.

1. Mechanical
   Unbalanced rotating masses.
   Reciprocating masses.
   Fluctuating mechanical forces or torques.
   Fluctuating loads.
   Fluctuating mass or stiffness.
   Poorly formed moving components.
   Mechanical looseness.
   Misalignment.

2. Transformation from another form of energy.
   Varying electrical fields.
   Varying hydraulic forces.
   Aerodynamic forces.
   Acoustic excitation.
   Varying thermal conditions.

Sometimes the source of the vibratory force is readily apparent or well known from experience. At other times use of some measuring instruments can be invaluable in tracking down sources.

Here are some examples:

Stroboscopic observation of a cam and follower showed that above a certain speed the follower did not remain in contact with the cam during parts of the cycle. When the cam periodically came into contact with the follower after the period of separation, a serious impact occurred, which resulted in excessive vibration and noise. (Figure 9-3).

223

Figure 9-3. Sequence of photographs shows misbehaving cam and follower. The cam is rotating at 2000 rpm. The photographs were taken with stroboscopic illumination at different phases of the cam cycle to show the bouncing action when the cam rotates above a critical speed.

224

A frequency analysis of a vibration often shows up strong components whose frequencies can be related to certain shaft speeds or gear-tooth meshing frequencies, and in this way the source can be tracked down. Sometimes, however, the relations are not simple. As pointed out by L. S. Wirt (1962) the gear-tooth meshing frequency may be modulated at rates determined by shaft speeds, because of run out, and by the rate at which the torsional loading varies (Figure 9-4).

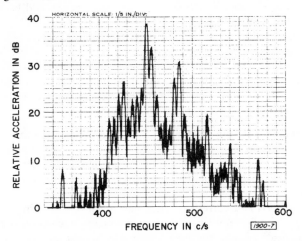

Figure 9-4. A part of the recorded frequency analysis of the vibration of a gear-belt drive. The tooth-contact rate of 450 impacts per second determines the frequency of the dominating component, and the gear belt with its speed of 5 rps introduces a host of components spaced about the main component by multiples of 5 hertz. The torque pulsations from the 1800 rpm synchronous motor and the 120-Hz magnetically driven vibration in the motor also influence the spectrum.

For devices that are electrically driven, strong vibration components at frequencies that are multiples of 120 Hz are good indications that these vibration components are electro-magnetically excited. Sometimes one can check this deduction by monitoring the level of such components, first when the device is operating normally, and then when the electric power is suddenly disconnected. Usually the driven devices will coast long enough so that the mechanical forces will not change rapidly even though the electrical forces are changed abruptly.

When a device can be driven at varying speeds, the effect of changed speeds on the frequencies and amplitudes of the various important components can be an important clue in tracking down the sources of those components. Here the changes in shaft speeds and mesh frequencies can be related to changing or steady frequencies. This technique is particularly helpful if the relative speeds of some parts can be changed or if a clutch can be used to deactivate some sections.

When the indication on the meter of a vibration meter or of a broad-band analyzer fluctuates erratically over a range of 2 to 1 (6 dB) or more, the vibration is usually random in character, and the source is then probably to be found in some rattle, friction-induced vibration, turbulence, poor ball bearings, gases or liquids in motion, or combustion processes. The relative value of a peak and average reading also serves to differentiate this type of vibration from the simpler harmonic motion of rotating unbalanced masses.

For simple harmonic motion the peak value will be about 1.5 times the average value (and the peak-to-peak, about 3 times). For random signals the ratio is usually much higher, that is 3 to 4 times (or 6 to 8 times for peak-to-peak).

Listening by means of a pair of earphones to the signal picked up by the vibration pickup can be helpful in determining the cause of a vibration, particularly if the source is defective ball or needle bearings or air leaks, which give a rough quality to the sound. The earphones should have a good pair of ear cushions or muffs to keep out extraneous sound.

Once the mechanism producing the vibratory force is recognized, a review of the possible means for reducing the force is in order. Thus, balancing techniques can be applied, better gears or bearings can be substituted, proper lubrication can be applied, the mechanical structure can be improved (for example by lightening the moving members and increasing the weight of stationary members), and gas or liquid velocities can be reduced.

9.5.2 Balancing Rotating Machinery. Unbalance in rotating devices is one of the chief causes of excessive vibration. This single cause is so important that extensive discussions of it will be found in a number of the books listed at the end of this chapter. See, for example, Muster and Senger (1961) and Wilcox (1967).

Balancing criteria and current practice have been reviewed by Muster and Flores (1969). The degree of balance that is sought depends on the type of device, its applications, and the rotor speed. The highest quality of balance is required for gyroscopes and precision grinders, and the poorest quality is tolerated for the crankshaft drives of slow, rigidly mounted engines. A standard has been published by the Association of German Engineers (VDI 2060-October 1966) for recommended allowable degrees of unbalance, and some indirect criteria have been published in terms of acceptable vibration at a bearing housing.

9.5.3 Reducing Response to Driving Force. A further important step in the process of vibration reduction is to reduce the response to the driving force (Morrow, 1963, pp 56 ff). Here, too, measurement techniques can be valuable in guiding the approach to reducing the response. For example, exploring for maxima in vibration level may show up resonance modes of vibrations of plates and other structural members. It can show where damping may be most effective or where resonant absorbers can be added. It may also show where detuning can be used.

Resonance Effects. The phenomenon of resonant vibration occurs frequently; for example, resonant vibration is essential to the operation of most musical instruments. The undesired resonances in some automobiles at certain speeds can be very annoying.

The effects of resonant vibration in rotating machinery can be so serious that the design of these devices includes the calculation of the critical speeds (resonance frequencies). These calculations are used to make certain that whenever possible, the critical speeds are not included in the normal operating range of the device.

The resonance or natural modes of vibration for many types of simple structures have been calculated. Some of these are beams, shafts, plates, and stretched wires. The frequencies of resonance depend, for example, on the shape, dimensions, stresses, mounting, and material characteristics. The frequencies can also be affected by coupling to other structures.

The nature of resonance is readily illustrated by vibration of a table on which a mass is flexibly mounted with the table driven at a constant amplitude but at different frequencies. At a certain critical frequency the motion of the mass will be greater than for frequencies just slightly higher and slightly lower. This frequency at which a maximum in vibration occurs is a resonance frequency. If the structure being shaken is relatively complex, many such maxima can be observed. (It is often helpful to use a stroboscopic technique to make this motion visible at a slowed-down rate.) Minima of motion may also be due to resonances.

In an actual operating device, resonant conditions may be obvious because of excessive noise or observed vibration at certain speeds. Exploring by means of a vibration pickup, for the points at which vibration is much greater than for other places on the device, will often locate the resonant elements. The resonances may be of the simple type where a mass is mounted on a flexible support, or they may be of the plate-mode type, where the mass and flexibility of a plate or sheet are in resonance, so that different parts of the plate are moving differently. In this latter instance very complicated motions may result.

Unless there is some significant dissipation of energy (damping) as the system vibrates, the resonance amplitude of motion may become very large, even with a relatively small driving force. These large amplitudes must ordinarily be avoided. The two principal ways of reducing these amplitudes are detuning and damping. If the driving force is at a relatively fixed frequency, it may be relatively easy to move the frequency of resonance out of the operating range by a change of the resonant-element mass or stiffness or both. The use of damping devices or highly damped materials is the other important possibility.

Many techniques for damping vibration have been developed. They include dashpots and other viscous absorbing systems, mastic coatings, sandwich-type dissipative materials, inherently dissipative plastics or metals, electromagnetic damping, frictional rubbing devices, and dynamic absorbers.

Measurements of the vibration levels at various parts of the device under study can help to show where damping devices can be applied most effectively. Thus if a resonance condition is to be damped, an analyzer tuned to the frequency of resonance should be used on the output of a pickup. Then when the measurements are made at different points on the vibrating device, only the vibration component at the resonance frequency will be observed, so that the actual resonance maxima can be obtained without being obscured by high-amplitude low-frequency vibrations. When such measurements are made, the vibration pickup must be light in weight compared with the mass of the resonant element, so that it does not appreciably detune the resonant system. Whenever possible stroboscopic observations should be made, since this can be done without affecting the vibration.

As an example of the effectiveness of damping in reducing vibration, Ruzicka (1964) reports on an aluminum chassis for electronic modules that was giving trouble because of fatigue failures and incorrect operation because of the collision of modules during vibration of the chassis. The installation of stiffening plates made of visco-elastic-damped material reduced the vibration amplification at the main resonance modes by factors of 3 to 4, and the vibration-caused problems were eliminated.

Oscillating Conditions. In most instances resonance is exhibited when the natural-mode frequency of a vibrating member coincides with, or is very close to, one of the component frequencies of the driving force. Certain unstable systems, however, do not require this coincidence when the conditions make the system self-oscillatory. They require what is essentially a reasonably steady driving force. Galloping transmission lines and some forms of machine-tool chatter, electrical brush squeal and automobile shimmy are examples of this type of excitation.

The galloping and torsional oscillations in some suspension bridges are aerodynamically induced forms of vibration. Such torsional oscillations destroyed the first Tacoma Narrows Bridge on November 7, 1940. The proper aerodynamic design of such a structure can essentially eliminate this vibration (Steinman, 1956).

The Mackinac Bridge as a matter of fact is a classic example of the possible tremendous value that can accrue from careful control of vibration. In its design the vibratory driving force produced by wind was made essentially zero by the particular open structure used. This new design also made possible great savings in the structure. As an additional precaution the deck openings and roadway are arranged to damp any vibration that may occur.

Variation of Parameters. In any of these procedures for tracking down vibration troubles, it is often helpful to change some element, for example the mass, and observe how the change affects the vibration levels. This technique can be classed as the method of variation of parameters. In other words, change things and see what happens. The way of "seeing" is, of course, to use measurements that will give a good basis for judging what has changed and by how much. In general, one follows a logical guessing procedure. The results of the experiments help one to eliminate or confirm the various possible sources of vibration effects.

9.5.4. Vibration Isolation. The reduction of the effects of vibration by isolation is widely used. (Crede, 1951; Den Hartog, 1956; Vigness, 1965; SAE Committee G-S, 1962). This isolation technique is usually illustrated with a vibrating device mounted on a foundation by means of soft springs or other resilient devices. If the isolation system is properly designed, the vibratory force transmitted to the foundation will be less when the springs are used than when the device is clamped directly to a foundation. The device itself, however, will ordinarily vibrate with a greater amplitude when mounted on a soft mount. Thus it is essential to realize that the isolation is working in only one direction, that is, the original source of vibratory force is not reduced by this isolation. Of course, if the foundation is vibrating as a result of some other driving force, one can reduce the effects of the vibration on a device by suspending it on a suitable soft mount. Some scientific instruments must be isolated in this way from building vibrations in order to operate satisfactorily.

Many commercial vibration isolators, or shock mounts, are available, and the manufacturers of these mounts usually supply information for their proper use. It is most important in applying isolators to avoid having the natural frequency of the mass of the device and the resilient suspension be nearly the same as the frequency of the driving force. When such a condition occurs, the transmitted vibration may be greater with the use of isolators than without. A frequency analysis of the vibration, which gives the component frequencies of the driving force, and a knowledge of the mechanical constants should make it possible to avoid this simple resonance effect.

Supports should be located to avoid cross coupling from one mode of vibration to another. Such a requirement ordinarily means that the line of action of the support should pass through the center of gravity of the device being supported.

The foundation, the isolating suspension system, and the supported structure will have, individually and in combination, resonant modes at frequencies higher than the first natural resonance. Sometimes these higher modes cause trouble, because the isolation is reduced from that normally expected (Plunkett, 1958).

The usual commercial vibration isolators include sufficient damping so that effects of the higher-order resonances in the isolator are not serious. But the isolation is usually significantly less at high frequencies than one would expect on the basis of the simple idea of a weight supported on a spring.

Torsional vibration is isolated by the use of flexible couplings, flexible shafts, and belts. These, too, include some damping, and they also introduce resonant modes of torsional vibration in conjunction with the rotational inertia of the coupled system.

Multiple isolators need careful design in order to be effective. When two isolator units are used in cascade, serious effects that interfere with satisfactory isolation may occur (Skudrzyk, 1959).

9.5.5 Maintenance. When maintenance of proper performance or acceptable noise and vibration levels is the goal, symptoms are used as a guide to discover the source of any trouble that may develop and to decide on the remedy. Before these symptoms are reviewed, it is also helpful to keep in mind the many ways that machine performance is affected by changes that occur with time. A systematic classification of the sources of these changes should serve to point up the many possibilities that exist. They are:

1. Wear

2. Erosion

3. Corrosion

4. Aging
   Curing
   Crystalization and fatigue
   Solidifying of grease or packing
   Loss of adhesion or bonding

5. Inelastic behavior
   Parts stressed out of shape
   Bent parts
   Increased tolerances

6. Loosening of fastenings

7. Broken or damaged parts

8. Incorrect or inadequate lubrication

9. Foreign matter
   Dirt chips, dust, grit
   Contaminants
   Humidity
   Ice accumulation
   Paint and other finishes

229

10. Environmental changes
    Temperature
    Humidity
    Pressure
11. Chemical changes in materials

The existence of a vibration problem may be first noticed in a routine survey of the vibration levels on the machines in a plant, or it may become evident the performance of a machine may be obviously not so good as it should be. In either situation the usual first step in tracking down the trouble is to locate the point or area where the vibration level is the highest. Inspection at this point may show the real source of the trouble. It is important to remember, however, that vibration is transmitted very readily by metal, and occasionally the point at which the trouble is best corrected is some distance from the point of maximum vibration.

The next step in the search is often a study of the character of the vibration signal, that is, the dominant frequency (low or high), whether it is a tone, random in nature (a rough, rushing or roaring noise in the earphones at the output of a vibration meter), or an impact-type vibration.

The measurement of displacement tends to emphasize low-frequency vibration, and acceleration emphasizes high-frequency vibration. Thus a vibration meter that can measure both these quantities in addition to velocity is helpful in diagnosis. When high-frequency vibration or impact vibration is significant, listening to the character of the vibration signal can often provide an additional clue. For example, poor ball bearings have a characteristic rough tone that may wax and wane.

The nature of the vibration can be organized into three broad classes with a host of possible faults. By the use of the position information and the possible pertinent faults listed in the following classification, one may be able to track down the specific fault in a given case. Or at most only a few possibilities need to be considered and a process of elimination used. For a specific machine, the following list, if not pertinent, at least, may suggest the possibilities that must be considered.

1. Low-frequency vibration (frequency of order of shaft or belt speeds)
    Unbalanced rotor (worn, eroded, broken, or corroded parts)
    Misalignment (induces significant axial vibration)
    Eccentric shafts
    Slipping clutches
    Mechanical looseness
    Loose foundation bolts
    Oil whirl or whip (1/2 or less times shaft speed)
    Worn belts
    Belts and pulleys out of adjustment
    Aerodynamically driven galloping and twisting
    Changed reciprocating elements that introduce added torsional vibration.
2. High-frequency vibration
    Defective bearings (random or rough vibration)
    Inadequate lubrication
    Poor gears
    Slipping clutches
    Rubbing or binding parts

Air leaks

Hydraulic leaks

3. Impact vibration and rattles

Parts colliding

Broken or loose pieces

Electromagnetically driven loose pieces

Water hammer

Surge

In addition to position, frequency, and character of the vibration, timing may also furnish an important clue to the nature of the difficulty. Here, stroboscopic observation with a photoelectric pickoff to trigger the stroboscope can be helpful, as illustrated by the cam and follower study previously mentioned.

When stroboscopic observation is not possible, the vibration signal may be observed on an oscilloscope with timing supplied by the photoelectric pickoff.

9.5.6 Conclusion. If a simple solution is not obvious, the quantitative results of measurements are often essential elements in the efficient analysis and solution of the problem. As various control procedures are used, vibration measurements can show the progress being made and when the attack on the vibration problem must be shifted from one form or place to another.

REFERENCES

AIMA (1971-72), *Performance Data, Architectural Acoustical Materials,* Bull. #31, Acoustical and Insulating Materials Association, 206 West Touhy Avenue, Park Ridge, Illinois, 60068.

American Foundrymen's Society (1966), *Foundry Noise Manual,* American Foundrymen's Society, Des Plaines, Ill., 2nd edition.

AIHA (1966), *Industrial Noise Manual,* American Industrial Hygiene Association, 14125 Prevost, Detroit, Michigan 48227, 2nd edition.

ASHRAE (1967), *ASHRAE Guide and Data Book, Systems and Equipment,* American Society of Heating, Refrigerating and Air-conditioning Engineers, Inc., 345 East 47th Street, New York, N. Y. 10017.

L. L. Beranek, ed. (1971), *Noise and Vibration Control,* McGraw-Hill., New York.

L. L. Beranek, ed (1960), *Noise Reduction,* McGraw-Hill, New York.

British Internal Combustion Engine Research Association (1958), *A Handbook on Torsional Vibration,* University Press, Cambridge, England.

C. E. Crede (1951), *Vibration and Shock Isolation,* John Wiley & Sons, Inc., New York.

J. P. Den Hartog (1956), *Mechanical Vibrations,* McGraw-Hill, New York.

C. Duerden (1970), *Noise Abatement,* Butterworths, London.

W. Furrer (1964), *Room and Building Acoustics and Noise Abatement,* Butterworth, London.

C. M. Harris, ed (1957), *Handbook of Noise Control,* McGraw-Hill, New York.

C. M. Harris and C. E. Crede (1961), *Shock and Vibration Handbook,* McGraw-Hill, New York.

E. M. Kerwin, Jr., (1959), "Damping of Flexural Waves by a Constrained Viscoelastic Layer," *J Acoust Soc Am,* Vol 31, #5, July, pp 952-962.

V. O. Knudsen and C. M. Harris (1950), *Acoustical Designing in Architecture,* John Wiley & Sons, Inc., New York.

G. Kurtze (1964), *Physik und Technik der Larmbekampfung,* G. Braun, Karlsruhe.

B. J. Lazan (1968), *Damping of Materials and Members in Structural Mechanics,* Pergamon Press, New York.

P. Lord and F. L. Thomas, ed. (1963), *Noise Measurement and Control,* Heywood & Company Ltd, London.

J. N. MacDuff and J. R. Curreri (1958), *Vibration Control,* McGraw-Hill, New York.

R. T. McGoldrick (1957), *A Vibration Manual for Engineers,* US Navy, PB131785, December, 2nd edition.

R. T. McGoldrick (1960), *Ship Vibration*, David Taylor Model Basin Report 1457, December.

C. T. Morrow (1963), *Shock and Vibration Engineering*, John Wiley & Sons, Inc., New York.

D. Muster and W. I. Senger (1961), "Balancing of Rotating Machinery," Vol 3, Chapter 39, of Harris and Crede (1961).

D. Muster and B. Flores (1969), "Balancing Criteria and Their Relationship to Current American Practice," *J Engineering for Indus*, Trans ASME, Vol 91, Series B, #4, Nov, pp 1035-1046.

National Physical Laboratory (1962), *The Control of Noise*, Symposium No. 12, Her Majesty's Stationery Office, London.

P. H. Parkin and H. R. Humphreys (1963), *Acoustics, Noise, and Buildings*, Faber and Faber, London, 2nd edition.

R. Plunkett (1958), "Interaction Between a Vibratory Machine and Its Foundation," *Noise Control*, Vol 4, #1, Jan, pp 18-22.

M. Rettinger (1968), *Acoustics, Room Design and Noise Control*, Chemical Publishing Co., New York.

D. Ross, E. E. Ungar, and E. M. Kerwin, Jr. (1959), "Damping of Plate Flexural Vibrations by Means of Viscoelastic Laminae," in Ruzicka (1959).

J. E. Ruzicka, ed (1959), *Structural Damping*, American Society of Mechanical Engineers, New York, N. Y.

J. E. Ruzicka (1964), "Vibration Control: Applications," *Electro-Technology*, Vol 73, #1, Jan, pp 75-82.

J. E. Ruzicka (1971), "Fundamental Concepts of Vibration Control," *Sound and Vibration*, Vol 5, #7, July 1971, pp 16-23.

H. J. Sabine (1950), *Less Noise—Better Hearing*, Celotex Corporation, Chicago.

SAE Committee G-5 (1962), Aerospace Shock and Vibration, *Design of Vibration Isolation Systems*, Society of Automotive Engineers, New York.

E. Skudrzyk (1959), "Theory of Noise and Vibration Isolation of a System with Many Resonances," *J Acoust Soc Am*, Vol 31, #1, Jan, pp 68-74.

E. Skudrzyk (1968), *Simple and Complex Vibratory Systems*, Penn State Univ. Press, University Park, Pennsylvania.

D. B. Steinman (1956), "The Design of the Mackinac Bridge for Aerodynamic Stability", *J Franklin Inst*, Vol 262, #6, Dec, pp 453-468.

G. W. Van Santen (1953), *Mechanical Vibrations*, Philips Technical Library, Elsevier, Publishing Co., Amsterdam.

VDI-2060 (October 1966), *Beurteilungsmass-stabe fur den Auswuchtzustand rotierender starrer Korper*, Verein Deutscher Ingenieure, Dusseldorf.

I. Vigness (1965), "Vibration Isolation," *Physics Today*, Vol 18, #7, July, pp 42-48.

J. B. Wilcox (1967), *Dynamic Balancing of Rotating Machinery*, Sir Isaac Pitman & Sons Ltd., London.

W. K. Wilson (1959), *Vibration Engineering*, Charles Griffin, London.

L. S. Wirt (1962), "An Amplitude Modulation Theory for Gear-Induced Vibrations," Chapter 17 in P, K. Stein (1962), *Measurement Engineering*, Stein Engineering Services, Tempe, Arizona.

L. F. Yerges (1969), *Sound, Noise, and Vibration Control*, Van Nostrand Reinhold Company, New York.

T. P. Yin (1969), "The Control of Vibration and Noise," *Scientific Amer*, Vol 220, #1, Jan, pp 98-107.

T. P. Yin, T. J. Kelly and J. E. Barry (1967), "A Quantitative Evaluation of Constrained Layer Damping," *J of Engineering for Indus*, Trans ASME, Vol 89, Series B, #4, Nov, pp 773-784.

Chapter 10

Some Case Histories

In order to illustrate some of the procedures given in this book, we shall describe in this chapter how some industrial noise problems might be handled. They are taken from actual experience, and where instruments are mentioned, the latest equipment is named, although some of the instruments actually used were earlier models. The principles and techniques illustrated remain unchanged, and the slight departure from authenticity is made up for by the greater usefulness of reference to a current instrument.

10.1 NOISE FROM AN AIR COMPRESSOR.

Engineers in a group of offices were annoyed by an intense low-frequency noise whenever an air compressor in another part of the same building was running. The noise was most intense when the office windows were open; the air intake for the compressor was about 50 ft away on the near side of the building. Furthermore, the noise level varied markedly in the office; that is, in the middle of the office the noise was hardly noticeable, but near the windows or the door on the opposite wall the noise was loudest. This standing-wave pattern was confirmed by a quick check on a sound-level meter, with weighting control in the flat position, to show that the maxima were about 162 inches apart. When the windows were closed, the maxima were not obvious because of other background noises. With one or more windows open, the pattern was relatively unaffected by opening or closing the door.

The obvious explanation of this behavior was that the pulses produced at the air intake were propagated through the windows and excited a resonant mode of the office. But one of the engineers suggested that the result might be produced in a different fashion. He suggested that the driving force could be a vibration transmitted through the building and that the windows needed to be open in order for the room resonance to coincide with the frequency of the driving force. (He admitted this explanation was far fetched.)

In order to decide what to do about the problem, some simple measurements were made. Since the annoying noise was low in frequency, it was decided to use the combination of a Type 1560-9531 1-inch Ceramic Microphone Set driving a Type 1564 Sound and Vibration Analyzer, which could measure noise components at frequencies as low as 2.5 Hz. A Type 1562 Sound-Level Calibrator was used to set the level controls. The microphone was set up at one of the maximum level points near the door, and the third-octave analysis shown in Figure 10-1a was obtained. The strong components near 16 and 40 Hz were remeasured with the 1/10-octave bandwidth to be actually at 14 and 37 Hz. The strong component at 37 Hz appeared to be the major offending noise.

A Type 1560-P52 Vibration Pickup was connected to the Type 1564. This combination was calibrated by means of a Type 1557 Vibration Calibrator.

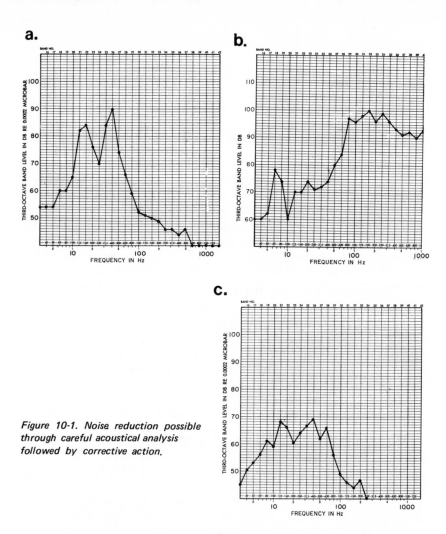

Figure 10-1. Noise reduction possible through careful acoustical analysis followed by corrective action.

Then some exploration of the office floor for a 37-Hz component indicated nothing significant. An analysis of the vibration of the pump structure produced the result shown in Figure 10-1b. These measurements satisfied the one engineer that his explanation based on vibration was probably incorrect.

Since the 37-Hz component was so dominant, it could be assessed as a pure-tone. The equal-loudness contours of Figure 3-3 indicated that its loudness level was about 70 phons. Although the rating procedures of Chapter 3 apply generally to broad-band noise, it is obvious from those ratings that a significant drop in level for this very loud tone would be necessary in order to make it acceptable. If it could be lowered to 40 phons, it would probably be unobjectionable. This drop would require a decrease in sound-pressure level to 70 dB.

Many possibilities for correcting the annoying condition were considered, for example, changes in the offices so that they would not resonate at the troublesome frequency, a change in compressor speed, and rerouting of the air intake. The solution adopted was to add a pneumatic filter to the air

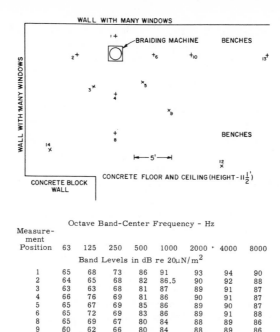

WALL WITH MANY WINDOWS

BRAIDING MACHINE   BENCHES

WALL WITH MANY WINDOWS

BENCHES

CONCRETE BLOCK WALL

CONCRETE FLOOR AND CEILING (HEIGHT - 11½')

Octave Band-Center Frequency - Hz

Measure-ment Position	63	125	250	500	1000	2000	4000	8000
Band Levels in dB re 20μN/m²								
1	65	68	73	86	91	93	94	90
2	64	65	68	82	86.5	90	92	88
3	63	63	68	81	87	89	91	87
4	66	76	69	81	86	90	91	87
5	65	67	69	85	86	89	90	87
6	65	72	69	83	86	89	91	88
8	65	69	67	80	84	88	89	86
9	60	62	66	80	84	88	89	86
10	65	69	68	80	85	88	89	87
12	62	60	64	78	83	86	87	84
13	61	60	65	78	81	85	86	83
14	65	70	69	81	85	89	90	87

Microphone on analyzer - 42" above floor.

Figure 10-2. An octave-band analysis of braiding-machine noise (paragraph 10-2).

intake. With the data on the significant components at hand, it was easy to design a proper filter. A thirty-foot pipe was already being used from the air intake to the compressor, and calculations showed that it could form part of the filter. An air tank was added at the center of this pipe, and the noise was so reduced that it was no longer troublesome. The noise analysis in the office after this change is shown in Figure 10-1c.

10.2 BRAIDING-MACHINE NOISE.

When a manufacturer introduced a process of putting a braided nylon sheath around a cable of wires, the employees in the vicinity of the braiding machine complained about the noise it made. In common with other machines of this type, this was a broad-band noise source, and the obvious instrument to use was an octave-band analyzer.

A 1933 Precision Sound-Level Meter and Analyzer was used to analyze the noise at a number of places around the machine. Some of the results are shown in Figure 10-2.

A study of the machine indicated that it would be very difficult to modify it to reduce the level at the operators' ears without reducing the production rate. The machine was run intermittently for only a fraction of the day, and this intermittency provided some margin to protect the operator. But it was decided to supply protective earmuffs for the operator as an added margin of safety. To protect the other workers, the machine was put in a separate room heavily treated with acoustical tile. In addition, to avoid troubles from open windows in the summer bypassing the wall barriers, the room was air-conditioned. The air conditioning made it unnecessary to open the windows, and it made it possible to wear the earmuffs with comfort even in the summer.

10.3 REDUCTION OF FLUTTER IN A TAPE RECORDER.

Measurements of the flutter (variations in tape speed) of a tape recorder showed strong components at 15, 30, and 75 Hz and other minor components. Although it was expected that eccentricities in the drive produced some of this flutter, a check on the effects of vibration was made.

A Type 1560-P54 Vibration Pickup was mounted on the tape deck and connected through a Type 1560-P40 Preamplifier to a Type 1564 Sound and Vibration Analyzer. The analyzed vibration showed strong components at 30 and 75 Hz, but very little at 15 Hz. The 30 Hz component corresponded to the motor speed. Although the motor and attached flywheel had been balanced before being mounted, the vibration was easily reduced by rebalancing of these in place. After balancing, the flutter component at 30 Hz was negligible, and the 75 Hz component was markedly reduced also.

The 15-Hz component corresponded to the capstan speed, and it was the largest remaining component. The fact that there was no appreciable vibration at this frequency seemed surprising at first. The flutter could be reduced significantly by the placing of eccentric weights on the capstan flywheel; but then the vibration of the tape deck increased markedly at 15 Hz. Obviously, this flutter component was caused by eccentricity in the capstan, and the vibration introduced was canceling the effects of eccentricity.

Measurements at the capstan bearing showed that the vibration at 75 Hz was a maximum there. What was happening here, apparently, was that the capstan flywheel and shaft structure had a vibration resonance at 75 Hz that was excited either by the fifth harmonic of the capstan rotation frequency or, more likely, by a combination of a multiple of the motor rotation frequency and the capstan rotation frequency. Because of the resonance, very little energy was required to produce a significant vibration. This mode could be reduced significantly by a change in the resonant frequency, but the balancing of the motor and flywheel had already reduced it so that the 15-Hz component was the only significant one remaining.

10.4 AN OIL-PUMP PROBLEM.

An oil pump, used in a production setup to supply oil at high pressure to a number of hydraulic presses, was so noisy that the workmen objected to using it. This pump had been installed to speed up production with new presses, but the men preferred to use an earlier production method because it was not then necessary to use the noisy pump. The problem was to find out what should be done to make the noise less objectionable.

In this example, it was assumed that the pump itself could not be modified to reduce the noise, since correcting basic design faults would be a major problem. Errors in alignment or looseness of mounting, as the source of the high noise levels, however, should be taken into consideration. On that basis, the apparent procedure was to investigate these possibilities, to measure the noise produced by the machine, to measure the background noise level, and then to decide what recommendations should be made.

The following instruments were chosen to take to the factory:

Type 1562 Sound-Level Calibrator.

Type 1933 Precision Sound Level Meter and Analyzer.

Type 1568 Wave Analyzer.

Type 1560-P11B Vibration Pickup System, comprising Type 1560-P52 Vibration Pickup and Type 1560-P21B Control Box.

Pair of high-fidelity earphones.

Two sponge-rubber pads.

Before going to the factory each instrument was given a maintenance check to see that it was operating properly, since it is easier to correct any faults at the home office than it is to correct them in a noisy factory where service facilities are limited. The procedure was as follows:

a. All equipment was turned on.

b. Batteries were checked.

c. The analyzers were calibrated by means of their own built-in calibration circuits.

d. A Type 1562 Sound-Level Calibrator was used to check the calibration of the 1933.

The instruments were taken in an automobile to the factory, where they were loaded on a rubber-tired cart and taken to the noisy pump on the ground floor. Incidentally, this type of cart is a convenient support for instruments during measurements. At the pump, the obvious data were recorded. It was rated at 5 gallons per minute at 3000 psi, and it was 6 in. long and 5 1/2 in. in diameter, with seven knobs projecting from the outer cylinder. These knobs apparently corresponded to the seven cams of the pump. The pump was driven through a three-pronged flexible coupling by a 10-hp, 60 Hz, 1730-rpm induction motor. This motor was air-cooled. The oil storage and heat-exchanger tank was about 25-in. long and 15-in. in diameter. These three main items − the pump, the motor, and the tank − as well as a mounting board, some gages and a line switch, were mounted on a 37-in.-square, heavy, steel base. Steel I-beams were welded underneath as a part of this base and these were securely bolted to the floor, which was a reinforced cement slab. Four heavy, brass, pipe lines were connected to the storage tank. Two of these were for water cooling, and the other two were for the oil. These lines ran directly to the heavy masonry wall nearby, and they were securely anchored in many places to the wall as they ran to the different presses.

The factory itself was of heavy reinforced concrete construction with no acoustical treatment. Numerous small machines, benches, storage racks, cartons, and other items were arranged in orderly fashion throughout the large factory space where this pump was located.

When the pump was turned on, it was clear why the men complained. It was very noisy. There were no obvious rattles from loose pieces, however, and there seemed to be no mounting troubles. The floor did not seem to be transmitting vibration, and this conclusion was verified later. The vibration in the oil lines could be felt by touch, but they did not seem to be an important source of noise. For example, a check using the sound-level meter carried along near the lines showed that the noise level dropped noticeably as one went away from the pump. The units mounted on the steel frame appeared to be the main source of noise, and listening nearby indicated that the pump itself was the major source.

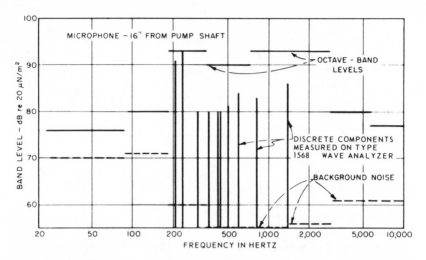

Figure 10-3. Frequency analysis of the noise produced by a pump. Levels measured with the octave-band analyzer are shown together with components measured on the Type 1568 Wave Analyzer. Background band levels are shown by horizontal dashed lines; solid horizontal lines represent pump noise plus background.

A preliminary survey around and over the structure but some 5 ft away was made in octave-bands. As expected, there was no obvious directional pattern.

The first measurement was made close to the pump. The microphone, only 16 in. from the pump shaft was on the 1933, which in turn was set on an empty cardboard packing case on the concrete floor. This first position was selected at this point to make certain that the background noise from other machines would not obscure any significant components.

With the pump turned on, the output from the analyzer was monitored by the pair of earphones. Listening to the output of the various bands showed that the noise in the 1000 and 2000-Hz bands was the dominating part of the annoying, loud noise heard from the machine.

The complete analysis was made at this point as shown on the graph of Figure 10-3. Then the pump was turned off, and the background noise was analyzed. In all frequency bands but the lowest, this background noise was so low that it could be neglected. It was obvious from this analysis that most of the noise was in the range from 200 to 2800 Hz.

There were no apparent characteristic, pitched sounds in the noise heard from the machine, but it could be expected that some would be present. Just to make sure that nothing important would be overlooked, an analysis of the noise was also made with the Type 1568-A wave analyzer on the output of the 1933. The only discrete components (definite peaks in response as the analyzer was tuned) that were observed are shown on the graph. Of these components, the one at 205 Hz was the basic pumping rate of seven times the rotational speed. A comparison of the levels from this analysis with that in octave-bands showed that most of the energy in the range from 200 to 700 Hz was from discrete components, but above that the noise was generally unpitched.

The next step was to use a vibration test to find out if the mounting was satisfactory. The vibration pickup and control box were connected to the analyzer. Exploration with the pickup and the analyzer showed the following behavior. The pump itself was vibrating most strongly; the high-frequency and low-frequency components were all present. The driving motor was not vibrating seriously. The storage tank vibrated most strongly at low frequencies. As the probe was moved about the mounting base toward the concrete floor the amplitude of motion decreased. At the floor the motion was insignificant. This vibration test confirmed that the mounting was not faulty.

The final measurements were octave-band analyses at a number of points 5 ft from the pump and one point 12 ft away. The results of these analyses are shown in the data sheet of Figure 10-4.

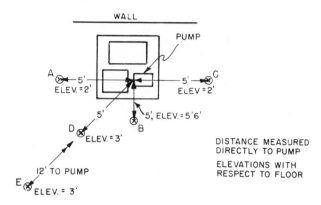

MICROPHONE LOCATION	SOURCE	OVER-ALL	OCTAVE BAND CENTER FREQUENCY							
			63	125	250	500	1000	2000	4000	8000
A	Pump + Bkgd*	86	72-76	78	76	80	78	81	76	74
A	Bkgd	76-78	72-76	72	65	61	58	58	62	63
B	Pump + Bkgd	89	72-76	74-73	81	85-86	81-83	82-83	76	75
B	Bkgd	76	70-74	86	82	61	59	64	70	66
C	Pump + Bkgd	88	74-78	76-73	80	84	82	82-83	77-78	75
C	Bkgd	76-78	72-74	72-74	60	57	56	56	62	62
D	Pump + Bkgd	87-88	72-76	75-77	82	82	·79	82	74	72
E	Pump + Bkgd	84-85	70-74	74	78	80	76	76	72	71

*Bkgd = Background

Figure 10-4. A diagram of the several positions used in making octave-band analyses of pump noise. Results obtained at the various locations are given in the table.

The nearest workmen were about 7 feet from the pump, so that the levels at 5 feet were nearly representative of the conditions they encountered. A comparison of the levels from the pump with the background data and with the speech-interference criteria given in Chapter 3 indicated that a 20-dB reduction in noise level in the bands from 250 to 2000 Hz would have been desirable.

Therefore, as a solution to the problem, the following suggestions were made:

One possible solution is to use a different pump based on a principle of operation that produces less noise as a byproduct.

Another possible solution is to enclose the whole pump in a tight housing with lined ducts for air ventilation. The housing should be treated on the inside with acoustic absorbing materials.

239

A third solution is to move the pump to another location outside the working area, and this solution was adopted. The pump was moved to a nearby boiler room.

The use of earplugs, sometimes a solution to noise problems, was not adopted here because of the need for communications and the reluctance of personnel to wear such devices except as a last resort.

What had been accomplished by these measurements? First, they had ruled out the possibility of a simple solution, such as isolating the whole structure by vibration mounts, putting flexible couplings in the pipe lines, or using acoustic baffles. Second, they provided the data needed for a preliminary design of a housing, so that its probable cost could be weighed against other possible solutions. In short, these measurements provided the necessary data for a decision by management.

10.5 SUMMARIES OF SOME EXAMPLES FROM THE LITERATURE.

As an example of vibration isolation, Miller and Dyer (1958) report tests on the vibration levels induced in a concrete floor by a printing press. When used with 1/4-in. cork mounting, the press produced such high vibration levels in a concrete floor that the noise in the engineering offices below was excessive. Replacement of these mounts by a much thicker felt mount reduced the vibration amplitudes in the floor to about 1/10 the previous values in the important frequency range of 75 to 600 Hz.

As an example of detection of resonant modes of vibration, Austen and Priede (1958) found excessive vibration of the valve cover and the timing cover of a diesel engine. They found, by exploring with a vibration pickup and by making a narrow-band analysis of the vibration signal, that the valve cover was vibrating strongly at 1150 Hz, while the timing cover had strong components of vibration at 760, 1350, and 2800 Hz. Replacing the cast aluminum covers by "deadened" covers eliminated this excessive vibration.

Feinberg (1965) analyzes an interesting example of a gyrocompass mounted in a conventional vibration-isolation system. The performance of the gyrocompass was unsatisfactory when subjected to vibration in the frequency range from 220 to 350 Hz. The criterion for acceptable vibration levels was determined by vibrating the gyrocompass as a function of frequency and observing the level at which the performance became unacceptable. This vibration tolerance showed a minimum of 2 cm/s^2 rms (66 dB re 10^{-5} m/s^2 rms) in the frequency range from 240 to 350 Hz. In order to achieve the required low vibration level in this frequency range a tuned two-degrees-of-freedom filter was designed. Compared to the original simple isolation system, the resulting vibration levels at frequencies below 150 Hz were generally higher, but the criterion level was not exceeded, and the levels in the sensitive region from 240 to 350 Hz were, with the new system, sufficiently low that the criterion was satisfied everywhere.

Judd (1969) describes methods of controlling furnace noise. He shows the result of modifying burner tips to reduce the effects of firebox resonance as observed in an octave-band analysis of the noise. The very high levels in the octave bands from 2000 to 8000 Hz were reduced by the use of a mixer with a larger spud to permit a lower fuel gas pressure. These high-frequency levels were also reduced by the use of enclosures and intake silencers.

Mills (1969) shows how small but significant reductions in noise in a textile weaving mill were obtained by the acoustical treatment of the ceiling, walls and floor, by replacement of metal with nylon pinion gears in the drive assembly, and by other minor modifications of the looms. The important reductions in level were obtained in the octave bands from 250 to 8000 Hz.

Judd and Spence (1969) show how significant reductions in noise from electric motors can be obtained by selection of the proper type, by the use of a treated fan shroud, or by full enclosures. The differences in level were mainly in the octave bands above 250 Hz, except for the full enclosure where 20- to 25-dB reductions in level were obtained over the full audible range.

Torpey (1969) describes how power-generating equipment can be made quieter by a variety of techniques. Among these are sound-attenuating ducts for air intake and exhaust and covering surfaces with sound-absorbing materials. His experiments were based mainly on measurements of the noise with octave or 1/3-octave-band analyzers. He used an analyzer with an even narrower band to find that a very high 250-Hz octave-band level was caused by the tone produced by a generator cooling fan with a fundamental blade pulsing frequency in that band.

Hudson and Crocker (1970) show the effects of a barrier in reducing noise from an air-cooled refrigerant compressor. Noise reductions of from 7.5 to 16 dB(A) were achieved, and they proved adequate in satisfying complaints.

Excessive vibration of a cooling tower (Buscarello, 1968) was traced to tower resonance excited by impulses from rotating fan blades. Stroboscopic observation showed that the tip of each fan blade rose about 3 in. as it passed over a nearby drive shaft. The resulting impulses occurred 900 times per min, which was the resonant frequency of the tower. The excessive vibration was avoided by stiffening the tower to raise its resonant frequency.

Many examples of noise or vibration reduction are given in Chapter 11 of the AIHA *Industrial Noise Manual* (1966), in Chapter 7 of the *Foundry Noise Manual* (American Foundrymen's Society, 1966), in Harris (1957) and in Harris and Crede (1961).

REFERENCES

American Foundrymen's Society (1966), *Foundry Noise Manual*, American Foundrymen's Society, Des Plaines, Ill, 2nd edition.

AIHA (1966), *Industrial Noise Manual*, American Industrial Hygiene Association, 14125 Prevost, Detroit, Mich 48227, 2nd edition.

A.E.W. Austen and T. Priede (1958), "Origins of Diesel Engine Noise," *Proceedings of the Symposium on Engine Noise and Noise Suppression,* London, Institution of Mechanical Engineers, Oct, pp 19-32.

L. L. Beranek, ed. (1971), *Noise and Vibration Control*, McGraw-Hill, New York.

R. T. Buscarello (1968), "Practical Solutions for Vibration Problems," *Chem Eng,* Vol 75, Aug 12, pp 157-166.

M. Feinberg (1965), "New Methods Simplify Analysis of Vibration Isolation Systems," Part I, *Mach Des,* Vol 37, #18, Aug 5, pp 142-149.

C.M. Harris, ed (1957), *Handbook of Noise Control*, McGraw-Hill, New York.

C. M. Harris and C. E. Crede (1961), *Shock and Vibration Handbook*, McGraw-Hill, New York.

R. R. Hudson and M. J. Crocker (1970), "The Practical Problems Associated with Quieting a Refrigerant Compressor," *Applied Acoustics* Vol. 3 #4, Oct, pp 251-258.

S. H. Judd (1969), "Engineering Control of Furnace Noise," *Amer Indust Hyg Assoc J,* Vol 30, #1, Jan-Feb, pp 35-40.

S. H. Judd and J. A. Spence (1969), "Noise Control for Electric Motors," *Amer Indust Hyg Assoc J,* Vol 30, #6, Nov-Dec, pp 588-595.

L. N. Miller and I. Dyer (1958), "Printing Machine Isolation," *Noise Control,* Vol 4, #4, July, pp 21-23.

R. O. Mills (1969), "Noise Reduction in a Textile Weaving Mill," *Amer Indust Hyg Assoc J,* Vol 30, #1, Jan-Feb, pp 71-76.

P. J. Torpey (1969), "Noise Control of Emergency Power Generating Equipment," *Amer Indust Hyg Assoc J,* Vol 30, #6, Nov-Dec 1969, pp 588-595.

Appendixes

Appendix I

Decibel Conversion Tables

It is convenient in measurements and calculations to use a unit for expressing a logarithmic function of electric or acoustic power ratios. The *decibel* (1/10th of the bel) on the briggsian or base-10 scale is in almost universal use for this purpose.

Table I and Table II on the following pages have been prepared to facilitate making conversions in either direction between the number of decibels and the corresponding power and pressure ratios.

Decibel — The number of decibels N_{dB} corresponding to the ratio between two amounts of power W_1 and W_2 is

$$N_{dB} = 10 \log_{10} \frac{W_1}{W_2} \qquad (1)$$

When two pressures P_1 and P_2 operate in the same or equal impedances.

$$N_{dB} = 20 \log_{10} \frac{P_1}{P_2} \qquad (2)$$

To Find Values Outside The Range of Tables

Values outside the range of either Table I or Table II on the following pages can be readily found with the help of the following simple rules:

Table I: Decibels to Pressure and Power Ratios

Number of decibels positive (+): Subtract +20 decibels successively from the given number of decibels until the remainder falls within range of Table I. *To find the pressure ratio*, multiply the corresponding value from the right-hand voltage-ratio column by 10 for each time you subtracted 20 dB. To find the power ratio, multiply the corresponding value from the right-hand power-ratio column by 100 for each time you subtracted 20 dB.

Example — Given: 49.2 dB
    49.2 dB — 20 dB — 20 dB = 9.2 dB
    Pressure ratio: 9.2 dB →
        2.884 x 10 x 10 = 288.4
    Power ratio: 9.2 dB →
        8.318 x 100 x 100 = 83180

Number of decibels negative (−): Add +20 decibels successively to the given number of decibels until the sum falls within the range of Table I. For the pressure ratio, divide the value from the left-hand pressure-ratio column by 10 for each time you added 20 dB. For the power ratio, divide the value from the left-hand power-ratio column by 100 for each time you added 20 dB.

Example — Given: −49.2 dB
 −49.2 dB + 20 dB + 20 dB = −9.2 dB
 Pressure ratio: −9.2 dB →
  .3467 x 1/10 x 1/10 = .003467
 Power ratio: −9.2 dB →
  .1202 x 1/100 x 1/100 − .00001202

Table II: Pressure Ratios to Decibels

For ratios smaller than those in table — Multiply the given ratio by 10 successively until the product can be found in the table. From the number of decibels thus found, subtract +20 decibels for each time you multiplied by 10.

Example — Given: Pressure ratio = .0131
 .0131 x 10 x 10 = 1.31
 From Table II, 1.31 →
 2.34 dB − 20 dB − 20 dB = −37.66 dB

For ratios greater than those in table — Divide the given ratio by 10 successively until the remainder can be found in the table. To the number of decibels thus found, add +20 dB for each time you divided by 10.

Example — Given: Pressure ratio = 712
 712 x 1/10 x 1/10 = 7.12
 From Table II, 7.12 →
 17.05 dB + 20 dB + 20 dB = 57.05 dB

Use of Tables to Convert Vibration Readings

These decibel tables offer a convenient means of converting decibel vibration readings obtained with the sound-level meter and vibration pickup into displacement in inches, velocity in inches per second, and acceleration in inches per second per second.

Each control box nameplate is inscribed with a conversion table, which applies when that control box is used with the pickup and sound-level meter indicated on the nameplate. The conversion figures for the Type 1560-P21B Control Box are:

Parameter	English Units		Metric Units	
	SLM* Reading (dB)	Vibration (rms)	SLM$^+$ Reading (dB)	Vibration (rms)
Acceleration	50	1 in./s/s	80	1 m/s/s
Velocity	90	1 in./s	120	1 m/s
Displacement	120	1 in.	90	1 mm

*SLM sensitivity set for −40 dB re 1V/N/m² (−60 dB re 1 V/μ bar)
+SLM sensitivity set for −38.1 dB re 1 V/N/m² (−58.1 dB re 1 V/μ bar)

N.B. For Types 759-P36 and 1560-P21 Control Boxes, the conversion figures are different from the above. When these control boxes are used, substitute values given on the nameplate for those used below to obtain correct conversion.

NOTE: In Tables I and II, the term "pressure ratio" is equivalent to the term "voltage ratio" as used in the following instructions.

To Convert dB SLM Readings
Into RMS Amplitude in In.

1. Note decibel readings of sound-level meter when vibration pickup is in contact with vibrating surface and control box switch is set at DISPlacement.
2. If reading for Step 1 is below 120 dB: Subtract +20 dB successively from 120 minus dB reading until the remainder falls within the range of Table I of decibel tables. To determine rms amplitude in inches, multiply the voltage ratio (left-hand column) corresponding to the dB remainder by 0.1 for each time you subtracted 20 dB. Figures obtained are expressed directly in inches rms amplitude.

If reading for Step 1 is above 120 dB: Subtract +20 dB successively from dB reading minus 120 dB until the remainder falls within the range of Table I. To determine amplitude in inches, multiply the voltage ratio (right-hand voltage ratio column) corresponding to the dB remainder by 10 for each time you subtracted 20 dB. Figures obtained are expressed directly in inches rms amplitude.

To Convert dB SLM Readings
Into RMS Velocity in in./s

1. Note dB reading of sound-level meter with vibration pickup in contact with vibrating surface and control box switch set at VELocity.
2. If reading for Step 1 is below 90 dB: Subtract +20 dB successively from 90 minus dB reading until the remainder falls within the range of Table I of decibel tables. To determine rms velocity in inches per second, multiply the voltage ratio (left-hand voltage ratio column) corresponding to the dB remainder by 0.1 for each time you subtracted 20 dB. The value obtained is velocity expressed directly in inches per second rms.

If reading for Step 1 is above 90 dB: Subtract +20 dB successively from dB reading minus 90 until the remainder falls within the range of Table I. To determine rms velocity in inches per second, multiply the voltage ratio (right-hand voltage ratio column) corresponding to the dB remainder by 10 for each time you subtracted 20 dB. The value obtained is velocity expressed in inches per second rms.

To Convert dB SLM Readings
Into RMS Acceleration in in./s/s

1. Note dB reading of sound-level meter with vibration pickup in contact with vibrating surface and control box switch set at ACCeleration.
2. If reading of Step 1 is below 50 dB: The value obtained from the left-hand ratio column corresponding to 50 minus dB reading is acceleration expressed directly in inches per second per second rms.

If reading for Step 1 is above 50 dB (maximum 132 dB): Subtract +20 dB successively from dB reading minus 50 until the remainder falls within the range of Table I. To determine rms acceleration in inches per second per second, multiply the voltage ratio (right-hand voltage ratio column) corresponding to the dB remainder by 10 for each time you subtracted 20 dB. The value obtained is acceleration expressed directly in inches per second per second rms.

246

Example:

With the vibration pickup placed in contact with some vibrating surface and the control box switch, let us say, on DISPlacement, a reading of 54 dB is obtained. Then, following outlined procedure:

1. DB reading = 54 dB.
2. 120 − 54 = 66 dB.

   66 − (+20) − (+20) − (+20) = 6 dB remainder.

Voltage ratios corresponding to 6 dB (left-hand column) equal 0.5012; 20 dB was subtracted from 66 dB three times; therefore 0.5012 should be multiplied by 0.1 three times.

Result = 0.0005012 or (to 2 significant figures) 0.00050 inch rms amplitude.

Like procedure should be followed for the calculation of velocity or acceleration.

Acceleration and Velocity Level

In order to convert the readings obtained with the sound-level meter and vibration pickup system into acceleration level re 10^{-3} cm/sec^2 (often called adB) or velocity level re 10^{-6} cm/sec (often called vdB), proceed as follows:

When the conversion figures on the nameplate are:

Velocity   90 dB = 1 in./sec
Acceleration   50 dB = 1 in./sec^2

add 38.1 dB to sound-level meter reading to get velocity level when the control box is set to velocity, and add 18.1 dB to sound-level meter reading to get acceleration level when the control box is set to acceleration.

TABLE I

GIVEN: Decibels   TO FIND: Power and Pressure Ratios

TO ACCOUNT FOR THE SIGN OF THE DECIBEL

For positive (+) values of the decibel — Both pressure and power ratios are greater than unity. Use the two right-hand columns.

For negative (−) values of the decibel — Both pressure and power ratios are less than unity. Use the two left-hand columns.

Example—*Given:* ± 9.1 dB. *Find:*

	Power Ratio	Pressure Ratio
+9.1 dB	8.128	2.851
−9.1 dB	0.1230	0.3508

− dB +

Pressure Ratio	Power Ratio	dB	Pressure Ratio	Power Ratio	Pressure Ratio	Power Ratio	dB	Pressure Ratio	Power Ratio
1.0000	1.0000	0	1.000	1.000	.5623	.3162	5.0	1.778	3.162
.9886	.9772	.1	1.012	1.023	.5559	.3090	5.1	1.799	3.236
.9772	.9550	.2	1.023	1.047	.5495	.3020	5.2	1.820	3.311
.9661	.9333	.3	1.035	1.072	.5433	.2951	5.3	1.841	3.388
.9550	.9120	.4	1.047	1.096	.5370	.2884	5.4	1.862	3.467
.9441	.8913	.5	1.059	1.122	.5309	.2818	5.5	1.884	3.548
.9333	.8710	.6	1.072	1.148	.5248	.2754	5.6	1.905	3.631
.9226	.8511	.7	1.084	1.175	.5188	.2692	5.7	1.928	3.715
.9120	.8318	.8	1.096	1.202	.5129	.2630	5.8	1.950	3.802
.9016	.8128	.9	1.109	1.230	.5070	.2570	5.9	1.972	3.890
.8913	.7943	1.0	1.122	1.259	.5012	.2512	6.0	1.995	3.981
.8810	.7762	1.1	1.135	1.288	.4955	.2455	6.1	2.018	4.074
.8710	.7586	1.2	1.148	1.318	.4898	.2399	6.2	2.042	4.169
.8610	.7413	1.3	1.161	1.349	.4842	.2344	6.3	2.065	4.266
.8511	.7244	1.4	1.175	1.380	.4786	.2291	6.4	2.089	4.365
.8414	.7079	1.5	1.189	1.413	.4732	.2239	6.5	2.113	4.467
.8318	.6918	1.6	1.202	1.445	.4677	.2188	6.6	2.138	4.571
.8222	.6761	1.7	1.216	1.479	.4624	.2138	6.7	2.163	4.677
.8128	.6607	1.8	1.230	1.514	.4571	.2089	6.8	2.188	4.786
.8035	.6457	1.9	1.245	1.549	.4519	.2042	6.9	2.213	4.898
.7943	.6310	2.0	1.259	1.585	.4467	.1995	7.0	2.239	5.012
.7852	.6166	2.1	1.274	1.622	.4416	.1950	7.1	2.265	5.129
.7762	.6026	2.2	1.288	1.660	.4365	.1905	7.2	2.291	5.248
.7674	.5888	2.3	1.303	1.698	.4315	.1862	7.3	2.317	5.370
.7586	.5754	2.4	1.318	1.738	.4266	.1820	7.4	2.344	5.495
.7499	.5623	2.5	1.334	1.778	.4217	.1778	7.5	2.371	5.623
.7413	.5495	2.6	1.349	1.820	.4169	.1738	7.6	2.399	5.754
.7328	.5370	2.7	1.365	1.862	.4121	.1698	7.7	2.427	5.888
.7244	.5248	2.8	1.380	1.905	.4074	.1660	7.8	2.455	6.026
.7161	.5129	2.9	1.396	1.950	.4027	.1622	7.9	2.483	6.166
.7079	.5012	3.0	1.413	1.995	.3981	.1585	8.0	2.512	6.310
.6998	.4898	3.1	1.429	2.042	.3936	.1549	8.1	2.541	6.457
.6918	.4786	3.2	1.445	2.089	.3890	.1514	8.2	2.570	6.607
.6839	.4677	3.3	1.462	2.138	.3846	.1479	8.3	2.600	6.761
.6761	.4571	3.4	1.479	2.188	.3802	.1445	8.4	2.630	6.918
.6683	.4467	3.5	1.496	2.239	.3758	.1413	8.5	2.661	7.079
.6607	.4365	3.6	1.514	2.291	.3715	.1380	8.6	2.692	7.244
.6531	.4266	3.7	1.531	2.344	.3673	.1349	8.7	2.723	7.413
.6457	.4169	3.8	1.549	2.399	.3631	.1318	8.8	2.754	7.586
.6383	.4074	3.9	1.567	2.455	.3589	.1288	8.9	2.786	7.762
.6310	.3981	4.0	1.585	2.512	.3548	.1259	9.0	2.818	7.943
.6237	.3890	4.1	1.603	2.570	.3508	.1230	9.1	2.851	8.128
.6166	.3802	4.2	1.622	2.630	.3467	.1202	9.2	2.884	8.318
.6095	.3715	4.3	1.641	2.692	.3428	.1175	9.3	2.917	8.511
.6026	.3631	4.4	1.660	2.754	.3388	.1148	9.4	2.951	8.710
.5957	.3548	4.5	1.679	2.818	.3350	.1122	9.5	2.985	8.913
.5888	.3467	4.6	1.698	2.884	.3311	.1096	9.6	3.020	9.120
.5821	.3388	4.7	1.718	2.951	.3273	.1072	9.7	3.055	9.333
.5754	.3311	4.8	1.738	3.020	.3236	.1047	9.8	3.090	9.550
.5689	.3236	4.9	1.758	3.090	.3199	.1023	9.9	3.126	9.772

TABLE I (continued)

Pressure Ratio	Power Ratio	dB	Pressure Ratio	Power Ratio	Pressure Ratio	Power Ratio	dB	Pressure Ratio	Power Ratio
.3162	.1000	10.0	3.162	10.000	.1585	.02512	16.0	6.310	39.81
.3126	.09772	10.1	3.199	10.23	.1567	.02455	16.1	6.383	40.74
.3090	.09550	10.2	3.236	10.47	.1549	.02399	16.2	6.457	41.69
.3055	.09333	10.3	3.273	10.72	.1531	.02344	16.3	6.531	42.66
.3020	.09120	10.4	3.311	10.96	.1514	.02291	16.4	6.607	43.65
.2985	.08913	10.5	3.350	11.22	.1496	.02239	16.5	6.683	44.67
.2951	.08710	10.6	3.388	11.48	.1479	.02188	16.6	6.761	45.71
.2917	.08511	10.7	3.428	11.75	.1462	.02138	16.7	6.839	46.77
.2884	.08318	10.8	3.467	12.02	.1445	.02089	16.8	6.918	47.86
.2851	.08128	10.9	3.508	12.30	.1429	.02042	16.9	6.998	48.98
.2818	.07943	11.0	3.548	12.59	.1413	.01995	17.0	7.079	50.12
.2786	.07762	11.1	3.589	12.88	.1396	.01950	17.1	7.161	51.29
.2754	.07586	11.2	3.631	13.18	.1380	.01905	17.2	7.244	52.48
.2723	.07413	11.3	3.673	13.49	.1365	.01862	17.3	7.328	53.70
.2692	.07244	11.4	3.715	13.80	.1349	.01820	17.4	7.413	54.95
.2661	.07079	11.5	3.758	14.13	.1334	.01778	17.5	7.499	56.23
.2630	.06918	11.6	3.802	14.45	.1318	.01738	17.6	7.586	57.54
.2600	.06761	11.7	3.846	14.79	.1303	.01698	17.7	7.674	58.88
.2570	.06607	11.8	3.890	15.14	.1288	.01660	17.8	7.762	60.26
.2541	.06457	11.9	3.936	15.49	.1274	.01622	17.9	7.852	61.66
.2512	.06310	12.0	3.981	15.85	.1259	.01585	18.0	7.943	63.10
.2483	.06166	12.1	4.027	16.22	.1245	.01549	18.1	8.035	64.57
.2455	.06026	12.2	4.074	16.60	.1230	.01514	18.2	8.128	66.07
.2427	.05888	12.3	4.121	16.98	.1216	.01479	18.3	8.222	67.61
.2399	.05754	12.4	4.169	17.38	.1202	.01445	18.4	8.318	69.18
.2371	.05623	12.5	4.217	17.78	.1189	.01413	18.5	8.414	70.79
.2344	.05495	12.6	4.266	18.20	.1175	.01380	18.6	8.511	72.44
.2317	.05370	12.7	4.315	18.62	.1161	.01349	18.7	8.610	74.13
.2291	.05248	12.8	4.365	19.05	.1148	.01318	18.8	8.710	75.86
.2265	.05129	12.9	4.416	19.50	.1135	.01288	18.9	8.811	77.62
.2239	.05012	13.0	4.467	19.95	.1122	.01259	19.0	8.913	79.43
.2213	.04898	13.1	4.519	20.42	.1109	.01230	19.1	9.016	81.28
.2188	.04786	13.2	4.571	20.89	.1096	.01202	19.2	9.120	83.18
.2163	.04677	13.3	4.624	21.38	.1084	.01175	19.3	9.226	85.11
.2138	.04571	13.4	4.677	21.88	.1072	.01148	19.4	9.333	87.10
.2113	.04467	13.5	4.732	22.39	.1059	.01122	19.5	9.441	89.13
.2089	.04365	13.6	4.786	22.91	.1047	.01096	19.6	9.550	91.20
.2065	.04266	13.7	4.842	23.44	.1035	.01072	19.7	9.661	93.33
.2042	.04169	13.8	4.898	23.99	.1023	.01047	19.8	9.772	95.50
.2018	.04074	13.9	4.955	24.55	.1012	.01023	19.9	9.886	97.72
.1995	.03981	14.0	5.012	25.12	.1000	.01000	20.0	10.000	100.00
.1972	.03890	14.1	5.070	25.70					
.1950	.03802	14.2	5.129	26.30					
.1928	.03715	14.3	5.188	26.92					
.1905	.03631	14.4	5.248	27.54					
.1884	.03548	14.5	5.309	28.18					
.1862	.03467	14.6	5.370	28.84					
.1841	.03388	14.7	5.433	29.51					
.1820	.03311	14.8	5.495	30.20					
.1799	.03236	14.9	5.559	30.90					
.1778	.03162	15.0	5.623	31.62					
.1758	.03090	15.1	5.689	32.36					
.1738	.03020	15.2	5.754	33.11					
.1718	.02951	15.3	5.821	33.88					
.1698	.02884	15.4	5.888	34.67					
.1679	.02818	15.5	5.957	35.48					
.1660	.02754	15.6	6.026	36.31					
.1641	.02692	15.7	6.095	37.15					
.1622	.02630	15.8	6.166	38.02					
.1603	.02570	15.9	6.237	38.90					

Pressure Ratio	Power Ratio	dB	Pressure Ratio	Power Ratio
3.162×10^{-1}	10^{-1}	10	3.162	10
	10^{-1}	20	10	10^2
3.162×10^{-2}	10^{-3}	30	3.162×10	10^3
	10^{-2}	40	10^2	10^4
3.162×10^{-3}	10^{-5}	50	3.162×10^2	10^5
	10^{-3}	60	10^3	10^6
3.162×10^{-4}	10^{-7}	70	3.162×10^3	10^7
	10^{-4}	80	10^4	10^8
3.162×10^{-5}	10^{-9}	90	3.162×10^4	10^9
10^{-5}	10^{-10}	100	10^5	10^{10}

249

TABLE II

GIVEN: { Pressure } Ratio   TO FIND: Decibels

POWER RATIOS

To find the number of decibels corresponding to a given power ratio—Assume the given power ratio to be a pressure ratio and find the corresponding number of decibels from the table. The desired result is exactly one-half of the number of decibels thus found.

Example—*Given:* a power ratio of 3.41. *Find:* 3.41 in the table:

3.41→10.655 dB × ½ = 5.328 dB

Pressure Ratio	.00	.01	.02	.03	.04	.05	.06	.07	.08	.09
1.0	.000	.086	.172	.257	.341	.424	.506	.588	.668	.749
1.1	.828	.906	.984	1.062	1.138	1.214	1.289	1.364	1.438	1.511
1.2	1.584	1.656	1.727	1.798	1.868	1.938	2.007	2.076	2.144	2.212
1.3	2.279	2.345	2.411	2.477	2.542	2.607	2.671	2.734	2.798	2.860
1.4	2.923	2.984	3.046	3.107	3.167	3.227	3.287	3.346	3.405	3.464
1.5	3.522	3.580	3.637	3.694	3.750	3.807	3.862	3.918	3.973	4.028
1.6	4.082	4.137	4.190	4.244	4.297	4.350	4.402	4.454	4.506	4.558
1.7	4.609	4.660	4.711	4.761	4.811	4.861	4.910	4.959	5.008	5.057
1.8	5.105	5.154	5.201	5.249	5.296	5.343	5.390	5.437	5.483	5.529
1.9	5.575	5.621	5.666	5.711	5.756	5.801	5.845	5.889	5.933	5.977
2.0	6.021	6.064	6.107	6.150	6.193	6.235	6.277	6.319	6.361	6.403
2.1	6.444	6.486	6.527	6.568	6.608	6.649	6.689	6.729	6.769	6.809
2.2	6.848	6.888	6.927	6.966	7.008	7.044	7.082	7.121	7.159	7.197
2.3	7.235	7.272	7.310	7.347	7.384	7.421	7.458	7.495	7.532	7.568
2.4	7.604	7.640	7.676	7.712	7.748	7.783	7.819	7.854	7.889	7.924
2.5	7.959	7.993	8.028	8.062	8.097	8.131	8.165	8.199	8.232	8.266
2.6	8.299	8.333	8.366	8.399	8.432	8.465	8.498	8.530	8.563	8.595
2.7	8.627	8.659	8.691	8.723	8.755	8.787	8.818	8.850	8.881	8.912
2.8	8.943	8.974	9.005	9.036	9.066	9.097	9.127	9.158	9.188	9.218
2.9	9.248	9.278	9.308	9.337	9.367	9.396	9.426	9.455	9.484	9.513
3.0	9.542	9.571	9.600	9.629	9.657	9.686	9.714	9.743	9.771	9.799
3.1	9.827	9.855	9.883	9.911	9.939	9.966	9.994	10.021	10.049	10.076
3.2	10.103	10.130	10.157	10.184	10.211	10.238	10.264	10.291	10.317	10.344
3.3	10.370	10.397	10.423	10.449	10.475	10.501	10.527	10.553	10.578	10.604
3.4	10.630	10.655	10.681	10.706	10.731	10.756	10.782	10.807	10.832	10.857
3.5	10.881	10.906	10.931	10.955	10.980	11.005	11.029	11.053	11.078	11.102
3.6	11.126	11.150	11.174	11.198	11.222	11.246	11.270	11.293	11.317	11.341
3.7	11.364	11.387	11.411	11.434	11.457	11.481	11.504	11.527	11.550	11.573
3.8	11.596	11.618	11.641	11.664	11.687	11.709	11.732	11.754	11.777	11.799
3.9	11.821	11.844	11.866	11.888	11.910	11.932	11.954	11.976	11.998	12.019
4.0	12.041	12.063	12.085	12.106	12.128	12.149	12.171	12.192	12.213	12.234
4.1	12.256	12.277	12.298	12.319	12.340	12.361	12.382	12.403	12.424	12.444
4.2	12.465	12.486	12.506	12.527	12.547	12.568	12.588	12.609	12.629	12.649
4.3	12.669	12.690	12.710	12.730	12.750	12.770	12.790	12.810	12.829	12.849
4.4	12.869	12.889	12.908	12.928	12.948	12.967	12.987	13.006	13.026	13.045
4.5	13.064	13.084	13.103	13.122	13.141	13.160	13.179	13.198	13.217	13.236
4.6	13.255	13.274	13.293	13.312	13.330	13.349	13.368	13.386	13.405	13.423
4.7	13.442	13.460	13.479	13.497	13.516	13.534	13.552	13.570	13.589	13.607
4.8	13.625	13.643	13.661	13.679	13.697	13.715	13.733	13.751	13.768	13.786
4.9	13.804	13.822	13.839	13.857	13.875	13.892	13.910	13.927	13.945	13.962
5.0	13.979	13.997	14.014	14.031	14.049	14.066	14.083	14.100	14.117	14.134
5.1	14.151	14.168	14.185	14.202	14.219	14.236	14.253	14.270	14.287	14.303
5.2	14.320	14.337	14.353	14.370	14.387	14.403	14.420	14.436	14.453	14.469
5.3	14.486	14.502	14.518	14.535	14.551	14.567	14.583	14.599	14.616	14.632
5.4	14.648	14.664	14.680	14.696	14.712	14.728	14.744	14.760	14.776	14.791
5.5	14.807	14.823	14.839	14.855	14.870	14.886	14.902	14.917	14.933	14.948
5.6	14.964	14.979	14.995	15.010	15.026	15.041	15.056	15.072	15.087	15.102
5.7	15.117	15.133	15.148	15.163	15.178	15.193	15.208	15.224	15.239	15.254
5.8	15.269	15.284	15.298	15.313	15.328	15.343	15.358	15.373	15.388	15.402
5.9	15.417	15.432	15.446	15.461	15.476	15.490	15.505	15.519	15.534	15.549

TABLE II (continued)

Pressure Ratio	.00	.01	.02	.03	.04	.05	.06	.07	.08	.09
6.0	15.563	15.577	15.592	15.606	15.621	15.635	15.649	15.664	15.678	15.692
6.1	15.707	15.721	15.735	15.749	15.763	15.778	15.792	15.806	15.820	15.834
6.2	15.848	15.862	15.876	15.890	15.904	15.918	15.931	15.945	15.959	15.973
6.3	15.987	16.001	16.014	16.028	16.042	16.055	16.069	16.083	16.096	16.110
6.4	16.124	16.137	16.151	16.164	16.178	16.191	16.205	16.218	16.232	16.245
6.5	16.258	16.272	16.285	16.298	16.312	16.325	16.338	16.351	16.365	16.378
6.6	16.391	16.404	16.417	16.430	16.443	16.456	16.469	16.483	16.496	16.509
6.7	16.521	16.534	16.547	16.560	16.573	16.586	16.599	16.612	16.625	16.637
6.8	16.650	16.663	16.676	16.688	16.701	16.714	16.726	16.739	16.752	16.764
6.9	16.777	16.790	16.802	16.815	16.827	16.840	16.852	16.865	16.877	16.890
7.0	16.902	16.914	16.927	16.939	16.951	16.964	16.976	16.988	17.001	17.013
7.1	17.025	17.037	17.050	17.062	17.074	17.086	17.098	17.110	17.122	17.135
7.2	17.147	17.159	17.171	17.183	17.195	17.207	17.219	17.231	17.243	17.255
7.3	17.266	17.278	17.290	17.302	17.314	17.326	17.338	17.349	17.361	17.373
7.4	17.385	17.396	17.408	17.420	17.431	17.443	17.455	17.466	17.478	17.490
7.5	17.501	17.513	17.524	17.536	17.547	17.559	17.570	17.582	17.593	17.605
7.6	17.616	17.628	17.639	17.650	17.662	17.673	17.685	17.696	17.707	17.719
7.7	17.730	17.741	17.752	17.764	17.775	17.786	17.797	17.808	17.820	17.831
7.8	17.842	17.853	17.864	17.875	17.886	17.897	17.908	17.919	17.931	17.942
7.9	17.953	17.964	17.975	17.985	17.996	18.007	18.018	18.029	18.040	18.051
8.0	18.062	18.073	18.083	18.094	18.105	18.116	18.127	18.137	18.148	18.159
8.1	18.170	18.180	18.191	18.202	18.212	18.223	18.234	18.244	18.255	18.266
8.2	18.276	18.287	18.297	18.308	18.319	18.329	18.340	18.350	18.361	18.371
8.3	18.382	18.392	18.402	18.413	18.423	18.434	18.444	18.455	18.465	18.475
8.4	18.486	18.496	18.506	18.517	18.527	18.537	18.547	18.558	18.568	18.578
8.5	18.588	18.599	18.609	18.619	18.629	18.639	18.649	18.660	18.670	18.680
8.6	18.690	18.700	18.710	18.720	18.730	18.740	18.750	18.760	18.770	18.780
8.7	18.790	18.800	18.810	18.820	18.830	18.840	18.850	18.860	18.870	18.880
8.8	18.890	18.900	18.909	18.919	18.929	18.939	18.949	18.958	18.968	18.978
8.9	18.988	18.998	19.007	19.017	19.027	19.036	19.046	19.056	19.066	19.075
9.0	19.085	19.094	19.104	19.114	19.123	19.133	19.143	19.152	19.162	19.171
9.1	19.181	19.190	19.200	19.209	19.219	19.228	19.238	19.247	19.257	19.266
9.2	19.276	19.285	19.295	19.304	19.313	19.323	19.332	19.342	19.351	19.360
9.3	19.370	19.379	19.388	19.398	19.407	19.416	19.426	19.435	19.444	19.453
9.4	19.463	19.472	19.481	19.490	19.499	19.509	19.518	19.527	19.536	19.545
9.5	19.554	19.564	19.573	19.582	19.591	19.600	19.609	19.618	19.627	19.636
9.6	19.645	19.654	19.664	19.673	19.682	19.691	19.700	19.709	19.718	19.726
9.7	19.735	19.744	19.753	19.762	19.771	19.780	19.789	19.798	19.807	19.816
9.8	19.825	19.833	19.842	19.851	19.860	19.869	19.878	19.886	19.895	19.904
9.9	19.913	19.921	19.930	19.939	19.948	19.956	19.965	19.974	19.983	19.991

Pressure Ratio	0	1	2	3	4	5	6	7	8	9
10	20.000	20.828	21.584	22.279	22.923	23.522	24.082	24.609	25.105	25.575
20	26.021	26.444	26.848	27.235	27.604	27.959	28.299	28.627	28.943	29.248
30	29.542	29.827	30.103	30.370	30.630	30.881	31.126	31.364	31.596	31.821
40	32.041	32.256	32.465	32.669	32.869	33.064	33.255	33.442	33.625	33.804
50	33.979	34.151	34.320	34.486	34.648	34.807	34.964	35.117	35.269	35.417
60	35.563	35.707	35.848	35.987	36.124	36.258	36.391	36.521	36.650	36.777
70	36.902	37.025	37.147	37.266	37.385	37.501	37.616	37.730	37.842	37.953
80	38.062	38.170	38.276	38.382	38.486	38.588	38.690	38.790	38.890	38.988
90	39.085	39.181	39.276	39.370	39.463	39.554	39.645	39.735	39.825	39.913
100	40.000	—	—	—	—	—	—	—	—	—

251

Appendix II

Chart for Combining Levels of Uncorrelated Noise Signals*

TO ADD LEVELS

Enter the chart with the NUMERICAL DIFFERENCE BETWEEN TWO LEVELS BEING ADDED. Follow the line corresponding to this value to its intersection with the curved line, then left to read the NUMERICAL DIFFERENCE BETWEEN TOTAL AND LARGER LEVEL. Add this value to the larger level to determine the total.

Example: Combine 75 dB and 80 dB. The difference is 5 dB. The 5-dB line intersects the curved line at 1.2 dB on the vertical scale. Thus the total value is 80 + 1.2 or 81.2 dB.

TO SUBTRACT LEVELS

Enter the chart with the NUMERICAL DIFFERENCE BETWEEN TOTAL AND LARGER LEVELS if this value is less than 3 dB. Enter the chart with the NUMERICAL DIFFERENCE BETWEEN TOTAL AND SMALLER LEVELS if this value is between 3 and 14 dB. Follow the line corresponding to this value to its intersection with the curved line, then either left or down to read the NUMERICAL DIFFERENCE BETWEEN TOTAL AND LARGER (SMALLER) LEVELS. Subtract this value from the total level to determine the unknown level.

Example: Subtract 81 dB from 90 dB. The difference is 9 dB. The 9-dB vertical line intersects the curved line at 0.6 dB on the vertical scale. Thus the unknown level is 90 − 0.6 or 89.4 dB.

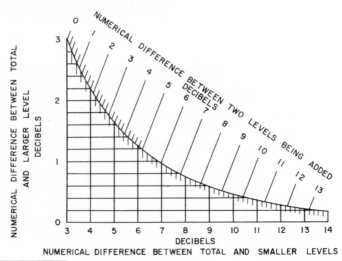

NUMERICAL DIFFERENCE BETWEEN TOTAL AND SMALLER LEVELS

*This chart is based on one developed by R.Musa.

Appendix III

Table for Converting Loudness to Loudness Level

A simplified relation between the loudness in sones and the loudness level in phons has been standardized internationally (ISO/R131-1959). This relation is a good approximation to the psychoacoustical data and is useful for engineering purposes, but it should not be expected to be accurate enough for research on the subjective aspects of hearing.

The relation is

$$S = 2^{(P-40)/10}$$

where S is the loudness in sones and P is the loudness level in phons.

A table of loudness in sones for loudness levels ranging from 20 to 130 phons in increments of 1 phon, calculated from the above relation, is given below.

Examples:

Given — loudness level of 72 phons.

Find — in table under "+2" in the "70" row — 9.2 sones.

Phons	LOUDNESS IN SONES									
	0	+1	+2	+3	+4	+5	+6	+7	+8	+9
20	.25	.27	.29	.31	.33	.35	.38	.41	.44	.47
30	.50	.54	.57	.62	.66	.71	.76	.81	.87	.93
40	1	1.07	1.15	1.23	1.32	1.41	1.52	1.62	1.74	1.87
50	2	2.14	2.30	2.46	2.64	2.83	3.03	3.25	3.48	3.73
60	4	4.29	4.59	4.92	5.28	5.66	6.06	6.50	6.96	7.46
70	8	8.6	9.2	9.8	10.6	11.3	12.1	13.0	13.9	14.9
80	16	17.1	18.4	19.7	21.1	22.6	24.3	26.0	27.9	29.9
90	32	34.3	36.8	39.4	42.2	45.3	48.5	52.0	55.7	59.7
100	64	68.6	73.5	78.8	84.4	90.5	97	104	111	119
110	128	137	147	158	169	181	194	208	223	239
120	256	274	294	315	338	362	388	416	446	478

Appendix IV

Vibration Conversion Charts

The charts on the following pages illustrate the relationship between frequency, velocity, acceleration, and displacement (refer to Chapter 2).

Figures IV-1 and IV-2 are general conversion charts for frequency, displacement, velocity, and acceleration. Enter the chart with any two of these parameters to solve for the other two. In Figure IV-1, displacement, velocity, and acceleration are given in inches, inches/second, and inches/second^2, respectively, while Figure IV-2 uses metric units.

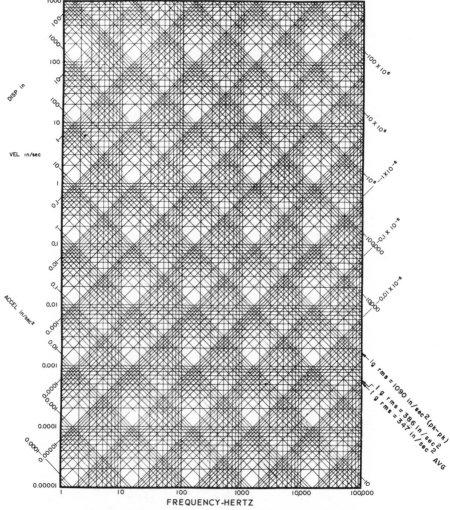

Figure IV-1. Conversion chart for vibration parameters, for use with Type 1553-A Vibration Meter.

254

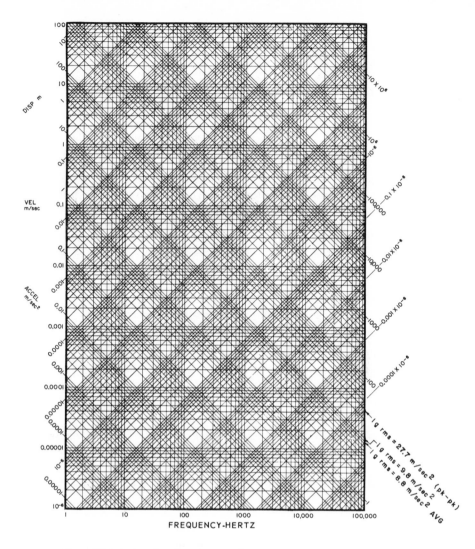

Figure IV-2. Conversion chart for vibration parameters,
for use with Type 1553-AK Vibration Meter.

255

Appendix V

Definitions

This section on definitions includes most of the technical terms used in this handbook. Most of the definitions are selected from the American National Standard Acoustical Terminology (S1.1-1960 (R1971)), and those definitions are marked with an asterisk. They are printed with permission.

Many have been shortened by putting them in the usual dictionary form. A number of these standard definitions are very technical in order to be precise. Some readers may find it easier to refer to the discussion in the main text of this handbook to obtain a general understanding of those terms.

The nonstandard definitions have been adapted especially for this handbook.

ACCELERATION*

vector that specifies the time-rate-of-change of velocity. Note 1: Various self-explanatory modifiers such as peak, average, rms are often used. The time interval must be indicated over which the average (for example) was taken. Note 2: Acceleration may be (1) oscillatory, in which case it may be defined by the acceleration amplitude (if simple harmonic) or the rms acceleration (if random), or (2) nonoscillatory, in which case it is designated "sustained" or "transient" acceleration.

ALIAS

in sampled, equally spaced data, two frequencies are aliases of one another if sinusoids of those frequencies cannot be distinguished by the sampled values.

AMPLITUDE DENSITY DISTRIBUTION (PROBABILITY DENSITY DIS-TRIBUTION) (FREQUENCY DISTRIBUTION)

a function giving the fraction of time that the pressure, voltage, or other variable dwells in a narrow range.

AMPLITUDE DISTRIBUTION FUNCTION (DISTRIBUTION FUNCTION) (PROBABILITY FUNCTION) (CUMULATIVE FREQUENCY FUNCTION)

a function giving the fraction of time that the instantaneous pressure, voltage or other variable lies below a given level.

ANALYZER

a combination of a filter system and a system for indicating the relative energy that is passed through the filter system. The filter is usually adjustable so that the signal applied to the filter can be measured in terms of the relative energy passed through the filter as a function of the adjustment of the filter response-vs-frequency characteristic. This measurement is usually interpreted as giving the distribution of energy of the applied signal as a function of frequency.

ANECHOIC ROOM (FREE-FIELD ROOM)*

a room whose boundaries absorb effectively all the sound incident thereon, thereby affording essentially free-field conditions.

AUDIOGRAM (THRESHOLD AUDIOGRAM)

a graph showing hearing-threshold level (HTL) as a function of frequency.

AUDIOMETER

an instrument for measuring hearing threshold level.

AUTOCORRELATION

a measure of the similarity of a function with a displaced version of itself as a function of the displacement. The displacement is usually in terms of time and, when the displacement is zero, the value of the autocorrelation is equal to the mean square value of the function.

AUTOSPECTRUM (POWER SPECTRUM)

a spectrum with the coefficients of the components expressed as the square of the magnitudes.

BAFFLE*

a shielding structure or partition used to increase the effective length of the external transmission path between two points in an acoustic system as, for example, between the front and back of an electroacoustic transducer.

COHERENCE.

a measure of the reliability of a transfer function estimate. It is zero when the transfer function has no statistical validity and unity when the estimate is not contaminated by interfering noise.

CONFIDENCE LIMITS

the upper and lower values of the range over which a given percent probability applies. For instance, if the chances are 99 out of 100 that a sample lies between 10 and 12, the 99% confidence limits are said to be 10 and 12.

CRITICAL SPEED*

a speed of a rotating system that corresponds to a resonance frequency of the system.

CROSSCORRELATION.

a measure of the similarity of two functions with the displacement between the two used as an independent variable. The displacement is usually in terms of time. When the two functions are alike, a crosscorrelation is an autocorrelation.

CROSS-SPECTRUM

a measure in the frequency domain of the similarity of two functions.

DATA WINDOW

the interval that includes all the sampled values in a calculation, also the form of a weighting function that is regarded as multiplying the data that enters into a calculation.

DEAD ROOM* (See also ANECHOIC ROOM)

a room that is characterized by an unusually large amount of sound absorption.

DECAY RATE (See RATE OF DECAY)

DECIBEL*

one-tenth of a bel. Thus, the decibel is a unit of level when the base of the logarithm is the tenth root of ten, and the quantities concerned are proportional to power. Note 1: Examples of quantities that qualify are power (any form), sound pressure squared, particle velocity squared, sound intensity, sound energy density, voltage squared. Thus the decibel is a unit of sound-pressure-squared level; it is common practice, however, to shorten this to sound pressure level because ordinarily no ambiguity results from so doing. Note 2: The logarithm to the base the tenth root of 10 is the same as ten times the logarithm to the base 10: e.g., for a number x^2, $\log_{10}{}^{0.1} x^2 = 10 \log_{10} x^2 = 20 \log_{10} x$. This last relationship is the one ordinarily used to simplify the language in definitions of sound pressure level, etc.

DEGREES OF FREEDOM (STATISTICAL)

a measure of stability relating to the number of independent equivalent terms entering into a distribution.

DIRECTIVITY FACTOR*

1. of a transducer used for sound emission is the ratio of the sound pressure squared, at some fixed distance and specified direction, to the mean-square sound pressure at the same distance averaged over all directions from the transducer. The distance must be great enough so that the sound appears to diverge spherically from the effective acoustic center of the sources. Unless otherwise specified, the reference direction is understood to be that of maximum response.
2. of a transducer used for sound reception is the ratio of the square of the open-circuit voltage produced in response to sound waves arriving in a specified direction to the mean-square voltage that would be produced in a perfectly diffused sound field of the same frequency and mean-square sound pressure.

Note 1: This definition may be extended to cover the case of finite frequency bands whose spectrum may be specified. Note 2: The average free-field response may be obtained, for example,
1. By the use of a spherical integrator
2. By numerical integration of a sufficient number of directivity patterns corresponding to different planes, or
3. By integration of one or two directional patterns whenever the pattern of the transducer is known to possess adequate symmetry.

DIRECTIONAL GAIN (DIRECTIVITY INDEX)*

of a transducer, in decibels, is 10 times the logarithm to the base 10 of the directivity factor.

DISPLACEMENT*

a vector quantity that specifies the change of position of a body or particle and is usually measured from the mean position or position of rest. In general, it can be represented by a rotation vector or translation vector or both.

DISTRIBUTION

See AMPLITUDE DISTRIBUTION FUNCTION.

EARPHONE (RECEIVER)*

an electroacoustic transducer intended to be closely coupled acoustically to the ear. Note: The term "receiver" should be avoided when there is risk of ambiguity.

EFFECTIVE SOUND-PRESSURE (ROOT-MEAN-SQUARE SOUND PRESSURE)*

at a point is the root-mean-square value of the instantaneous sound pressures, over a time interval at the point under consideration. In the case of periodic sound pressures, the interval must be an integral number of periods or an interval long compared to a period. In the case of non-periodic sound pressures, the interval should be long enough to make the value obtained essentially independent of small changes in the length of the interval. Note: The term "effective sound pressure" is frequently shortened to "sound pressure."

FFT (FAST-FOURIER TRANSFORM)

any of a number of calculation procedures that yields a set of Fourier coefficients (component amplitudes) from a time-series frame with much less computational effort for large frame sizes than is possible by the classical approach of successive calculation of each coefficient.

FILTER

a device for separating components of a signal on the basis of their frequency. It allows components in one or more frequency bands to pass relatively unattenuated, and it attenuates components in other frequency bands.

FOLDING FREQUENCY

reciprocal of twice the time interval between sampled values. The folding frequency is equal to its own alias.

FRAME

a set of points or values that are processed as a group.

FRAME SIZE

the number of sampled values in a frame.

FREE SOUND FIELD (FREE FIELD)*

a field in an homogeneous, isotropic medium, free from boundaries. In practice, it is a field in which the effects of the boundaries are negligible over the region of interest. Note: The actual pressure impinging on an object (e.g., electro-acoustic transducer) placed in an otherwise free sound field will differ from the pressure that would exist at that point with the object removed, unless the acoustic impedance of the object matches the acoustic impedance of the medium.

FREQUENCY (IN CYCLES PER SECOND OR HERTZ)

the time rate of repetition of a periodic phenomenon. The frequency is the reciprocal of the period.

FREQUENCY DISTRIBUTION (STATISTICAL)

see AMPLITUDE DENSITY DISTRIBUTION.

g*

quantity that is the acceleration produced by the force of gravity, which varies with the latitude and elevation of the point of observation. By international agreement, the value 980.665 cm/s^2 = 386.087 in./s^2 = 32.1739 ft /s^2 has been chosen as the standard acceleration of gravity.

GAUSSIAN DISTRIBUTION (NORMAL DISTRIBUTION)

a particular amplitude distribution of fundamental importance in the theory of probability. Its histogram is the familiar "bell-shaped curve." It describes many natural phenomena, and most stationary acoustic noise that is not periodic has an essentially Gaussian distribution.

HANNING
use of a smooth data window that has the form in the time domain of a raised cosine arch. The weighting is zero at the beginning and end of a frame and unity in the middle of the frame. (After Julius von Hann, an Austrian meteorologist.)

HEARING THRESHOLD LEVEL (OF AN EAR)***
amount in decibels by which the threshold of audibility for that ear exceeds a standard audiometric threshold.

HISTOGRAM
graph of an amplitude density distribution.

IMPACT*
a single collision of one mass in motion with a second mass which may be either in motion or at rest.

ISOLATION*
a reduction in the capacity of a system to respond to an excitation attained by the use of a resilient support. In steady-state forced vibration, Isolation is expressed quantitatively as the complement of transmissibility.

JERK*
a vector that specifies the time rate of change of the acceleration; jerk is the third derivative of the displacement with respect to time.

LEVEL*
in acoustics, the level of a quantity is the logarithm of the ratio of that quantity to a reference quantity of the same kind. The base of the logarithm, the reference quantity, and the *kind* of level must be specified. Note 1: Examples of kinds of levels in common use are electric power level, sound-pressure-squared level, voltage-squared level. Note 2: The level as here defined is measured in units of the logarithm of a reference ratio that is equal to the base of logarithms. Note 3: In symbols

$$L = \log_r (q/q_o)$$

where L = level of kind determined by the kind of quantity under consideration, measured in units of $\log_r r$

r = base of logarithms and the reference ratio

q = the quantity under consideration

q_o = reference quantity of the same kind.

Note 4: Differences in the levels of two quantities q_1 and q_2 are described by the same formula because, by the rules of logarithms, the reference quantity is automatically divided out:

$$\log_r(q_1/q_o) - \log_r(q_2/q_o) = \log_r(q_1/q_2)$$

LEVEL DISTRIBUTION
set of numbers characterizing a noise exposure, which gives the length of time that the sound-pressure level dwelled within each of a set of level intervals.

LINE COMPONENT
simple tone that may be part of a complex signal.

LIVE ROOM*
a room that is characterized by an unusually small amount of sound absorption.

LOUDNESS*
the intensive attribute of an auditory sensation, in terms of which sounds may be ordered on a scale extending from soft to loud. Note: Loudness depends primarily upon the sound pressure of the stimulus, but it also depends upon the frequency and wave form of the stimulus.

LOUDNESS CONTOUR*
a curve that shows the related values of sound pressure levels and frequency required to produce a given loudness sensation for the typical listener.

LOUDNESS LEVEL*
of a sound, in phons, is numerically equal to the median sound pressure level, in decibels, relative to 0.0002 microbar, of a free progressive wave of frequency 1000 Hz presented to listeners facing the source, which in a number of trials is judged by the listeners to be equally loud. Note: The manner of listening to the unknown sound, which must be stated, may be considered one of the characteristics of that sound.

LOUDSPEAKER (SPEAKER)*
an electroacoustic transducer intended to radiate acoustic power into the air, the acoustic waveform being essentially equivalent to that of the electrical input.

MASKING*
1. the process by which the threshold of audibility for one sound is raised by the presence of another (masking) sound.
2. the amount by which the threshold of audibility of a sound is raised by the presence of another (masking) sound. The unit customarily used is the decibel.

MECHANICAL IMPEDANCE*
the impedance obtained from the ratio of force to velocity during simple harmonic motion.

MECHANICAL SHOCK*
occurs when the position of a system is significantly changed in a relatively short time in a nonperiodic manner. It is characterized by suddenness and large displacement, and develops significant inertial forces in the system.

MEL*
a unit of pitch. By definition, a simple tone of frequency 1000 Hz, 40 decibels above a listener's threshold, produces a pitch of 1000 mels. The pitch of any sound that is judged by the listener to be n times that of a 1-mel tone is n mels.

MICROBAR, DYNE PER SQUARE CENTIMETER*
a unit of pressure commonly used in acoustics. One microbar is equal to 1 dyne per square centimeter. Note: The term "bar" properly denotes a pressure of 10^6 dynes per square centimeter. Unfortunately, the bar was once used to mean 1 dyne per square centimeter, but this is no longer correct.

MICROPHONE*
an electroacoustic transducer that responds to sound waves and delivers essentially equivalent electric waves.

NNI

the noise and number index based on perceived noise level. It is used for rating airplane flyby noise.

NOISE*

1. any undesired sound. By extension, noise is any unwanted disturbance within a useful frequency band, such as undesired electric waves in a transmission channel or device.
2. an erratic, intermittent, or statistically random oscillation.

Note 1: If ambiguity exists as to the nature of the noise, a phrase such as "acoustic noise" or "electric noise" should be used. Note 2: Since the above definitions are not mutually exclusive, it is usually necessary to depend upon context for the distinction.

NOISE LEVEL*

1. the level of noise, the type of which must be indicated by further modifier or context.

Note: The physical quantity measured (e.g. voltage), the reference quantity, the instrument used, and the bandwidth or other weighting characteristic must be indicated.

2. For airborne sound unless specified to the contrary, noise level is the weighted sound pressure level called sound level; the weighting must be indicated.

NORMAL DISTRIBUTION

See GAUSSIAN DISTRIBUTION.

NOYS

a unit used in the calculation of perceived noise level.

NYQUIST INTERVAL

period equal to the reciprocal of twice the frequency of that component of the signal having the highest frequency. It is the maximum sampling-time interval that permits reconstruction of a band-limited signal.

OCTAVE*

1. the interval between two sounds having a basic frequency ratio of two.
2. the pitch interval between two tones such that one tone may be regarded as duplicating the basic musical import of the other tone at the nearest possible higher pitch.

Note 1: The interval, in octaves, between any two frequencies is the logarithm to the base 2 (or 3.322 times the logarithm to the base 10) of the frequency ratio. Note 2: The frequency ratio corresponding to an octave pitch interval is approximately, but not always exactly, 2:1.

OSCILLATION*

the variation, usually with time, of the magnitude of a quantity with respect to a specified reference when the magnitude is alternately greater and smaller than the reference.

PEAK-TO-PEAK VALUE*

of an oscillating quantity is the algebraic difference between the extremes of the quantity.

PERCEIVED NOISE LEVEL

the level in dB assigned to a noise by means of a calculation procedure that is based on an approximation to subjective evaluations of "noisiness."

PERIODIC QUANTITY*
oscillating quantity whose values recur for certain increments of the independent variable.

PHON*
unit of loudness level. (See LOUDNESS LEVEL.)

PINK NOISE
noise whose noise-power-per-unit-frequency is inversely proportional to frequency over a specified range.

PITCH*
that attribute of auditory sensation in terms of which sounds may be ordered on a scale extending from low to high. Pitch depends primarily upon the frequency of the sound stimulus, but it also depends upon the sound pressure and wave form of the stimulus. Note 1: The pitch of a sound may be described by the frequency or frequency level of that simple tone, having a specified sound pressure level, which is judged by listeners to produce the same pitch.

POINT SOURCE See "SIMPLE SOUND SOURCE."

POWER LEVEL
in decibels, is 10 times the logarithm to the base 10 of the ratio of a given power to a reference power. The reference power must be indicated. [The reference power is taken as 1.0×10^{-12} watt in this handbook.]

PRESBYCUSIS
the condition of hearing loss specifically ascribed to aging effects.

PRESSURE SPECTRUM LEVEL
of a sound at a particular frequency is the effective sound-pressure level of that part of the signal contained within a band 1 cycle per second wide, centered at the particular frequency. Ordinarily this has significance only for sound having a continuous distribution of energy within the frequency range under consideration. The reference pressure should be explicitly stated.

PRIMITIVE PERIOD (PERIOD)*
of a periodic quantity is the smallest increment of the independent variable for which the function repeats itself. Note: If no ambiguity is likely, the primitive period is simply called the period of the function.

PROBABILITY DENSITY DISTRIBUTION
See AMPLITUDE DENSITY DISTRIBUTION.

PSIL (THREE-BAND PREFERRED-OCTAVE SPEECH-INTERFERENCE LEVEL) (SPEECH INTERFERENCE LEVEL)
average, in dB, of the sound-pressure levels of a noise in the three octave bands of center frequency 500, 1000, and 2000 Hz. The speech interference level, or SIL, without the qualifying "PREFERRED" is usually the arithmetic average of the sound-pressure levels in the older series of three octave bands: 600 to 1200, 1200 to 2400, and 2400 to 4800 Hz.

PURE TONE See SIMPLE TONE.

QUANTIZATION
conversion of a value into one of a limited set of values. The limited set is usually a discrete series of total number equal to two raised to an integer power, that is, a binary set.

RANDOM NOISE*

an oscillation whose instantaneous magnitude is not specified for any given instant of time. The instantaneous magnitudes of a random noise are specified only by probability distribution functions giving the fraction of the total time that the magnitude, or some sequence of magnitudes, lies within a specified range. Note: A random noise whose instantaneous magnitudes occur according to Gaussian distribution is called Gaussian random noise.

RATE OF DECAY*

the time rate at which the sound pressure level (or other stated characteristic) decreases at a given point and at a given time. A commonly used unit is the decibel per second.

RESONANCE*

of a system in forced oscillation exists when any change however small in the frequency of excitation causes a decrease in the response of the system. Note: Velocity resonance, for example, may occur at a frequency different from that of displacement resonance.

RESONANCE FREQUENCY
(RESONANT FREQUENCY)*

a frequency at which resonance exists. Note: In case of possible confusion the type of resonance must be indicated: e.g., velocity resonance frequency.

RESPONSE*

of a device or system is the motion (or other output) resulting from an excitation (stimulus) under specified conditions. Note 1: Modifying phrases must be prefixed to the term response to indicate kinds of input and output that are being utilized. Note 2: The response characteristic, often presented graphically, gives the response as a function of some independent variable such as frequency or direction. For such purposes it is customary to assume that other characteristics of the input (for example, voltage) are held constant.

REVERBERATION*

1. the persistence of sound in an enclosed space, as a result of multiple reflections after the sound source has stopped.
2. the sound that persists in an enclosed space, as a result of repeated reflection or scattering, after the source of sound has stopped.

Note: The repeated reflections of residual sound in an enclosure can alternatively be described in terms of the transient behavior of the modes of vibration of the medium bounded by the enclosure.

REVERBERATION TIME*

of a room is the time that would be required for the mean squared sound pressure level therein, originally in a steady state, to decrease 60 dB after the source is stopped.

ROOT-MEAN SQUARE (rms)

square root of the arithmetical mean of the squares of a set of instantaneous amplitudes, or of a set of values of a function of time or other variable.

SAMPLING

transformation of a continuous function into a discrete series of values in appropriate order.

SIGMA (σ)

See STANDARD DEVIATION.

264

SIMPLE SOUND SOURCE*

a source that radiates sound uniformly in all directions under free-field conditions.

SIMPLE TONE (PURE TONE)*

1. a sound wave, the instantaneous sound pressure of which is a simple sinusoidal function of the time.
2. a sound sensation characterized by its singleness of pitch.

Note: Whether or not a listener hears a tone as simple or complex is dependent upon ability, experience, and listening attitude.

SOCIOCUSIS

increase in hearing-threshold level resulting from noise exposures that are part of the social environment, exclusive of occupational-noise exposure, physiologic changes with age, and otologic disease.

SONE*

a unit of loudness. By definition, a simple tone of frequency 1000 Hz, 40 dB above a listener's threshold, produces a loudness of 1 sone. The loudness of any sound that is judged by the listener to be n times that of the 1-sone tone is n sones. Note 1: A millisone is equal to 0.001 sone. Note 2: The loudness scale is a relation between loudness and level above threshold for a particular listener. In presenting data relating loudness in sones to sound pressure level, or in averaging the loudness scales of several listeners, the thresholds (measured or assumed) should be specified.

SONICS*

the technology of sound in processing and analysis. Sonics includes the use of sound in any noncommunication process.

SOUND*

1. an oscillation in pressure, stress, particle displacement, particle velocity, etc., in a medium with internal forces (e.g. elastic, viscous), or the superposition of such propagated alterations.
2. an auditory sensation evoked by the oscillation described above.

Note 1: In case of possible confusion the term "sound wave" or "elastic wave" may be used for concept (1), and the term "sound sensation" for concept (2). Not all sound waves can evoke an auditory sensation: e.g. ultrasound. Note 2: The medium in which the source exists is often indicated by an appropriate adjective: e.g. airborne, waterborne, structureborne.

SOUND INTENSITY (SOUND POWER DENSITY)
(SOUND-ENERGY FLUX DENSITY)*

in a specified direction at a point is the average rate of sound energy transmitted in the specified direction through a unit area normal to this direction at the point considered.

SOUND-LEVEL (NOISE LEVEL)**

weighted sound-pressure level measured by the use of a metering characteristic and weighting A, B, or C, as specified in American National Standard Specification for Sound-Level Meters, S1.4-1971, or the latest approved revision thereof. The weighting employed must be indicated, otherwise the A weighting is understood. The reference pressure is 20 micronewtons per square meter (2×10^{-4} microbar).

SOUND-PRESSURE LEVEL*

in dB, is 20 times the logarithm to the base 10 of the ratio of the pressure of this sound to the reference pressure. The reference pressure shall be explicitly stated. Note 1: The following reference pressures are in common use;

(a) 2×10^{-4} microbar [$20\ \mu N/m^2$]

(b) 1 microbar

Reference pressure (a) is in general use for measurements concerned with hearing and with sound in air and liquids, while (b) has gained widespread acceptance for calibrations of transducers and various kinds of sound measurements in liquids.

[The reference pressure used in this handbook is 20 micronewtons per square meter ($20\ \mu N/m^2$).] Note 2: Unless otherwise explicitly stated, it is to be understood that the sound pressure is the effective (rms) sound pressure. Note 3: It is to be noted that in many sound fields the sound-pressure ratios are not the square roots of the corresponding power ratios.

SPECTRUM*

1. of a function of time is a description of its resolution into components, each of different frequency and (usually) different amplitude and phase.
2. also used to signify a continuous range of components, usually wide in extent, within which waves have some specified common characteristic; e.g., "audio-frequency spectrum."

Note 1. The term is also applied to functions of variables other than time, such as distance.

SPECTRUM LEVEL (ACOUSTICS)

ten times the common logarithm of the ratio of the squared sound-pressure-per-unit-bandwidth to the corresponding reference quantity. The unit bandwidth is the hertz and the corresponding reference quantity is $(20\ \mu N/m^2)^2/Hz$.

SPEECH INTERFERENCE LEVEL

See PSIL.

STANDARD DEVIATION (SIGMA, σ)

linear measure of variability equal to the square root of the variance.

STANDING WAVE*

periodic wave having a fixed distribution in space which is the result of interference of progressive waves of the same frequency and kind; characterized by the existence of nodes or partial nodes and anti-nodes that are fixed in space.

STATIONARY (STATISTICAL)

term that describes a noise whose spectrum and amplitude distribution do not change with time.

THRESHOLD OF AUDIBILITY
(THRESHOLD OF DETECTABILITY)*

for a specified signal is the minimum effective-sound-pressure level of the signal that is capable of evoking an auditory sensation in a specified fraction of the trials. The characteristics of the signal, the manner in which it is presented to the listener, and the point at which the sound pressure level is measured must be specified. Note 1: Unless otherwise indicated, the ambient noise reaching the ears is assumed to be negligible. Note 2: The threshold is usually given as a sound-pressure level in decibels, relative to 0.0002 microbar. Note 3: Instead of the method of constant stimuli, which is implied by the phrase "a specified fraction of the trials," another psychophysical method (which should be specified) may be employed.

THRESHOLD OF FEELING (OR TICKLE)*

for a specified signal is the minimum sound-pressure level at the entrance to the external auditory canal which, in a specified fraction of the trials, will stimulate the ear to a point at which there is a sensation of feeling that is different from the sensation of hearing.

TIF (TELEPHONE INFLUENCE FACTOR)

an index of the potential interfering effect of a particular power circuit on a telephone circuit. (See AIEE Trans. Vol. 79, Part I, 1960, pp. 659-664.)

TIME SERIES

values ordered in time, a succession of discrete observations made at points in time or covering discrete intervals of time. The spacing of observations is ordinarily uniform on the time scale.

TONE*

(a) a sound wave capable of exciting an auditory sensation having pitch.

(b) a sound sensation having a pitch.

TRANSDUCER*

a device capable of being actuated by waves from one or more transmission systems or media and of supplying related waves to one or more other transmission systems or media. Note: The waves in either input or output may be of the same or different types (e.g., electric, mechanical, or acoustic).

TRANSFER FUNCTION

measure of the relation between the output signal and the input signal of a system or device, ordinarily the ratio of the output signal to the input signal.

TRANSIENT VIBRATION*

temporarily sustained vibration of a mechanical system. It may consist of forced or free vibration or both.

ULTRASONICS*

the technology of sound at frequencies above the audio range. Note: Supersonics is the general subject covering phenomena associated with speed higher than the speed of sound (as in the case of aircraft and projectiles traveling faster than sound). This term was once used in acoustics synonomously with "ultrasonics;" such usage is now deprecated.

VARIANCE

quadratic measure of variability, the average of the mean squares of the deviations from the arithmetic mean of a set of values of a variable.

VELOCITY*

a vector that specifies the time-rate-of-change of displacement with respect to a reference frame. Note: If the reference frame is not inertial, the velocity is often designated relative velocity.

VIBRATION*

an oscillation wherein the quantity is a parameter that defines the motion of a mechanical system.

VIBRATION ISOLATOR*

a resilient support that tends to isolate a system from steady-state excitation.

VIBRATION METER (VIBROMETER)*

an apparatus for the measurement of displacement, velocity, or acceleration of a vibrating body.

WAVEFORM

instantaneous amplitude as a function of time.

WAVEFORM AVERAGING (SUMMATION ANALYSIS)

summing of corresponding ordinates of selected frames of a wave. The summed values may be divided by the number of frames summed to convert to an average.

WEIGHTING**

prescribed frequency response provided in a sound-level meter.

WHITE NOISE

power per-unit-frequency is substantially independent of frequency over a specified range. Note: White noise need not be random.

---

*This material is reproduced from the American National Standard Acoustical Terminology, S1.1-1960, copyrighted by ANSI, copies of which may be purchased from the American National Standards Institute at 1430 Broadway, New York, N. Y. 10018.
**ANSI S1.4-1971.
***ANSI S3.6-1969

Appendix VI

Words Commonly Used to Describe Sounds

The words listed below are commonly used to describe sounds of various types. Such words are often helpful in conveying information on the general nature of a sound.

BANG	CLUCK	HUM	RING	SWOOSH
BARK	CLUNK	JINGLE	RIPPLING	TAP
BEEP	CRACK	JANGLE	ROAR	TATTOO
BELLOW	CRACKLE	KACHUNK	RUMBLE	TEARING
BLARE	CRASH	KNOCK	RUSHING	THROB
BLAST	CREAK	MEW	RUSTLE	THUD
BLAT	DINGDONG	MOAN	SCREAM	THUMP
BLEAT	DRIP	MOO	SCREECH	THUNDER
BONG	DRUMMING	MURMUR	SCRUNCH	TICK
BOOM	FIZZ	NEIGH	SHRIEK	TICK-TOCK
BRAY	GLUG	PATTER	SIZZLE	TINKLE
BUZZ	GNASHING	PEAL	SLAM	TOOT
CACKLE	GOBBLE	PEEP	SNAP	TRILL
CHEEP	GRATING	PING	SNARL	TWANG
CHIME	GRINDING	POP	SNORT	TWITTER
CHIRP	GROAN	POW	SPLASH	WAIL
CLACK	GROWL	POUNDING	SPUTTER	WHEEZE
CLANG	GRUMBLE	PULSING	SQUAWK	WHINE
CLANK	GRUNT	PURR	SQUEAK	WHIR
CLAP	GURGLE	PUT-PUT	SQUEAL	WHISPER
CLATTER	HISS	RAP	SQUISH	WHISTLE
CLICK	HOOT	RAT-A-TAT	STAMP	YAP
CLINK	HOWL	RATTLE	SWISH	YELP
				ZAP

Appendix VII

Standards and Journals

Standards

The following standards in acoustics and mechanical shock and vibration can be purchased from the American National Standards Institute, (ANSI) 1430 Broadway, New York, N.Y., 10018.

S1.1-1960	Acoustical Terminology
S1.2-1962	Physical Measurement of Sound
S1.4-1971	Sound Level Meters
S1.5-1963	Loudspeaker Measurements
S1.6-1967	Preferred Frequencies for Acoustical Measurements
S1.7-1970	Method of Test for Sound Absorption of Acoustical Materials in Reverberation Rooms
S1.8-1969	Preferred Reference Quantities for Acoustical Levels
S1.10-1966	Calibration of Microphones
S1.11-1966	Octave, Half-Octave, and Third-Octave Band Filter Sets
S1.12-1967	Laboratory Standard Microphones
S1.13-1971	Measurement of Sound Pressure Levels
S2.2-1959	Calibration of Shock and Vibration Pickups
S2.3-1964(R1970)	High-Impact Shock Machine for Electronic Devices
S2.4-1960(R1966)	Specifying the Characteristics of Auxiliary Equipment for Shock and Vibration Measurements
S2.5-1962	Specifying the Performance of Vibrating Machines
S2.6-1963	Specifying the Mechanical Impedance of Structures
S2.7-1964	Terminology for Balancing Rotating Machinery
S2.10-1971	Analysis and Presentation of Shock and Vibration Data
S2.11-1969	Calibrations and Tests for Electrical Transducers Used for Measuring Shock and Vibration
S2.15-1971	Design Construction and Operation of Class HI (High-Impact) Shock-Testing Machine for Lightweight Equipment
S3.1-1960	Criteria for Background Noise in Audiometer Rooms
S3.2-1960	Measurement of Monosyllabic Word Intelligibility
S3.3-1960	Measurement of Electroacoustical Characteristics of Hearing Aids
S3.4-1968	Computation of the Loudness of Noise
S3.5-1969	Calculation of the Articulation Index
S3.6-1969	Specifications for Audiometers
S3.8-1967	Expressing Hearing Aid Performance
S3.13-1971	Artificial Head-Bone for the Calibration of Audiometer Bone Vibrators
S3-W-39	Effects of Shock and Vibration on Man
S5.1-1971	CAGI-PNEUROP Test Code for the Measurement of Sound from Pneumatic Equipment
Y32.18-1968	Symbols for Mechanical and Acoustical Elements as Used in Schematic Diagrams
Z24.9-1949	Coupler Calibration of Earphones
Z24.21-1957	Specifying the Characteristics of Pickups for Shock and Vibration Measurement
Z24.22-1957	Measurement of the Real-Ear Attenuation of Ear Protectors at Threshold
Z24.24-1957	Calibration of Electroacoustical Transducers (Particularly Those for Use in Water)
Z24-X-2	The Relations of Hearing Loss to Noise Exposure

The following are recommendations of the International Organization for Standardization: (available from ANSI)

ISO/R16-1965	Standard Tuning Frequency
ISO/R31/Part VII-1965	Quantities and Units of Acoustics
ISO/R131-1959	Expression of the Physical and Subjective Magnitudes of Sound or Noise
ISO/R140-1960	Field and Laboratory Measurements of Airborne and Impact Sound Transmission
ISO/R226-1961	Normal Equal-Loudness Contours for Pure Tones
ISO/R266-1962	Preferred Frequencies for Acoustical Measurements
ISO/R354-1963	Measurement of Absorption Coefficients in a Reverberation Room
ISO/R357-1963	Power and Intensity Levels of Sound or Noise
ISO/R362-1964	Measurement of Noise Emitted by Vehicles
ISO/R389-1964	Reference Zero for Pure-Tone Audiometers
ISO/R454-1965	Relation Between Sound Pressure Levels of Narrow Bands of Noise in a Diffuse Field and in a Frontally-Incident Free Field for Equal Loudness
ISO/R495-1966	Preparation of Test Codes for Measuring the Noise Emitted by Machines
ISO/R507-1970	Describing Aircraft Noise Around an Airport
ISO/R532-1966	Calculating Loudness Level
ISO/R717-1968	Rating of Sound Insulation for Dwellings
ISO/R1761-1970	Monitoring Aircraft Noise Around an Airport

The following are standards of the International Electrotechnical Commission: (available from ANSI)

IEC/50-08(1960)	International Electrotechnical Vocabulary Group 08: Electro-Acoustics
IEC/118(1959)	Measurements of the Electro-Acoustical Characteristics of Hearing Aids
IEC/123(1961)	Sound Level Meters
IEC/124(1960)	Rated Impedances and Dimensions of Loudspeakers
IEC/126(1961)	IEC Reference Coupler for the Measurement of Hearing Aids Using Earphones Coupled to the Ear by Means of Ear Inserts
IEC/177(1965)	Pure Tone Audiometers for General Diagnostic Purposes
IEC/178(1965)	Pure Tone Screening Audiometers
IEC/179(1965)	Precision Sound Level Meters
IEC/184(1965)	Specifying the Characteristics of Electromechanical Transducers for Shock and Vibration Measurements
IEC/200(1966)	Measurement of Loudspeakers
IEC/222(1966)	Specifying the Characteristics of Auxiliary Equipment for Shock and Vibration Measurement
IEC/225(1966)	Octave, Half-Octave and Third-Octave Band Filters Intended for the Analysis of Sounds and Vibrations
IEC/263(1968)	Scales and Sizes for Plotting Frequency Characteristics
IEC/303(1970)	IEC Provisional Reference Coupler for the Calibration of Earphones Used in Audiometry
IEC/327(1971)	Precision Method for Pressure Calibration of One-inch Standard Condenser Microphones by the Reciprocity Technique

American Society for Testing and Materials, 1916 Race St., Philadelphia, PA 19103

Methods of Test for:

C367-57	Strength Properties of Prefabricated Architectural Acoustical Materials
C384-58	Impedance and Absorption of Acoustical Materials by the Tube Method

271

C423-66	Sound Absorption of Acoustical Materials in Reverberation Rooms (S1.7-1970)
C522-69	Airflow Resistance of Acoustical Materials
C643-69	Painting Ceiling Materials for Acoustical Absorption Tests

Recommended Practices for:

E90-70	Laboratory Measurement of Airborne Sound Transmission Loss of Building Partitions
E336-67T	Measurement of Airborne Sound Insulation in Buildings
C636-69	Installation of Metal Ceiling Suspension Systems for Acoustical Tile and Lay-In Panels

Definition of Terms Relating to:

| C634-69 | Acoustical Tests of Building Constructions and Materials |

Standards Prepared by Professional Societies

American Society of Heating, Refrigerating and Air-Conditioning Engineers (ASHRAE), 345 East 47th Street, New York, N.Y. 10017

36-62	Measurement of Sound Power Radiated from Heating, Refrigerating and Air Conditioning Equipment
36A-63	Method of Determining Sound Power Levels of Room Air-Conditioners and Other Ductless, Through-the-Wall Equipment
36B-63	Method of Testing for Rating the Acoustic Performance of Air Control and Terminal Devices and Similar Equipment
36R-Feb 1970 (Draft)	Method of Testing for Sound Rating Heating, Refrigerating and Air Conditioning Equipment

Instrument Society of America, 400 Stanwix St., Pittsburgh, PA 15222.

| RP37.2 | Guide for Specifications and Tests for Piezoelectric Acceleration Transducers for Aerospace Testing (1964). |
| S37.10 | Specification and Tests for Piezoelectric Pressure and Sound-Pressure Transducers (1969) |

Institute of Electrical and Electronic Engineers, 345 East 47th Street, New York, N.Y. 10017

IEEE 85	Airborne Noise Measurements on Rotating Electric Machinery (1965)
IEEE 219	Loudspeaker Measurements (ANSI S1.5-1963)
IEEE 258	Methods of Measurement for Close-Talking Pressure Type Microphones (January 1965)
IEEE 269	Method for Measuring Transmission Performance of Telephone Sets (May 1966)

Society of Automotive Engineers, 345 East 47th Street, New York, N.Y. 10017
  SAE Committee A-21, Aircraft Noise Measurement

ARP 796	Measurements of Aircraft Exterior Noise in the Field
AIR 817	A Technique for Narrow Band Analysis of a Transient
AIR 852	Methods of Comparing Aircraft Takeoff and Approach Noises
ARP 865a	Definitions and Procedures for Computing the Perceived Noise Level of Aircraft Noise
ARP 866	Standard Values of Atmospheric Absorption as a Function of Temperature and Humidity for Use in Evaluating Aircraft Flyover Noise
ARP 876	Jet Noise Prediction
AIR 902	Determination of Minimum Distance from Ground Observer to Aircraft for Acoustic Tests
AIR 923	Method for Calculating the Attenuation of Aircraft Ground to Ground Noise Propagation During Takeoff and Landing
ARP 1080	Frequency Weighting Network for Approximation of Perceived Noise Level for Aircraft Noise
AIR 1115	Evaluation of Headphones for Demonstration of Aircraft Noise

SAE Sound Level Committee
J6a	Ride and Vibration Data Manual
J336	SAE Recommended Practice, Sound Level for Truck Cab Interior
J366	SAE Recommended Practice, Exterior Sound Level for Heavy Trucks and Buses
J377	SAE Standard, Performance of Vehicle Traffic Horns
J672a	SAE Standard, Exterior Loudness Evaluation of Heavy Trucks and Buses
J919	SAE Recommended Practice, Measurement of Sound Level at Operator Station
J952a	SAE Standard, Sound Levels for Engine Powered Equipment
J986a	SAE Standard, Sound Level for Passenger Cars and Light Trucks
J994	SAE Recommended Practice, Criteria for Backup Alarm Devices

Industry Groups

Air Conditioning and Refrigeration Institute (ARI), 1815 North Fort Meyer Drive, Arlington, Virginia 22209

ARI 443-66	Rooms Fan-Cool Air Conditioner
ARI 270-67	Sound Rating of Outdoor unitary Equipment

Air Diffusion Council (ADC), 435 North Michigan Ave., Chicago, Ill 60611

AD-63	Measurement of Room-to-Room Sound Transmissions Through Plenum Air Systems
1062-R2	Equipment Test Code

Air Moving and Conditioning Association (AMCA), 205 West Touhy Avenue, Park Ridge, Ill 60068

Bulletin 300-67	Test Code for Sound Rating
Bulletin 301-65	Method of Publishing Sound Ratings for Air Moving Devices
Bulletin 302-65	Application of Sone Loudness Ratings for Non-Ducted Air Moving Devices
Bulletin 303-65	Application of Sound Power Level Ratings for Ducted Air Moving Devices
Publication 311-67	AMCA Certified Sound Ratings Program for Air Moving Devices

American Gear Manufacturers Association (AGMA), One Thomas Circle, Washington, D.C. 20005

295.02	AGMA Standard Specification for Measurement of Sound in High Speed Helical and Herringbone Gear Units, November 1965.

The Anti-Friction Bearing Manufacturers Association, Inc., 60 East 42nd Street, New York, N.Y. 10017

	AFBMA Standard, Section 13, Roller Bearing Vibration and Noise

Association of Home Appliance Manufacturers, 20 North Wacker Drive, Chicago, Ill 60606

Standard RAC-2-SR	Room Air Conditioner Sound Rating, January 1971

Compressed Air and Gas Institute (CAGI), 122 East 42nd Street, New York, N.Y. 10017 (see ANSI S5.1-1971)

National Electrical Manufacturers Association (NEMA), 155 East 44th St., New York, N.Y. 10017

SM33-1964	Standards Publication, Gas Turbine Sound and Its Reduction
MG1	Motors and Generators
Section 4.3.2	Method of Measuring Machine Noise
TR1-1963	Transformers, Regulators and Reactors (Sections 9-04 and 9-05)

273

National Fluid Power Association, Thiensville, Wisconsin 53092

NFPA T3.9-70.12   Method of Measuring Sound Generated by Hydraulic Fluid
                        Power Pumps

National Machine Tool Builders Association (NMTBA), 2139 Wisconsin Ave., Washington,
D.C. 20007

                     Noise Measurement Techniques, June 1970

Journals in the Field of Sound and Vibration.

Acustica, S. Hirzel, Stuttgart 1, Birkenwaldstr. 44, Postfach 347, Germany. (An international journal on acoustics.)

Akusticheskii Zhurnal, (in Russian), Academy of Sciences of USSR, Moscow.

Applied Acoustics, Elsevier Publishing Co. Ltd., Ripple Road, Barking, Essex, England. (An international journal.)

IEEE Transactions on Audio and Electroacoustics, The Institute of Electrical and Electronics Engineers, Inc., 345 East 47 Street, New York, N.Y. 10017.

The Journal of the Acoustical Society of America, Acoustical Society of America, 335 East 45 Street, New York, N.Y. 10017. (The most comprehensive scientific journal in acoustics with occasional papers on vibration. The Society also publishes cumulative indexes to the *Journal* and to other acoustical literature.)

The Journal of the Acoustical Society of Japan, (in Japanese), Acoustical Society of Japan, Ikeda Building/2-7-7, Yoyogi, Shibuya-Ku, Tokyo, Japan.

Journal of the Audio Engineering Society, Audio Engineering Society, Room 929, Lincoln Building, 60 East 42nd Street, New York, N.Y. 10017.

Journal of Auditory Research, The C. W. Skilling Auditory Research Center, Inc., Box N, Groton, Connecticut 06340.

Journal of Sound and Vibration, Academic Press, Inc., Limited, Berkeley Square House, Berkeley Square, London W1X 6BA and Academic Press Inc., 111 Fifth Avenue, New York, N.Y. 10003. (An official medium of publication for the British Acoustical Society.)

Kampf Dem Lärm, (in German), J. F. Lehmanns Verlag, Agnes-Bernauerplatz 8, 8000 München 21, Germany.

Lärmbekämpfung, (in German), Verlag Für Angewandte Wissenschaften GmbH, Hardstrasse 1, 757 Baden-Baden, Germany.

NOISE/NEWS, Institute of Noise Control Engineering, P. O. Box 1758, Poughkeepsie, NY 12601. (Published in cooperation with the Acoustical Society of America).

Revue D' Acoustique (in French), G.A.L.F. (Groupement des Acousticiens de Langue Francaise), Secretariat, *Départment Acoustique du CNET, 22-Lannion, France.*

Sound and Vibration, Acoustical Publications, Inc., 27101 E. Oviatt Road, Bay Village, Ohio 44140.

Numerous other societies in the United States are interested in sound and vibration measurements, for example:

     American Hearing Society
     American Industrial Hygiene Association
     American Medical Association
     American Psychological Association
     American Society of Heating, Refrigerating and Air-Conditioning Engineers
     American Society for Testing and Materials
     American Speech and Hearing Association
     American Society of Mechanical Engineers
     Institute of Electrical and Electronic Engineers
     Institute of Environmental Sciences
     Instrument Society of America
     Society of Automotive Engineers
     Society of Experimental Psychologists
     Society of Experimental Stress Analysis

Many others in other countries, and many trade journals, publish occasional papers on acoustics, noise control and vibration.

Appendix VIII

Hearing-Loss Statutes

The following tables are a compilation of hearing loss statutes in effect in 1972 in the various states of the United States and in the Canadian provinces. They were prepared by Meyer S. Fox, M.D., Medical Acoustics, Inc., Portland, Oregon.

They are abstracted by permission of the author and from *National Safety News,* Vol 105, No. 2, Feb 1972 (pp 50-56) in an article by Dr. Fox entitled "In the U.S. and Canada — Hearing Loss Statutes." They are reprinted with permission.

	JURISDICTION	Is Occupational Hearing Loss Due to Continuous Noise Exposure Compensable?	Do You Have Any Regulation Regarding Noise Exposure?	Basic of Compensation (Per Week—One Ear)	Basic Compensation (Per Week—Both Ears)	Maximum Compensation—One Ear	Maximum Compensation—Both Ears	Must Employee Leave Noisy Work for Any Period Before Filing Claim?	Method or Formula Used for Determining Hearing Impairment	Do You Deduct for Presbycusis?	Is Any Award Made for Tinnitus?	Do You Compensate for Non-Organic Hearing Loss?	Is Provision Made for Hearing Aid?	Is Credit Given for Improvement with Hearing Aid?
1	ALABAMA	No	No	53 Weeks	163 Weeks	$ 2,650	$ 8,150	No	Medical Evidence*	•	•	•	•	No
2	ALASKA	Yes	•	52 Weeks	200 Weeks	$ 3,000	$10,000	No	AMA	Possibly	Possibly	Possibly	Yes	No
3	ARIZONA	*Possibly	No	20 Months	60 Months	$11,000	$33,000	No	AMA	Possibly	Possibly	Possibly	Yes	Not Decided
4	ARKANSAS	Yes	No	40 Weeks	150 Weeks	$ 1,960	$ 7,350	No	AMA	No	Possibly	*es	Yes	Yes
5	CALIFORNIA	Yes	Yes	60 Weeks	240 Weeks	$ 3,150	$12,600	No	AMA Plus 3000 Hz Frequency	Possibly	Yes	Possibly	Yes	Yes
6	COLORADO	No	Yes	—	—	$ 2,082	$ 8,270	—	AMA*	—	—	—	Yes	—
7	CONNECTICUT	Yes	No	52 Weeks	156 Weeks	$ 4,368	$13,104	No	ME*	No	No	Law Uncertain	Yes	No
8	DELAWARE	Yes	No	75 Weeks	175 Weeks	$ 5,625	$13,125	No	ME	—	—	No	Yes	No
9	DIST OF COLUMBIA	Yes	No	52 Weeks	200 Weeks	$ 3,640	$14,000	No	AMA	Possibly	Possibly	Possibly	Yes	No
10	FLORIDA	Yes	No	40 Weeks	150 Weeks	$ 2,240	$ 8,400	No	ME*	Yes	No	Possibly	No	—
11	GEORGIA	Yes	No	60 Weeks	150 Weeks	$ 3,000	$ 7,550	No	ME*	Possibly	No	Possibly	No	—
12	HAWAII	Yes	Yes	52 Weeks	200 Weeks	$ 5,850	$22,500	No	AMA	No	Yes	Yes	Yes	No
13	IDAHO	No	No	35 Weeks	175 Weeks	$ 1,505	$ 6,450	No	ME	Possibly*	Possibly*	Possibly*	Yes	No
14	ILLINOIS	Yes	No	50 Weeks	125 Weeks	$ 3,200	$ 8,500	No	AMA	No	No	Possibly	No	—
15	INDIANA	No	No	75 Weeks	200 Weeks	$ 4,275	$11,400	No	ME	No	No	No	No	—
16	IOWA	No	No	50 Weeks	175 Weeks	$ 2,800	$ 9,800	No	ME	Yes	—	—	Yes	Yes
17	KANSAS	Yes	No	30 Weeks	110 Weeks	$ 1,680	$ 5,560	No		—	—	—	—	—
18	KENTUCKY	Yes	No	75 Weeks	150 Weeks	$ 3,825	$ 7,650	No	ME	No	No	No	Possibly	—
19	LOUISIANA	No	—	—	—	—	—	Yes	ME	—	—	—	No	—
20	MAINE	Yes	No	50 Weeks	100 Weeks	$ 3,646	$ 7,292	6 Months	AMA	Yes ½ dB After Age 40	Yes	No	No	—
21	MARYLAND	Yes	No	75 Weeks	233 Weeks	$ 1,875	$ 9,370	—	AMA	—	Possibly	—	Yes	—
22	MASSACHUSETTS	Yes*	No	150 Weeks	400 Weeks	$ 3,750	$10,000	No	AMA ME	Possibly	Possibly	Possibly	Yes	No
23	MICHIGAN	Yes*	No	•	•	•	•	No	ME	No	Yes	—	Yes	—
24	MINNESOTA	Yes	Yes	85 Weeks	170 Weeks	$ 6,205	$12,410	No	ME	No	Possibly	Possibly	Yes	No
25	MISSISSIPPI	Yes	No	40 Weeks	150 Weeks	$ 1,600	$ 6,000	No	ME	No	—	—	Yes	No
26	MISSOURI	Yes	No	40 (Noise) 44 (Traumatic)	148 (N) 168 (T)	$ 2,540 (N) $ 2,794 (T)	$ 9,398 (N) $10,668 (T)	6 Months	AMA	Yes ½ dB After Age 40	Yes	Yes	No	—
27	MONTANA	Yes*	Yes*	•		•	•	•		•	•	•	•	•
28	NEBRASKA	No	No	50 Weeks	100 Weeks	$ 2,750	$ 5,500	No	AMA	No	Yes	Yes	Yes	No
29	NEVADA	Yes	Yes*	20 Months	60 Months	$ 5,600	$16,800	No	AMA	No	No	No	Yes	No
30	NEW HAMPSHIRE	Yes	Yes*	52 Weeks	214 Weeks	$ 4,174	$19,688	No	AMA	Possibly	—	—	Yes	No
31	NEW JERSEY	Yes	No	60 Weeks	200 Weeks	$ 2,400	$ 8,000	No	ME	No	Yes	Yes	Yes	No
32	NEW MEXICO	No	No	40 Weeks	150 Weeks	$ 1,920	$ 7,280	—	ME	—	—	—	—	—
33	NEW YORK	Yes	Yes*	60 Weeks	150 Weeks	$ 4,800	$12,000	Yes 6 Months	AMA	No	Yes	Yes	Yes	No
34	NORTH CAROLINA	Yes	No	70 Weeks	150 Weeks	$ 3,500	$ 7,500	6 Months	AMA	½ dB for Each Year After Age 38	No	No	No	No
35	NORTH DAKOTA	Yes	Yes*	50 Weeks	200 Weeks	$ 1,575	$ 6,300	No	AMA ME	Possibly	No	No	Yes	No
36	OHIO	Yes	No	25 Weeks	125 Weeks	$ 1,400	$ 7,000	No	ME	Possibly	No	No	No	No
37	OKLAHOMA	Yes*	No	100 Weeks	200 Weeks	$ 4,300	$ 8,600	No	ME*	No	Yes	Yes	No	No
38	OREGON	Yes	Yes	60 ¢	192 ¢	$ 3,300	$10,560	No	AMA	Possibly	No	No	Yes	No
39	PENNSYLVANIA	Yes	Yes	—	180 Weeks		$10,800	No	ME	No	No	No	No	—
40	RHODE ISLAND	Yes	No	17 Weeks	100 Weeks	$ 765	$ 4,500	6 Months	AMA	Yes ½ dB for Each Year After Age 40	No	No	Yes	No
41	SOUTH CAROLINA	Yes	No	70 Weeks	150 Weeks	$ 3,500	$ 7,500	No	ME	No	Possibly	Possibly	Yes	No
42	SOUTH DAKOTA	Yes	No	50 Weeks	150 Weeks	$ 2,500	$ 7,500	—	ME	Possibly	Yes	No	Yes	Yes
43	TENNESSEE	Yes	No	75 Weeks	150 Weeks	$ 3,525	$ 7,050	No	ME	No	No	No	Yes	No
44	TEXAS	Yes	No	—	150 Weeks	—	$ 7,350	No	AMA	Possibly	Yes	Yes	Yes	No
45	UTAH	Yes	Yes	—	100 Weeks	—	$ 7,900	6 Months	AMA	½ dB After Age 40	No	No	Yes	No
46	VERMONT	No	No	52 Weeks	215 Weeks	$ 3,172	$13,115	No	ME	No	No	No	Yes	No
47	VIRGINIA	Yes	No	50 Weeks	100 Weeks	$ 3,100	$ 6,200	No	ME	No	Yes	Yes	Yes	No
48	WASHINGTON	Yes	Yes			$ 2,400	$14,400	No	AMA	No	Yes	Yes	Yes	No
49	WEST VIRGINIA	Yes	No	60 Weeks	180 Weeks	$ 3,390	$11,790	No	AMA	Possibly	Yes	No	Yes	No
50	WISCONSIN	Yes	Yes	36 Weeks (N) 55 Weeks (T)	216 Weeks (N) 330 Weeks (T)	$ 1,800 (N) $ 2,750 (T)	$10,800 (N) $16,500 (T)	6 Months	AMA	No	Yes*	Yes*	Yes	No
51	WYOMING	No	No	•	•	$ 3,000	$ 6,000	No	ME	No	No	No	Yes	No
52	PUERTO RICO	Yes	Yes	50 Weeks	200 Weeks	$ 2,250	$ 9,000	No	AMA	No	Possibly	Possibly	Yes	No
53	CANADIAN PROVINCES	Yes	Yes	•	•	•	•	Yes*	•	•	•	•	Yes *	•

"See "Comments" far right column   AMA—American Medical Association "Guide to the Evaluation of Permanent Impairment"   ME—Medical Evidence

Jurisdiction	Comments
1 ALABAMA	*Workmen's Compensation laws administered by courts. May use any criteria appropriate to determine issue.
2 ALASKA	Awards for tinnitus and non-organic loss if it affects hearing and is due to work. (Plan to adopt OSHA noise guidelines.)
3 ARIZONA	Noise-induced hearing loss recognized under gradual theory — series of traumatic incidents. Compensation for tinnitus; non-organic loss based on medical evidence of impairment of function and inability to work.
4 ARKANSAS	Might provide hearing aid and credit for improvement as done with glasses.
5 CALIFORNIA	Rating values based on age and occupation of worker. Uses AMA formula plus 3,000 Hz frequency. Awards for tinnitus and non-organic loss on non-scheduled basis — depends on medical evidence. Frequent claims experienced.
6 COLORADO	At present time only traumatic hearing loss is compensable. Consideration being given to include noise-induced hearing loss. Have adopted Walsh Healey regulations.
7 CONNECTICUT	
8 DELAWARE	All Workmen's Compensation acts are being reviewed by the assembly.
9 DIST. OF COLUMBIA	Award for tinnitus and non-organic hearing loss if associated with hearing loss.
10 FLORIDA	Compensation for non-organic hearing loss possible on medical evidence if related to employment.
11 GEORGIA	Compensation for noise-induced hearing loss decided by court decision. Treated as accidental (traumatic) loss. Provision for temporary as well as scheduled loss depends upon medical opinion for various criteria used.
12 HAWAII	Have regulation on noise exposure above 90 dBA. Compensation for tinnitus and non-organic loss on medical, psychiatric basis.
13 IDAHO	Consideration of presbycusis, tinnitus, and non-organic loss based on medical evidence.
14 ILLINOIS	Occupational safety bill passed Apr. 29, 1971 (like Walsh Healey). Hearing loss must be total in one or both ears.
15 INDIANA	
16 IOWA	Credit for improvement with hearing aid. Mean between improved and unimproved hearing.
17 KANSAS	Uses modified weighted AMA formula of 1942.
18 KENTUCKY	Provision for hearing aid if medically indicated.
19 LOUISIANA	Compensation based upon 65 per cent of wages during disability not beyond 300 weeks if temporary, or 400 weeks if total, and must leave work to prove disability.
20 MAINE	Deduction for presbycusis — 1/2 dB each year after age 40.
21 MARYLAND	
22 MASSACHUSETTS	*Must be total loss of hearing for all practical purposes to be compensable.
23 MICHIGAN	Hearing loss must be total in one or both ears to be compensable. Compensation based on wage loss and inability to work.
24 MINNESOTA	Award for tinnitus and non-organic hearing loss on basis of wage loss. Award on one ear up to 85 weeks — 90 dBA used.
25 MISSISSIPPI	Award for tinnitus and non-organic hearing loss if job-related.
26 MISSOURI	Deduction for presbycusis — 1/2 dB for each year after 40. Separate schedule for loss resulting from noise and trauma.
27 MONTANA	Legislature passed law covering occupational hearing loss to become effective Jan. 1, 1972.
28 NEBRASKA	Compensate for tinnitus if associated with hearing loss. Non-organic on neurosis basis. Has frequent claims.
29 NEVADA	Has general safety rule applying to noise exposure.
30 NEW HAMPSHIRE	*Anticipate adoption of federal noise exposure standards.
31 NEW JERSEY	Large number of cases — 607 in 1969, more in 1970.
32 NEW MEXICO	District courts administer the compensation act.
33 NEW YORK	Formulating safety code after Walsh Healey act. Compensation for tinnitus and non-organic loss if causally related.
34 NORTH CAROLINA	Legislation enacted to compensate for noise-induced hearing loss. Effective Oct. 1, 1970. Deduction for presbycusis after age 38.
35 NORTH DAKOTA	Use Walsh Healey guidelines for noise exposure.
36 OHIO	Loss must be total in one or both ears to be compensable.
37 OKLAHOMA	Considered as series of traumatic incidents. Permit use of live voice tests at measured distances.
38 OREGON	Schedule is based on degrees rather than weeks. Each degree is worth $55.
39 PENNSYLVANIA	Must have complete loss of hearing in both ears. Receives compensation at rate of 66 per cent of weekly wages for 180 weeks (180 x $60 = $10,800). Legislation suggested but has not been enacted. Passed specific safety rule for hearing protection in noise.
40 RHODE ISLAND	Legislation effective Sept. 1, 1969. Deduction for presbycusis, 1/2 dB each year after 40. Benefits were reduced.
41 SOUTH CAROLINA	
42 SOUTH DAKOTA	Occupational noise compensable as of July 1, 1971. Credit for improvement with hearing aid.
43 TENNESSEE	
44 TEXAS	Texas law effective June 9, 1971 provides compensation of noise-induced hearing loss. Compensation for noise-induced hearing loss is based on both ears only.
45 UTAH	Impairment computed on binaural hearing only.
46 VERMONT	Department of Health uses Walsh Healey criteria. May pass legislation in 1972.
47 VIRGINIA	Hearing table slightly different than AMA. Impairment begins at 17 dB and ends at 80 dB.
48 WASHINGTON	Noise exposure criteria like Walsh Healey. Award for tinnitus and non-organic hearing loss on medical evidence.
49 WEST VIRGINIA	Presbycusis and tinnitus given consideration based on medical evidence.
50 WISCONSIN	Award for tinnitus and non-organic hearing loss if it is disabling and related to employment. Has separate schedule for noise and traumatic hearing loss cases.
51 WYOMING	Rated as percentage loss similar to rating for impairment of vision.
52 PUERTO RICO	
53 CANADIAN PROVINCES	The statutes and provisions in the Canadian Provinces show slight variations. In general they compensate for noise-induced hearing loss and have specific guidelines (Walsh Healey) for noise exposure and for the use of personal hearing protection devices. Compensation is based upon the percentage of the body as a whole, and varies from three to five per cent for total loss in one ear to thirty per cent for each ear. They use a modification of the AMA formula as follows: No award for average loss less than 25 dB, ASA scale or 35 dB, ISO scale. Complete loss if average is 70 dB on ASA scale or 80 dB on ISO scale. The determination of binaural hearing loss varies from one-to-five to one-to-nine ratio. Most provinces require the applicant to remove himself from noise exposure to collect an award (pension). Some provinces have a presbycusis deduction of 1/2 dB for each year over 50; some start at 60, and some provinces have no presbycusis deduction. There is provision for furnishing a hearing aid where medically indicated, but no credit is allowed for improvement by use of a hearing aid.

Appendix IX

Product Directory

The following pages include detailed specifications for GenRad sound- and vibration-measuring instruments and accessories. Specifications given are subject to change without notice.

1933 Precision Sound-Level Meter and Analyzer

- three instruments in one
  - precision sound-level meter
  - precision impulse sound-level meter
  - octave-band analyzer

- ideal for OSHA and a broad variety of noise measurements

- compact, lightweight, and fully portable

- virtually mistake-proof operation with:
  - OPTI-RANGE
  - easy-to-read meter display
  - extendible microphone mast

- can be used with low-cost dc recorders

- compatible with companion cassette data recorder

A precision sound laboratory The 1933 is a precision measuring instrument that conforms to U. S. and international standards for a precision sound-level meter, octave-band analyzer, and impulse sound-level meter. An impact (true peak) measuring capability is also provided. The 1933 measures true rms values (there are no approximations) and automatically warns of invalid readings due to overloads. The complete instrument is in a package one-half the size and weight of conventional analyzers.

An easy-to-use instrument Set the upper knob to Weighting and the 1933 becomes a sound-level meter with a pushbutton choice of A, B, or C weighting or flat response from 5 Hz to 100 kHz. Fast and slow meter speeds are also pushbutton selected. Another button allows impulse testing, according to the proposed amendment to IEC 179, or impact (peak sound-pressure level) testing often used for the measurement of industrial impact noise.

Conversion to an octave-band analyzer is equally simple; turn the knob to the desired octave band — there are 10 to choose from, with center frequencies from 31.5 Hz to 16 kHz.

Virtually mistake-proof measurement A single control is sufficient to set the meter range, even when the instrument is used as an octave-band analyzer. In other analyzers, two are required: An input range control to set the "all-pass" level and an analyzing range control to provide an on-scale meter indication after the desired octave filter has been selected. (Both are necessary to obtain the maximum analyzing range and maximum dynamic range.) But in the 1933 a unique *automatic* attenuator system is used (OPTI-RANGE). With this feature, you need only set a single range control for an on-scale indication. A second control is provided for situations where the automatic system may not be suitable, as with some measurements of transient signals.

The unusual meter scale also enhances the ease of operation. The meter spans a full 20-dB range, is graduated *linearly* over the entire range, and displays the attenuator setting on the meter face. These features reduce the number of range changes necessary and aid in rapid, error-free interpretation of the readings.

An expandable sound laboratory Often it is desirable to record field measurements for further analysis later in the laboratory. With the 1933 and its companion recorder, the 1935, it is easy to make accurate recordings of such measurements. In addition to an ac signal output to drive one channel of the recorder, the 1933 also provides a level-range-code signal that is stored on a second channel of the recorder. On playback, the level-range setting used for the sound-level meter is indicated by a digital display on the panel of the tape recorder. Thus, the tape stores both data and absolute level information.

A dc output, proportional to the meter deflection (linear in dB), is provided to drive a low-cost dc recorder for hard-copy records of the level vs time. This output has a dynamic range of 40 dB plus an additional 20-dB crest-factor allowance.

Other features The microphones fit atop a telescoping 12-inch extension to reduce the effects of the instrument and operator on the sound field. There is rarely a need for extension cables and tripod. If these are necessary, however, a 60-foot cable and tripod are available. A 10-foot cable is supplied as standard equipment. Measurements are unaffected by the cables because the preamplifier in the 1933 is detachable and connects to the cable at the microphone end, to prevent signal loss.

A complete line of electret-condenser and ceramic microphones can be used with the 1933. Most users will want at least two: The one-half-inch random-incidence microphone, supplied, for smooth high-frequency response and nearly ideal directional characteristics, and the one-inch random-incidence microphone for measurements of very low sound levels. To simplify changing from one microphone to the other, two sensi-

279

tivity presets are provided in the 1933. You can use two microphones alternately, in a series of measurements, without recalibration; merely turn the sensitivity switch to the position corresponding to the microphone being used.

For field or lab use The 1933 operates for up to 20 hours on self-contained batteries. A companion instrument, the 1940 Power Supply and Charger, allows the analyzer to be operated from the ac line and provides rechargeable batteries and a charging circuit.

Several versions to choose from Four versions of the basic instrument are offered, the difference among them being the number and types of microphones supplied. Versions with flat perpendicular-incidence response microphones are offered for the convenience of customers in those countries (particularly in Europe) where it has become customary to measure with this type of microphone. It should be noted that all versions offered comply with IEC 179.

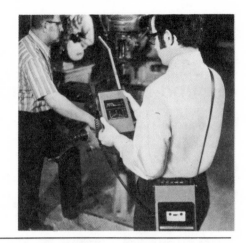

1933 Sound Analysis Systems

1933-9712

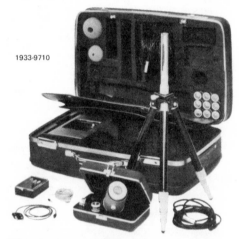

1933-9710

The 1933 Precision Sound-Level Meter and Analyzer is the heart of several systems available from GR to meet varying measurement and budget needs. All of the system instruments and accessories you require for different measurement situations have a special compartment in the system case and are readily at hand when you need them. Typical components in the systems available include: windscreens for outdoor measurements; a tripod for remote microphone mounting; an acoustic calibrator for on-the-spot calibration checks; earphones for aural monitoring; spare batteries; microphone extension cables; etc.

The 1933-9712* includes . . . 1933 Precision Sound-Level Meter and Analyzer with ½-inch and 1-inch flat random-incidence-response electret-condenser microphones (conforms to ANSI S1.4-1971 Type 1 and IEC

*The 1933-9713 system is identical except for the microphones which have flat perpendicular-incidence response (conforms to IEC 179).

179), microphone attenuator, tool kit, 10-foot microphone extension cable, and batteries . . . 1935 Cassette Data Recorder with interconnecting cables to the 1933, microphone for voice notes, three 30-minute cassettes, earphone, head-maintenance and tool kits . . . ½-inch dummy microphone . . . ½-inch and 1-inch windscreens . . . 1562 Sound-Level Calibrator with battery, adaptors, and carrying case . . . 60-foot microphone extension cable . . . tripod . . . large system carrying case . . . and instruction manuals for all instruments.

The 1933-9710 (ANSI and IEC conformance) or 1933-9711 (IEC conformance) systems contain all the items in the 1933-9712 and -9713 systems except for the 1935 Recorder and its accessories. These systems are offered for those buyers who do not have an immediate need or budget for the 1935 but plan to acquire one at a later date. The carrying-case insert has compartments for the recorder and its accessories.

280

For those who have no need for a recorder, now or in the foreseeable future, the 1933-9714 (ANSI and IEC conformance) or 1933-9715 (IEC conformance) are logical system selections. These systems are offered in a smaller carrying case and include the following items: 1933 Precision Sound-Level Meter with ½-inch and 1-inch electret-condenser microphones, microphone attenuator, tool kit, 10-foot microphone extension cable, and batteries . . . 1562 Sound-Level Calibrator with battery and adaptors (but without carrying case) . . . ½-inch dummy microphone . . . ½-inch and 1-inch windscreen . . . earphone . . . small system carrying case . . . and instruction manuals.

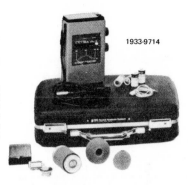

1933-9714

Popular Accessories for the 1933

Vibration Integrator System

The 1933-9610 Vibration Integrator System expands the capabilities of the 1933 to include vibration measurements with readout of acceleration (L_a), velocity (L_v), and displacement (L_d). This added capability increases the versatility of the 1933 for noise-reduction work by permitting the measurement and analysis of structure-borne vibration. It also adds preventive maintenance to the 1933's functions since vibration analysis is often used to detect potential parts' failures in machinery and equipment.

The system consists of a vibration pickup (accelerometer) with a magnetic clamp and keeper, a vibration integrator that mounts on the 1933 preamplifier in place of a microphone, an 8-foot cable to connect the pickup to the integrator, a storage case, and a slide rule.

With the integrator, the 1933 reads directly in dB re the standard references for acceleration, velocity, and displacement. A special, easy-to-use slide rule is included in the system to permit simple readout directly in vibration units. This eliminates the need to refer to special conversion tables or to become involved in complex dB calculations.

Power Supply and Charger

The 1940 Power Supply and Charger allows either the 1933 or the 1935 to be operated from an ac line, independent of their internal batteries. It is supplied with five rechargeable cells (to replace the ordinary C cells supplied in the analyzer or recorder) and a battery charger. There are no internal connections to make; the instrument simply plugs into the 1940 and is supported at a convenient angle for bench-top operation.

Calibrator

The 1562-A Sound-Level Calibrator is used to check the 1933 instrument calibration before and after each series of measurements. It generates 114 dB at 125 Hz, 250 Hz, 500 Hz, 1 kHz, and 2 kHz. It is supplied with adaptors for ½-inch and 1-inch microphones.

Extension Cable and Tripod

The 1933-9601 60-foot Extension Cable and 1560-9590 Tripod are used in applications where the observer must be a considerable distance from the microphone and sound field.

Popular Accessories for the 1933 (Cont'd)

Windscreens

Windscreens are used to reduce the effects of wind-generated noise and to protect the microphone diaphragm against contamination in oily, misty, or dusty environments. One-half inch and one-inch sizes are available.

Earphone

The 1935-9601 Earphone can be used with the 1933 to permit audible monitoring of the signal being measured. It is particularly useful for matching the annoying component of a noise source with an audible signal from a particular octave band.

Dummy Microphone

The 1560-P9 Dummy Microphone is used in place of the 1962 ½-inch Electret-Condenser Microphone to determine instrument noise floor. A BNC input connector is provided to connect to a signal source.

Carrying Cases

The 1933-9603 Carrying Case (small) and the 1933-9604 Carrying Case (large) may be purchased separately. They provide custom-fitted protection for the 1933 and its commonly used accessories.

SPECIFICATIONS

1933 PRECISION SOUND-LEVEL METER AND ANALYZER

Specifications meet ANSI S1.4-1971 for Type 1 (precision) Sound-Level Meters: IEC 179-1973 for Precision Sound-Level Meters; IEC 123-1961 for Sound-Level Meters; ANSI S1.11-1966 for Octave, Half-Octave, and Third-Octave Band Type 0 Class II Filter Sets; IEC 225-1966 for Octave, Half-Octave, and Third-Octave Band Filters for the Analysis of Sound and Vibrations; and Proposed IEC 179 amendment for impulse measurement.

Level Range: 10 dB to 130 dB re 20 $\mu N/m^2$ with 1-in. microphone, 20 dB to 140 dB with ½-in. microphone. Typical minimum measurable level (noise floor 5 dB below minimum measurable level) with 1-in. microphone, 22 dBA; with ½-in. microphone, 31 dBA; lower in octave bands.

Frequency: 5 Hz to 100 kHz essentially flat response, 10 octave bands with center frequencies from 31.5 Hz to 16 kHz; plus A, B, and C weighting.

Display: METER: 20-dB scale linearly marked in dB and lower, center, and upper values automatically indicated on scale. RESPONSE: Fast, slow, absolute peak, and impulse (per IEC 179 amendment), pushbutton selected. Precise rms detection for signals with ≤20-dB crest factor at full scale, crest-factor capacity greater below full scale. OVERLOAD: Signal peaks monitored at 2 critical points to provide positive panel-lamp warning. RANGING: Automatic system (OPTI-RANGE) maximizes analyzing range and signal-to-noise ratio for each level range-control setting; manual control provides override. Increment between ranges, 10 dB.

Filters: WEIGHTING: A, B, C, and flat; pushbutton selected. OCTAVE BANDS: 10, manually selected, with 3.5 ±1-dB attenuation at nominal cutoff, >18-dB attenuation at ½ and 2X center frequency, >70-dB ultimate attenuation. EXTERNAL FILTERS can be substituted for internal weighting networks and octave-band filters; connect to 2 miniature phone jacks.

Input: ½-in. or 1-in. electret-condenser microphone mounted with detachable preamplifier on 12-in. extendible mast, or on 10-ft. extension cable supplied, or on 60-ft. cable available. Input can also be from tape recorder. INPUT IMPEDANCE: 1 GΩ//<3 pF.

Output: SIGNAL OUTPUT: 0.632 V rms behind 600Ω corresponding to full-scale meter deflection, any load permissible. RANGE CODE: Contact closure provides sound-level-meter range information to 1935 Cassette Data Recorder. DETECTED OUTPUT: 4.5 V dc behind 4.5 kΩ corresponding to full-scale meter deflection, output is linear in dB at 0.1 V/dB over 60-dB range (40-dB normal range plus 20-dB crest-factor allowance), any load permissible.

Calibration: FACTORY: Fully tested and calibrated to all specifications; acoustical response and sensitivity are measured in a free field by comparison with a WE640AA Laboratory Standard Microphone whose calibration is traceable to the U.S. National Bureau of Standards. ON-SITE: Built-in calibrator provides quick test of electrical circuits; GR 1562 Sound-Level Calibrator is available for simple test of over-all calibration, including microphones.

Environment: TEMPERATURE: −10 to +50°C operating, −40 to +60°C storage with batteries removed. HUMIDITY: 0 to 90% RH. VIBRATION AND MICROPHONICS: Conform to applicable ANSI and IEC standards.

Magnetic Field: 1-Oersted (80 A/m) 60-Hz field causes 43 dB C-weighted indication when meter is oriented for maximm sensitivity to field using ½-in. microphone; 34 dB using 1-in. microphone.

Power: 4 alkaline energizer C cells supplied provide ≈ 20-h operation; 1940 Power Supply and Charger allows line operation of 1933 and includes rechargeable batteries and charging source. Battery check provided on 1933.

Supplied: Microphone attenuator, tool kit, 10-ft microphone extension cable, batteries.

Mechanical: (1933 Instrument) Small, rugged, hand-held case with standard 0.25-20 threaded hole for tripod mounting. DIMENSIONS (wxhxd): 6.19x9x3 in. (158x229x76 mm). WEIGHT: 5.5 lb (2.5 kg) net, 10 lb (4.6 kg) shipping.

(1933 Systems): DIMENSIONS (wxhxd): 1933-9710, -9711, -9712, -9713: 22.5x15.5x8.25 in. (573x394x210 mm); 1933-9714 and -9715: 19x14.5x6 in. (483x370x152 mm). WEIGHT: 1933-9710 and -9711: 21 lb (9.6 kg) net, 24 lb (11 kg) shipping; 1933-9712 and -9713: 31 lb (14 kg) net, 34 lb (15.5 kg) shipping; 1933-9714 and -9715: 15 lb (7 kg net), 17 lb (8 kg) shipping.

1935 CASSETTE DATA RECORDER

Recording Format: 0.150-in.-wide tape cassette (Coplanar Type CPII), two-channel, two-track.

Normal Recording Duration: 30 minutes using C60 tape. TAPE SPEEDS: 1⅞ in./s ±2%, electronically controlled.

Inputs: Input impedance at signal input, each channel, 100 kΩ. Signal level corresponding to normal maximum record level is adjustable from 0.5 to 3 V rms. RANGE CODE AND VOICE NOTES: Second channel normally records range code or voice notes simultaneously with data from a sound-level meter. Range code is provided automatically by 1933 Precision Sound-Level Meter and Analyzer or manually by switch on recorder. Voice-note input has 1-MΩ input impedance and automatic level control.

Frequency Response: Typical response ±2 dB, 20 Hz to 12 kHz using 1935-9603 series cassettes. Guaranteed limits as shown. PLAYBACK EQUALIZATION: EIA std for Coplanar Type CPII (playback T.C. 1590μs and 120μs) (1⅞"/s). FLUTTER AND WOW: 0.3% rms as tested in accordance with NAB Standard (April 1965). SIGNAL TO NOISE RATIO: 50 dB minimum from 3% harmonic distortion to A-weighted noise level.

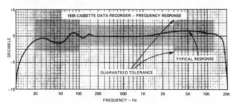

Output (each channel): 0.5 V behind 600 Ω corresponds ₊o normal maximum record level (which allows 10-dB crest-factor capacity). Any load can be connected.

Peak Monitors: Both channels include peak detectors that monitor peaks of both polarities and display on panel meters.

Tape Position Counter: Built-in mechanical counter provides index number for relocating tape position.

Supplied: Head demagnetizer, head cleaning kit, interconnecting cables to 1933 Precision Sound-Level Meter and Analyzer, earphone, microphone for voice notes, cassettes, and batteries.

Environment: TEMPERATURE: 10 to 50°C operating. −40 to +60°C storage with batteries and tape removed. HUMIDITY: 0 to 90% RH operating.

Power: 5 size-C energizers, supplied, provide about 10-hour operation. 1940 Power Supply and Charger allows line operation of 1935 and recharges suitable batteries (included with power supply).

Mechanical: DIMENSIONS (wxhxd): 6.5x10.87x3.56 in. (165x 276x90 mm). WEIGHT: 7.5 lb (3.4 kg) net, 12 lb (5.2 kg) shipping.

1940 POWER SUPPLY AND CHARGER

Power Source: 5 V for line operation of 1933, 6.5 V for line operation of 1935; 250 mA max.

Charging Source: 200 mA max for charging batteries in 1933 or 1935; automatically reduces to ≈ 30-mA trickle charge when batteries are charged. Charging time ≈ 16 h.

Supplied: 5 rechargeable nickel-cadmium C cells to replace non-rechargeable batteries in 1933 or 1935.

Power: 100 to 125 or 200 to 250 V, 50 to 400 Hz, 11 W.

Mechanical: DIMENSIONS (wxhxd): 4.38x4.25x9.44 in. (111x 108x240 mm). WEIGHT: 3.5 lb (1.5 kg) net, 5 lb (2.3 kg) shipping.

1933-9610 VIBRATION INTEGRATOR SYSTEM
(See Specifications on the following page.)

Description	Catalog Number
1933 Precision Sound-Level Meter and Analyzer	
With ½-in. and 1-in. microphones (random incidence)*	1933-9700
With ½-in. microphone only (random incidence)*	1933-9701
With ½-in. and 1-in. microphones (perpendicular incidence)**	1933-9702
With ½-in. microphone only (perpendicular incidence)**	1933-9703
SOUND ANALYSIS SYSTEMS	
1933-9710 Sound Analysis System*	1933-9710
1933-9711 Sound Analysis System**	1933-9711
1933-9712 Sound Analysis System*	1933-9712
1933-9713 Sound Analysis System**	1933-9713
1933-9714 Sound Analysis System*	1933-9714
1933-9715 Sound Analysis System**	1933-9715
ACCESSORIES AVAILABLE	
1935 Cassette Data Recorder	1935-9700
Cassette, 30-minute	1935-9603
1933 Vibration Integrator System	1933-9610
1940 Power Supply and Charger (with rechargeable cells)	1940-9701
1560-9619 Audiometer Calibration Accessory Kit	1560-9619
1562-A Sound-Level Calibrator	1562-9701
1560-P9 Dummy Microphone	1560-9609
Electret-Condenser Microphones	
Flat random-incidence response, 1-in.	1961-9601
Flat perpendicular-incidence response, 1-in.	1961-9602
Flat random-incidence response, ½-in.	1962-9601
Flat perpendicular-incidence response, ½-in.	1962-9602
Ceramic Microphone Cartridge and Adaptor, 1-in.	1971-9601
Earphone	1935-9601
Tripod	1560-9590
Cables	
Microphone extension cable, 60 ft.	1933-9601
Miniature phone plug to 1933 microphone mast	1933-9602
Cable to Simpson Recorder	1560-9675
Miniature phone plug to double banana plug	1560-9677
Miniature phone plug to standard phone plug	1560-9678
Miniature phone plug to BNC	1560-9679
Windscreens	
For ½-in. microphone, set of 4	1560-9522
For 1-in. microphone, set of 4	1560-9521
Carrying Case (small)	1933-9603
Carrying Case (large)	1933-9604
Batteries	
Spare for 1933, uses 4 (non-rechargeable)	8410-1500
Spare for 1935, uses 5 (non-rechargeable)	8410-1500
Rechargeable, set of 5	1940-9500

*Conforms to ANSI S1.4-1971 Type 1 and IEC 179
**Conforms to IEC 179

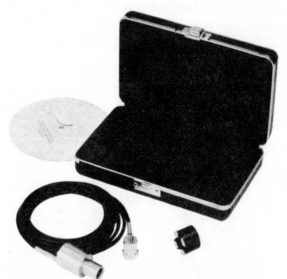

1933-9610 Vibration Integrator System

- **extends capabilities of 1933 Precision Sound-Level Meter and Analyzer**

- **direct readout in dB re standard references for:**
  - acceleration
  - velocity
  - displacement

- **handy slide rule gives metric and English vibration units**

The 1933-9610 Vibration Integrator System extends the capabilities of the 1933 Precision Sound-Level Meter and Analyzer to include vibration measurements with readout of acceleration (L_a), velocity (L_v), and displacement (L_d). This added capability increases the versatility of the 1933 for noise-reduction work by permitting the measurement and analysis of structure-borne vibration as well as airborne noise. It also adds preventive maintenance to the 1933's functions since vibration analysis is often used to detect potential parts' failures in machinery and equipment.

The system consists of a vibration pickup (accelerometer) with a magnetic clamp and keeper, a vibration integrator that mounts on the 1933 preamplifier in place of a microphone, an 8-foot cable to connect the pickup to the integrator, a storage case, and a slide rule.

The 1933 reads directly in dB re the standard references for acceleration, velocity, and displacement. A special, easy-to-use slide rule is included in the system to permit simple readout directly in vibration units. This precludes the need to refer to special conversion tables or to become involved in complex dB calculations.

SPECIFICATIONS

Measurement Range: ACCELERATION: L_a in dB re 10^{-5} m/s²; (octave) 30 to 140 dB (3.16 x 10^{-4} to 100 m/s²), (flat) 46 to 140 dB (2 x 10^{-3} to 100 m/s²). VELOCITY: L_v in dB re 10^{-8} m/s²; (octave) 60 to 150 dB (1 x 10^{-5} to 0.316 m/s), (flat) 76 to 150 dB (6.31 x 10^{-5} to 0.316 m/s). DISPLACEMENT: L_d in dB re 10^{-5} m; (octave) 50 to 150 dB (3.16 x 10^{-7} to 3.16 x 10^{-2} m), (flat) 66 to 150 dB (2 x 10^{-6} to 3.16 x 10^{-2} m).

System Environment: TEMPERATURE: -10 to $+50°C$ operating; -40 to $+70°C$ storage. HUMIDITY: 0-95% RH operating (45°C). VIBRATION: Withstand: 0.030" pk-pk vibration 10 to 55 Hz.

Transducer Environment: (Endevco Model 2217E) VIBRATION: ±1000 pk g, sinusoidal, any direction. TEMPERATURE: -54 to $+177°C$. HUMIDITY: All welded hermetic seal.

Mechanical: (System in storage case). DIMENSIONS (wxhxd): 7.562x2.000x4.625 in. (190x51x117 mm). WEIGHT: 1.5 lb (0.7 kg) net, 3 lb (1.35 kg) shipping.

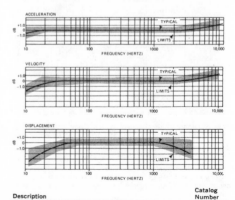

Description	Catalog Number
1933-9610 Vibration Integrator System	1933-9610

1982 Precision Sound-Level Meter and Analyzer

- a versatile, all-purpose instrument
  precision sound-level meter
  peak and impulse noise meter
  octave-band analyzer

- ideal for OSHA and a broad variety
  of noise measurements

- digital and analog displays
  for error-free reading

- compact and lightweight
  (3 lb) for easy handling

The 1982 Precision Sound-Level Meter and Analyzer combines measurement versatility with simplicity of operation to give you a practical, economical solution to a variety of noise measurements.

Now you can use a single instrument, without plug-in filters or other add-on accessories, to make A-, B-, or C-weighted sound-level measurements from 30 to 140 dB, octave-band analyses from 31.5 Hz to 16 kHz, and peak or impulse noise measurements.

The 1982 satisfies many noise-measurement requirements In a typical industrial facility, a company safety engineer, noise-control specialist or hired consultant may be required to make several types of noise measurements in a single day. With the GR 1982, the following measurements can be made without the need for any accessories or additional instrumentation.

1. A-weighted sound-level measurements to locate noise-hazard areas.
2. Peak and impulse measurements of short-duration noises caused by punch presses, metal-stamping equipment, riveting machines, etc.
3. Octave-band analyses required for:
   a. Ear-protector selection
   b. Noise-barrier material selection
   c. Noise-source identification for engineering-control programs
   d. Audiometric booth-site surveys

Beyond its many uses in industrial safety and hearing-conservation programs, the 1982 has broad application in:

1. General noise measurements made by acoustic consultants.
2. Environmental noise programs at the federal, state, and community levels.

Alternatives to the single-instrument 1982 solution are separate instruments for each measurement function or sound-level meters with cumbersome plug-in or add-on accessories. The combined cost of separate instruments and accessories usually exceeds the cost of the 1982. Also, these alternatives require operating knowledge of different instruments and increase the chances for confusion and measurement errors.

The 1982 is easy to use With all of its versatility, the 1982 is extremely easy to use and does not require special technical training. Switching its operating mode from sound-level measurement to octave-band analysis, to peak or impulse measurement requires only the push of a slide switch or turn of a knob.

Precision sound-level measurement The 1982's conformance to ANSI Type 1 and IEC Type 1 (June 1976 Draft) for Precision Sound-Level Meters is your assurance of the most accurate performance offered in a sound-level meter. To make a measurement you simply switch to the weighting and meter response (fast or slow) you desire, switch on the meter and set the attenuator to the range that gives you an on-scale reading. Then you read the measured levels from either the digital display or analog meter.

Octave-band analysis The octave-band filters in the 1982 are the most accurate offered in a portable instrument. This assures a high degree of confidence in your octave-band measurements. In addition, the 1982 eliminates the often confusing two-attenuator system used in other instruments. The 1982 features a single attenuator which allows you to set the range desired, switch on the instrument, and read the measured level from either display. Should the range level be set too low, an overload light on the meter face alerts you to change to a higher level, thus avoiding incorrect readings.

Peak and impulse measurement The 1982's peak detector is the fastest available for measuring impact- or impulse-type noise. With a 50-microsecond rise time, the detector ensures reading the true peak of the signal, up to 140 dB. An accessory 10-dB microphone attenuator extends this range to 150 dB. An impulse detector which meets IEC R179A is also built-in.

A significant feature of the 1982 allows you to capture and hold the peak or rms reading on the digital display without inhibiting successive readings on the analog meter. This lets you take ambient level readings immediately after the impact occurs without losing the peak reading. Also, in this mode it is not necessary to wait for the peak detector to decay before reading a lower level peak. A press of the capture button resets the long decay time of the peak detector allowing you to read a lower peak immediately following the previous measurement. This is especially useful when making measurements of forging hammers, metal stamping, and similar operations.

Easy, accurate reading The digital display allows quick, accurate, error-free reading with a resolution of 0.1 dB. Set the display mode to continuous and the digital display tracks the analog meter. Other operating modes allow you to "capture and hold" a reading on the digital display. You can automatically capture and hold the highest level measured during a measurement period or push a button to

capture the level at a specific moment during the period. In either of these modes, the analog meter continues to track the ambient level.

You will find the analog meter easy to read, also. It is calibrated linearly in 1-dB increments and the dB levels are clearly visible on the meter face.

Systems The 1982 is offered in a sound analysis system which includes the accessories supplied with the 1982 plus a tripod for remote mike positioning, 1562-A Sound-Level Calibrator (five frequencies at 114 dB), and 60-ft cable, all contained in a padded, luggage-type carrying/storage case.

SPECIFICATIONS

Standards: Meets the following (use 1562-A or 1567 Sound-Level Calibrator): ANSI Standard specifications for sound-level meters S1.4-1971, Type 1 (Precision); IEC Recommendation Publication 179-1965, Precision Sound-Level Meters; IEC Recommendation Publication 179A-1973; Precision Sound-Level Meters (impulse characteristics); IEC Recommendation Publication 123-1961, Sound-Level Meters; Draft Consolidated Revision of IEC Publication R123 and R179 (June 1976), Type 1 (Precision); ANSI standard specification for Octave, Half-octave, and Third-octave Band Filter Sets S1.11-1966, Type O, Class II; IEC Recommendation Publication 225-1966, Octave, Half-octave, and Third-octave Band Filters for the Analysis of Sounds and Vibrations.

Level Range: 30-130 dB re 20 μpA rms (140-dB PEAK). May be extended to 140-dB rms (150-dB PEAK) using 10-dB microphone attenuator (1962-3200) supplied. Typical minimum measurable level, 34 dBA; lower in octave bands. Noise floor at least 5 dB below minimum measurable levels.

Frequency Response: A, B, and C weighting; 10 octave-band filters ranging in center frequency from 31.5 Hz to 16 kHz; a FLAT response (+0.5, −3 dB) from 10 Hz to 20 kHz.

Detector Characteristics: DETECTOR RESPONSE*: Fast, Slow, Impulse (per IEC R179A), and Absolute Peak (<50 μsec rise time), switch selected. Precise rms detection for signals with crest factors as high as 20 dB to 120 dB** (10 dB at 130 dB). OVERLOAD: Signal peaks monitored at two critical points to provide positive panel lamp warning of overload.

Display: ANALOG: Meter with 3-inch scale marked in 1-dB increments, four ranges: 30-80 dB, 50-100 dB, 70-120 dB, 90-140 dB. DIGITAL: 4-digit LED display with 0.1-dB resolution. Direct reading on all ranges. DIGITAL DISPLAY MODES: OFF, for minimum battery drain; CONTINUOUS, like

*U.S. Patent No. 3,681,618.
**10 dB higher when 10-dB microphone attenuator is used.

meter except present reading can be "captured" by pushbutton; MAXIMUM, automatically holds highest level in measurement interval, until reset by pushbutton.

Microphone: TYPE: ½-inch Electret-Condenser Microphone with flat random (-9700) or perpendicular (-9710) incidence response. MOUNTING: Mounted with detachable preamplifier (1981-4000) that plugs into nose of instrument, or may be remoted with 10-foot cable (1933-0220) supplied or 60-foot cable (1933-9801) available. INPUT IMPEDANCE: Approximately 2 GΩ // <3 pF.

Outputs: AC OUTPUT: 0.4 V rms nominal behind 5 kΩ corresponding to full scale deflection, any load permissible. DC OUTPUT: 3 V behind 30 kΩ corresponding to full scale meter deflection. Output is linear in dB at 60 mv/dB over 70-dB range (50-dB display range plus 20 dB crest-factor allowance). Any load permissible.

Calibration: FACTORY: Fully tested and calibrated to all specifications; acoustical response and sensitivity are measured in a free field by comparison with a Western Electric Type 640AA Laboratory Standard Microphone whose calibration is traceable to the U.S. National Bureau of Standards. FIELD: GR 1562-A or 1567 Sound-Level Calibrators are available for making an overall pressure calibration. GR 1562-A, included in 1982-9720 and 1982-9730 Sound Analysis Systems, has acoustic output of 125, 250, 500, 1000, and 2000 Hz at sound-pressure level of 114 dB. 1567 has acoustic output of 1000 Hz only at 114 dB.

Environment: TEMPERATURE: −10 to +50°C operating, −40 to +60°C storage with batteries removed, 15 to 50°C during battery charging. HUMIDITY: 0-90% RH operating.

Supplied (1982-9700, -9710): Battery pack assembly; battery charger; microphone extension cable (10-foot); 10-dB microphone attenuator; calibration screwdriver; wrist strap; miniature phone plug (2); instruction manual; microphone windscreen. (1982-9720 and -9730 Systems): precision sound-level meter and analyzer; carrying case; tripod; 1562-A Sound-level Calibrator; microphone extension cable (60-foot).

Available: Carrying Case (includes space for calibrator, 60-ft cable, tripod, misc. access.); battery pack assembly; microphone extension cable (60-foot); calibrator, 1562-A, five-frequency; calibrator, 1567, single frequency; dummy microphone, 35 pF with BNC female input; tripod — will mount either 1982 or preamplifier; windscreen (package of 4); adaptor cables for connection to outputs, all 3 feet (0.9 mm) long; 1560-9619 Audiometer Calibration Accessory Kit.

Power: Removable battery pack containing 3 AA-size nickel-cadmium rechargeable cells with charger interlock. Battery life between charges 3 to 4.5 hours depending on digital display usage. Battery charger supplied operates on 115/220 volts ac 50-60 Hz; full recharge accomplished in about 4 hours. Three AA-size alkaline cells (not rechargeable) may be used in place of the battery pack.

Mechanical: DIMENSIONS: (wxhxd): 3.9x16.8x2.3 in. (99x 425x59 mm). WEIGHT: 3 lb (1.36 kg) net.

Description	Catalog Number
1982 Precision Sound-Level Meter and Analyzer (supplied with ½-inch flat random incidence response electret condenser microphone).†	1982-9700
1982 Precision Sound-Level Meter and Analyzer (supplied with ½-inch flat perpendicular incidence response electret condenser microphone).††	1982-9710
1982 Sound Analysis System includes 1982-9700 Sound-Level Meter, 1562-A Sound-Level Calibrator, 60-foot microphone extension cable, tripod, accessories, and attache-type carrying case.†	1982-9720
1982 Sound Analysis System includes 1982-9710 Sound-Level Meter, 1562-A Sound-Level Calibrator, 60-foot microphone extension cable, tripod, accessories, and attache-type carrying case.††	1982-9730
1562-A Sound-Level Calibrator	1562-9701
1567 Sound-Level Calibrator	1567-9701
1560-9619 Audiometer Calibration Accessory Kit	1560-9619
Microphone Extension Cable, 60-foot	1933-9601
Carrying Case (includes space for Calibrator, 60-ft cable, tripod and miscellaneous accessories)	1982-9610
Tripod	1560-9590
Windscreen (package of 4)	1560-9522

†Conforms to ANSI S1.4 Type I and IEC 179
††Conforms to IEC 179

1981 and 1981-B Precision Sound-Level Meters

- digital and analog displays
- digital display can hold maximum level
- 70 to 120 dBA (1981)
- 30 to 120 dBA (1981-B)
- digital display can be "frozen" at any instant
- 50-dB analog scale has 1-dB linear calibration
- meets ANSI S1.4-1971 Type S1A and IEC 179

The 1981 Series introduces a new concept in sound-level meters by combining both digital and analog displays in a single instrument. The dual-display capability of the 1981s simplifies accurate data collection and the digital display gives you the advantage of more accurate (repeatable) readings, even for the most inexperienced users of sound-level meters.

The 1981 spans the single range of 70 to 120 dBA, and the 1981-B spans 30 to 120 dBA in two switch-selectable 50-dB ranges.

Digital display The digital display on the 1981 has three operating modes for maximum ease of use in a variety of measurement situations; CONTINUOUS, MAXIMUM HOLD, and CAPTURE DISPLAY.

In the CONTINUOUS mode the digital display tracks the reading on the analog meter. This mode is normally used for general-purpose noise surveys, giving the user the option of reading the measured level on either the digital or analog display.

The CAPTURE DISPLAY mode lets you capture and hold a reading on the digital display at any given moment by simply pushing a button. This mode is especially useful when you wish to measure the sound level of a specific event. You need only press the CAPTURE DISPLAY button when the event occurs and the sound level will be displayed and held constant. The level is held until you release the button so that you have adequate time to record the reading.

In the MAXIMUM HOLD mode of operation the digital display may be set to update and hold the maximum A-weighted sound level automatically during a measurement period. This eliminates meter watching and operator interpretation of the analog display when you wish to measure the maximum sound level encountered. This mode is particularly significant for vehicle passby measurements. It permits you to measure and hold the maximum level during the passby and, at the same time, to observe the sound level rise and fall on the analog meter to ascertain that a valid measurement has been made.

Two models To satisfy users who must comply with either or both American and International Standards, the 1981 Series is available in two versions. One version is supplied with a flat random-incidence response GR Electret-Condenser Microphone. This model conforms to IEC 179 and, when used with either a GR 1567 or 1562-A Sound-Level Calibrator, it conforms to ANSI S1.4-1971 Type S1A.

The second version is supplied with a flat perpendicular-incidence response GR Electret-Condenser Microphone and conforms to IEC 179. This model is designed for use in countries where ISO Recommendations apply.

Systems and sets Most buyers of the 1981s will select a set or system because it offers convenience in selecting and ordering the meter with its commonly used accessories. For those contemplating vehicle noise measurements, a system is the logical choice because it includes accessories usually required for such measurements . . . tripod, windscreen, 60- or 66-ft cable assembly, calibrator, etc. When the use of a tripod or remote microphone positioning is not required, a 1981 Set with its meter and calibrator will satisfy almost all other measurement requirements. All systems and sets include a 1567 Sound-Level Calibrator, except the 1981-9710 which includes a 1562-A.

SPECIFICATIONS

Standards: Instruments with a GR ½-in. flat *random-incidence* response Electret-Condenser Microphone conform to IEC 179 and ANSI S1.4-1971 Type S1A when used with a GR Sound-Level Calibrator.

Instruments with a GR ½-in. flat *perpendicular-incidence* response Electret-Condenser Microphone conform to IEC 179 only.

Measurement Range and Response Characteristics: 1981: SOUND LEVEL RANGE: 70 to 120 dBA in single range; 0-dB reference is 20 μpA. FREQUENCY RESPONSE: "A" weighting. DETECTOR* CHARACTERISTICS: Rms response. Crest-factor capacity, X5 at full scale. DYNAMICS: Fast and slow, switch selected.

Measurement Range and Response Characteristics: 1981-B: SOUND LEVEL RANGE: 30 to 120 dB in two 50-dB switch-selectable ranges; 0-dB reference is 20 μpA. FREQUENCY RESPONSE: "A" weighting. DETECTOR* CHARACTERISTICS: Rms response. Crest-factor capacity, X5 at full scale. DYNAMICS: Fast and slow, switch selected.

Displays: 1981: ANALOG: Meter 3-in. scale, 70 to 120 dBA; increments 1 dB. **1981-B:** ANALOG: Meter 3-in. scale, 30 to 80 and 70 to 120 dBA; increments 1 db. DIGITAL READOUT: 4-digit with decimal point, "LED," 7-segment numerals; increments 0.1 dB. DIGITAL-DISPLAY MODES: OFF, for minimum battery drain; CONTINUOUS, like meter except present reading can be "captured" by pushbutton; MAXIMUM, automatically holds highest level in measurement interval, until reset by pushbutton.

Microphone and Terminals: MICROPHONE: GR ½-in. electret-condenser, 2 response types (see description). MICROPHONE CONNECTOR: Input impedance approx 1 GΩ, parallel 5 pF. AC OUTPUT: Weighted, 500 mV nominal full scale, behind 5 kΩ. DC OUTPUT: Approx 10 mV/dB, linear, 500 mV nominal full scale, behind 100 kΩ. Both outputs are short-circuit-proof; both receive subminiature phone plugs (0.097 in., 2.5 mm dia.). EXT PREAMPLIFIER INPUT: **1981:** Switching jack disables internal preamp when miniature phone plug (0.14 in., 3.5 mm dia.) is inserted. Adjacent 6 V OUTPUT subminiature jack provides power. Use 1981-9601 cable (connects to both jacks) and 1972-9600 preamp (contains microphone connector). INPUT: **1981-B:** ½-in. electret-condenser microphone with flat response (random or perpendicular incidence); mounted with detachable preamplifier (1933-4000) that plugs into nose of instrument, or may be remoted with accessory 60-ft cable (1933-9601).

*U.S. Patent 3,681,618.

Calibration: FACTORY: The sound-level meter with microphone is fully tested and calibrated to all specifications; acoustical response and sensitivity are measured in a free field by comparison with a Western Electric Type 640AA Laboratory Standard Microphone whose calibration is traceable to the U.S. National Bureau of Standards. FIELD: GR 1562-A or 1567 Sound-Level Calibrators are available for making an overall pressure calibration. Calibrator included in systems 1981-9710, -9711, -9712, -9713, -9760, -9761, -9762, and -9763.

Environment: TEMPERATURE: −10 to +50°C operating, 15 to 50°C battery charging, −25 to +60°C storage with battery pack supplied. HUMIDITY: 0 to 90% RH, operating and storage.

Supplied: Wrist strap, battery pack, battery charger, screwdriver for calibration adjustment, miniature phone-plug connectors, instruction manual.

Available: Rechargeable battery pack, spare, microphone extension cables (66-ft for 1981, 60-ft for 1981-B), carrying case (includes space for accessories), microphone windscreen (package of 4), tripod.

1981-9711

Power: Removable battery pack containing 3 AA-size nickel-cadmium rechargeable cells with charger interlock. Battery life between recharges, 5 to 10 hours depending on digital display usage. Battery charger (supplied) for 115/220 V ac 50-60 Hz operation; full recharge accomplished in about 4 hours. Instrument may be operated continuously from ac power by using charger; in this case battery pack is trickle-charged. Three AA-size primary cells (not rechargeable) may be used in place of the battery pack.

Mechanical: (-9700 or -9701): DIMENSIONS (wxhxd): 3.4x 10.6x2.3 in. (87x268x59 mm). WEIGHT: 28 oz (0.8 kg) net. (-9750 or -9751): DIMENSIONS (wxhxd): 3.4x11x2.3 in. (87x 292x59 mm). WEIGHT: 30 oz (0.8 kg) net. (-9710, -9711, -9760, or -9761): DIMENSIONS (wxhxd): 19x14.5x6 in. (483 x370x152 mm). WEIGHT: 15 lb (7 kg) net, 17 lb (8 kg) shipping.

Description	Catalog Number
1981 Precision Sound-Level Meter	
With ½-in. electret microphone (random incidence)*	1981-9700
With ½-in. electret condenser microphone (perpendicular incidence)**	1981-9701
1981 Precision Noise Measurement System*	1981-9710
1981 Precision Noise Measurement System**	1981-9711
1981 Precision Sound Measurement Set*	1981-9712
1981 Precision Sound Measurement Set**	1981-9713
1981-B Precision Sound-Level Meter	
With ½-in. electret condenser microphone (random incidence)*	1981-9750
With ½-in. electret condenser microphone (perpendicular incidence)**	1981-9751
1981-B Precision Noise Measurement System*	1981-9760
1981-B Precision Noise Measurement System**	1981-976¹
1981-B Precision Sound Measurement Set*	1981-9762
1981-B Precision Sound Measurement Set**	1981-9763
Carrying Case (includes space for system components)	1981-9610
Rechargeable Battery Pack, spare	1981-9602
Microphone Extension Cable, 66-foot (included in 1981-9710 and -9711 systems)	1981-9601
Microphone Extension Cable, 60-foot (included in 1981-9760 and -9761 systems)	1933-9601
Tripod	1560-9590
Windscreen (package of 4)	1560-9522

*Conforms to ANSI S1.4-1971 Type S1A and IEC 179
**Conforms to IEC 179

1551-C Sound-Level Meter

- **general purpose (Type 2)**
- **24-to-150 dB measurement range**
- **meets common standards:**
  ANSI Standard SI.4-1971
  IEC Publication 123, 1961
- **20-Hz to 20-kHz amplifier response**
- **internal calibration system**

The 1551-C is a convenient, highly accurate, general-purpose sound-level meter and is also the key instrument in a wide variety of sound-and-vibration measuring systems. In use as a sound-level meter alone, the 1551 is compact and easy to handle, rugged enough for severe environments, and simple to use.

This highly versatile Type-2 instrument will, for example, serve as a calibrated preamplifier in combination with other, related instruments such as spectrum analyzers, special-purpose microphones, calibrators, and vibration pickups. Many other accessories, such as scopes, headphones, graphic level recorders and tape recorders, can be operated from the sound-level-meter output.

This sound-level meter can also be used as a portable amplifier, attenuator, and voltmeter for laboratory measurements in the audio-frequency range.

Description The 1551-C consists of an omnidirectional microphone, a calibrated attenuator, an amplifier, standard weighting networks, and an indicating meter. The complete instrument, including batteries, is mounted in an aluminum case. The microphone can be used in several positions and, when not in use, folds down into a storage position, automatically disconnecting the batteries. An ac power-supply unit is available.

Sound level is indicated by the sum of the meter and attenuator readings. The clearly marked, open-scale meter covers a span of 16 dB.

Absolute acoustic sensitivity is factory calibrated at 500 Hz. Microphone response and sensitivity are measured in a free field from 20 Hz to 15 kHz by comparison with a WE 640AA laboratory-standard microphone with calibration traceable to the National Bureau of Standards. Complete electrical frequency-response measurements are made on each instrument.

The SLM case is fitted with soft rubber feet and amplifier is resiliently mounted for vibration isolation.

SPECIFICATIONS

Sound-Level Range: From 24 to 150 dB (re 20 μN/m²).

Frequency Characteristics: Four response characteristics as selected by panel switch. The A-, B-, and C-weighting positions are in accordance with ANSI Standard S1.4-1971 and IEC Publication 123, 1961. Response for the 20-kHz position is flat from 20 Hz to 20 kHz, to complement very wide-band microphones.

Microphone: GR 1971-9605.

Sound-Level Indication: METER: Calibration from −6 to +10 dB. ATTENUATOR: Calibrated in 10-dB steps from 30 to 140 dB above 20 μN/m².

Calibration Accuracy (absolute): ±1 dB at 500 Hz, in accordance with ANSI standard at all frequencies, when amplifier sensitivity has been standardized (use front-panel adjustment). *Note: The 1562-A Sound-Level Calibrator can be used for making periodic over-all acoustic checks.*

Output: 1.4 V behind 7000 Ω (meter at full scale). HARMONIC DISTORTION (panel meter at full scale): < 1%.

Input Impedance: 25 MΩ in parallel with 50 pF.

Meter: Rms response, fast and slow meter speeds in accordance with ANSI S1.4-1971 and IEC 123, 1961.

Environment: TEMPERATURE AND HUMIDITY: Operating, 0 to 60°C and 0 to 90% RH. (Specifications valid when SLM is standardized and meter indication > 0 dB). Storage, −30 to +95°C and 0 to 100% RH. MAGNETIC FIELDS: Residual indication ≤ 60 dB (C weighting) in a 60-Hz, 1 oersted (80 A/m) field. ELECTROSTATIC FIELDS: Negligible effect. VIBRATION: Residual indication or signal level < 45, 60, or 40 dB (C weighting) for vibration vertical, lengthwise, or sidewise, (respectively); shaker amplitude, 0.10 in. pk-pk; any frequency from 10 Hz to 55 Hz; the SLM standing on its feet.

Supplied: Telephone plug.

Available: 1551-P2 Leather Case (permits operation of instrument in case), 1562 Sound-Level Calibrator, 1560-P95 Adaptor Cable (connects output to 1521-B Level Recorder).

Power: Two 1½-V size D flashlight cells and one 67½-V battery (Burgess XX45 or equivalent), supplied.

Mechanical: Aluminum cabinet. DIMENSIONS (wxhxd): 7.25x 9.25x6.13 in. (185x235x156 mm). WEIGHT: 7.75 lb (3.6 kg) net, 16 lb (8 kg) shipping, batteries included. Add 2 lb (1 kg) for leather case.

Description	Catalog Number
1551-C Sound-Level Meter	**1551-9703**
1551-P2 Leather Carrying Case	**1551-9602**
Windscreen, for 1-in. microphone, pack of 4	**1560-9521**

Patent Number 3,012,197.

289

1565-B Sound-Level Meter

- 40-to-140 dB range
- meets ANSI Type 2 and IEC standards
- rugged ceramic microphone
- FET and integrated-circuit design combine performance with reliability
- convenient pocket proportions — small and light
- approved by Bureau of Mines

1565-B Sound-Level Meter
Type 2

The best of both worlds The 1565-B is a full-fledged standard sound-level meter — it conforms to both national and international standards, meets all criteria necessary for the noise provisions of the Occupational Safety and Health Act, and includes most of the features usually found in larger, more cumbersome, and more expensive instruments. Yet the 1565-B fits in the palm of your hand and operates in severe environments for up to 50 hours on self-contained batteries. There are no line cords to bother with or microphone cords to trip over, and an imaginative combination of controls permits one-hand operation and rapid interpretation of the result — just aim and read.

The 1565-B is the successor to the 1565-A, long popular for rapid measurements of plant, traffic and community noise.

The -B version is a total redesign to take advantage of the experience gained with its predecessor and of the latest advances in component and techniques — it is smaller, 40% lighter, and easier to use. It offers 50% longer life on batteries that are readily available. In common with the 1565-A, the 1565-B is approved by the Bureau of Mines for use in gassy coal mines.

Performance and versatility built-in The 1565-B uses a rugged, yet laboratory-quality, ceramic microphone that can be checked easily, when necessary, by such standard calibration devices as the GR 1562 Sound-Level Calibrator. An output jack is provided for use with headphones or recorders, and a lock is provided so the range control can be fixed in a single position. The instrument is housed in a tough plastic case, tapered at the microphone end to reduce the effects of case diffraction, and meets all ANSI requirements for a Type 2 general-purpose sound-level meter.

SPECIFICATIONS

Sound Level: 40 to 140 dB re 20 μN/m^2.

Weighting: A, B, and C. 1565-B conforms to ANSI S1.4-1971 Type 2 and IEC 123,1961.

Meter: Rms response with fast and slow speeds.

Input: MICROPHONE: Lead-zirconate-titanate ceramic. A 1560-P96 Adaptor converts input to 3-pin male A3 connector; for correct weighting, source impedance must be 380 pF ±5%. INPUT IMPEDANCE: ≈ 13 MΩ//15 pF.

Output: ≥1.2V rms behind 620 Ω with meter at full scale; will drive 1556 Impact-Noise Analyzer, 1558 Octave-Band Noise Analyzer, 1521 or 1523 recorders, oscilloscopes, or low-impe-

dance headphone. HARMONIC DISTORTION: ≤0.5% (0.1% typical) from 32 Hz to 8 kHz, C-weighted with meter at full scale.

Calibration: 1565-B can be acoustically calibrated at 125, 250, 500, 1000, and 2000 Hz with 1562-A Sound-Level Calibrator and at 1000 Hz with the 1567 Calibrator.

Environment: TEMPERATURE: −10 to +50°C operating; −40 to +60°C storage, with batteries removed. For 1565-B, coefficient of sensitivity ≈ +0.02dB/°C at 6 dB below full-scale meter reading. HUMIDITY: 90% RH. MAGNETIC FIELD: 1-Oersted (80 A/m) 50- or 60-Hz field causes ≈ 45 dB C-weighted indication when meter is oriented to maximum sensitivity to field.

Supplied: Carrying pouch, miniature phone plug to connect to output, screwdriver for calibration adjust, batteries.

Available: When used with 1560-P96 Adaptor: 1560-P52 Vibration Pickup, 1560-P73 or -P73B Extension Cable for remote microphone connection.

Power: Two 9-V batteries (Burgess 2U6 or equal) supplied, provide ≈ 50-h operation.

Mechanical: Shielded plastic case. DIMENSIONS (wxhxd): 3.63x6.5x2.09 in. (92x165x53 mm); WEIGHT: 1 lb (0.5 kg) net, 3 lb (1.4 kg) shipping.

Description	Catalog Number
1565-B Sound-Level Meter	1565-9702
Windscreens reduce wind noise and protect against contaminants, pack of 4	1560-9521
Battery, spare (2 required)	8410-3200

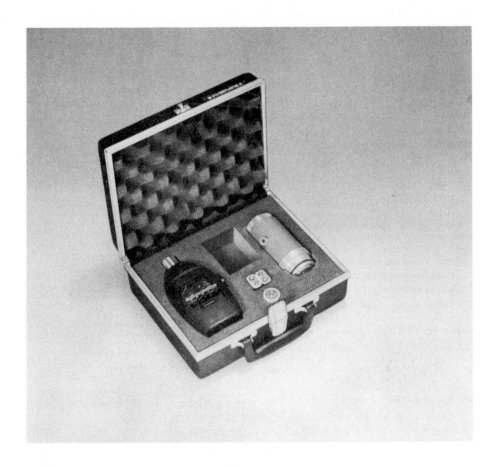

Sound-Level Measurement Sets

- measure noise levels
- calibrate "on the spot"

Convenient combination The GR sound-level measurement set is a practical buy for the person who needs to make sound-level measurements and wants to make his own periodic routine calibrations. Three versions of the set are offered, each containing a sound-level meter and a sound-level calibrator. The performance characteristics of each version are determined by the individual instruments in the set, as follows:

The 1565-B Sound-Level Meter meets ANSI Type 2 Standards.

The 1562-A Sound-Level Calibrator provides 5 frequencies, enabling you to test frequency response as well as to calibrate at a standard level. The 1567 Sound-Level Calibrator tests at 1000 Hz, for calibration of level only.

Both instruments in each set are battery operated to provide truly portable sound-level measurements and calibration in a convenient, easily carried package. The carrying case has the added advantage of keeping both instruments together in a single package. The calibrator

is therefore readily available for on-the-spot calibration of the sound-level meter.

SPECIFICATIONS

1565-9902 Sound-Level Measurement Set: 1565-B Sound-Level Meter, 1562-A Sound-Level Calibrator, carrying case, batteries, screwdriver for calibration adjust, miniature phone plug that connects to sound-level-meter output.

1565-9903 Sound-Level Measurement Set: 1565-B Sound-Level Meter, 1567 Sound-Level Calibrator, carrying case, batteries, screwdriver for calibration adjust, miniature phone plug that connects to sound-level-meter output.

Mechanical (any set): DIMENSIONS (wxhxd): 11.25x4.25x10 in. (286x108x254 mm). WEIGHT: 4.5 lb (2.1 kg) net, 12 lb (6 kg) shipping.

For all other specifications, refer to the individual descriptions of the instruments in these sets.

Description	Catalog Number
1565-9902 Sound-Level Measurement Set	1565-9902
1565-9903 Sound-Level Measurement Set	1565-9903
Carrying Case	1562-9600

1565-C Sound-Level Meter

- 30-to-130 dB range

- designed for community noise measurements

- meets ANSI S1.4-1971 Type 2 and IEC 123, 1961

- A, B, and C weighting

- small, light, and easy to use

Proven design The 1565-C incorporates the time-proven design of the popular 1565-B but has been modified to measure levels down to 30 dB to meet the requirements of community noise measurements. The operation of this sound-level meter has been simplified so that even new-comers to acoustic measurements may learn to use it properly with just a few minutes of instruction.

Versatile and dependable For maximum versatility in meeting different measurement requirements, the 1565-C has A-, B-, and C-weighting networks. Selection of the proper weighting is a simple pushbutton operation as is the se-

lection of fast or slow meter response. Another button is provided for an instant check of battery condition.

The 1565-C uses a rugged, laboratory-quality, ceramic microphone that can be checked easily, when necessary, by such standard calibration devices as the GR 1562 and 1567 Sound-Level Calibrators. An output jack is provided for use with headphones or recorders, and a lock is provided so the range control can be fixed in a single position. The instrument is housed in a tough plastic case, tapered at the microphone end to reduce the effects of case diffraction, and meets all ANSI requirements for a Type 2 general-purpose sound-level meter.

(See Specifications on the following page.)

Description	Catalog Number
1565-C Sound-Level Meter	1565-9703
Windscreens reduce wind noise and protect against contaminants, pack of 4	1560-9521
Battery, spare (2 required)	8410-3200

Sound-Level Measurement Set (Community Noise)

Whether or not your community has enacted noise ordinances, GR's 1565-9905 Sound-Level Measurement Set will be a valuable asset. The set consists of a 1565-C Sound-Level Meter for making noise measurements from 30 to 130 dB, a 1567 Sound-Level Calibrator for routine calibration of the meter, a windscreen, and a rugged carrying/storage case.

The 1565-C Sound-Level Meter has been specifically designed for community noise measurements. It meets the American National Standards Institute (ANSI) Type 2 Specifications, which detail the required instrument performance. The 1565-C is easy to operate and requires no prior knowledge of acoustics.

As is true with all measuring instruments, routine calibration is a must for measurements that have legal significance. The GR 1567 Sound-Level Calibrator is included in this set to permit on-the-spot calibration of your sound-level meter. Routine calibration is simple and takes only a few seconds.

292

Vehicle-Noise Measurement Set

Vehicle noise ordinances are currently second in number only to zoning noise ordinances. GR has designed the 1565-9906 Vehicle-Noise Measurement Set specifically to help communities measure vehicle noise and enforce related ordinances.

This GR set features simplicity of operation and calibration so that reliable measurements can be made by law enforcement officers who have had no prior experience in acoustic measurements. The set includes a GR 1565-9015 Sound-Level Meter that measures in the range of 50 to 140 dB. Since most vehicle-noise measurement regulations specify microphone location during measurement, with the observer out of the sound field, the set includes a remote microphone, extension cable, and tripod. The sound-level meter is designed to be direct reading when the extension cable is used so that correction factors are not required. This virtually eliminates measurement errors since the meter reading reflects the actual measurement. To prevent erroneous readings due to wind noise, a windscreen is provided. The windscreen also protects the microphone from dirt and other contaminants. Calibration of the sound-level meter for optimum measurement accuracy is easily performed in just a few seconds with the 1567 Sound-Level Calibrator, included in the set. The sound-level calibrator and sound-level meter are protected during storage and transportation from site to site by an impact-resistant, padded carrying case.

Should you desire to use the sound-level meter in this set for general measurements without the extension cable, the microphone is easily attached directly to the meter. Measurements from 30 to 120 dB are then possible by simply subtracting 20 dB from the meter reading.

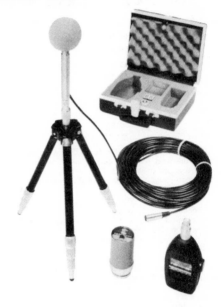

SET SPECIFICATIONS

1565-9905 Sound-Level Measurement Set: Consists of 1565-C Sound-Level Meter, 1567 Sound-Level Calibrator, windscreen, carrying case, batteries, screwdriver for calibration adjust, and miniature phone plug that connects to sound-level-meter output.

Mechanical: DIMENSIONS (wxhxd): 11.25x4.25x10 in. (286x 108x254 mm). WEIGHT: 4.5 lb (2.1 kg) net, 12 lb (6 kg) shipping.

1565-9906 Vehicle-Noise Measurement Set: Consists of 1565-9015 Sound-Level Meter, 1567 Sound-Level Calibrator, microphone, adaptor for microphone, tripod, extension cable (100 ft), windscreen, carrying case, batteries, screwdriver for calibration adjust, and miniature phone plug that connects to sound-level-meter output.

Mechanical: DIMENSIONS (wxhxd): 11.25x4.25x10 in. (286x 108x254 mm). WEIGHT: 4.5 lb (2.1 kg) net, 12 lb (6 kg) shipping.

For all other specifications, refer to "Instrument Specifications".

INSTRUMENT SPECIFICATIONS

1565-C Sound-Level Meter (included in 1565-9905 Sound-Level Measurement Set).

Sound Level: 30 to 130 dB re 20 μN/m^2, A weighted; 35 to 130 dB, B and C weighted.

1565-9015 Sound-Level Meter (included in 1565-9906 Vehicle-Noise Measurement Set).

Sound Level: (with remote microphone connected by 100-ft extension cable) 50 to 140 dB re 20 μN/m^2, A weighted; 55 to 140 dB, B and C weighted. When microphone is attached directly to sound-level meter without 100-ft extension cable, subtract 20 dB from meter reading to get true reading from 30 to 120 dB, A weighted; 35 to 120 dB, B and C weighted.

SPECIFICATIONS COMMON TO BOTH SOUND-LEVEL METERS

Weighting: A, B, and C in accordance with ANSI S1.4-1971 Type 2 and IEC 123, 1961.

Meter: RMS response with fast and slow speeds.

Input: MICROPHONE: Lead-zirconate-titanate ceramic. A 1560-P96 Adaptor converts input to 3-pin male A3 connector; for correct weighting, source impedance must be 380 pF ±5%. INPUT IMPEDANCE: ≈ 13 MΩ//15 pF.

Output: >1.2 V rms behind 6.2 kΩ with meter at full scale; will drive 1556 Impact-Noise Analyzer, 1558 Octave-Band Noise Analyzer, 1521 and 1523 recorders, oscilloscopes, or low-impedance headphone. HARMONIC DISTORTION: ≤0.5% (0.1% typical) from 32 Hz to 8 kHz, C-weighted with meter at full scale.

Calibration (with 1567 Sound-Level Calibrator): Can be acoustically calibrated at 1000 Hz; (with 1562 Sound-Level Calibrator): can be acoustically calibrated at 125, 250, 500, 1000, and 2000 Hz.

Environment: TEMPERATURE: −10 to +50°C operating; −40 to +60°C storage, with batteries removed. Coefficient of sensitivity ≈ +0.02 dB/°C at 6 dB below full-scale meter reading. HUMIDITY: 90% RH. MAGNETIC FIELD: 1-oersted (80 A/m) 50- or 60-Hz field causes ≈ 45-dB C-weighted indication when meter is oriented to maximum sensitivity to field.

Power: Two 9-V batteries (Burgess 2U6 or equal) supplied, provide ≈ 50-h operation.

Mechanical: Shielded plastic case. DIMENSIONS (wxhxd): 3.63x6.5x2.09 in. (92x165x53 mm); WEIGHT: 1 lb (0.5 kg) net, 3 lb (1.4 kg) shipping.

Description	Catalog Number
1565-9905 Sound-Level Measurement Set	1565-9905
1565-9906 Vehicle-Noise Measurement Set	1565-9906
1565-C Sound-Level Meter	1565-9703
1567 Sound-Level Calibrator	1567-9701

1983 Sound-Level Meter

- ideal for OSHA and vehicle-noise measurements
- approved by Bureau of Mines
- meets ANSI S1.4-1971 Type S2A
- one range, 70 to 120 dBA
- no range switching; turn on and read
- easy-to-read scale calibrated in 1-dB increments

This GenRad sound-level meter is specially designed to satisfy the need for a low-cost, easy-to-use sound-level meter. It meets ANSI S1.4-1971 Type S2A as required for OSHA noise measurements, plus IEC Recommendation Publication 123, 1961.

Utmost simplicity The GR 1983 is the latest in design and operating simplicity. Its tapered case minimizes reflections which could cause erroneous readings. Readings are always in dBA since the A weighting is built-in. A single range, 70 to 120 dBA, eliminates the need to make any special settings or adjustments. To make a measurement, you simply push the ON/OFF switch, orient the meter to the proper position, and read the scale. The big meter scale is extremely easy to read because of its clearly marked 1-dB increments over the entire 50-dB range. The 1983 is set to operate in the SLOW meter-response mode but a simple internal adjustment lets you switch to FAST meter response, normally used for vehicle-noise measurements.

Design features For reliable operation in tough industrial environments, a rugged ceramic microphone and solid-state circuitry are used to ensure accurate measurements in temperature extremes from −10 to +50°C and in environments of up to 95% relative humidity. The low current requirement of the 1983's circuitry permits continuous operation on a single 9-volt transistor-radio-type battery for up to 60 hours and a dc output lets you operate low-cost dc recorders and other accessories.

The 1983 is supplied with a removable microphone for remote measurements with optional extension cables. This permits the microphone to be located at the measurement point and the observer with the meter to be located away from the sound field to eliminate interference with the measurement.

Measurement sets Good measurement practice dictates periodic calibration of your sound-level meter. Many laws, including current OSHA regulations, require calibration of measuring instruments every day that measurements are made. For convenience in ordering and storing the 1983 Sound-Level Meter and a GR 1567 Sound-Level Calibrator, both of these instruments are included in the GR 1983-9915 Sound-Level Measurement Set. The set also includes a carrying/storage case plus a windscreen, screwdriver for calibration adjustment, batteries for both instruments, and a miniature plug to connect to the 1983's output.

The GR 1567 Sound-Level Calibrator lets you check the calibration of the 1983 and other acoustic instruments in a matter of seconds. It has an acoustic output of 1000 Hz at 114 dB and meets the accuracy requirements of OSHA regulations.

SPECIFICATIONS

Sound Level: 70 to 120 dBA re 20 μN/m².

Weighting: A; conforms to ANSI S1.4-1971 Type S2A and IEC 123, 1961.

Meter: Rms response, slow. Internal connection allows selection of fast response.

Output: 0.25 V behind 100 kΩ at full scale (120 dB), will drive recorders or other accessories.

Calibration: Can be pressure calibrated with GR 1562-A or GR 1567 Sound-Level Calibrator.

Environment: TEMPERATURE: −10 to +50°C operating; −40 to +60°C storage, with batteries removed. HUMIDITY: 0 to 95% RH. MAGNETIC FIELD: Reads less than 70 dB when placed in a 50- to 60-Hz magnetic field of 25 oersteds.

Supplied: Carrying pouch, miniature phone plug to connect to output, screwdriver for calibration adjust, battery.

Available: Carrying case, windscreen (package of 4).

Power: One 9-V battery (Burgess 2U6 or equal) supplied, provides 60-h operation.

Mechanical: (Meter): Shielded plastic case. DIMENSIONS: (wxhxd): 3.5x7.95x1.87 in. (89x202x48 mm); WEIGHT: 12 oz (0.34 kg) net, 3 lb (1.4 kg) shipping. (Set): DIMENSIONS: (wxhxd): 11.25x4.25x10 in. (286x108x254 mm); WEIGHT: 4.5 lb (2.1 kg) net, 12 lb (6 kg) shipping.

Description	Catalog Number
1983 Sound-Level Meter	1983-9730
1983 Sound-Level Measurement Set	1983-9915
1567 Sound-Level Calibrator	1567-9701
Carrying Case for sound-level measurement set	1983-9610
Battery, spare for meter and calibrator (1 required for each)	8410-3200
Windscreen (package of 4)	1560-9522

1983 Vehicle-Noise Measurement Set

- a complete, low-cost system
- for pass-by, start-up, and muffler testing
- meets ANSI S1.4-1971 Type S2A
- 50-dB meter display eliminates range switching
- easy-to-read linear scale, 1-dB increments

This noise measurement set has been specifically designed to satisfy vehicle-noise-measurement requirements specified by legislation at the federal, state, and local levels. The set features simplicity of operation and calibration so that reliable measurements can be made by law enforcement officers and others who have not had prior experience in acoustic measurements.

Easy to use and read The 1983 Sound-Level Meter, the heart of the set, is designed for ease of use. It has a large, linear meter, calibrated in 1-dB increments for easy reading. It spans the instrument's entire 50-dB range (70 — 120 dBA) so that you need not keep switching ranges to get an on-scale reading. Simply turn it on and read the level indicated. A-weighting is built-in so that readings are always dBA and fast or slow meter response is selectable.

The 1983 is supplied with a remote microphone, and the set includes a 20-foot extension cable and tripod. A 60-foot extension cable is available as an accessory. This permits the microphone to be located at the measurement point and the observer with the meter to be located away from the sound field to eliminate interference with the measurement.

Special set-up for muffler measurements A special tripod set-up is featured for low-to-the-ground muffler-noise measurements. With the microphone positioned near the muffler, the observer can sit at the vehicle's controls with the sound-level meter and regulate the engine's rpm while observing the meter readings.

A windscreen is supplied to negate the effects of moderate breezes on the measurement and to protect the microphone from dust, dirt and other airborne contaminants. It is good practice to check calibration at the beginning and end of each day that measurements are made, and on-the-spot calibration checks of the sound-level meter can be made in a matter of seconds with the GR 1567 Sound-Level Calibrator included in the set.

SPECIFICATIONS

1983 VEHICLE NOISE MEASUREMENT SET

Supplied: 1983-9730 Sound-Level Meter, 1567 Sound-Level Calibrator, carrying case, tripod, 20-foot extension cable, windscreen, spare batteries.

Available: 1933-9601 60-foot extension cable.

1983-9730 Sound-Level Meter

Sound Level: 70 to 120 dB re 20 μN/m².

Weighting: A; conforms to ANSI S1.4-1971 Type S2A and IEC 123, 1961.

Meter: Rms response, slow. Internal connection allows selection of fast response.

Output: 0.25 V behind 100 kΩ at full scale (120 dB), will drive recorders or other accessories.

Calibration: Can be pressure calibrated with GR 1562-A or GR 1567 Sound-Level Calibrator.

Environment: TEMPERATURE: −10 to +50°C operating; −40 to +60°C storage, with batteries removed. HUMIDITY: 0 to 95% RH. MAGNETIC FIELD: Reads less than 70 dB when placed in a 50- to 60-Hz magnetic field of 25 oersteds.

Supplied: Miniature phone plug to connect to output, screwdriver for calibration adjust, battery.

Power: One 9-V battery (Burgess 2U6 or equal) supplied provides 60-h operation.

Mechanical: (Meter): Shielded plastic case. DIMENSIONS (wxhxd): 3.5x7.95x1.87 in. (89x202x48 mm); WEIGHT: 12 oz (0.34 kg) net, 3 lb (1.4 kg) shipping. (Set, excluding tripod): DIMENSIONS: (wxhxd): 11.25x4.25x10 in. (286x108x254 mm); WEIGHT: 6.5 lb (2.9 kg) net, 14 lb (6.4 kg) shipping.

Description	Catalog Number
1983 Vehicle Noise Measurement Set	**1983-9910**
1933-9601 60-foot accessory cable	1933-9601
Windscreens for ½-in. microphone, pack of 4	1560-9522

1954 Noise Dosimeter

... consists of Monitor and Indicator as follows

1954 Noise-Exposure Monitor

- user adjustable threshold and criterion levels
- small, shirt-pocket size
- light weight, 10 oz
- tamper-proof
- built-in and remote mike
- conforms to applicable portions of ANSI S1.4-1971, and IEC Type 2 Sound-Level Meters

1954 Indicator

- only one required for any number of monitors
- built-in sound-level calibrator checks complete system including microphone
- readout available only to authorized persons
- all electronic, including bright light-emitting-diode display — no moving parts
- powered by monitor battery

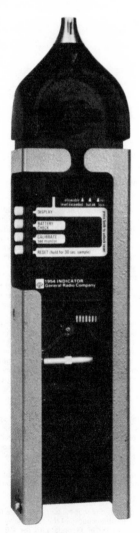

1954 Monitor   1954 Indicator

Why use a noise dosimeter? The 1954 Noise Dosimeter is designed to save you time and money in the measurement of noise for computation of personal noise dose. In industrial environments where noise levels vary constantly, noise-dose measurements are the easiest method of determining both the risk of hearing damage and compliance with the law. Computing noise dose in virtually every industrial environment would necessitate tedious day-long measurements with a sound-level meter and timing with a stop watch. This is necessary because noise dose is computed by the formula:

$$D = \frac{C_1}{T_1} + \frac{C_2}{T_2} + \ldots \frac{C_n}{T_n}$$

where D is noise dose, C is the actual duration (in hours) at a given steady noise level, and T is the noise exposure limit (in hours) from the table below.

Sound level (dBA)	90	95	100	105	110	115
Time permitted (hours)	8	4	2	1	0.5	0.25

Computing noise dose with a sound-level meter is generally impractical and expensive. A noise dosimeter performs the measuring, timing, and computing automatically. You need only read the computed answer at the end of the measurement period.

Unsurpassed for noise-dose measurements The primary function of the 1954 is automatic monitoring of sound levels and computing personal noise dose based on current OSHA noise limits and other established standards. Should the limits change, you can re-adjust the 1954 yourself, quickly and easily. A screwdriver is all you will need to adjust the exchange rate, criterion level, threshold level, and maximum allowable level. There is no expense or lost measurement time since the 1954 need not be returned to the factory or a service center for adjustment.

Noise-dose measurements are simple and automatic At the start of the workday or other monitoring period, your noise-program supervisor turns on the small wearable monitor by means of a concealed on-off switch. Operating controls are concealed to discourage tampering. The monitor is then calibrated (about 10 seconds), clipped in a pocket or on a belt or waistband, and the tiny microphone is positioned at the ear, on a collar, or wherever you desire. Noise levels to which the wearer is exposed are then monitored continually throughout the workday, and noise dose is computed automatically without any effort or operating requirements on the part of the employee or noise-program supervisor.

Reading the noise dose is quick and easy At the end of the measurement period the monitor is plugged into the 1954 Indicator. You simply push a button to retrieve the computed noise dose which is then displayed on a 4-digit electronic display. The number is the actual percentage of the OSHA criterion limit. A display of 085.0, for example, means that the total noise dose is 85% of the OSHA maximum, a safe level. A reading of 145.0 indicates that the noise dose exceeds OSHA limits by 45% and that some corrective action is required.

Since the OSHA maximum allowable noise level is 115 dBA, the 1954 is designed to indicate if 115 dBA was exceeded during the measurement. This is shown by a lamp on the indicator that lights during readout of the noise dose.

Push the "Display" button for a clear, digital indication of the computed dose (actual percentage of OSHA maximum), and to see if 115 dBA was exceeded. This does not reset monitor memory to zero.

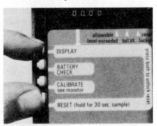

Press "Display" and "Reset" buttons simultaneously to reset monitor to zero for start of a new measurement period.

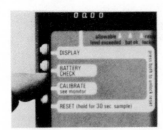

Microphone is secured in calibration cavity by spring-loaded clip. Press the "Calibrate" button and read prescribed level in just under ten seconds. Continuous adjustment, if necessary, can be made quickly with screwdriver supplied.

Calibration takes less than 10 seconds The 1954 Indicator features a built-in calibrator that lets you check the complete instrument from the microphone to the display at the push of a button. Unlike other dosimeters, the 1954 can be continuously adjusted during the calibration period, with the screwdriver supplied. An opening in the monitor case provides access to the calibration adjustment so that the case need not be taken apart. The procedure is as simple as calibrating a sound-level meter.

A complete calibration check takes less than 10 seconds and is recommended at the beginning and end of each measurement period. A separate calibrator is not required, as with other systems.

Work area noise-exposure measurements You can use the 1954 to measure the noise dose of specific work areas. These measurements are also completely automatic. The procedure is simple. Just switch on the monitor, plug it into the indicator, position the microphone on the microphone extension, and place the 1954 on a table or set it up on a tripod in the area to be measured. At any time during the measurement period, you can check the computed noise-dose answer by pushing the "display" button. This does not erase the memory and allows you to continue the measurement for the full period.

Equivalent sound-level measurements Noise-survey measurements, usually made with a sound-level meter, are another function of the 1954. Again you plug the monitor into the indicator and position the microphone on the removable extension. Sound-level measurements are made by pressing the "Reset" button. In a few seconds, you'll get a reading on the digital display that you can convert to dBA by simply reading the conversion chart printed on the monitor face.

Users concerned with community-noise measurements can select a 3-dB exchange rate monitor which allows L_{eq} measurements prescribed in many community-noise ordinances.

User adjustable Obsolescence due to changes in OSHA or other noise criteria is not a factor when you buy the GR 1954. Provision is made for you, the user, to readjust the 1954 to meet most changes when they occur. And all you need is a screwdriver. There is no service charge to be concerned with, and no time lost in returning your instrument to the factory or a service center.

The versatility of the 1954 precludes the need to buy a separate sound-level meter and/or area noise monitor for many users. And if community-noise measurements become a factor in the future, an additional monitor is all you need for L_{eq} measurements.

SPECIFICATIONS
NOISE-EXPOSURE MONITOR: (5-dB Exchange Rate) 1954-9710

The 1954-9710 Noise-Exposure Monitor integrates the noise in conformance with OSHA Regulations (90-dB Threshold, 5-dB Exchange rate). The integrated level is stored in a low-power MOS-type counter which is permanently connected to the battery. The Monitor can be converted in the field by changing plug-in jumpers to provide an 80, 85, or 90 dB threshold and an exchange rate of either 3 or 5 dB.

Noise Level Exposure: Maximum permissible exposure of 100% in accordance with OSHA is accumulated for the following combinations: (Range control set to 80-130).

Sound Level dB (A)	Exposure (hours per day)
90	8
95	4
100	2
105	1
110	0.5
115	0.25

Sound level is interpolated between the above points. The integrator cuts off sharply below 90 dB (A).

Level Ranges: Selectable by switch on top of Monitor.

Sound-Level Range (dB)	Threshold Level (dBA)	Peak Level W/O Overload (dB)	Allowable Level Exceeded Indication (dBA)
80-130	90	143	115
60-110	70	123	95
40- 90	50	103	75

Weighting: "A" in accordance with ANSI Standard S1.4-1971, Type 2 and IEC publication R123, 1961.

Accuracy: At 116.5 dB, 1 kHz, 23°C, 760 mm Hg; ±7% of indicated reading ($\approx$ ±0.5 dB). Temperature coefficient of sensitivity typically +0.03 dB/°C. Unit calibrated for a reading at the mid-point of the allowable calibration range using the built-in calibrator.

Linearity: Within selected sound-level range: ±1 dB (measured at 1 kHz with reference to a level 35 dB above threshold).

Standards: Satisfies all applicable sections of ANSI S1.4-1971 for Type 2 sound-level meters and IEC Publication R123, 1961.

Detector*: True rms response with SLOW dynamic characteristics in accordance with ANSI S1.4-1971, IEC Publication R123, 1961. Crest-factor capacity at 115 dB is greater than 25 dB.

Allowable Level Exceeded: If on the 80-130 dB sound-level range, 115-dB sound level is exceeded, this information is stored in the monitor unit and read out on the indicator. On the 60-110 dB and 40-90 dB ranges, an indication is given if level during monitoring period ever exceeds 90 and 75 dB respectively.

Microphone: Ceramic type. Remote from monitor (32" extension cable).

Environment: TEMPERATURE: −10 to +50°C operating, −40 to +60°C storage with batteries removed. HUMIDITY: 0 to 90% RH at 40°C.

*Patent Number 368,168

298

Effect of Magnetic Field: On the 80-130 dB range, the monitor will accumulate equivalent to a level less than 80 dB when placed in a magnetic field of 100 oersteds at 50 or 60 Hz, or less than 40 dB in a 6-oersted magnetic field at 50 or 60 Hz on any range.

Supplied: Three earloops, one windscreen set (contains 2 windscreen assemblies), one 9-V alkaline battery, three battery sleeves.

Available: 1954-9610 Windscreen Set (contains 4 windscreen assemblies), 1954-9630 Microphone Assembly (includes 32-inch cable and plug), 8410-3400 9-V alkaline battery, Mallory Type MN 1604 or equivalent.

Power: One 9-V alkaline battery supplied, provides 40 hours of typical operation. MOS-counter and latch-storing data are permanently connected to the battery and can store accumulated noise dose and maximum level exceeded data for three months (monitor alone), one month with monitor plugged into indicator.

Mechanical: Shielded microphone and metal case. DIMENSIONS (wxhxd): 2.5x6.0x1.2 in. (63x153x31 mm). WEIGHT: 10.3 oz (0.29 kg) net.

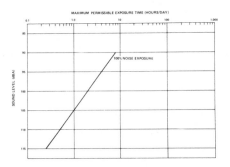

NOISE-EXPOSURE MONITOR (3-dB Exchange Rate) 1954-9700

Specifications same as 1954-9710 except those below.

The 1954-9700 Noise-Exposure Monitor integrates noise in accordance with ISO 1999 (August 1975). The integrated level is stored in a low-power, MOS-type counter which is permanently connected to the battery. The monitor can be converted in the field by changing plug-in jumpers to provide an 80, 85, or 90 dB threshold and an exchange rate of either 3 or 5 dB.

Noise Level Exposure: The noise exposure index number displayed doubles when exposed time is doubled or when exposure level is increased by 3 dB. A level change of 3 dB can be traded for a factor of two in time. The monitor operates linearly over a dynamic range of 60 dB above the threshold level selected. This 60-dB range includes an allowance of 13 dB for signal crest factor. Exposure index numbers from 00.00 to 9999 are stored for display on the indicator.

Level Ranges: Selectable by switch on top of monitor.

Sound-Level Range (dB)	Threshold Level (dBA)	Peak Level W/O Overload (dB)	Allowable Level Exceeded Indication (dBA)
80-130	80	143	130
60-110	60	123	110
40- 90	40	103	90

Accuracy: At 116.5 dB, 1 kHz, 23°C, 760 mm Hg atmospheric pressure; ±11% of indicated reading (≈±0.5 dB). Temperature coefficient of sensitivity typically +0.03 dB/°C. (Unit calibrated for a reading at the midpoint of the allowable calibration range using the built-in calibrator.)

Standards: Satisfies ISO 1999 (1975) and applicable portions of IEC Publication R123, 1961, and ANSI Standard S1.4-1971 for Type 2 Sound-Level Meters.

Detector*: True rms response with SLOW dynamic characteristics in accordance with IEC Publication R123, 1961, and ANSI Standard S1.4-1971, Type 2. Crest-factor capacity at high end of range is 13 dB.

Allowable Level Exceeded: If the upper limit of the selected range is exceeded (i.e., 130, 110, or 90 dB), this information is stored in the monitor unit and read out on the indicator.

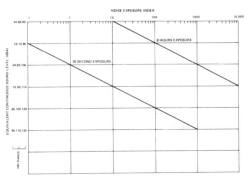

NOISE-EXPOSURE MONITOR: (3-dB Exchange Rate) 1954-9730

Specifications same as 1954-9710 except those below.

The 1954-9730 Noise-Exposure Monitor integrates noise in accordance with ISO 1999 (August 1975). The integrated level is stored in a low-power, MOS-type counter which is permanently connected to the battery. The monitor can be converted in the field by changing plug-in jumpers to provide an 80, 85, or 90 dB threshold and an exchange rate of 3 or 5 dB.

Noise Level Exposure: Same as 1954-9700.

Level Ranges: Same as 1954-9700.

Weighting: "A" in accordance with ANSI Standard S1.4-1971 and Draft Consolidated Revision of IEC Publications R123 and R179 (June 1976) for Type 2 Sound-Level Meters.

Accuracy: Same as 1954-9700.

Standards: Satisfies ISO 1999 (1975) and applicable portions of Draft Consolidated Revision of IEC Publications R123 and R179 (June 1976) and ANSI Standard S1.4-1971 for Type 2 Sound-Level Meters.

Detector*: True rms response with SLOW dynamic characteristics in accordance with Draft Consolidated Revision of IEC Publications R123 and R179 (June 1976) and ANSI Standard S1.4-1971, Type 2. Crest-factor capacity at high end of range is 13 dB.

Allowable Level Exceeded: Same as 1954-9700.

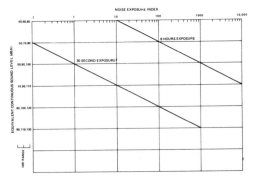

NOISE-EXPOSURE MONITOR (4-dB Exchange Rate) 1954-9780

Specifications same as 1954-9710 except those below.

The 1954-9780 Noise-Exposure Monitor integrates noise in accordance with AFR 161-35. The integrated level is stored in a low-power, MOS-type counter which is permanently connected to the battery. The monitor can be converted in the field by changing plug-in jumpers to provide an 80, 85, or 90 dB threshold and an exchange rate of either 3, 4, or 5 dB.

Noise Level Exposure: The percentage exposure displayed doubles when exposed time is doubled or when exposure level is increased by 4 dB. A level change of 4 dB can be traded for a factor of two in time. Percentage exposure numbers from 00.00 to 9999 are stored for display on the indicator.

Level Ranges: Selectable by switch on top of monitor.

Sound-Level Range (dB)	Threshold Level (dBA)	Peak Level W/O Overload (dB)	Allowable Level Exceeded Indication (dBA)
80-130	80	137	115
60-110	60	117	95
40- 90	40	97	75

Accuracy: At 116.5 dB, 1 kHz, 23°C, 760 mm Hg atmospheric pressure; ±9% of indicated reading (≈±0.5 dB). Temperature coefficient of sensitivity typically +0.03 dB/°C. (Unit calibrated for a reading at the midpoint of the allowable calibration range using the built-in calibrator.)

Standards: Same as 1954-9700.

Detector*: True rms response with SLOW dynamic characteristics in accordance with IEC Publication R123, 1961, and ANSI Standard S1.4-1971, Type 2.

Allowable Level Exceeded: If, on the 80-130 sound-level range, 115-dB sound level is exceeded, this information is stored in the monitor unit and read out on the indicator. On the 60-110 dB and 40-90 dB ranges, an indication is given if the level (during the monitoring period) ever exceeds 90 and 75 dB respectively.

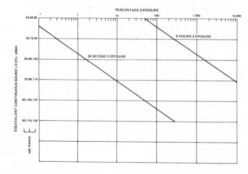

INDICATOR 1954-9720

The 1954-9720 Indicator converts the information stored in the 1954 Noise-Exposure Monitor and displays it as a four digit number. This number has different designations depending on the monitor in use. The indicator is also used to calibrate and reset the monitor as well as check the monitor battery.

Readout: The display will indicate either percentage exposure or index number and have a range of either 0.000 to 999.9 or 00.00 to 9999. The indication and display range are dependent on the monitor in use (see 1954 Noise-Exposure Monitor Specifications).

Allowable Level Exceeded: When the DISPLAY button is depressed, a light indicates if the specified ALLOWABLE LEVEL for the monitor in use (see 1954 Noise-Exposure Monitor Specifications), was exceeded during the monitoring period. The allowable level exceeded circuit in the monitor is reset when the RESET button is depressed.

Calibration: A sound-level calibrator is included in the indicator. The calibrator tests all circuits in the monitor including the integrator. The calibration signal is applied as a steady tone. The calibration cycle will repeat automatically every 0.9 sec. by resetting the monitor, allowing calibration adjustment in a matter of seconds.

The calibrator operates at a frequency of 1000 Hz with an output level of 116.5 ±0.5 dB re 20 μpA. Temperature coefficient is ±0.02 dB/°C. Atmospheric pressure correction chart supplied.

Battery Check: The monitor battery voltage is checked by lighting an LED on the indicator if it is above the minimum operating voltage. Additionally, all eights are activated on the readout to (1) check the readout digits and (2) apply a heavier than normal load to the battery.

30-Second Sample Operation Mode: This mode is initiated by depressing and holding the RESET button. The display automatically indicates exposure when 30 (28.8 actual) seconds have lapsed. This number multiplied by 1000 predicts the 8-hour exposure.

Environment: TEMPERATURE: −10 to +50°C operating, −40 to +60°C storage. HUMIDITY: 0-90% RH at 40°C.

Supplied: An accessory slide rule allows "equivalent continuous sound level" to be computed by entering the measurement period and the percentage or index number displayed. Jeweler's screwdriver is supplied for calibration, activation of monitor controls, and access to battery compartment. Microphone extension assembly supports microphone on indicator when L_{eq} measurements are being made.

Available: 1954-9600 Carrying Case includes space for one indicator, ten monitors, microphone extension assembly, ten batteries, and miscellaneous small accessories.

Power: Supplied by battery in monitor.

Mechanical: DIMENSIONS (wxhxd): 3.31x14.5x2.39 in. (84x 368x61 mm). WEIGHT: 2.75 lb (1.25 kg).

Description	Catalog Number
1954 Noise-Exposure Monitor, 5-dB exchange rate, meets U.S.A. OSHA requirements	1954-9710
1954 Noise-Exposure Monitor, 3-dB exchange rate, meets U.S.A. EPA requirements for L_{eq}	1954-9700
1954 Noise-Exposure Monitor, 3-dB exchange rate, meets JSO recommendations and IEC standards	1954-9730
1954 Noise-Exposure Monitor, 4-dB exchange rate, meets USAF AFR 161-35 requirements	1954-9780
1954 Indicator, one indicator and at least one monitor comprise a complete dosimeter. Only one indicator is required for any number of monitors	1954-9720
1954-9785 Personal Noise Dosimeter, contains 5 each 1954-9780, one 1954-9720 and one 1954-9600 (meets USAF requirements)	1954-9785
1954 Carrying Case, holds up to 10 monitors and one indicator	1954-9600
1954 Windscreen Set, contains 4 windscreen assemblies	1954-9610
1954 Microphone Assembly, includes 32-in. cable and connector, used on -9700, -9710, -9780 monitors	1954-9630
1954 Microphone Assembly, includes 32-in. cable and connector, used on -9730 monitor	1954-9640
Spare Battery, only one required to power both monitor and indicator	8410-3400

1562-A Sound-Level Calibrator

- 125 to 2000 Hz
- ±0.3-dB accuracy at 500 Hz
- fits many microphones
- approved by Bureau of Mines

A handful of precision The 1562-A is a self-contained unit for making accurate field calibrations on microphones and sound-measuring instruments. This calibrator fits in the palm of your hand, operates on its own battery power, features a single fumble-free control, and provides a precisely known sound-pressure level at five ANSI-preferred frequencies.

Adaptors supplied with the 1562-A permit calibration of any GR 1⅛", 1", or ½" microphone. Optional adaptors are available to permit calibration of most other standard-size microphones.

An electrical signal output is provided for tests on instruments without microphones, and a built-in indicator lamp checks for adequate battery voltage.

Typical GR instruments that can be calibrated with the 1562-A are sound-level meters, octave-band analyzers, and sound and vibration analyzers.

SPECIFICATIONS

Acoustic Output: FREQUENCIES: 125, 250, 500, 1000, and 2000 Hz; ±3%. SOUND-PRESSURE LEVEL: 114 dB re 20 $\mu N/m^2$; accuracy at 23°C and 760 mm Hg is, for WE 640AA or

equivalent microphone, ±0.3 dB at 500 Hz and ±0.5 dB at other frequencies; and, for other microphones, ±0.5 dB at 500 Hz and ±0.7 dB at other frequencies.

Electrical Output: 1 V ±20% behind 6 kΩ, flat ±2% with <0.5% distortion; available at phone jack.

Environment: TEMPERATURE: 0 to 50°C operating. Temperature coefficient of sound-pressure level is 0 to −0.012 dB/°C; correction chart supplied. HUMIDITY: 0 to 100% RH.

Supplied: Carrying case, adaptors for ½- and 1-in. microphones (fits 1⅛-in. microphones without adaptor), battery.

Available: 1560-9561 Coupler Adaptor Set, for coupling 1562 to ⅛, ¼, and ½-in. B&K microphones.

Power: Battery operated (9 V, Burgess PM6 or equal); 120 h use

Mechanical: DIMENSIONS: 5 in. (127 mm) long x 2.25 in. (57 mm) dia. WEIGHT: 1 lb (0.5 kg) net, 4 lb (1.9 kg) shipping

Description	Catalog Number
1562-A Sound-Level Calibrator ⊛	**1562-9701**
Coupler Adaptor Set, adapts 1562-A to ⅛, ¼, and ½-in. microphone	**1560-9561**
Battery, spare (1 required)	**8410-3000**

1567 Sound-Level Calibrator

Economical Calibration The 1567 Sound-Level Calibrator is specially designed for you who wish to check instrument sensitivity only (not frequency response). The 1567 has a single-level output and is well suited for calibrating the 1563 and 1565-B Sound-Level Meters at 1 kHz.

SPECIFICATIONS

Acoustic Output: FREQUENCY: 1000 Hz, ±3%. SOUND-PRESSURE LEVEL: 114 dB re 20 $\mu N/m^2$; accuracy (at 23°C and 760 mm Hg) is ±0.5 dB for 1565-B, ±1 dB for 1563.

Environment: TEMPERATURE: 0 to 55°C operating. Temperature coefficient of sound-pressure level is zero ±0.01 dB/°C,

0 to 23°C; −0.017 ± 0.008 dB/°C, 23 to 50°C. Pressure-correction chart supplied. HUMIDITY: 0 to 95% RH.

Supplied: Carrying case, adaptors for ½- and 1-in. microphones (fits 1⅛-in. microphones without adaptor), battery.

Power: Battery operated, using 9-V Burgess 2U6 or equivalent; 100 h of use.

Mechanical: Cylindrical housing. DIMENSIONS (dia x h): 2.38x 4.44 in. (61x113 mm). WEIGHT: 1 lb (0.5 kg) net, 4 lb (1.9 kg) shipping.

Description	Catalog Number
1567 Sound-Level Calibrator	**1567-9701**
Battery, spare (1 required)	**8410-3200**

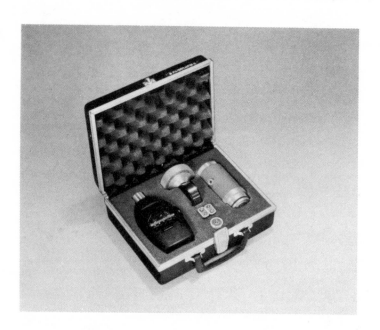

1562-Z Audiometer Calibration Set

The **1562-Z — faulty hearing or faulty audiometer?** Studies have revealed that audiometers may have only a 50-50 chance of being accurate. Deficiencies include sound pressure at or beyond tolerance limits, faulty earphone performance, frequency outside limits, excessive harmonic distortion, and extraneous instrument noise.

With this fact in mind the 1562-Z Audiometer Calibration Set was conceived — mini-systems with maxibenefits for tight budgets. Each contains a sound-level meter and earphone coupler to measure the output level and frequency response of the audiometer, a sound-level calibrator to ensure accurate readings from the sound-level meter, a calibration chart, a full set of instructions, and a convenient carrying case to keep everything together.

Earphone Couplers The set includes a 1560-P83 Earphone Coupler that fits GR 1-inch-diameter microphones and Type L laboratory standard microphones such as the WE640AA. The set can be used for calibrating the Telephonics TDH-39 and TDH-49 earphones with the earphone cushions (MX-41/AR) left in place.

SPECIFICATIONS
1562-Z AUDIOMETER CALIBRATION SET

Supplied: 1565-B Sound-Level Meter, 1562 Sound-Level Calibrator, earphone coupler, spare batteries, storage case.

Mechanical: DIMENSIONS (wxhxd): 11.25x4.25x10 in. (286x 108x254 mm). WEIGHT: 5 lb (2.3 kg) net, 12 lb (6 kg) shipping.

EARPHONE COUPLER

1560-P83: GR 9A (modified version of NBS type 9-A). VOLUME: 5.642 cm³ including volume added by microphone. AXIAL HOLDING FORCE: 450 grams nominal.

Frequency: 125 Hz to 8 kHz audiometric frequencies; response is equal to that obtained with NBS 9-A coupler within 1 dB to 4 kHz and 1.5 dB to 8 kHz when it is used with TDH-39 or TDH-49 earphone in MX-41/AR earcushion.

Mechanical: 1560-P83: DIMENSIONS: Coupler, 2.94 in. dia x 1.25 in. high (75x32 mm); over-all (wxhxd), 2.94x3.5x3.5 in. (75x90x90 mm). WEIGHT: 0.5 lb (0.3 kg) net, 2 lb (1 kg) shipping.

Description	Catalog Number
1562-Z Audiometer Calibration Set	**1562-9901**
1560-P83 Earphone Coupler, GR type 9A	**1560-9683**
Battery, spare for 1565-B (2 required)	**8410-3200**
Battery, spare for 1562-A (1 required)	**8410-3000**

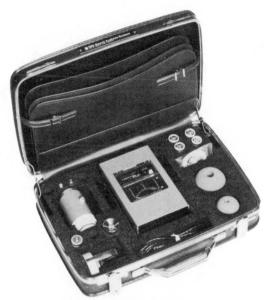

1933 Audiometer Calibration System

Your best choice for compliance with current and proposed OSHA regulations

• The system lets you calibrate audiometers and check attenuator linearity over the range of 10 dB to 90 dB HL
• Calibration chart documents sound-level-meter readings for popular TDH -39,-49, and -50 earphones to simplify calibration
• Precision sound-level meter gives you A-, B-, and C-weighting and impulse/impact capability, plus octave-band analysis to perform many other OSHA-required measurements

No matter how well planned a hearing conservation program may be or how carefully the equipment has been selected, the entire effort can be jeopardized by insufficient evidence that instruments have been performing properly. OSHA recognizes this and requires that audiometers be calibrated periodically.

Key elements in the system for audiometer calibration are a 1933 Precision Sound-Level Meter and Analyzer, a 1562-A Sound-Level Calibrator, and a 1560-P83 Earphone Coupler. The earphone coupler couples a TDH-39, -49, or -50 earphone to the sound-level meter's microphone in a sealed cavity of standard size and shape and simulates compliance of the human ear. A calibration chart, included, documents sound-level-meter readings at 70 and 90 HL, eliminating cumbersome manual calibration. Basic microphone-pressure-response data are also provided to facilitate more detailed investigations.

Other items included with the system make it a versatile tool for a number of other OSHA-required measurements. These accessories are listed in the specifications section and comprise a very complete measurement system with which you can make plant noise surveys of both continuous and impact noise, audiometric booth-site surveys, measurements for noise reduction, hearing protector evaluations, and other general-purpose measurements.

The 1933 has several features to help simplify accurate measurements. The microphone is mounted on a 12-inch extension mast to eliminate reflections from the meter case and observer. An automatic attenuator system eliminates wrong settings and a linear meter scale (20-dB range) makes meter reading virtually mistake proof.

SPECIFICATIONS
1933-9716 AUDIOMETER CALIBRATION SYSTEM

Supplied: 1933-9700 Precision Sound-Level Meter and Analyzer, including $\frac{1}{2}$-inch and 1-inch random-incidence electret-condenser microphones, microphone attenuator, tool kit, microphone extension cable (10-ft) and batteries; dummy microphone; $\frac{1}{2}$-inch and 1-inch windscreen (one each); earphone; 1562-A Sound-Level Calibrator, with adaptors for $\frac{1}{2}$-inch and 1-inch microphones, and batteries; 1560-P83 Earphone Coupler; 1933-9603 Carrying Case with custom-padded insert to accommodate all system components plus a compartment for instruction manuals and other paperwork.

Mechanical: DIMENSIONS (wxhxd): 19x14.5x6 in. (483x370x 152 mm.)   WEIGHT: 15 lb (7 kg) net, 17 lb (8 kg) shipping.

1560-P83 EARPHONE COUPLER

GR 9A, fulfills the requirements of NBS type 9-A.

Volume: 5.642 cm³ including volume added by microphone.

Axial Holding Force: 450 grams nominal.

Frequency: 125 Hz to 8 kHz, audiometric frequencies; response is equal to that obtained with NBS 9-A coupler within 1 dB to 4 kHz and 1.5 dB to 8 kHz when it is used with TDH-39, -49, or -50 earphone in MX-41/AR earcushion.

Mechanical: DIMENSIONS: Coupler, 2.94 in. dia. x 1.25 in. high (75x32 mm); over-all (wxhxd), 2.94x3.5x3.5 in. (75x90x 90 mm).   WEIGHT: 0.5 lb (0.3 kg) net.

Description	Catalog Number
1933 Audiometer Calibration System	1933-9716

1560-9619
Audiometer Calibration Accessory Kit

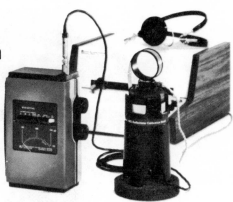

- **permits field calibration of audiometers with accuracy comparable to factory calibration**
- **stable, bench-mounted base for microphone and earphone coupler**
- **supplied with precision, one-inch electret-condenser microphone**
- **includes all necessary calibration data**

The 1560-9619 Audiometer Calibration Accessory Kit is designed to be used with either the GenRad 1982 or 1933 Precision Sound-Level Meter and Analyzer for the precise calibration of audiometers. When used with these meters, it permits the periodic calibration of audiometers as required by OSHA and other agencies, to the sound-pressure-level values specified in ANSI S3.6 1969 or other standards which require the NBS Type 9-A coupler to be used in the measurement procedure.

The kit contains all the necessary components needed to measure the acoustic output of audiometers when used with the 1982 or 1933. An optional acoustic calibrator such as the GenRad 1562-A or 1567 enables the user to make an independent acoustical check of the measuring system. Included in the kit are a GR 1560-P83 Earphone Coupler which fulfills the requirements of NBS Type 9-A, a 1-inch GenRad Electret-Condenser Microphone, an adaptor (1-inch to ½-inch thread), audiometer calibration stand assembly, calibration chart, and instruction sheet.

Calibration Data The calibration chart in the kit documents octave band sound-pressure levels for 125 Hz to 8000 Hz. Data are given for an audiometer setting of 70 dB HL for the TDH-39 earphone, and 70 dB HL and 90 dB HL for the TDH-49 and TDH-50 earphones. Readings are given for the flat and A-weighted scale on the 1982 and 1933 Precision Sound-Level Meters and Analyzers.

Pressure-response corrections for the supplied microphone in a P83 coupler are provided for octave-band frequencies 125 Hz to 8000 Hz.

Stable stand assembly The audiometer calibration stand assembly is a cast metal stand which supports the 1-inch microphone, earphone coupler, and 1982 or 1933 preamplifier. It has a polyethylene-foam base for isolation against shock and vibration during the measurement.

The stand eliminates mounting the earphone coupler directly on the sound-level meter and the subsequent risk of the meter falling over.

Easy set-up and use 1. To use the 1560-9619 kit with a 1982 or 1933 Precision Sound-Level Meter and Analyzer, the preamplifier and microphone must be removed from the meter. This simple procedure is detailed in the 1982 and 1933 instruction manuals.

2. Install the 10-foot extension cable on the 1982 or 1933. This cable is supplied with both meters.

3. Feed the free end of the cable through the legs on the stand assembly and through the opening in the middle of the stand, and connect the preamplifier to the cable.

4. Screw the 1-inch microphone, supplied with the 1560-9619, onto the preamplifier and gently lower it into the stand cavity.

5. Place the 1562 or 1567 Calibrator over the 1-inch microphone and calibrate the sound-level meter in accordance with standard calibration procedure.

6. Install the earphone coupler on the microphone. The system is now ready for use.

SPECIFICATIONS

Frequency Range: 125 Hz to 8 kHz.

Accuracy: The electret microphone response in a P83 NBS Type 9-A coupler is calibrated to be equal to the response of a type L microphone in an NBS 9-A coupler when used to calibrate TDH-39, TDH-49 and TDH-50 earphones mounted in a MX41/AR ear cushion. MICROPHONE/COUPLER CALIBRATION: (Factory), ±0.2 dB — 125 Hz to 4 kHz; ±0.3 dB — 6 kHz to 8 kHz. System accuracy when used with 1933-9700 or 1982-9700 and the microphone supplied with the 1560-9619 and calibrated with the 1562 or 1567 Acoustic Calibrator is within 1 dB at audiometric test frequencies 125 Hz to 4 kHz; 1.5 dB at audiometric test frequencies 6 kHz and 8 kHz.

Earphone Coupler: The GR P83 9-A type coupler fulfills the volume requirements for the NBS 9-A coupler specified in ANSI S3.7 1973 when used with the GR 1961-9601 one-inch electret microphone. VOLUME: 5.633 cm³ ±0.030 cm³ including volume added by microphone. AXIAL HOLD FORCE: 450 grams nominal.

Microphone: GR 1961-9601 1-inch electret-condenser microphone, random-incidence response with pressure-response corrections given for audiometer test frequencies.

Environmental: (1961-9601 1-inch microphone only). TEMPERATURE: −20 to +55°C and 90% RH operating.

Supplied: (1560-9619): 1560-9683 Earphone Coupler, 1961-9601 Microphone, 1560-9618 Audiometer Calibration Stand Assembly, Calibration Chart, Instruction Sheet, adaptor.

Available: 1560-9618 Audiometer Calibration Stand Assembly, supplied as part of the 1560-9619, is also available separately. This offers the present user of the 1933-9716 Audiometer Calibration System a stable, bench-mounted stand for the earphone coupler and microphone.

Mechanical: DIMENSIONS: 1560-9618 Stand Assembly, 10 in. high x 3.87 in. dia (254 x 98 mm). WEIGHT: 2.4 lb (1.1 kg) net, 5 lb (2.3 kg) shipping.

Description	Catalog Number
Audiometer Calibration Accessory Kit	1560-9619
Audiometer Calibration Stand Assembly	1560-9618

1557-A Vibration Calibrator

- **calibrates vibration pickups, meters**
- **generates 1 g at 100 Hz**
- **portable, battery-operated**

This calibrator provides a single-frequency (100 Hz), single-level (1 g) check on the GR Vibration Pickups, the 1553 Vibration Meter, or any pickup whose total mass is 300 grams or less. It can provide on-the-spot calibration of vibration-measuring systems immediately before and after important measurements and can also be used to compare transducers or to calibrate working transducers against a standard transducer.

Operation of the calibrator is simple. A pickup of known mass is attached to the shaker, either in place of one of the removable 50-gram disks or to one of the disks by double-faced, pressure-sensitive tape. The user adjusts the Level control until the panel meter, calibrated in grams, indicates the mass of the pickup. The pickup will then be automatically subjected to an acceleration of 1 g at 100 Hz.

The 1557-A is a small, battery-operated unit consisting of a transistorized electromechanical oscillator and a cylindrical shaker. The acceleration output of the calibrator appears at two pillbox-shaped, 50-gram disks mounted on an internal cylinder that projects through the sides of the instrument.

View of the calibrator with Type 1560-P52 Vibration Pickup attached.

SPECIFICATIONS

Output: ACCELERATION: 1 g rms ±10%. 1 g = 386 in./s² (9.81 m/s²). VELOCITY: 0.614 in./s (15.6 mm/s) rms. DISPLACEMENT: 0.000978 in. (0.0248 mm) rms: 0.00277 in. (0.0704 mm) pk-pk. FREQUENCY: 100 Hz ±1% for 50-gram load; 100 Hz +0, −2% for 300-gram load.

Power: Battery operated (Eveready 724 or equivalent dry cell).

Supplied: Leather carrying case.

Mechanical: Aluminum case. DIMENSIONS (wxhxd): 4x8x4 in. (105x205x105 mm). WEIGHT: 3.25 lb (1.5 kg), net; 5.25 lb (2.4 kg) shipping.

Description	Catalog Number
1557-A Vibration Calibrator (with dry battery)	**1557-9702**
Replacement Dry Cell, 1 req'd	**8410-1050**

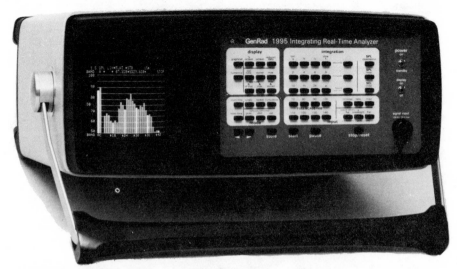

1995 Integrating Real-Time Analyzer

- 25 Hz to 20 kHz or 2.5 Hz to 20 kHz
- 1/3-octave and full-octave real-time analysis
- built-in display scope features bar-graph display or numerical listing
- small and lightweight
- power-line or battery operation for truly portable use
- 50-dB display range
- integration times from 1/8-second to 24 hours
- spectrum comparison capability

The 1995 is designed to satisfy a broad range of noise-measurement requirements in real time, on the spot without the need to make tape recordings for detailed analysis back in the laboratory. A compact, lightweight, microprocessor-based instrument, it can operate from optional rechargeable batteries for truly portable on-site measurements. This is the first instrument in its class that is not dependent on an external power source.

The 1995 is a one-third and full-octave real-time analyzer with long-term integration capabilities. It also operates as an integrating analyzer or integrating sound-level meter to display A-weighted sound level, Flat response, or any selected band level as a function of time.

A built-in display scope features a bar-graph display of one-third-octave or full-octave bands, and a pushbutton allows the user to convert the bar graph to a numerical display with standard deviations listed for each band. Spectrum storage is also built-in, allowing the storage of a spectrum for recall and comparison with new data. The stored spectrum can be retained for a long period of time since the internal memory is powered by a separate battery.

The 1995 is an excellent tool for industrial-noise, community-noise and product-noise applications. Typical applications include:

- Plant and machinery noise reduction
- Sound-power measurements per EPA standards
- Machine-tool measurements per NMTBA
- Aircraft-noise measurements per FAR-36
- Motor-vehicle-passby measurements
- Community-noise measurements (e.g., L_{eq})
- Product-noise rating and reduction

Please use one of the cards at the rear of this catalog to request complete information.

SPECIFICATIONS

Standards: FILTERS: One-third-octave filters in accordance with: ANSI Standard Specification for Octave, Half-Octave and Third-Octave-Band Filter Sets S1.11 1966, Type E, Class III; IEC Recommendation Publication 225-1966, Octave, Half-Octave and Third-Octave-Band Filters for the Analysis of Sound and Vibration; DIN 45 652, 1964 Third-Octave-Band Filters for Electroacoustical Measurements. A-weighting characteristics and Fast and Slow responses in accordance with: ANSI Standard Specification for Sound-Level Meters S1.4-1971, Type 1; IEC Recommendation Publication 179-1973 Precision Sound-Level Meters; DIN 45 633/1, 1970, Precision Sound-Level Meters General Requirements.

Preamplifier Input: MICROPHONES AND ACCELEROMETERS: Preamplifier has 0.460 x 60 thread for direct connection to one-half inch electret-condenser or air-condenser microphone and various adaptors for use with other microphones and accelerometers. Switchable polarizing voltage for use with air-condenser microphones is provided. ELECTRICAL SIGNALS: BNC to the amplifier thread adaptor supplied.

Level Range for Direct Reading in dB re 20 μPa

Nominal Microphone Sensitivity dB re 1 V/Pa	Microphone Sensitivity Range dB re 1 V/Pa	Level Range* For Direct Reading dB re 20 μPa	Corresponding Voltage Range
−30	−26 to −36	120 to 20	.63 V to 6.3 μV
−40	−36 to −46	130 to 20	.63 V to 2 μV
−50	−46 to −56	140 to 20	.63 V to .63 μV
−60	−56 to −66	140 to 30	.2 V to .63 μV

*Lower level may be limited due to noise depending on the capacitance of the microphone used, its exact sensitivity, and the particular pass band or weighting. Limits apply with preamplifier set to X1 gain. Lower limit may be extended by setting the preamplifier to X10 gain.

Typical sensitivity of GR 1971 Ceramic and 1962 Electret-Condenser Microphones is −40 dB re 1 V/Pa. Equivalent A-weighted noise for 1971 Ceramic Microphone: 21 dB; for 1962 Electret-Condenser Microphone: 27 dB. One-third-octave band levels are typically less than 10 dB for bands from 25 Hz to 20 kHz with 1971 Microphone. One-third-octave band levels decrease with increasing frequency for 1962 Microphone, ranging from typically 30 dB at 25 Hz to 12 dB at 20 kHz.

IMPEDANCE: Approximately 2 GΩ in parallel with less than 6 pF. CALIBRATION ADJUSTMENT: Rear-panel screwdriver adjustment with 10-dB total range. MAXIMUM INPUT: For linear operation ±5 V peak.

Tape Input (rear panel): CONNECTOR: Tape input connector; BNC. SENSITIVITY: Nominally 1 V rms full scale. Independent of full-scale range selected and continuously adjustable from 0.316 V to 3.16 V rms full scale. IMPEDANCE: 100 kΩ, ac coupled. MAXIMUM INPUT: For linear operation, a peak signal 20 dB above full-scale setting; ±32 V peak without damage. Maximum dc input, ±30 V without damage.

Overload Indication: Indication of overload on display when peak input voltage exceeds linear range (non-latching).

Filters: FREQUENCY RANGE: 1995-9700 and 1995-9720: 25 Hz-to-20 kHz one-third-octave center frequencies (standard bands 14 to 43), or 31.5 Hz to 16 kHz, one-octave-band center frequencies (bands 15 to 42); 1995-9710 and 1995-9730: 2.5 Hz-to-20 kHz (bands 4 to 43) one-third octave or 4 Hz-to-16 kHz octave-band center frequencies (bands 6 to 42). BANDWIDTH: Bandwidths of one-third octave or one octave (octaves derived by summing 1/3 octaves). Either result may be displayed at completion of analysis. CHARACTERISTICS: One-third-octave filters have nominal 6-pole Butterworth response.

Weighting: A.

Preweighting: Flat or A ahead of filters.

AC Output: Flat output unfiltered provides 0.5 V rms nominal at full scale, output provided from 5 kΩ shortable source.

Video Output: Composite video; negative sync; 1 V p-p into 75 Ω. 8-MHz picture element rate.

Detector and Integrator: DETECTOR RESPONSE: True Square Law (rms). SOUND-PRESSURE LEVEL: Sound-pressure level with either integration or exponential averaging as selected by operator. SOUND-EXPOSURE LEVEL: Sound-exposure level (time reference one second) selected by operator. INTEGRATION TIMES: 1/8, 1/4, 1/2, 1, 2, 4, 8, 9, 10, 15, 24 seconds, minutes or hours selectable by operator in linear modes; 1/8, 1/4, 1/2, 1, 2, 4, 8, 9, 10, 15, 24 seconds or minutes selectable by operator in exponential mode. In exponential mode, time constants of 1/8 second and 1 second correspond to FAST and SLOW sound-level meter responses, respectively. DYNAMIC RANGE: Dynamic range, including 10-dB allowance for crest factor above full scale, is 63 dB. Linearity error less than ±0.75 dB for sine wave inputs ranging from +7 dB to −40 dB re full scale and less than ±1 dB for inputs ranging from −40 to −50 dB re full scale. Resolution is 0.25 dB. CREST FACTOR: At least 10 dB at full scale. OVERLOAD INDICATION: Indication of overload on display when the integrated level in any band exceeds full scale (non-latching).

Display: TYPE: Five-inch raster-scan display with tube face recessed to permit viewing in bright ambient light. POWER: Controlled by front-panel switch. Display may be turned off to conserve battery power without affecting performance of instrument. RANGE: 50 dB displayed. Full-scale sensitivity selectable from 70 to 140 dB re 20 μPa in 10-dB steps. LEVEL-VS-FREQUENCY: Bar-graph display of one-third-octave or one-octave band levels plus A-weighted and flat-response levels. A second result, previously stored, may be displayed as a line graph, superposed on the bar graph, for comparison. Status information and one band level (selected by "cursor") displayed alphanumerically. LEVEL-VS-TIME: Bar graph of up to 32 sequential integration results plus status information and one integration result (selected by "cursor") displayed alphanumerically. NUMERICAL RESULT: All band numbers, levels, and standard deviations (except for octaves) are listed numerically along with status information. In level-vs-time mode, all integration periods and corresponding levels and standard deviations (except for octaves) are displayed. CURSOR: A cursor operates in the graphical mode to display the band number, level, and standard deviation of any one selected band. The bar corresponding to the selected band is intensified for identification. STORAGE: A displayed result may be stored and then recalled and displayed alone or superposed

on a "real time" result. A composite one-third-octave spectrum developed from one-third-octave band-level maximums in a series of integrations is stored and may be displayed alone or superposed on a "real time" or stored spectrum. DATA REDUCTION: In the REDUCED DATA mode, A-weighted and flat-response sound levels and Speech Interference Level are displayed.

Calibration: A built-in noise source permits an overall check on all channels. Overall system calibration, including accessory preamplifier, microphone, or accelerometer, can be performed using any acoustic or vibration calibrator.

Basic Input/Output Interface to Accessories: VIDEO OUTPUT: A composite video output signal permits use of large external monitors for display. START-STOP-PAUSE: A TTL compatible input allows remote control of panel START, STOP, and PAUSE functions.

Optional Interface to Accessories: X-Y RECORDER: An optional output interface in the 1995-9720 and -9730 supplies a 1-V full-scale signal for an X-Y plotter or level recorder. Recorder calibration voltages of 1-V full scale for both axes are available. LEVEL RECORDER: Synchronizing and pen lift circuits permit use of GR 1523 recorders. IEEE 488 INTERFACE: Optional output interface supplies digital data in IEEE 488 format, permitting use of data printers, computers, calculators, and other accessories compatible with the standard.

Environment: OPERATING TEMPERATURE RANGE: 0 to 50°C. STORAGE TEMPERATURE RANGE: −40 to +70°C with power supply; −40 to +60°C with batteries. HUMIDITY: Operating, up to 90% RH at 40°C.

Power Supply: LINE POWER SUPPLY: 1995-3040 plugs into rear-panel recess. Can be removed and replaced with optional rechargeable battery pack plug-in. Power consumption from line is 40 W maximum. Operates from 90 to 125 V or 180 to 250 V, 50 to 60 Hz. Used either to power the instrument or to recharge the batteries. BATTERY POWER SUPPLY: Optional rechargeable battery plug-in 1995-3030 provides at least one hour of operation with display on, at least two hours with display off. Battery is charged from power supply to 80% of full capacity in approximately eight hours. BATTERY VOLTAGE INDICATION: Low battery voltage is indicated on the display.

Accessories Supplied: Rear-panel mating connector with unterminated 5-foot cable, 2 each; front-panel cable connector lock; preamplifier; 10-foot preamplifier cable; BNC to preamplifier thread adaptor.

Accessories Available: Rechargeable battery pack and accessories; camera adaptor set; carrying case.

Mechanical: OVERALL DIMENSIONS (not including handle): (wxhxd): 17×7×17.5 in. (432×178×444 mm). WEIGHT (including removable ac power supply): 1995-9700, 41 lb (18.6 kg); 1995-9710, 42.5 lb (19.3 kg); 1995-9720, 42 lb (19.0 kg); 1995-9730, 43.5 lb (19.7 kg).

Description	Catalog Number
1995 Integrating Real-Time Analyzer (25 Hz to 20 kHz)	**1995-9700**
1995 Integrating Real-Time Analyzer (2.5 Hz to 20 kHz)	**1995-9710**
1995 Integrating Real-Time Analyzer (25 Hz to 20 kHz) with output interface	**1995-9720**
1995 Integrating Real-Time Analyzer (2.5 Hz to 20 kHz) with output interface	**1995-9730**
Rechargeable Battery Pack and Accessories	**1995-9600**
Camera Adaptor Set (includes hood, bracket, and close-up lens)	**1995-9601**
Carrying Case: provides space for calibrator, 60-ft cable, battery pack, tripod, microphones, and pre-amplifiers	**1995-9602**
Rechargeable Battery Pack	**1995-3030**

1925 Multifilter

- **3.15 Hz to 80 kHz**
- **1/3-octave or octave bands**
- **calibrated channel attenuators**
- **display with standard scale factor**
- **scanned, parallel, and summed outputs**

Spectrum shaper or analyzer building block The 1925 Multifilter contains up to 30 parallel octave-band or one-third-octave-band filters from 3.15 Hz to 80 kHz and is supplied with attenuators that permit independent control of the gain in each band. The attenuators let you use the multifilter as an equalizer or spectrum shaper to simulate or to compensate for irregularities in the frequency response of electrical or acoustical transmission systems or transducers. You can also use it as the basis for a serial or parallel frequency analysis system.

A variety of outputs The outputs from the individual filters are presented simultaneously in parallel, summed in a single output, and selected individually by manual switching, by external switch closure, or by a remote scanner control unit. Additional outputs provide the un-

filtered input signal and the signal with A, B, or C weighting imposed. Peak detectors located before and after the filters drive a metering circuit that selects the highest peak and gives you an indication in decibels referred to the overload level.

Attenuator for each band Each attenuator provides 50 dB of gain control in 1-dB steps, accurate to ±0.25 dB. Thumbwheel switches control the attenuation and a panel display indicates the "transmission" of the instrument. This display has the same scale as the 1521-9463 chart paper used with the 1564-A Sound and Vibration Analyzer (5 in./decade horizontal, 10 dB/in. vertical). A key-operated lock guards against unintended changes in the attenuator control settings.

Filters meet American and international standards The filters, built on plug-in etched boards (three per board) for easy interchange, are available with either octave or one-third-octave bandwidths that conform to both American and international standards. The A-, B-, and C- weighting characteristics also conform to the requirements of the various standards for sound-level meters.

— See **GR Experimenter** for May-June 1969 (Reprint E122).

SPECIFICATIONS

Frequency: 3.15 Hz to 80 kHz.

Bandwidth: 1/3 octave; octave and 1/10 octave available.

Peak Monitor: A peak detector senses levels at two circuit points and drives a panel meter calibrated in dB referred to overload level. A signal proportional to meter indication is available at a rear connector to drive a dc recorder; 1 mA for full-scale reading.

Input: Connects to rear BNC or microphone connector. GAIN: 0 dB nominal. MAXIMUM INPUT: 35 V dc, 17 V peak ac. IMPEDANCE: 100 kΩ.

Attenuation: +6 to −12-dB continuous gain adjustment common to all channels plus +25 to −25-dB attenuation in 1-dB steps with ±0.25-dB accuracy (re +25-dB setting) by means of a panel thumbwheel switch for each band. Attenuation of each band is indicated by a dot on panel display and represents the transmission between input and summed output. Display has standard 50-dB per decade scale factor; 10-dB per in. vertical, 5 in. per decade horizontal. Lock on panel prevents accidental changes in attenuator settings.

Response: 30 6-pole Butterworth filters with 1/3-octave effective (noise) bandwidths that conform to ANSI S1.11-1966 Class III (high attenuation) and IEC 225-1966 standards or with 1-octave bandwidths that conform to ANSI S1.11-1966 Class II (moderate rate but highest for octave-band filters) and IEC 225-1966 standards. ACCURACY of center frequency: ±2%. LEVEL UNIFORMITY: Within ±0.50 dB at 25°C, ±0.75

dB from 0 to 50°C, at center frequency with attenuator at +25 dB. PASSBAND RIPPLE: 0.5 dB max pk-pk. NOISE: <15 μV equivalent input noise. HARMONIC DISTORTION: <0.25% at 1-V output for bands centered below 25 Hz, <0.1% at 1-V output for 25 Hz and above. WEIGHTING: A, B, C, conforming to ANSI S1.4, IEC 123, and IEC 179.

Outputs: PARALLEL BAND OUTPUTS: ±4.2 V max (3 V rms) behind 20 Ω nominal; 3 kΩ min load for max output voltage. SCANNED BAND OUTPUT: ±4.2 V max (3 V rms) behind 20 Ω; 3-kΩ min load for max output voltage. Two chassis can be wired in parallel for up to 60 scanned outputs. SUMMED OUTPUT (for equalizing and shaping applications): ±4.2 V max open circuit behind 600 Ω; impedance of load does not affect output linearity. WEIGHTED AND UNFILTERED OUTPUTS: 0-dB nominal gain at 1 kHz, behind 20 Ω nominal; 30 kΩ min load for max output voltage.

Supplied: Power cord, two 36-pin type 57 plugs to mate with rear connectors.

1925-9670 Transmission Record Sheets available: thin Mylar* sheets, of same size and scale factor as attenuator display, attach to window with self-contained adhesive and can be used to record position of dots in window with china- or glass-marking pencil or crayon.

Available: 1560-P40 and -P42 PREAMPLIFIERS, 1566 MULTICHANNEL AMPLIFIER (input scanner).

Power: 100 to 125 and 200 to 250 V, 50-60 Hz, 17 W.

Mechanical: Bench or rack models. DIMENSIONS (wxhxd): Bench, 19.75x9.13x12.25 in. (502x232x311 mm); rack, 19x 8.75x12.25 in. (483x222x311 mm). WEIGHT: Bench, 49 lb (23 kg) net, 58 lb (27 kg) shipping; rack, 39 lb (18 kg) net, 47 lb (22 kg) shipping.

* Registered trademark of E. I. du Pont de Nemours and Co. Inc.

Description	Catalog Number	
**1925 Multifilter ** **		
One-Third-Octave Bands	Bench	Rack
25 Hz to 20 kHz	**1925-9700**	**1925-9701**
12.5 Hz to 10 kHz	**1925-9702**	**1925-9703**
3.15 Hz to 2.5 kHz	**1925-9704**	**1925-9705**
100 Hz to 80 kHz	**1925-9706**	**1925-9707**

** 45-band models, 1/10-octave-band models, mixed 1/10, 1/3, and 1-octave-band models, or special bandwidths available on special order.

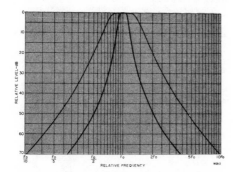

RELATIVE FREQUENCY

1564-A Sound and Vibration Analyzer

- **2.5 Hz to 25 kHz**
- **2 bandwidths: 1/3- and 1/10-octave**
- **use direct from microphone or vibration pickup**
- **ac or portable battery operation**
- **automatic spectrum plots with 1521 recorder**

The 1564-A Sound and Vibration Analyzer is designed primarily for measuring the amplitude and frequency of the components of complex sound and vibration spectra. Its 1/3-octave (23%) and 1/10-octave (7%) noise bandwidths provide the flexibility needed for analysis of both the noise and its causes.

Input sources The high input impedance of the analyzer permits direct connection of piezoelectric transducers for measuring sound pressures from 44 to 150 dB re $20\mu N/m^2$ and acceleration from 0.0007 g to 100 g.

The 1560-P42 and 1560-P40 Preamplifiers are available to extend the full scale sensitivity of the analyzer by 20 dB (10:1) and to allow use of the transducer at the end of a long extension cable. Alternatively, for higher sensitivity, the analyzer can be driven from a sound-level meter or vibration meter.

Automatic analysis Automatic range switching is provided so that the 1521-B Graphic Level Recorder can record automatically the spectrum of a signal under analysis. The combination of analyzer and recorder is available as the 1911-A Recording Sound and Vibration Analyzer for continuous spectrum plots. This combination is particularly well suited to measurements in accordance with MIL Standard 740B.

Noise filter The analyzer can be used in conjunction with the 1390-B, 1381, or 1382 random-noise generators for transfer and reverberation measurements using 1/3- or 1/10-octave bands of random noise.

Description The 1564-A consists of a high impedance amplifier, a continuously tunable filter having a noise bandwidth of either 1/3 or 1/10 octave, an output amplifier, and a meter. The center frequency of the filter is continuously adjustable. An all-pass, or flat, characteristic permits measurement of the over-all signal amplitude.

SPECIFICATIONS

Frequency: RANGE: 2.5 Hz to 25 kHz in four decade ranges. DIAL CALIBRATION: Logarithmic. ACCURACY OF CALIBRATION: ±2% of frequency-dial setting.

Filter Characteristics: Noise bandwidth is either 1/3 octave or 1/10 octave. One-third-octave characteristic has at least

30-dB attenuation at one-half and twice the selected frequency. One-tenth-octave characteristic has at least 40-dB attenuation at one-half and twice the selected frequency. Ultimate attenuation is 70 dB or greater for both characteristics. For both bandwidths, peak response is uniform ±1 dB from 5 Hz to 10 kHz and ±1.5 dB from 2.5 Hz to 25 kHz. An all-pass, or flat, characteristic is also included.

Detector Characteristics: Rms with three averaging times. Faster two speeds conform with ANSI standard for sound-level meters.

Input: IMPEDANCE: 25 MΩ in parallel with 80 pF (independent of attenuator setting). VOLTAGE RANGE: 0.3 mV to 30 V full scale in 10-dB steps. MICROPHONE: 1971-9606 Microphone Assembly or the 1560-P42 or 1560-P40 Preamplifiers are recommended.

Output: VOLTAGE: At least 1.0 V open circuit, when meter reads full scale. IMPEDANCE: 6000 Ω. Any load can be connected. METER: Three scales, 0 to 3 V; 0 to 10 V; −6 to +10 dB.

Recording Analyzer: Automatic range switching at the end of each frequency decade allows convenient continuous recording of spectra with the 1521-B Graphic Level Recorder.

Calibration: Built-in, feedback-type calibration system permits amplitude calibration at any frequency.

Available: 1971-9606 Microphone Assembly, 1560-P52, -P53 Vibration Pickups, 1560-P40 and -P42 Preamplifiers (power for preamp available at input connector).

Power: Operates from 105 to 125 or 210 to 230 V, 50-60 Hz, or from nickel-cadmium battery supplied. Battery provides 25 h of operation when fully charged and requires 14 h for charging.

Mechanical: Flip-Tilt case and rack mount. DIMENSIONS (wxhxd): Portable, 10.25x8.13x8 in. (260x206x203 mm); rack, 19x10.5x6 in. (482x267x152 mm). WEIGHT: Portable, 15 lb (7 kg) net, 17 lb (8 kg) shipping; rack, 16 lb (8 kg) net, 28 lb (13 kg) shipping.

Description	Catalog Number
1564-A Sound and Vibration Analyzer	
Portable Model, 115 V ◈	1564-9701
Rack Model, 115 V ◈	1564-9820
Portable Model, 230	1564-9702
Rack Model, 230 V	1564-9821
Replacement Battery	8410-0410

Patent Number 3,012,197.

◈ National stock numbers are listed before the Index.

310

1568-A Wave Analyzer

- **20 Hz to 20 kHz**
- **1% constant-percentage bandwidth**
- **portable, battery-operated**
- **85-dB rejection**

The 1568-A is an important instrument for high-resolution frequency analyses, whether for measuring vibration and noise components or the spectrum of a complex electrical signal. Good design combines the excellent filter shape of a wave analyzer with the convenient, simple operation of constant-percentage-bandwidth analyzers in a portable, low-cost instrument.

The voltage sensitivity and input impedance, adequate for most uses, can be improved to 10 microvolts full-scale and > 500 megohms, respectively, by the use of a 1560-P42 Preamplifier and a 1560-P62 Power Supply.

High resolution Narrow bandwidth permits separation of closely spaced frequencies; wide dynamic range, high stop-band attenuation, and low distortion allow measurement of small components in the presence of components up to 80 dB larger. These capabilities are vital to the identification of unwanted vibration and noise components and to the measuring of discrete frequencies in complex electrical waveforms. At low frequencies, bandwidth is narrower, stability better, and calibration more accurate than those of fixed-bandwidth heterodyne wave analyzers.

The 1568 excels in such applications as

- harmonic distortion measurements at low frequencies
- harmonic analysis — 1% bw yields 50 components
- detailed analysis of machinery noise and vibration
- separation of close, discrete, low frequencies

Automatic analysis In combination, the 1568-A and 1521-B Graphic Level Recorder produce spectrum plots with as much as a 70-dB recording range. Automatic range switching is included for ease and speed in making spectrum analyses.

SPECIFICATIONS

Frequency: RANGE: 20 Hz to 20 kHz in six half-decade ranges. DIAL CALIBRATION: Logarithmic. ACCURACY OF FREQUENCY CALIBRATION: 1%.

Filter Characteristics: BANDWIDTH between 3-dB points on selectivity curve: 1% of selected frequency. ATTENUATION, at 20% above and at 20% below selected frequency: > 50 dB referred to the level at the selected frequency. Attenuation at twice and at one-half the selected frequency is ≥ 75 dB referred to the level at the selected frequency. Ultimate attenuation is > 85 dB. UNIFORMITY of filter peak response with tuning: ±1 dB from 20 Hz to 6.3 kHz and ±2 dB from 20 Hz to 20 kHz.

Input: IMPEDANCE: 100 kΩ. VOLTAGE RANGE: 100 µV to 300 V, full scale, in 3-10 series steps. DISTORTION: Input-circuit distortion is lower than −80 dB relative to input-signal level.

Output: IMPEDANCE: 6000 Ω. Any load can be connected. VOLTAGE: At least one volt open circuit when meter reads full scale. CREST-FACTOR CAPACITY: Greater than 13 dB.

Output Meter: CALIBRATION: Voltage (see above) and dBm, with reference at 1 mW into 600 Ω (775 mV). DAMPING: 2 modes, Fast and Slow, for manual measurements of noise.

Analyzing Range: 80 dB. Components of an input signal that differ in amplitude by as much as 80 dB can be measured.

Automatic Recording: Automatic range switching is provided to allow convenient, continuous spectrum plotting when the 1521 Graphic Lever Recorder is used. Medium-speed motor is recommended. Chart paper is Catalog No. 1521-9475. Frequency scale is logarithmic, 10 inches per decade; vertical

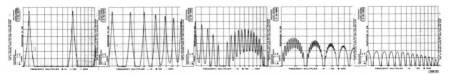

Frequency spectrum analysis of a 1.0-ms pulse at a 70-Hz repetition rate. The 1% bandwidth yields high resolution at low frequencies, shows the envelope at high frequencies.

scale is 4 inches for 20, 40, or 80 dB, depending on the potentiometer used in the recorder.

Calibrator: A built-in, feedback-type calibration system permits amplitude calibration at any frequency.

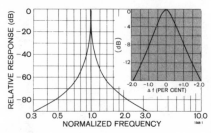

Attenuation characteristics of the filter.

Supplied: Power cord; 1568-2090 Detented Knob and Dial Assembly, used to facilitate measuring the components of an input signal as a percentage or in decibels with an arbitrary voltage reference.

Available: 1560-P42 and 1560-P40 Preamplifiers; Link Unit 1521-P15, with Sprocket Kit 1521-P16 for mechanical coupling to 1521-B Graphic Level Recorder equipped wtih Drive Unit 1521-P10B; Chart Paper 1521-9475.

Power: 100 to 125 or 200 to 250 V, 50 to 60 Hz. 2 W for normal operation, 3.5 W for battery charging. A rechargeable nickel-cadmium battery is supplied. Battery provides about 20 hours of operation when fully charged and requires 16 hours for charging. Internal charger operates from the power line.

Mechanical: Flip-Tilt case. DIMENSIONS (wxhxd): With case closed, 13.25x13x8.25 in. (337x330x210 mm). WEIGHT: 22 lb (10 kg) net, 27 lb (13 kg) shipping.

Description	Catalog Number
1568-A Wave Analyzer	
Portable Model, 115 V ac ⊛	1568-9000
Portable Model, 230 V ac	1568-9010
Replacement Battery	8410-0410

Frequency-Response and Spectrum Recorder Assembly

Several GR instruments can be used with the 1521-B Graphic Level Recorder for automatic plotting of the frequency response of a device or the frequency spectrum of (for example) acoustic noise or of a complex electrical waveform. Automatic plotting with these instruments replaces tedious point-by-point manual methods and provides much more information in the form of finer-resolution curves.

The component items can be ordered individually to convert existing equipment into fully automatic recording assemblies.

Custom assemblies of GR analysis equipment and sound and vibration instruments can be built to order to meet a variety of special requirements.

1911-A Recording Sound and Vibration Analyzer

This assembly will generate continuous frequency plots of the 1/3- or 1/10-octave spectrum of sound and vibration signals over the range of 4.5 Hz to 25 kHz. Thus 1/3-octave measurements can be made in accordance with several common military and industrial noise-control specifications. While the third-octave bandwidth is convenient for testing compliance to a specification for maximum allowable noise or vibration level, the 1/10-octave bandwidth permits precise identification of individual frequency components, leading to their reduction or elimination. The analyzer will accept signals from a sound-level meter, vibration meter, or other stable amplifier, or directly from a microphone or vibration pickup. It includes a storage drawer and system power control.

SPECIFICATIONS

The 1911-A consists of the following:

1564-A Sound and Vibration Analyzer, rack model

1521-B Graphic Level Recorder with 40-dB Potentiometer (1521-9602) and medium-speed motor

1521-P10B Drive Unit (1521-9467)

1521-P15 Link Unit (1521-9615), with 16-tooth sprocket installed (standard 24-tooth sprocket also included)

Chart Paper, 10 rolls (1521-9469), calibrated 2.5-25 normalized, logarithmic.

Adaptor Cable, double banana to right-angle phone plug.

Available: 1560-P40 and -P42 Preamplifiers; 1961, 1962, and 1971 microphones; 80-dB potentiometer; choice of vibration pickups.

Mechanical: Assembled in cabinet. DIMENSIONS (wxhxd): 19.75x31.25x15.75 in. (502x794x400 mm). WEIGHT: 101 lb (46 kg) net, 158 lb (72 kg) shipping.

Description	Catalog Number
1911-A Recording Sound and Vibration Analyzer	
60-Hz 115-V Model	1911-9701

1521-B Graphic Level Recorder

- 7 Hz to 200 kHz
- 1-mV ac sensitivity — 0.8-mA dc
- linear dB plot of rms ac-voltage level
- 20-, 40-, or 80-dB range
- convenient, disposable pens

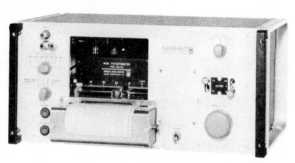

Stands alone This recorder produces a permanent, reproducible strip-chart record of ac-voltage level as a function of time or of some other quantity. Record, for example, the frequency response of a device or the frequency spectrum of noise or of a complex electrical signal.

The wide range of paper speed facilitates long-period studies (such as traffic-noise) as well as short-duration-transient measurements (such as auditorium-reverberation). Writing speeds and low-frequency cutoff are selected by a single switch. The frequency response can be extended downward to 4.5 Hz with the slower writing speeds, which filter out abrupt level variations. You get a smoothed plot without loss of accuracy.

The 1521 is a solid-state, single-channel, servo-type recorder with interchangeable logarithmic potentiometers, of 20-, 40-, and 80-dB ranges, and a linear potentiometer for dc recording. The 1521 can be calibrated and relied upon for recording absolute levels as well as changes.

Or in combination This graphic level recorder can be mechanically or electrically coupled to various GR analyzers and oscillators to synchronize the frequency scale of the chart paper with the instrument's calibrated tuning-control dial. With a sound-level meter, the recorder can plot sound levels over a wide dynamic range as a function of time; the writing speed is sufficiently high for the measurement of reverberation time and other transient phenomena.

SPECIFICATIONS

AC Recording: RANGE: 40 dB full-scale with the potentiometer supplied, 20- and 80-dB potentiometers available for ac level recording. LINEARITY: ±(1% of full-scale dB value plus a frequency error of 0.5 dB at 100 kHz and 1.5 dB at 200 kHz).

Frequency Response and Writing Speed, for AC Level Recording: High-frequency response ±2 dB, up to 200 kHz. Low-frequency sine-wave response depends on writing speed, as shown in following table: (With the 80-dB pot, writing speed < 300 dB/s, i.e., 15 in./s.)

Writing Speed (approx), with 0.1-in. overshoot		Low-Frequency Cutoff (< 1 dB down)
20 in./s	508 mm/s	100 Hz
10	254	20 Hz
3	76	7 (3 dB down at 4.5 Hz)
1	25	7 (3 dB down at 4.5 Hz)

Dc Recording: RANGE: 0.8 to 1 V (0.8 to 1.0 mA) full-scale, with zero position adjustable over full scale. RESPONSE: 3 dB down at 8 Hz (pk-pk amplitude < 25% of full scale). LINEARITY: ±1% of full scale.

Resolution: ±0.25% of full scale.

Input: AC LEVEL RECORDING: Sensitivity is 1 mV (at 0 dB) into 10 kΩ, attenuator has 60-dB range in 10-dB steps, max limit is 100 V rms. DETECTOR RESPONSE: True rms, within 0.25 dB for multiple sine waves, square waves, or noise. Detector operating level is 1 V. DC RECORDING: Sensitivity is 0.8 or 1 V full scale, into 1 kΩ.

External Dc Reference: An external dc reference voltage of 0.5 to 1.5 V can be applied internally to correct for variations of up to 3 to 1 in the signal source of the system under test.

Paper Speeds
HIGH-SPEED MOTOR: Paper speeds of 2.5, 7.5, 25, 75 in./min. Used for high-speed-transient measurements.
MEDIUM-SPEED MOTOR: Paper speeds of 0.5, 1.5, 5, 15 in./min. Used with analyzers and in level-vs-time plots.
LOW-SPEED MOTOR: Paper speeds of 2.5, 7.5, 25, 75 in./h. Used for measurements from 1 hour to > 2 weeks.

Chart Paper: 4-in. recording width on 5-in. paper, 100 feet long. See separate listing of accessories.

Supplied: 40-dB potentiometer, 12 disposable pens with assorted ink colors, 1 roll of 1521-9428 chart paper, power cord, 1560-P95 Adaptor Cable (phone to double plug).

Available: Potentiometers, chart paper, pens, high-, medium-, and low-speed motors, drive and link units.

Power: 105 to 125 or 210 to 250 V, 50 or 60 Hz, 35 W.

Mechanical: Rack-bench cabinet. DIMENSIONS (wxhxd): Bench, 19x9x13.5 in. (483x229x343 mm); rack, 19x8.75x 11.25 in. (483x222x286 mm). WEIGHT: 50 lb (23 kg) net, 62 lb (29 kg) shipping.

Description	Catalog Number
Graphic Level Recorder, 40-dB potentiometer, * high-speed motor	
1521-B 60-Hz Bench Model	1521-9802
1521-B 60-Hz Rack Model	1521-9812
Graphic Level Recorder, 40-dB potentiometer, medium-speed motor	
1521-B 60-Hz Bench Model	1521-9833
1521-B 60-Hz Rack Model	1521-9834

* Other potentiometers available; see accessory pages following.

Graphic Level Recorder Accessories

Drive and Link Units for Coupling to Generator and Analyzers

1521-P10B Drive Unit

Provides mechanical-drive output from 1521-B to operate any link unit.

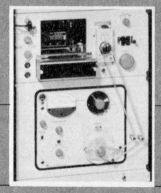

1521-9467

1521-P15 Link Unit

For mechanical coupling to 1564 or 1568 analyzers. Fitted with 24-tooth sprocket. Includes chain.

1521-9615

1521-P16 Sprocket Kit, contains 5 sizes of interchangeable sprockets for 1521-P15: 40, 36, 32, 20, and 16 teeth. Provides choice of scale factor in proportion to that with normal 24-tooth sprocket. Includes chain.

Industry Scale Factors

Industry Standard	Scale Factor (dB/decade)	Decade Length (Inches) for 1304 Generator	Sprocket (teeth)	Pot (dB)
Institute of High Fidelity Manufacturers	20	2.0	16	40
Proposed International Standard	25	2.5	20	40
Electronic Industries Association	30	3.0*	24	40
Institute of High Fidelity Manufacturers	20	4.0	32	20
Hearing Aid Industry	45	4.5	36	40
Proposed International Standard	50	5.0	40	40
Proposed International Standard	50	5.0**	16	40

* Chart paper available for 1304-B Beat-Frequency Audio Generator.
** Decade length applies to 1564-A Sound and Vibration Analyzer; chart paper available.

1521-9616

Graphic Level Recorder Accessories (cont'd)

Chart Papers

Dimensions: 5 in. wide x 100 ft long; recording width, 4 in. (127 mm x 30.5 m; 102 mm).

Associated Instrument	Calibration Horizontal	Vertical (Div)	Chart Length (in.) Cal.	Blank	Catalog Number
1304-B Generator	20 Hz to 20 kHz, log	80	9	4 ½	1521-9427*
1900-A Analyzer with 1900-P1 or 1900-P3 Link Units	0-1 or 0-10 kHz, linear	40	20	0	1521-9464
1900-A Analyzer with 1900-P1 Link Unit	0-50 kHz, linear	40	16	0	1521-9465
1564-A Analyzer with 1521-P15 Link Unit and 24-tooth sprocket	2.5-25 normalized, log	40	7½	1½	1521-9493
1564-A Analyzer with 1521-P15 Link Unit and 16-tooth sprocket (or with 1564-P1 Dial Drive continuous mode)	2.5-25 normalized, log	40	5	1	1521-9469
1564-A Analyzer with 1564-P1 Dial Drive (stepped mode)	Third-octave bands 3.15 Hz-25 kHz	40	10	0	1521-9460
1568-A Analyzer with 1521-P15 Link Unit	2-20 normalized, log	40	10	2	1521-9475
1554-A Analyzer	2.5 Hz-25 kHz, log	40	18	3	1521-9463
General use	Continuous ¼-in. div.	40	Continuous		1521-9428

* Use with 40-dB potentiometer; has 50-dB per decade scale factor required by many testing standards, particularly the ANSI S3.8-1967, "Method of Expressing Hearing Aid Performance."

Potentiometers

1521-P1 20-dB Potentiometer   1521-9601
1521-P2 40-dB Potentiometer**   1521-9602
1521-P3 80-dB Potentiometer   1521-9603
1521-P4 Linear Potentiometer (for dc)   1521-9604
** Normally supplied with the recorder

Optional Motors †

Chart Speeds

High-Speed Motors Used for high-speed-transient measurements and with **1304 Beat-Frequency Audio Generator**. Not for use with 1564-A and 1568 analyzers.	**1521-P19** (for 60-Hz supply) normally supplied in recorder†	2.5-75 in./min	1521-9619
Medium-Speed Motors Used with analyzers and in level-vs-time plots; must be used with 1564-P1 Dial Drive.	**1521-P23** (for 60-Hz supply)	0.5-15 in./min	1521-9623
Low-Speed Motors Used for level-vs-time measurements 1-24 hours.	**1521-P20B** (for 60-Hz supply)	2.5-75 in./h	1521-9513

† Recorder can be supplied with low- or medium-speed motor installed, at same price as with standard motor.

fastrak® Pen Sets and Conversion Kit

The pen used in the 1521-B recorder combines ink reservoir and writing point in a single disposable unit, eliminates refilling. Each cartridge has about twice the life of one old-style pen refill and can outlast three rolls of chart paper. The pen consists of a sealed plastic cartridge with a fiber plastic point that requires only about 2 grams of force to operate properly.

The pens are available with red, green, and blue ink and are supplied in sets of four pens. A set of assorted colors is included with the recorder and with the conversion kit.

For converting older 1521-A and 1521-B recorders to use the improved pen, a kit is available that contains a pen holder, set of 12 assorted-color pens, and conversion instructions.

fastrak® Marker Set, Red   1522-9614
fastrak® Marker Set, Green   1522-9615
fastrak® Marker Set, Blue   1522-9616
fastrak® Recorder Marker Conversion Kit   1521-9439

1523 Graphic Level Recorder

An excellent recorder with plug-in modules for:

- level recordings
- frequency-response measurements
- ⅓-octave-band analysis
- narrow-band wave analysis
- fast plots of real-time analyzer output

- 1-Hz to 500-kHz frequency range
- 100-μV sensitivity
- up to 100-dB dynamic range
- up to 0.1-dB linearity
- 5 recorders in one with plug-in versatility
- remotely programmable — a systems natural

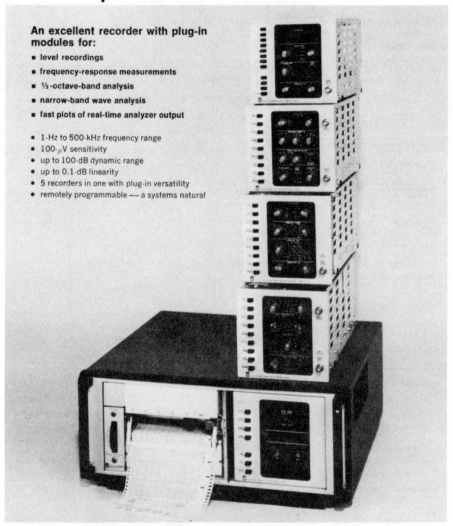

Automatic measurements – simply and graphically The 1523 is *not* just another recorder; it is a measurement center. It incorporates the latest refinements of the recorder field with those of the sweep-oscillator and sound-analyzer fields and does so in one instrument that eliminates the usual bother of trying to keep everything synchronized. Simply connect your signal or device, set up the desired measurement conditions, and push a button — the 1523 does the rest, automatically and without constant attention or control manipulation.

Narrow-band wave analysis for

- product-noise reduction programs
- spectrum-signature work
- vibration studies
- preventive maintenance programs
- distortion measurement
- network analysis

The 1523-P4 Wave Analyzer plug-in gives you the capability to perform high-resolution spectral analysis, swept-frequency analysis with a tuned detector, and amplitude-vs-time measurements at selected frequencies.

The 1523-P4 provides analysis bandwidths of 10 Hz and 100 Hz and an all-pass mode covering the range from 10 Hz to 80 kHz. Most signals can be handled without preamplification, because the analyzer will accommodate inputs over a 140-dB range (3 μV to 30 V), with capabilities to detect and display any 80-dB portion.

The analyzer conveniently provides two frequency display modes. A logarithmic display with 2.0-, 2.5- and 5.0-inch decades and a linear display with scale factors of 50 Hz, 500 Hz, and 5 kHz per inch. The logarithmic mode is useful when you use the tracking analyzer feature for network measurements or plotting spectra over a wide frequency range. The linear mode is most useful for obtaining a detailed analysis over a narrower frequency range. For maximum versatility, this analyzer has controls for setting both the analysis start and stop points anywhere within the 10 Hz-to-80 kHz range.

Through the use of the plug-in approach, GR offers you two instruments — a graphic-level recorder and a wave analyzer — in a single coordinated package, capable of handling an entire measurement requirement from data acquisition and processing to hard-copy data recording. Additionally, the plug-in approach accommodates present needs while allowing for economical future expansion with other GR plug-ins.

Precise 1/3-octave-band analysis for
- product-noise reduction
- plant- and field-noise studies
- materials testing

Insert the 1523-P3 Stepped 1/3-Octave-Band Analyzer plug-in and your recorder becomes a 1/3-octave-band analyzer with a frequency range of 1 Hz to 80 kHz (ANSI standard bands 0 through 49.) You can perform analysis on selected portions within the full range, and you can switch in an all-pass channel to display the over-all level at the start of a record. You can also select any one of 11 automatic programs to provide recordings with constant averaging times or, as a unique feature, to provide analyses with statistical confidences of up to 90% to within ±0.5 dB. You can record measurements singly on a new chart, successively on a single chart for comparison, or successively on new charts, simply by the turn of a single knob.

Simple response measurements for
- filter and network response testing
- loudspeaker, amplifier, and tape-recorder evaluation
- performance tests for microphones, hydrophones, and hearing aids
- general medical and educational applications

With the 1523-P2 Sweep Oscillator plug-in, which incorporates a sweep oscillator, your recorder produces frequency-response recordings at the push of a button. You can set the oscillator to sweep the full 1-Hz to 500-kHz range, or various portions of it, at output levels continuously adjustable from 500 μV to 5 V behind 600 Ω. A unique and versatile constant-Q mode of operation can be selected to speed the recording in many applications by increasing the sweep rate automatically as the frequency increases. Under many conditions, recordings can be made in the constant-Q mode in ½ to ⅓ the time normally required.

The accuracy and stability of the generator, plus the resolution of the recorder and the variety of chart speeds and averaging-time programs, permit precise response measurements of almost any device — performed with the ease and economy of a single instrument rather than with the clutter and confusion of two.

Versatile level recording for
- A-weighted level-vs-time recordings
- reverberation-time measurements
- general level-recording applications

Select the 1523-P1A Preamplifier plug-in for the best in general recorder performance. The 1523-P1A gives you a broad frequency coverage from 1 Hz to 500 kHz, a sensitivity of 100 μV, and 18 chart speeds from as slow as 20 hours per inch to as fast as half a second per inch. Continuously adjustable attenuation from 0 to 70 dB provides the utmost in recording resolution, and a choice of nine averaging times from 10 ms to 5 s allows supreme flexibility.

DC recording capability for the 1921 Real-Time Analyzer
- automatic plotting of real-time analysis data
- automatic spectrum overlay capability
- easy to use

The 1523-P5 DC Preamplifier is specifically designed to provide plots of spectra measured with the GR 1921 Real-Time Analyzer.

The instrument simplifies and automates plotting of spectra analyzed by the 1921. Simplicity is evidenced by the absolute minimum number of controls on the 1523-P5. Logic circuits in the plug-in permit synchronized, automatic plotting, controlled from the 1921 Real-Time Analyzer panel. Thirty ⅓-octave bands are plotted in less than 25 seconds.

It is often desirable to make more than one recording on the same chart to compare the effects of changes on the system being tested. This is automated by a "repeat chart" mode which rewinds the chart for replotting immediately after the completion of a plot. Readily interchangeable pens, available in red, green, and blue, can be used to distinguish each successive spectrum.

Conveniences standard All plug-ins feature remote programmability, a variety of inputs and outputs to synchronize recorder operation with that of other instruments, and a choice of several potentiometers with dynamic ranges from 10 dB to 100 dB to tailor the instrument to your specific requirement.

For convenience, a chart take-up reel is included but the paper also can be fed out directly for immediate inspection and use. For interpretation, an event marker can be recorded by the simple push of a button at the desired time. For reliability, a stepper motor drives the chart (there are no gears or clutches to wear out, slip, or jam), and clog-free disposable pens eliminate messy refilling and provide clear, easily read, and skip-free traces even at the fastest writing speeds. You have a choice of colors and a choice of marker types: the fastrak® Marker for general purposes and the Slow-Speed Marker for particularly slow-moving records or those with much retracing over a part of the chart. GO/NO-GO limit adjustments are included to provide LO, GO, and HI electrical outputs for external alarm or control applications.

317

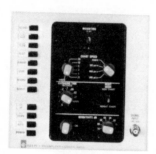

with 1523-P1A Preamplifier Plug-in

for level-vs-time recordings

- frequencies to 500 kHz
- 100-μV sensitivity
- up to 100-dB dynamic range
- for A-weighted level-vs-time recordings
- 1-MΩ input impedance
- 18 chart speeds

with 1523-P2 Sweep Oscillator Plug-in

contains sweep generator for level-vs-frequency recordings

- frequencies to 500 kHz
- 100-μV sensitivity
- up to 100-dB dynamic range
- 1-MΩ input impedance

Input: Chart 0-level can be 0 dB (100 μV) to 70 dB; set in 10-dB steps plus a continuous vernier. This corresponds to a chart 0-level of 34 dB with the 1560-P42 Preamplifier in the X10 gain position and a −40 dB re 1 V/N/m² microphone. See Maximum Input Sensitivity under 1523 Mainframe Specifications. MAXIMUM INPUT: ±10 V pk ac to 250 kHz, +5 V pk ac to 500 kHz, re dc component of ±350 V max. IMPEDANCE: 1 MΩ//30 pF at plug-in; 3.35 kΩ ±1% direct to potentiometer via internal switch. CONNECTORS: Front and rear BNC and rear 3-pin A3 mike connector that also provides power for 1560-P40 or -P42 Preamplifier.

Input Frequency: FLAT or A-weighted selected by switch on front panel. Response in FLAT, 1 Hz to 500 kHz ±0.1 dB to 100 kHz, ±2 dB to 500 kHz, except <3 dB down at 100 kHz on 0-dB range. A-weighted response conforms to ANSI S1.4-1971 Type 1. Response uniformity between FLAT and A-weighted, +0.2 dB at 1 kHz. Low-frequency and crest-factor cutoffs depend on averaging times (see table).

Pen: Three modes, UP, DOWN, AUTO. AUTO may be either internal automatic program or remote control of pen position. UP and DOWN positions override remote programming.

Recording: CHART SPEED: 0.5 s/in. to 20 h/in., in 18 ranges of 0.5, 1, 2, 5, 10, and 20 h, min, or s/in., plus fast scan of 2 in./s and slow scan of 2 in./min.; all synchronized to line frequency. RESET: Advances at fast scan rate to start of new chart or return to start of present chart as selected by toggle switch. AVERAGING TIMES: 10 ms to 5 s in 9 ranges, all remotely programmable. Sinusoidal low-frequency cutoff (< 1 dB down) and fundamental cutoff for 20-dB crest factor depend on averaging times as follows:

Input: Chart 0-level can be 0 dB (100 μV) to 70 dB; set in 10-dB steps. See also Maximum Input Sensitivity under 1523 Mainframe Specifications. MAXIMUM INPUT: ± 10 V pk ac to 500 kHz, re dc component of ± 40 V max. IMPEDANCE: 1 MΩ//30 pF at plug-in; 3.35 kΩ ± 1% direct to potentiometer via internal switch. CONNECTORS: Front and rear BNC and rear 3-pin A3 mike connector that also provides power for 1560-P40 or -P42 Preamplifier.

Input Frequency: 1 Hz to 500 kHz; flat within ±0.1 dB to 100 kHz, within ±2 dB to 500 kHz, except on 0-dB range, down < 3 dB at 100 kHz. Averaging times programmed automatically to avoid low-frequency cutoff; program can be inhibited by external input.

Recording: CHART SPEED: Automatically set by sweep time (see below) and decade length. Decade length can be set for 2, 2.5, 3, 4, 5, or 10 in./decade.

Sweep Frequency: 1 Hz to 500 kHz; automatically from lower to upper frequency. Lower frequency can be set to 1, 2, 5, 10, 20, 50, 100, or 200 Hz, 1, 10, or 100 kHz; upper frequency can be set to 10 or 100 Hz, 1, 2, 5, 10, 50, 100, 200, or 500 kHz. ACCURACY: ±1% of indicated frequency. STABILITY: ±0.05% over 10 min, ±0.25% over 24 h; after 30-min warm-up. SWEEP TIME: 5 s to 200 ks/decade in 5, 10, 20 sequence; or manual sweep. Averaging time decreases with frequency as follows: 2 s from 1 to 10 Hz, 200 ms from 10 to 100 Hz, 50 ms from 100 Hz to 100 kHz, and 20 ms from 100 to 500 kHz. SWEEP RESOLUTION: 3000 discrete logarithmically scaled steps per decade (0.08% step). SWEEP VOLTAGE: Dc output proportional to log of swept frequency available at rear connector.

Sweep Amplitude: 500 μV to 5 V rms into open circuit behind 600 Ω. > 10 mW into 600 Ω, available at front BNC connector; set in four decade ranges of 5 mV to 5 V full-scale open-circuit plus continuous vernier; flat within ±0.1 dB to 100 kHz, within ±1 dB to 500 kHz. DISTORTION: < 0.2% from 1 Hz to 100 kHz with any linear load. HUM: < 0.03%. SPURIOUS (discrete non-harmonic): −55 dB. NOISE: > 60 dB below carrier in 100-kHz bandwidth.

Avg Time	Low-Frequency Cutoff Sinusoidal	Full Crest Factor	Avg Time	Low-Frequency Cutoff Sinusoidal	Full Crest Factor
10 ms	400 Hz	1 kHz	500 ms	2 Hz	8 Hz
20 ms	100 Hz	500 Hz	1 s	1 Hz	3.5 Hz
50 ms	20 Hz	120 Hz	2 s	<1 Hz	1.6 Hz
100 ms	10 Hz	35 Hz	5 s	<1 Hz	1 Hz
200 ms	5 Hz	16 Hz			

with 1523-P3 Stepped 1/3-Octave-Band Analyzer Plug-in

contains 1/3-octave-band filters for spectrum recording

- 1 Hz to 80 kHz
- Fifty 1/3-octave bands
- 100-μV sensitivity
- 1-MΩ input impedance
- averaging times varied automatically for fast constant-confidence results

Input: Chart 0-level can be 0 dB (100 μV) to 70 dB; set in 10-dB steps plus a continuous vernier. MAXIMUM INPUT: ± 10 V pk ac to 100 kHz, re dc component of ± 90 V max. IMPEDANCE: 1 MΩ//30 pF at plug-in, 3.35 kΩ ± 1% direct to potentiometer via internal switch. CONNECTORS: Front and rear BNC and rear 3-pin A3 mike connector that also provides power for 1560-P40 or -P42 Preamplifier.

Input Frequency: 1 Hz to 80 kHz center frequencies; fifty 1/3-octave noise-bandwidth (bands 0 thru 49) 4-pole Butterworth filters with Class II (moderate attenuation) Type O characteristics that conform to ANSI S1.11-1966 for sound-level recordings, switch-selected flat-response (all pass) channel at start of chart displays over-all level. Also available, with filter characteristics conforming to IEC 225, as Type 1523-P3I. CENTER-FREQUENCY ACCURACY: ±3%. LEVEL UNIFORMITY: ±1 dB at center frequencies. PASSBAND RIPPLE: 1 dB pk-pk max. NOISE: Equivalent input noise below 0 dB (re 100 μV) for all pass, and bands 0-39, increasing 1 dB/band to below 10 dB in band 49. HARMONIC DISTORTION: < 0.1% for signals of 1 V rms at band centers. STOP-BAND ATTENUATION: > 60 dB for frequencies of > 8 and < 1/8 times center frequency. OUTPUT: Filtered input signal available at rear connector. PEAK MONITOR included with panel lamp to indicate overload.

Input-Frequency Scan: Adjustable; automatically steps from lower frequency to (but not thru) upper frequency. Lower center frequency can be set to 1, 2, 10, 20, 100, or 1000 Hz; upper center frequency can be set to 0.1, 1, 2, 10, 20, or 100 kHz.

Analysis Programs: NO. OF PROGRAMS: 11, designated A, B, C . . . L. VARIETY: Program A provides constant averaging time per band; others, combinations of the same with a series of steps of constant confidence (averaging time ≈ proportional to one over analysis bandwidth). CONFIDENCE: For random noise, for 90% confidence, averaging time is adequate for ±0.5-dB accuracy along the "staircase" labeled ±0.5 dB. See chart. Similarly, ±1.5 dB, for the staircase so labeled. Any part of a program above a staircase has greater confidence. No program operates below the "sine" staircase on the left; thus averaging time is always sufficient to keep the detector operating above its low-frequency cutoff. AVERAGING TIME: 5 s for 1-, 1.25-, and 1.6-Hz bands; 5, 2, 1 . . . 0.05 s for higher-freq bands, depending on selected program. *Examples:* (See chart). Program B uses 5-s avg'g time below 2 Hz, 2-s for 2 Hz and above. Program H uses 5-s avg'g time up to 8 Hz, constant confidence (± 1.5 dB) from 8 through 100 Hz, and 0.5-s avg'g time from 100 Hz through 100 kHz. Location of program letter on chart indicates shortest avg'g time for the

program. (Imagine that each arrow, like K, extends to right.) SEQUENCE: Analyzer steps to a band, dwells for stabilization, then records the level, at 2 in./s chart speed. DWELL PERIOD: 6 x "averaging time," except at your selected Start Frequency band of each analysis (and "all-pass") 18 x avg'g time.

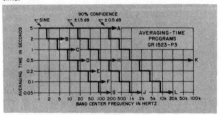

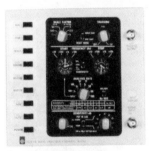

with 1523-P4 Wave Analyzer Plug-in

for detailed noise and vibration analysis

- 80-dB dynamic range
- 10-Hz and 100-Hz bandwidths
- Tracking output
- 10 Hz-to-80 kHz analysis range
- Linear and log frequency displays

Main Input: Chart 0-level can be − 30 dB (3.16 μV) to + 50 dB; set in 10-dB steps supplemented by a 12-dB continuous vernier. TOTAL MEASUREMENT RANGE: 140 dB (3.16 μV to 31.6 V). DYNAMIC RANGE: 80 dB, without changing attenuators, may be displayed with the 100-dB potentiometer. MAXIMUM INPUT: 30 V rms to 80 kHz, re dc component of ± 50 V Max. INPUT OVERLOAD: Detected by peak monitor and indicated on front panel. IMPEDANCE: 1MΩ//30 pF. CONNECTORS: Front and rear BNC and rear 3-pin A3 mike connector that also provides power for 1560-P40 or -P42 Preamplifier. ACCURACY OF RECORDED LEVEL: ± 0.5 dB below 10 kHz, ± 1 dB above (with 50-dB pot).

Analyzer Characteristics: FREQUENCY: 10 Hz to 80 kHz. SWEEP RANGE: 10 Hz to 10 kHz (10-Hz bandwidth); start and stop frequencies each set by 4-position switch and 10-turn dial. BANDWIDTH: 10 Hz, 100 Hz, and "all pass," switch selected. PASS-BAND SHAPES: 3-dB bandwidth = 10 ± 1 Hz, 60-dB bandwidth ≤ 60 Hz; 80-dB bandwidth ≤ 120 Hz; 3-dB bandwidth = 100 ± 10 Hz, 60-dB bandwidth ≤ 400 Hz, 80-dB bandwidth ≤ 800 Hz. ACCURACY OF RECORDED FREQUENCY: ± 2% or ± 5 Hz, whichever is greater. STABILITY: (After 30-min warmup) ± 0.05% (10 min), ± 0.25% (24 h). DISTORTION: Internally generated distortion and hum products ≥ 75 dB below full scale. NOISE: < 1 μV in a 10-Hz bandwidth. IMAGE REJECTION: ≥ 80 dB (100 to 180 kHz). I-F REJECTION: ≥ 80 dB (50 kHz).

Analysis Modes: AUTOMATIC: Linear sweep between start and stop frequency settings with automatic decade ranging. Analysis rates are 100, 50, 10, 5, 1, 0.5 and 0.1 Hz/s. Chart-scale factors of 50, 500 or 5000 Hz/in. Logarithmic sweep over single or multiple decades with automatic decade ranging provides the following types of analysis: (a) 100, 50, 10, 5, 1, 05, 0.1 Hz/s and (b) 5, 10, 50, 100, 500 s/decade. Chart-scale factors are 2.0, 2.5, and 5.0 in./decade. Sweep rate, automatically controlled. Averaging time and pen lift, also automatically controlled unless overridden by remote control. MANUAL: Frequency may be manually set or swept with START frequency control and range multiplier. LEVEL vs TIME: Analyzer may be set manually to any frequency or all pass and level recorded vs time.

Secondary Inputs: Remote control by switch or DTL/TTL ground closures of numerous factors such as pen lift, chart scan, run, stop, averaging time, event markers, etc.

Tracking Output: FREQUENCY: Follows analyzer center frequency. LEVEL: 1 V across 600 Ω (or less, by manual control). DISTORTION: < 0.2%.

Other Outputs: I-F: Filtered signal at 50 kHz, amplitude proportional to analyzer output. RETRANSMITTING: DC voltage proportional to pen excursion. SWEEP: DC voltage proportional to analyzer frequency. DIGITAL: Signals indicating system status, such as pen lift, chart direction and rate, run, stop, averaging time, limits, etc.

with 1523-P5 DC Preamplifier Plug-in

for fast plots of 1921 Real-Time Analyzer output

Input: VOLTAGE: 0 to 1 V dc ± 10% can be calibrated to produce 5.00 in. or 12.0 cm deflection on 1523 Level Recorder equipped with 1523-9625 Potentiometer. IMPEDANCE: 10 kΩ. MAX SAFE INPUT VOLTAGE: ± 15 V peak.

Recording: With the 1523-9625 potentiometer, a linear plot is produced which matches the 60-dB display range of the 1921 Real-Time Analyzer.

Over-all System Accuracy: ± 1.2% of 5-in. full-scale deflection, when end points are calibrated, including -P5 log conformity, recorder deadband, and potentiometer linearity. NOTE: This represents 0.75 dB for 60-dB full-scale display of 1921 Real-Time Analyzer output.

Speed: In PLOT mode, paper moves at 2 in./s; 500 ms dwell at beginning of each channel. Draws 30 band 1921 plot, including reset to new chart, in less than 25 s.

Control: PLOT is initiated remotely from the 1921 Real-Time Analyzer. Termination of PLOT produces automatic RESET. RESET may also be initiated by front-panel control. Reset direction is controlled by RESET MODE toggle switch. Paper may be scanned at 2 in./s using FAST FORWARD and FAST REVERSE. Pen may be UP, DOWN, or AUTO. PEN AUTO lowers pen automatically during PLOT, otherwise raises pen. Two calibrate potentiometers provide full-scale and bottom-scale calibration. Controls are non-interactive if bottom-scale calibration is done first.

MAINFRAME SPECIFICATIONS

Dynamic Range: Up to 100 dB, depending on potentiometer. POTENTIOMETERS: 5 available, all easily interchanged and all with 5-in. scales except for 60 dB which has 12-cm scale. 10 dB (with ±0.1-dB linearity); 25 dB (±0.15 dB), 50 dB (±0.25 dB), recommended for general use; 60 dB (±0.3 dB), for use with 1523-P3 only; and 100 dB (±0.5 dB). MAXIMUM INPUT SENSITIVITY: 100 μV rms for averaging times 0.1 s or greater, 1 mV rms for averaging times < 0.1 s; except for 10-dB pot, max sensitivity 1 mV; minimum averaging time 50 ms. DEAD BAND: ±0.15% of full scale; except ±0.25% with 0.01, 0.02 and 0.05 s averaging times. DETECTION: True rms, error ≤ 0.1 dB for 15-dB crest factor, < 0.5 dB for full 20-dB crest factor for frequencies above crest-factor cutoff frequency. NOISE: Equivalent input noise < 40 μV rms. RETRANSMITTING POTENTIOMETER: Provides dc output voltage, proportional to ac input, of 0 to 10.4 V dc (2 V/in. of pen deflection).

Pen Control: Pushbutton switches or external DTL or TTL signals control pen position (up, down, or automatically positioned). Pen status is also indicated by DTL outputs.

Chart Control: Pushbutton switches or external DTL or TTL ground closures start or stop recording, reset paper to start of same chart or advance it to start of next chart, and provide fast forward or reverse. Switch settings are also indicated by DTL outputs. CHART SPEED (see Chart Speed under individual plug-in headings): Can be externally programmed except with 1523-P3. MOTOR: Stepper motor moves paper in 0.0067-in. increments (0.17 mm) at rates up to 300 increments per second (2 in./s). Pulses supplied by internal clock or by external DTL or TTL input at rates of ≤ 300 pps. Pulses also available as an output to synchronize other recorders. There is exactly one increment for each pulse. PHOTOCELL: DTL ground-closure output corresponds to black marks printed on paper.

Limits and Event Markers: LIMITS: 3 DTL outputs provide HI, GO, and LO continuous indications of the recording level vs 2 adjustable limits. EVENT MARKERS: 2 pens; pushbutton switch controls one pen to mark selected events on paper; external DTL or TTL signal activates either or both pens. (These markers act more like "rubber stamps" than "pens.")

Interface: All plug-in pushbutton-control functions can be remotely indicated or controlled; other controls cannot be except for Chart Speed and Averaging Time controls on -P1 and -P2 and Sweep Time Per Decade on -P2. Levels are standard DTL or TTL, i.e., "low" is closure to ground or 0 to +0.5 V; "high" is +3.5 to +5.0 V. Logic-circuit input and output connections are available at 2 double 19-pin etched-board terminals, at rear of main frame, when plug-in is installed.

Supplied: 3-ft BNC-terminated patch cord, 2 rolls of chart paper, fastrak® Marker Set (4 red, 4 green, 4 blue pens), Event Marker Set of 4 red and 4 black pens, 3 potentiometer contacts, 2 paper cap assemblies, 50 chart-mounting sheets, power cord; double 19-pin etched-board connectors (1 or 2) for external programming (inputs and outputs) with each plug-in.

Power: 100 to 125 or 200 to 250 V, 50 to 60 Hz; 90 W typical, 160 W max.

Mechanical: Bench or rack models. DIMENSIONS (wxhxd): Bench 19.56x8.44x19.63 in. (496x214x498 mm); rack, 19x7x19.69 in. (483x178x500 mm). WEIGHT: Bench, including plug-in, 63 lb (29 kg) net, 98 lb (45 kg) shipping; rack, including plug-in, 57 lb (26 kg) net, 92 lb (42 kg) shipping; plug-in when shipped separately, 8 lb (3.7 kg) net, 16 lb (8 kg) shipping.

Description	Catalog Number
1523 Graphic Level Recorder Mainframe	
without plug-in but with poten-	
tiometer noted	
Potentiometer Model	
50 dB bench	1523-9700
50 dB rack	1523-9701
25 dB bench	1523-9704
25 dB rack	1523-9705
60 dB bench	1523-9706
60 dB rack	1523-9707
60 dB bench (for use with	1523-9712
1523-P5 DC Preamplifier	
only)	
60 dB rack (for use with	1523-9713
1523-P5 DC Pre-	
amplifier only)	
100 dB bench	1523-9708
100 dB rack	1523-9709
Select at least 1 of the following plug-Ins	
1523-P1A Preamplifier	1523-9608
1523-P2 Sweep Oscillator	1523-9602
1523-P3 Stepped ⅓-Octave-Band	
Analyzer conforming to ANSI S1.11-1966	1523-9603
1523-P3I Stepped ⅓-Octave-Band	
Analyzer conforming to IEC 225	1523-9605
1523-P4 Wave Analyzer	1523-9604
1523-P5 DC Preamplifier	
(for use with 1921 Real-Time Analyzer;	
requires one 1523-9625 60-dB	
potentiometer, which is included in	
1523-9712 and -9713, and requires one	
1523-9690 Cable Set for connection	
to 1921)	1523-9607
Cable Set	1523-9690
Potentiometers	
Can be ordered as options; easily	
interchanged to suit various requirements	
10 dB Potentiometer	1523-9620
25 dB Potentiometer	1523-9621
50 dB Potentiometer	1523-9622
60 dB Potentiometer (used only with 1523-P3)	1523-9623
60 dB Potentiometer (used only with 1523-P5)	1523-9625
100 dB Potentiometer	1523-9624
Other Recorder Accessories	
Event-Marker Sets, 4 black and 4 red pens	1522-9612

Description	Catalog Number
Mounting Sheets, 8½ x 11 in. sheets with	
adhesive strips to mount charts for filing	
in 3-ring notebooks, 50 sheets per pack	1522-9639
fastrak® Marker Sets (general purpose)	
Set of 4 RED pens	1522-9614
Set of 4 GREEN pens	1522-9615
Set of 4 BLUE pens	1522-9616
Slow-Speed Marker Sets	
Set of 4 RED pens	1522-9634
Chart Paper	
Chart Paper, 140-ft rolls of 6.63-in. wide paper with	
5 in. vertical chart of 50 div (except 1523-9644° and	
-9646 which have 12-cm vertical chart area of 60 div);	
including timing marks for proper synchronization.	
FOR 1523-P1A PREAMPLIFIER:	
Linear, continuous scale of 0.2 in. per div	1523-9641
FOR 1523-P2 SWEEP OSCILLATOR:	
3⅓ 3-in. decades, starts at 10, ends at 20 k	1523-9650
5⅔ 2.5-in. decades, starts at 1, ends at 500 k	1523-9642
3⅓ 2.5 in. decades, starts at 1, ends at 2 k	1523-9661
3 5-in. decades, starts at 1, ends at 1 k	1523-9662
FOR 1523-P3 STEPPED ⅓-OCTAVE-BAND ANALYZER:	
3⅓ 2.5-in. decades, starts at 1, ends at 2 k	1523-9640
3⅓ 5-cm decades, starts at 1, ends at 2 k°	1523-9646
5 2.5-in. decades, starts at 1, ends at 100 k	1523-9647
5 5-cm decades, starts at 1, ends at 100k°	1523-9644
FOR 1523-P4 WAVE ANALYZER:	
Linear, continuous scale of 0.2-in. per div	1523-9660
3⅓ 2.5-in. decades, starts at 1, ends at 2 k	1523-9661
3 5-in. decades, starts at 1, ends at 1 k	1523-9662
Linear, labeled frequency scale, 2 decades,	
0.2-in. per div	1523-9664
FOR 1523-P5 DC PREAMPLIFIER:	
Ideal for use with 1921 Real-Time Analyzer, 25-dB/decade	
scale factors. Inch-ruled charts have 2.08-in/decade	
abscissas, centimeter-ruled charts have 5-cm/decade	
abscissas. Bands are ANSI preferred ⅓-octave	

Ordinate Scale	Bands	Abscissa Frequencies	
12dB/in.	11-40	12.59 Hz-10 kHz	1522-9645
12dB/in.	14-43	25 Hz-20 kHz	1522-9644
5dB/cm	5-49	3.15 Hz-80 kHz	1522-9654
5dB/cm	14-43	25 Hz-20 kHz	1522-9655

*For use only with 1523-9623 60-dB Potentiometer

GR 1985 DC Recorder

- Ideal for industrial, laboratory, and community noise recordings
- Meets ANSI and IEC Type 1 response when used with GenRad Type 1 meters
- Matched to dc outputs of GenRad sound-level meters for guess-free selection of input sensitivities/calibration
- Chart speeds from 2 cm/h to 60 cm/min
- 50-dB direct reading dynamic range
- Powered by built-in rechargeable battery for "go anywhere" operation; also operates from ac line or external dc source

Simple, accurate noise recording

The GR 1985 is a portable, lightweight, battery-powered strip-chart recorder that is designed to simplify the gathering of noise data in permanent, hard-copy form. Compatible with GenRad sound-level meters, (1933, 1981, 1982, 1983) it completes a sound-measurement/recording system that produces permanent plots of noise-level-vs-time without the usual complicated calibration procedures that often cause recording errors. The recorder may also be used with the GenRad 1945 Community Noise Analyzer.

Accuracy of the recorded data is a plus feature of the 1985 since the pen response is fast enough to meet the Type 1 requirements of ANSI and IEC fast and slow meter response when used with a GenRad Type 1 instrument.

Easy setup

A front-panel switch on the 1985 allows you to select the proper input sensitivity to match the dc output of each compatible GenRad instrument. There is no need to select an input sensitivity on the 1985 that will handle the voltage range of the output from the instrument. Just set the switch for the proper instrument, adjust the zero and span adjustments, and record. The zero and span adjustments are located on the front panel for quick and easy calibration.

Guesswork eliminated

The 1985 eliminates the usual guesswork about what full-scale deflection means. It has a 50-dB recording range that makes it directly compatible with GenRad wide-dynamic range instruments. This means that the recorder's full scale automatically coincides with the meter's full-scale setting.

A 50-dB range is always plotted for the GenRad 1933, 1981, 1982, and 1983 sound-level meters regardless of attenuator setting. The 100-dB dynamic range of the GR 1945 Community Noise Analyzer is divided into three 50-dB ranges.

Convenient paper and chart speeds

The chart paper for the 1985 comes in 20-meter lengths, is fan-folded and has provision in the margin to record all the pertinent data about the noise recording including all sound-level meter and recorder-switch settings. Chart speeds from 2 cm/h to 60 cm/min make recording convenient for practically any application.

Use it anywhere and as a stand alone

Built-in battery power lets you make recordings anywhere in the field. The rechargeable internal battery gives 8 hours of operation between 14-hour charges.

The 1985 can be used as a stand-alone recorder without a GenRad sound-level meter, powered by the internal battery, an external dc source or from an ac line. See specifications for input voltage ranges.

SPECIFICATIONS

Recorder Type: Portable, battery-powered, single-channel, strip-chart recorder with multiple speeds and with ranges matched to GenRad sound-level meters. Provides a direct reading, 50-dB dynamic range permanent recording of sound-level meter output data.

Standards: When used with the GR 1933, 1981, or 1982 Precision Sound-Level Meters or with the GR 1945 Community Noise Analyzer, the recording system meets the fast and slow meter-response requirements of ANSI S1.4-1971 Type 1, IEC Recommendation Publication

179-1973 Precision Sound-Level Meters, and the Draft Consolidated Revision of IEC Publications R123 and R179 (August 1976) Type 1 (Precision).

When used with the GR 1983, the recording system meets the fast and slow meter response requirements of ANSI S1.4-1971 Type 2, IEC Recommendation Publication 123-1961, Sound-Level Meters and the Draft Consolidated Revision of IEC Publications R123 and R179 (August 1976), Type 2.

Recording System: METHOD OF WRITING: Cable-driven disposable cartridge with integral marking tip and ink supply. STEP RESPONSE TIME: 500 ms from bottom scale to full scale - corresponding to a 50-dB step. Response time is proportional to step size. OVERSHOOT: 1.25% (0.6 dB) typical; 2% (1 dB) maximum. PEN LIFTER: Manual front panel lever. CHART PAPER: Z-fold, rectilinear with 10 cm active span corresponding to 50-dB dynamic range (1 dB graduations). Chart has 5-cm folds and is 20 m long. SCALEPLATE: Removable 50-0 uniform, right-hand zero.

Measuring System: SOURCE IMPEDANCE: Up to 100 kΩ maximum. INPUT IMPEDANCE: Potentiometric on all spans.
INPUT SENSITIVITIES: Seven switch-selectable spans are provided. Front panel switch selects span for specific GenRad instrument as follows:

GR Model No.	Span (baseline to full scale)
1983	0 to +250 mV dc
1981	0 to +500 mV dc
1945	
(30-80 dB range)	−1.2 to −3.2 V dc
1945	
(50-100 dB range)	−2.0 to −4.0 V dc
1945	
(70-120 dB range)	−2.8 to −4.8 V dc
1982	0 to +3.0 V dc
1933	0 to +5.0 V dc

COMMON MODE POTENTIAL: ±150 V dc maximum. COMMON MODE REJECTION: 120 dB at 100 V dc. MAXIMUM SAFE OVER-LOAD: Input protected up to ±100 V dc. MEASUREMENT AC-CURACY: ±0.5% (0.25 dB) of span with maximum offset drift of 30 μV/°C (0.005 dB/°C worst case with GenRad model 1983). DEAD-BAND: ±0.3% (0.15 dB) of chart span maximum. Included in measurement accuracy. CONTROLS: Zero and Span adjustments are provided on the front panel. Each allows for ±10% of full-scale adjustment. SIGNAL INPUT CONNECTIONS: (+), (−), and ground (⏚) banana jacks provided on the front panel.

Chart Drive System: FEED RATES: 2, 5, 10, 15, 30, and 60 cm/hour and cm/minute. CHART SPEED ACCURACY: ±1% at 23°C ±10°C; ±2% at 0°C to 50°C. CONTROLS: Six-position feed-rate selector, Hour/Minute and chart ON/OFF switches provided on the front panel. TRANSPORT FEATURES: Front loading, dual-ended sprocket drive, slide-out chart accumulator, thumbwheel advance and chart tear-off bar.

Environment: TEMPERATURE: 0 to 50°C operating and storage. HUMIDITY: 0 to 90% R.H. Due to size changes in chart paper, the recorder should be calibrated at the operating humidity.

Supplied: Chart paper, 1 pack, 20m; 1 pen; rechargeable battery; battery charger; cable (15 feet); screwdriver.

Available: Chart paper, 6 packs, 20 m each; replacement pens, pack of 6; replacement battery; carrying case.

POWER REQUIREMENTS: The instrument may be powered from any one of three configurations:

Internal DC Source: 12-volt, 4.5 AH, rechargeable gelled lead-acid battery. Approximately 8-hour operation with full charge (not stalled). The stalled condition exists when the instrument is off scale in either direction. Current drain with the instrument stalled is approximately doubled. BATTERY CONDITION INDICATOR: Continuous reading meter provided on the front panel. POWER DRAIN: Approximately 6 VA (not stalled); 10 VA maximum. Fuse protection is provided. BATTERY CHARGER: AC adaptor supplied. Output is approximately 12 V dc at 500 mA. Plugs into ac line and rear panel jack. Instrument is inoperative during charge period. Maximum charge time is 16 to 24 hours. Fuse protection is provided. BATTERY LIFE: Approximately 200 charge/discharge cycles.

External DC Source: Requires nominal 12 V dc supply (10.5 V dc to 15.0 V dc). Source connects to rear panel jack. Fuse protection is provided. POWER DRAIN: Approximately 6 VA (not stalled); 10 VA maximum.

External AC Source: Battery charger supplied for ac operation from 115 V ±10% or 230 V ±10%, 50 or 60 Hz. Plugs into ac line and rear panel jack. POWER DRAIN: Approximately 12 VA (not stalled). POWER CONTROLS: Three-position mode switch is provided on the rear panel to select internal, external, or charging power functions. Power ON/OFF switch is provided on the front panel. CIRCUIT PROTECTION: Two replaceable fuses are provided on the rear panel for internal and external sources.

Mechanical: DIMENSIONS: (wxhxd): 9.75 x 6.13 x 14.63 in. (248 x 156 x 372 mm). WEIGHT: Approximately 14 lbs (6.4 kg) with battery, net.

Description	Catalog Number
1985 DC Recorder	**1985-9700**
Chart Paper, 20m, pack of 6	1985-9600
Pens, pack of 6	1985-9601
Battery, replacement	1985-0402
Carrying Case	1985-9603

Optional carrying case

323

1945 Community Noise Analyzer

- on-site readout of:
  L exceedance levels, L_{dn}, and L_{eq}

- does not require tape recorders or calculators

- battery power eliminates ac line requirements

- low-cost, optional weatherproof microphone system

- weatherproof security enclosure available

- analysis durations from 10 minutes to 24 hours available

- data inhibit available

A stand-alone instrument The GR 1945 is designed to satisfy the need for a low-cost, easy-to-use community noise analyzer, without the need for tape recorders, calculators, or computers. It monitors noise levels for up to three sequential time periods having selectable durations from 30 minutes to 24 hours, or 10 minutes to 8 hours (1945-9006), and automatically computes and stores L exceedance levels, L_{dn}, and L_{eq} (optional), for each time period. Answers to the computed levels are instantly available at the push of appropriate pushbuttons. The 1945 displays the levels on an easy-to-read digital display. Sound-level measurements of existing ambient levels can also be made at the push of a button.

High reliability Unlike electro-mechanical systems that use a tape recorder for data storage, the 1945's functions are completely electronic. It does not have moving mechanical parts that are prone to wear out and which may malfunction in environmental extremes. In addition, the concern of proper recording on expensive certified tapes during widely fluctuating temperature extremes is eliminated.

The 1945 has a 100-dB dynamic range to ensure that data will not be lost during wide variations in noise levels. This capability, plus the completely automatic electronic operation of the 1945, contributes to the high reliability of its answers.

Economy and ease of use When you buy the 1945 and the microphone of your choice, you are ready to begin measuring and analyzing noise without further equipment expense. There is no need to purchase a programmable calculator, a computer, or expensive certified tape cassettes. You need only select the measurement site and follow the simple steps summarized in the instruction manual.

Security and Environmental Protection For optimum performance and protection of the 1945 at unattended measurement locations, a weatherproof microphone system and weatherproof enclosure are offered as accessories.

The 1945-9730 Weatherproof Microphone System is a complete weatherproof system for outdoor noise monitoring. It is designed to protect its integral 1560-P42 Preamplifier and a microphone (not included) in an outdoor environment. The windscreen system provided protects the microphone from damage and reduces the effect of wind on the noise measurement. A GR electret-condenser or ceramic microphone should be used with this system (see Specifications section).

The 1945-9640 Weatherproof Enclosure provides a weatherproof and vandal-resistant shelter for the 1945 analyzer. It is supplied with a bracket for mounting to a pole or building, and a base for free-standing operation. The enclosure is fabricated from heavy-gauge aluminum and has a tumbler lock for security.

SPECIFICATIONS

COMMUNITY NOISE ANALYZER

Sensitivity Range: Microphone input can be directly calibrated with microphone-preamplifier combinations having sensitivity of -35 to -45 dB re 1 V/N/m² (-55 to -65 dB re 1 V/μbar). AUX INPUT: (For use with 1935 Cassette Recorder) 0.5 V rms corresponds to 120 dB.

Maximum Detected Level: 120 dB rms; provides 14-dB crest factor.

Minimum Detected Level: 5 dB above typical noise floor, using 1972-9600 or 1560-P42 Preamplifier with indicated microphone as follows:

Microphone input with	A	C	FLAT
GR 1962 Microphone	27 dB	30 dB	40 dB
GR 1961 Microphone	23 dB	26 dB	38 dB
GR 1971 Microphone	25 dB	25 dB	29 dB
AUX Input	27 dB	26 dB	29 dB

Input Impedance: 20 kΩ.

Maximum Safe Input Voltage: ±15 V peak ac, 35 V dc.

Weighting: A, C, or FLAT selected by front panel slide switch. A and C per ANSI S1.4-1971 Type 1 and IEC 179-1973. FLAT response $+0.5$, -3 dB 10 Hz to 25 kHz re 1 kHz. D weighting optionally available, consult factory.

Detector: True rms with 14-dB crest-factor capacity at 120-dB level. FAST or SLOW dynamic detection characteristic per ANSI S1.4-1971 Type 1 and IEC 179-1973 selected by front panel slide switch.

Statistical Analysis: RESOLUTION: 1 dB. LINEARITY: 0.25 dB. ANALYSIS DURATION: Selected by front panel switch; choices listed below. NUMBER OF SAMPLES: Function of analysis duration as follows:

Analysis Duration	Number of Samples
4, 6, 8, 12 or 24 hours	65528
2 or 3 hours	32764
1 hour	16382
½ hour	8191

NUMBER OF ANALYSES: One, two or three independent consecutive analyses may be selected. L_{eq} ANALYSIS: When the 1945 is supplied with L_{eq} option, each sample is also used to compute L_{eq}, the equivalent continuous level, over the analysis period, or L_{dn} on a 24-hour run. L_{dn} is identical to L_{eq} except that a 10-dB penalty is added to all levels from 10:00 p.m. to 7:00 a.m. L_{eq} may be enabled on 24-h run by changing internal jumper prior to analysis. ANALYSIS TIMING: Start of first analysis may be delayed up to 24 hours from initial set up by use of internal clock.

325

Display: LEVEL dB: Current sound level may be displayed digitally with 1-dB resolution before, during or after analysis. It is updated every 0.22 second. EXCEEDANCE LEVELS: After analysis is complete, desired exceedance levels are pushbutton selected. The following exceedance levels are available: $L_{0.1}$, L_1, L_2, L_5, L_{10}, L_{20}, L_{50}, L_{90}, L_{99}, L_{min}, L_{max}. Also selectable are $L_{33.3}$, $L_{4.25}$, $L_{2.12}$, $L_{6.25}$, corresponding to HUD Circular 1390.2 requirements of level exceeded 8 hours of 24, 1 hour of 24, ½ hour of 24 and ½ hour of 8 hours. EQUIVALENT CONTINUOUS LEVEL: After analysis is complete, L_{eq} (or L_{dn}) is selected by pushbutton. See "L_{eq} Analysis" above.

Data Output (electrical): Remote output connector provides the following: DC OUTPUT: 4.8 V dc behind 5 kΩ corresponds to 120-dB level, output linear at 40 mv/dB over an 80 to 98-dB dynamic range (limited only by internal noise for microphone and weighting selected). DIGITAL: Cumulative distribution, with 1-dB resolution, available in serial form with clocks for decoding. Signals to identify analysis complete and selected memory are provided. All digital signals are buffered CMOS outputs, $\approx$8 V logic levels. EXTERNAL POWER: Input from external battery or power supply at 8-15 V, 70 mA max, allows extended operating periods. Input has polarity reversal protection.

Environmental: TEMPERATURE: -10 to $+60°$C operating, -40 to $+55°$C storage (batteries installed), -40 to $+75°$C storage (batteries removed). HUMIDITY: 0 to 90% RH operating. VIBRATION: 0.030" excursion 10-55 Hz.

Supplied: Screwdriver to adjust microphone CAL pot, two battery packs, 8 alkaline "D" cells, plug for microphone input, cable for remote output connector, instruction sheet.

Available: 1945-9640 Weatherproof Enclosure, 1945-9730 Weatherproof Microphone System, for outdoor use. Preamplifier, electret-condenser and ceramic microphones, cables and windscreens also available.

Power: 8 "D" cells provide 75 hours' continuous operation or permit 24 hours' running time and 1 week of idling memory contents at 25°C.

Mechanical: DIMENSIONS (wxhxd): Models 1945-9700 and -9710: 8.5x10.75x9.38 in. (216x273x238 mm). WEIGHT: Model 1945-9700: 16.5 lb (7.5 kg) net; model 1945-9710: 15.5 lb (7.1 kg) net.

COMMUNITY NOISE ANALYZER (1945-9006)

Specifications per the above with the following additions:

Statistical Analysis: A front panel switch permits selection of ANALYSIS DURATIONS of ½ hour to 24 hours as above or 10 minutes to 8 hours shown below.

Analysis Duration	Number of Samples
1.33, 2, 2.67, 4 or 8 hours	65528
40 minutes or 1 hour	32764
20 minutes	16382
10 minutes	8191

Data Inhibit: A front panel PAUSE/RUN switch may be used to manually inhibit the data from being stored in memory. While the PAUSE/RUN switch is in the PAUSE position, the run is stopped. The run will not be completed until the total selected run time has elapsed with the PAUSE/RUN switch in RUN. For example, if a 2-hour run is started at 3 p.m. and the PAUSE/RUN switch is in the PAUSE position for 30 minutes, the run will not be completed until 5:30 p.m. The PAUSE/RUN switch is useful to eliminate the effect of unrelated noises on measurement data.

WEATHERPROOF MICROPHONE SYSTEM

Gain: 1:1 or 10:1 (20 dB) $\pm$0.3 dB at 25°C, slide switch selected; $<\pm$0.3 dB change from that at 25°C from -30 to $+65°$C.

Frequency: Measured at 1 V rms output into open circuit with 600-Ω source, -30 to $+55°$C.

	3 Hz	5 Hz	20 Hz	100 kHz 300 kHz 500 kHz
1:1 gain	$\pm$3 dB	$\pm$1.0 dB	$\pm$0.25 dB	$\pm$1 dB
10:1 gain	$\pm$3 dB	$\pm$1.5 dB	$\pm$0.3 dB	$\pm$2 dB

Input Impedance: Approximately 2 GΩ in parallel with less than 6 pF. Driven shield reduces input capacitance loading for condenser microphones.

Output Impedance: Approximately 15 Ω in series with 3.3 μF. Up to 11 V pk-pk into open circuit with 15 V supply at frequencies up to 10 kHz. Decreasing to 2 V pk-pk for 1:1 gain and 1 V pk-pk for 10:1 gain at 100 kHz. Up to 10 mA rms output (sine wave) with 1560-9575 Power Supply.

Distortion: $<$0.25% harmonic distortion at 1 kHz with 1 V rms into open circuit load; $<$1% at 10 kHz with 1 V rms into 0.1 μF (equivalent to 2000 ft of cable).

Polarizing Voltage: $+200$ V $\pm$5% behind approximately 1.2 GΩ (dc source res) slide switch selected. Temperature coefficient approx $+0.1\%/°$C.

Noise: $<$3.5 μV equivalent input noise with 390 pF source capacitance, C weighted (10-kHz effective bandwidth).

Insert Terminals: Accepts insert calibration signal. Insert resistance 10Ω $\pm$20%. Nominal loss between connector and microphone terminals $<$0.5 dB. Maximum insert voltage 1 V rms.

Power: $+15$ to 25 V dc 1-2 mA idling (200 V polarizing supply off), 3-5 mA idling (200 V on).

Connectors: Input connector 0.460 x 60 thd for direct connection to microphones and adaptors. Output (signal) connector GR 4-pin shielded, (male). Supplied with 1560-2370 10-ft cable with GR 4-pin shielded (female) connector on one end and Switchcraft type A3 3-terminal connector on the other end. 1933-9601 60-ft extension cable (optional) may be connected between preamplifier output and 10-ft cable.

Environmental: WIND: 30-mph wind typically produces 65-dBA reading; 15-mph wind typically produces 55-dBA reading. RAIN: Saturation of windscreen from heavy rain typically reduces sensitivity $\leqslant$2 dB for frequency $\leqslant$20 kHz. HUMIDITY: 99% relative humidity at 50°C for a period of two weeks will not affect performance.

Supplied: Windscreen kit, desiccant cartridge, 1560-P42 Preamplifier, 10-ft cable, mast assembly.

Mechanical: DIMENSIONS (wxhxd): 5.4x23.7x3.0 in. (138x 601x76 mm). WEIGHT: 4 lb (2 kg) net.

WEATHERPROOF ENCLOSURE

Environment: SOLAR TEMPERATURE RISE: Less than 10°C in still air. Typically 3°C in light variable wind, 0-5 mph. RAIN: Rainproof for wind-driven fall angle of rain less than 45° from vertical. CONDENSING MOISTURE: Provides protection to instrument for at least 24 hours' exposure to fog or dew conditions. SNOW: Provides protection from snow with wind-driven fall angle less than 45° from vertical.

Accessories Supplied: Mounting bracket assembly with bolts to secure to enclosure. Four lag screws for securing to pole, U-bolts for securing mast, key, instruction sheet.

Mechanical: DIMENSIONS: (wxhxd): 13.5x16.25x13.12 in. (343x413x333 mm). WEIGHT: 19 lb (9 kg) net.

Description	Catalog Number
1945 Community Noise Analyzer (Requires a microphone and preamplifier	
With L_{eq}/L_{dn} option	1945-9700
Without L_{eq}/L_{dn} option	1945-9710
D-weighting option is available on special order	
Consult factory for ordering information	
Community Noise Analyzer (same as 1945-9700/-9710 plus additional analysis durations and Data Inhibit — see specifications	1945-9006
Weatherproof Microphone System	1945-9730
Weatherproof Enclosure	1945-9640
Microphones	
Select at least one of the following microphones	
Electret-Condenser, 1-in., random incidence	1961-9601
Electret-Condenser, 1-in., perpendicular incidence	1961-9602
Electret-Condenser, ½-in., random incidence	1962-9601
Electret-Condenser, ½-in., perpendicular incidence	1962-9602
Ceramic, 1-in.	1971-9601
1560-P42 Preamplifier (Included with 1945-9730 Weatherproof Microphone System)	1560-9642
1972 Preamplifier/Adaptor	1972-9600
Accessories	
L_{eq}/L_{dn} Board Kit (retrofit version of L_{eq}/L_{dn} option)	1945-9630
Extender Board (for servicing)	1945-9610
Windscreen Replacement Kit	1945-9650
Dessicant Kit	1945-9600
Extension Cable (60 ft)	1933-9601
Battery, spare, for 1945-9700, -9710, 8 required	8410-1510

Electret-Condenser Microphones

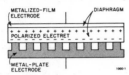

The **GR electret microphone** is a condenser microphone with a permanently-polarized solid dielectric diaphragm.

Use of a solid dielectric permits a simplified manufacturing process, and permanent polarization eliminates the need for a polarizing-voltage power supply. The net result is a high-performance laboratory-standard microphone at a moderate cost.

These microphones represent the very latest in microphone technology. They feature very uniform high-frequency performance in both flat random- and flat perpendicular-incidence versions, and are available in a variety of sizes. Since polarization voltage is not required, they can be used with inexpensive preamplifiers such as GR's 1972-9600.

1961 1-inch Electret-Condenser Microphones

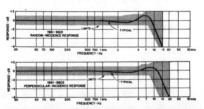

Frequency: Curves show typical response and guaranteed limits; individual response curve supplied with each microphone. Below 20 Hz, the microphone is typically flat ±1 dB down to 5 Hz. Microphone is essentially omnidirectional.

Sensitivity Level: NOMINAL: −38 dB re 1 V/N/m² (−58 dB re 1 V/μbar). TEMPERATURE COEFFICIENT: < ±0.02 dB/°C typically from 0 to +55°C. MAXIMUM SOUND PRESSURE LEVEL: 160 dB absolute max.

Impedance: 125 ±10 pF at 25°C and 1 kHz; temperature coefficient < +0.2 pF/°C at 1 kHz.

Environmental: −20 to +55°C and 90% RH operating; 1-year exposure in an environment of +55°C and 90% RH causes negligible sensitivity change.

Mechanical: TERMINALS: Coaxial, with 0.907-60 thread, adapted to 0.460-60 (thread per in.). DIMENSIONS: 0.936 ±0.001 in. dia. x 1.045 ±0.001 in. long (1.435 ±0.007 in. long with adaptor) (23.77 ±0.025 x 26.55 ±0.025 mm). WEIGHT: 1 oz (28 g) net, 1 lb (0.5 kg) shipping.

Typical performance
with 1560-P42 and 1972-9600 Preamplifiers (Unity Gain)

Microphone	Frequency Range	"System" Sensitivity re 1 V/N/m²	Dynamic Range* re 20 μN/m²
1961-9601	5 Hz to 12 kHz	−38 dB	20.5 to 140 dB
1961-9602	5 Hz to 15 kHz	−38 dB	20.5 to 140 dB

*A-weighted noise level to maximum rms sinewave signal without clipping.

Description	Catalog Number
1961 Electret-Condenser Microphones	
Flat random-incidence response, 1-inch	1961-9601
Flat perpendicular-incidence response, 1-inch	1961-9602

1962 ½-inch Electret-Condenser Microphones

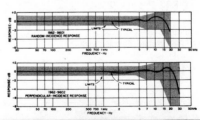

Frequency: Curves show typical response and guaranteed limits; individual response curve supplied with each microphone. Below 20 Hz, the microphone is typically flat ±1 dB down to 5 Hz. Microphone is essentially omnidirectional.

Sensitivity Level: NOMINAL: −40 dB re 1 V/N/m² (−60 dB re 1 V/μbar). TEMPERATURE COEFFICIENT: < ±0.02 dB/°C typically from 0 to +55°C. MAXIMUM SOUND-PRESSURE LEVEL: 170 dB absolute max.

Impedance: 35 ±5 pF, at 25°C and 1 kHz; temperature coefficient < +0.1 pF/°C, at 1 kHz.

Environmental: −20 to +55°C and 90% RH operating; 1-year exposure in an environment of +55°C and 90% RH causes negligible sensitivity change.

Mechanical: TERMINALS: Coaxial, with 0.460-60 thread. DIMENSIONS: 0.500 ±0.005 in. dia. x 0.815 ±0.001 in. long (12.70 ±0.127 x 20.70 ±0.025 mm). WEIGHT: 0.5 oz (14 g) net, 1 lb (0.5 kg) shipping.

Typical performance
with 1560-P42 and 1972-9600 Preamplifiers (Unity Gain)

Microphone	Frequency Range	"System" Sensitivity re 1 V/N/m²	Dynamic Range* re 20 μN/m²
1962-9601	5 Hz to 19 kHz	−41 dB	26 to 145 dB
1962-9602	5 Hz to 24 kHz	−41 dB	26 to 145 dB

*A-weighted noise level to maximum rms sinewave signal without clipping.

1962 Electret Condenser Microphones	
Flat random-incidence response, ½-inch	1962-9601
Flat perpendicular-incidence response, ½-inch	1962-9602

Ceramic Microphones

1-inch Ceramic Microphones

Three versions of the 1-inch ceramic microphone are offered; the differences are described below. All versions use the same microphone cartridge.

The 1971-9605 microphone comes with an adaptor base that plugs into a female three-terminal microphone connector. It mates directly with the 1560-P73 extension cable and can be mounted on a tripod in applications where the microphone will be remote from the instrument and no preamplifier is used.

The 1971-9601 comes with an adaptor that permits it to be mounted directly on the 1560-P42 or 1972-9600 pre-amplifiers.

The 1971-9606 microphone comes mounted on a flexible conduit that terminates in a three-terminal microphone connector. It is normally used with instruments such as the 1564 and 1934 to position the microphone away from the instrument case.

Frequency: Curve shows typical random response and guaranteed limits; individual response curve supplied with each microphone. Below 20 Hz, the microphone is typically flat ±1 dB down to 5 Hz re the 500-Hz level. Time constant of pressure-equalizing leak is typically 0.08 s with a corresponding 3-dB rolloff at 2 Hz.

Sensitivity Level: NOMINAL: −40 dB re 1 V/N/m² (−60 dB re 1 V/μbar); MINIMUM: −42 dB re 1 V/N/m² (−62 dB re 1 V/μbar). TEMPERATURE COEFFICIENT: ≈ −0.01 dB/°C. KEY SOUND-PRESSURE LEVELS: <1% distortion at 150 dB; at −184 and +174 dB peak, microphone may fail.

Impedance: For 1971-9601 and −9605, 385 pF ±15% at 23°C; for 1971-9606, 405 pF ±15% at 23°C. TEMPERATURE COEFFICIENT of Z, for both: 2.2 pF/°C from 0 to 50°C.

Environment: TEMPERATURE: −40 to +60°C operating: HUMIDITY: 0 to 100% RH operating.

Mechanical: TERMINALS: 1971-9601, Coaxial with 0.460-60 thread for mounting on 1560-P42 or 1972-9600 preamplifiers. Center terminal is signal, outer terminal (shell) is ground. 0.460-60 threaded adaptor may be removed for mounting on 1560-P40 preamplifier. 1971-9605, Microphone cartridge fitted with 3-terminal audio connector. 1971-9606, Microphone cartridge with flexible conduit and 3-terminal audio connector. DIMENSIONS: Cartridge only, 1.13 in. (29 mm) long, 0.936 ±0.002 in. (23.7 mm ±50 μm) dia; assembly, 1971-9601, 1.44 in. (36.5 mm) long; 1971-9605, 2.31 in. (59 mm) long; 1971-9606, 11.75 in. (298 mm) long. WEIGHT: 1971-9601, 1.5 oz (41 g) net, 1 lb (0.5 kg) shipping; 1971-9605, 2 oz (56.6 g) net, 1 lb (0.5 kg) shipping; 1971-9606, 10 oz (283 g) net, 2 lb (0.9 kg) shipping.

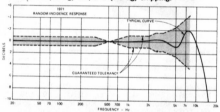

Typical performance of the 1971 Microphones with the 1560-P42 and 1972-9600 Preamplifiers (Unity Gain)

Frequency Range	"System" Sensitivity re 1 V/N/m²	Dynamic Range* re 20 μN/m²
5 Hz to 12.5 kHz	−40 dB	22 to 145 dB

* A-weighted noise level to maximum rms sinewave signal without clipping.

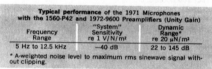

Description	Catalog Number
1971 1-inch Ceramic Microphone	
With adaptor to mike connector	1971-9605
With adaptor to preamplifier	1971-9601
Assembled with flexible conduit	1971-9606

Preamplifiers

1560-P42 Preamplifier

■ **For electret-condenser, air-condenser, and ceramic microphones and vibration pickups**

The 1560-P42 Preamplifier is a high-input impedance, low-noise preamplifier. It is particularly well suited for amplification of the output of capacitive sources, such as electret-condenser, air-condenser, and ceramic microphones and piezoelectric vibration pickups. It is an excellent choice for use with GR sound-level meters and analyzers when a long cable must be used between the microphone and the instrument. It is also a useful probe amplifier for other electrical signals where high input impedance and low noise are necessary. For example, it can increase the sensitivity and input impedance of analyzers, recorders, amplifiers, null detectors, counters, frequency meters, voltmeters, and oscilloscopes. Output from the preamplifier is through a removable 3-wire shielded cable and the required dc supply voltage is applied from one of the wires to ground.

Recommended Combination of Transducers, Adaptors, and Preamplifiers

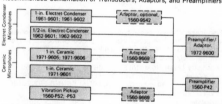

Gain: 1:1 or 10:1 (20 dB) ±0.3 dB at 25°C, slide-switch controlled; <±0.3-dB gain change, from that at 25°C, from −30 to +65°C.

Frequency Response (at 1-V rms open-circuit output behind 600 Ω, −30 to +55°C):

	3 Hz	5 Hz	20 Hz	100 kHz	300 kHz	500 kHz
1:1 gain	±3 dB	±1 dB	±0.25 dB		±1 dB	
10:1 gain	±3 dB	±1.5 dB	±0.3 dB	±2 dB		

328

Impedance: INPUT: $\approx$ 2 GΩ in parallel with <6 pF; driven shield reduces input-capacitance loading for condenser microphones. OUTPUT: $\approx$ 15 Ω in series with 3.3 μF.

Output: SIGNAL: Up to 11 V pk-pk to 10 kHz into open circuit with 15-V supply, decreasing to 2 V pk-pk for 1:1 gain and 1 V pk-pk for 10:1 gain at 100 kHz. Up to 10-mA rms output with 1560-P62 Power Supply. POLARIZING VOLTAGE: +200 V $\pm$5% behind $\approx$ 1.2 GΩ dc source resistance; on-off slide-switch controlled; temperature coefficient $\approx$ 0.1%/°C; frequency >50 kHz.

Noise: <3.5-μV equivalent input with 390-pF source capacitance, C-weighted, 10-kHz effective bandwidth.

Distortion: <0.25% harmonic distortion at 1 kHz with 1-V rms into open circuit load; <1% at 10 kHz with 1-V rms output into 0.1 μF (equivalent to 2000 ft of cable).

Insert Terminals: Accepts insert calibration signal. Insert resistance 10 Ω $\pm$20%. Nominal loss between connector and microphone terminals <0.5 dB. Maximum insert voltage 1 V rms.

Connectors: INPUT CONNECTOR: 0.460-60 thread for direct connection to $\frac{1}{2}$-inch microphones and adaptors. OUTPUT

(SIGNAL) CONNECTOR: (male) 4-pin shielded GR Type 1933-0410. Mates with 1560-2370 10-foot cable with Switchcraft Type A3 3-terminal microphone connector on opposite end.

Power: +15 to +25 Vdc, 1 to 2 mA idling (200 V off) or 3 to 5 mA idling (200 V on). Available directly from 1523, 1558, 1568, 1564, 1909, 1911, 1913, 1921, or 1925 Analyzers, 1525 Recorder, 1561 Sound-Level Meter, 1934 Noise-Exposure Meter, 1566 Multichannel Amplifier, or from 1560-P62 power supply when preamplifier is to be used with 1565 or 1551 Sound-Level Meter, 1553 Vibration Meter, and 1900 or 1910 Analyzer.

Mechanical: DIMENSIONS (less cable): 6.75 in. (170 mm) long x 0.5 in. (13 mm) dia. WEIGHT (with cable): 1 lb (0.5 kg) net, 3 lb (1.4 kg) shipping.

Description	Catalog Number
1560-P42 Preamplifier	**1560-9642**
Adaptor (to most 1-in. condenser microphones)	**1560-9542**
Adaptor (to vibration pickups and 1-in. ceramic microphones)	**1560-9669**

1972-9600 Preamplifier/Adaptor

The Preamplifier/Adaptor provides the high input impedance required by electret-condenser and ceramic microphones, unity voltage gain, and the capability to drive cables up to 100 feet in length. The amplifier requires a 9- to 25-volt dc power supply or normal connection to the 1560-P62 Power Supply or most any GR acoustic instrument.

The 1972-9600 has the same input connector as the 1560-P42 Preamplifier; unlike the latter, it does not provide polarization voltage for air-condenser microphones. It may be driven from the same kind of transducer as the 1560-P42 with the exception of any that require polarization voltage. (See block diagram.)

Gain: 0 dB, +0 −0.25 dB, at 1 kHz.

Frequency Response: $\pm$1 dB, 5 Hz to 100 kHz; $\pm$3 dB, 3 Hz to 500 kHz (at 0.1 V rms output into an open circuit, driven from 600-Ω source).

Input Impedance: $\approx$3 pF in parallel with 1 GΩ, at low audio frequencies.

Output Impedance: Less than 20 Ω in series with 6.8 μF.

Output: MAXIMUM VOLTAGE AVAILABLE: $\geqslant$10 V pk-pk, open circuit, at frequencies $\leqslant$100 kHz, with +15-V supply. CURRENT (available): >1 mA, pk, with +15-V supply.

Noise: <2.5 μV equivalent input noise voltage, with 390 pF source capacitance, C weighted.

Distortion: 0.1% total harmonic distortion for frequencies $\leqslant$100 kHz, at 1 V rms output level, open circuit, +15-V supply.

Terminals: INPUT: Coaxial, with 0.460 x 60 thread for direct connection to most microphones (see block diagram). OUTPUT: Switchcraft type A3M microphone connector, mates with 3-wire extension cables 1560-9665, -9666, -9667.

Power: 9 to 25 V (1 mA at 9 V). Available from most GR analyzers or 1560-P62 power supply. (See list with 1560-P42.)

Mechanical: DIMENSIONS: 0.75 in. dia x 3.44 in. long (19x 87 mm). WEIGHT: 3 oz (85 g) net.

1972 Preamplifier/Adaptor   **1972-9600**

1560-P40 Preamplifier

■ **For ceramic microphones and vibration pickups**

The 1560-P40 Preamplifier is a high input-impedance, low noise preamplifier similar to the 1560-P42 Preamplifier above except it produces no polarizing voltage and therefore cannot be used with condenser microphones.

A 1-inch ceramic microphone (1560-9570 cartridge, adaptor removed) plugs into the input end of the preamplifier case. The output from the preamplifier goes through a 3-terminal shielded connector, 1 terminal of which (with ground) brings in the required dc power.

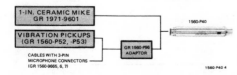

Frequency Response:

	3 Hz	5 Hz	20 Hz	250 kHz	500 kHz
1:1 gain			$\pm$1 dB	$\pm$0.25 dB	
10:1 gain	$\pm$3 dB	$\pm$1.5 dB	$\pm$0.25 dB	$\pm$1.5 dB	

Gain: 1:1 or 10:1 (20 dB) $\pm$0.3 dB at 25°C, slide-switch controlled; <$\pm$0.3-dB gain change (from that at 25°C) from −30° to +55°C.

Impedance: INPUT: 6 pF, >500 MΩ at low audio frequencies. OUTPUT: $\approx$20 Ω in series with 3.3 μF at 1:1 gain, $\approx$100 Ω in series with 3.3 μF at 10:1 gain.

Noise: <2.5-μV equivalent input with 400-pF source capacitance. C weighted, 10-kHz effective bandwidth.

Distortion: <0.25% harmonic distortion at audio frequencies with 1 V pk-pk open-circuit output; 1% at 1 kHz with 5 V pk-pk into 0.1 μF (equivalent to 200 ft of cable); 1% at 1 kHz with 2 V pk-pk into 0.01 μF.

Available: Ceramic microphones, vibration pickups, tripod, cables, and adaptors. **1560-P96** adaptor converts input to accept 3-pin mike connectors.

Power: +15 to +25 V dc, 1 to 2 mA. Available from same sources as 1560-P42.

Mechanical: DIMENSIONS: 6.88 in. (175 mm) long × 1.56 in. (30 mm) dia. WEIGHT: 0.6 lb (0.3 kg) net, 3 lb (1.4 kg) shipping.

1560-P40 Preamplifier	**1560-9640**
1560-P96 Adaptor, to microphone connector	**1560-9696**

Power Supply

1560-P62 POWER SUPPLY Required with 1560-P40, -P42, or 1972-9600 Preamplifiers when they are used with instruments that do not include a source of power such as the 1551 and 1565 Sound-Level Meters. Also useful when long cables are to be driven at high levels and as a charger for rechargeable batteries in the 1561 Sound-Level Meter or 1952 Universal Filter.

A single front-panel control selects operating mode: OFF, CHARGE ONLY, CHARGE AND OPERATE, OPERATE ONLY, REMOTE (off or operate-only mode selected remotely by instrument such as 1561 or 1564 analyzer), and BATTERY CHECK. The batteries are easily removed by a slide-out clip and fit into the same type of holder used in the 1952 Universal Filter.

Input: 100 to 125 or 200 to 250 V, 50 to 60 Hz.

Output: 18 to 21 V dc, 15 mA max; automatic limiting protects supply and prevents deep battery discharge. BATTERIES: Two rechargeable Ni-Cd batteries provide up to 225 mA-hours operation at room temperature between charges. RIPPLE: <5 mV rms in CHARGE-OPERATE mode. CHARGE TIME: 14 to 16 h for completely discharged battery, constant 22-mA battery-charging current. Rear-panel slide switch selects internal or external battery.

Interface: INPUT (from preamp): Power to, and signal from, preamplifier. Use Switchcraft type A3M microphone connector. OUTPUT (to analyzer): Signal from preamplifier and remote power control. Use Switchcraft type A3F microphone connector. ADDITIONAL OUTPUT: Miniature phone jack for connection to 1933 sound-level meter/analyzer and patch cable fitted with miniature phone plugs (listing follows).

Supplied: 1560-9665 4-ft cable to connect to 1551, 1561, 1564, etc; and cable to connect to 1561 charging terminals.

Remote Operation: With line voltage not connected, preamplifier can be set to Operate-Only mode by signal of +15 to 25 V at 300 μA.

Environmental: TEMPERATURE: −15 to +50°C operating.

Mechanical: Convertible Bench cabinet. DIMENSIONS (wx hxd): 8.5x3.84x5.5 in. (216x98x140 mm). WEIGHT: 3 lb (1.4 kg) net, 5 lb (2.3 kg) shipping.

Description	Catalog Number
1560-P62 Power Supply, Bench Model	**1560-9575**

Guide to Microphone System Selection

The microphones, preamplifiers and power supplies listed on the preceding pages may be put together to make complete microphone systems.

Microphone Selection First determine the frequency range and lowest sound level to be measured. Then, select a microphone that will fulfill these requirements. Note that the noise floor for each microphone will be lower if the measured signal is analyzed with full octave or narrower bandwidth filters.

Preamplifier Selection Three preamplifiers are offered. The 1560-P42 is the most versatile, as it can be used with all GR microphones and condenser microphones from other manufacturers. It can drive very long cables and provides a voltage-gain choice of 1 or 10 (0 or 20 dB). The 1972-9600 Preamplifier/Adaptor has the same input fitting as the 1560-P42; however, the former does not have the polarization voltage capability and, therefore, cannot be used with air-condenser microphones. This unity-voltage-gain preamplifier is recommended for driving cables up to 100 feet (30 m) long.

The 1560-P40 Preamplifier was designed for use with the 1971-9601 Microphone (with adaptor base removed). It will work well with accelerometers and other electrical inputs when used with the 1560-P96 Adaptor. This preamplifier provides a voltage-gain choice of 1 or 10 (0 or 20 dB) and may be used with cables of moderate length.

Power Supplies All the preamplifiers mentioned above require power to operate them; many GR sound measuring instruments supply it directly. (Consult the power specifications of the 1560-P42 or the specifications for the specific instrument of interest to see whether this power is supplied). If a separate power supply is required, use the 1560-P62. This should always be used (even with instruments that supply preamplifier power) if very long cables (over a few hundred feet) are to be driven, as the preamplifier power supplies built into most instruments have limited current capability.

Accessories for Acoustic Instruments

Microphone Windscreens

These microphone windscreens reduce the effects of ambient wind noise and protect the microphone diaphragm in oily, misty, or dusty environments. They attach easily to any 1-inch microphone and do not appreciably alter the sensitivity or frequency response of the microphone. The windscreens are made of reticulated polyurethane foam and can be conveniently washed if they become soiled.

Wind-Noise Reduction: 20 dB in winds ≤30 mph.

Microphone Sensitivity Loss: 0 dB to 3 kHz, ≈0.5 dB to 5 kHz, ≈2 dB to 12 kHz; see curve.

Windscreens are also available for ½-inch microphones. Their specifications are similar to those for 1-inch microphones.

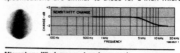

Microphone Windscreens, 4 each per pack	
For 1-in. microphones	**1560-9521**
For ½-in. microphones	**1560-9522**

Tripod

1560-9590 TRIPOD Versatile — accepts a variety of equipment. A ¼-20 threaded stud fits all GR sound-level meters and electronic stroboscopes, a 1-in. sleeve accepts the 1560-P40 and 1972-9600 Preamplifiers, and a ½-in. sleeve accepts the 1560-P42 Preamplifier.

Tripod	1560-9590

330

Vibration Pickups and Systems

The 1560-P11B Vibration Pickup System with the 1551-C Sound-Level Meter.

- accessories for sound-level meters
- select for:
  high-frequency performance
  general application, economy

For the measurement of solid-borne vibrations with the sound-level meter a vibration pickup is used in place of the microphone.

Each of these vibration pickup systems consists of a vibration pickup, a control box, and a connection cable. The vibration pickup is an inertia-operated, ceramic device, which generates a voltage proportional to the acceleration of the vibrating body. By means of integrating networks in the control box, voltages proportional to velocity and displacement can also be delivered to the sound-level meter. The desired response is selected by means of a three-position switch on the control box. Conversion data are supplied for translating the decibel indications of the sound-level meter into the vibration parameters of displacement, velocity, and acceleration.

Type 1560-P11B

This system uses a lead-zirconate-titanate pickup. Probe and probe tips are provided and a permanent-magnet mount is also available.

Type 1560-P13

For measurements at higher frequencies than the -P11B system affords, the -P13 combination is recommended, consisting of the 1560-P53 Vibration Pickup and the 1560-P23 Control Box. A small holding magnet is included.

This system with the Type 1551-C or -B Sound-Level Meter provides the flat frequency response and low-noise operation required by MIL-STD-740 (SHIPS) for vibration measurement. (The holding magnet is not used for measurements according to that standard.)

Pickup Systems	General Purpose 1560-P11B Vibration Pickup System	High Frequency 1560-P13 Vibration Pickup System
Ranges of Measurement Rms Acceleration (in./s²)	0.1 to 39,000 (100 g)†	0.3 to 390,000 (1000 g)†
Rms Velocity (in./s)	0.001 to 300 at 20 Hz* 100 at 60 Hz 10 at 600 Hz	0.001 to 1000 at 20 Hz** 1000 at 60 Hz* 100 at 600 Hz
Rms Displacement (in.)	0.00003 to 1 at 30 Hz* 0.1 at 100 Hz	0.00003 to 10 at 30 Hz* 1 at 100 Hz
Frequency Range Response characteristics for constant applied (1) acceleration, (2) velocity, and (3) displacement.		
Net Weight of System (lb)	1¾ (0.8 kg)	1¾ (0.8 kg)
Shipping Weight (lb)	5 (2.3 kg)	5 (2.3 kg)
Catalog Number	1560-9922	1560-9613 ◈
Pickup Characteristics		
Pickup Type Number	1560-P52	1560-P53
Sensitivity (mV/g, nominal)	70	70
Temp Coeff of Sens (dB/°C)	<−0.01	<0.02
Resonant Frequency (Hz)	3200	27,000
Capacitance (pF)	10,000	350
Temperature Range (°C)	−18 to 100	−54 to 177
Relative Humidity Range (%)	0 to 100	0 to 100
Cable Length (ft)	5 (1.55 m)	8 (2.5 m)
Dimensions (in.)	1⅝x1¼x⅝	⅝ (hex) x 0.7
(mm)	42x37x15	15.5x18
Net Weight (oz)	1.6 (45 grams)	1.1 (31 grams)
Catalog Number	1560-9652	1560-9653

† g = acceleration of gravity.
* Upper limit of displacement and velocity measurements depends upon frequency and is determined by the maximum acceleration possible before nonlinearity occurs (100 g for 1560-P11B, 1000 g for 1560-P13).
** Maximum reading of instrument.

331

Audio Test Instruments

1566 Multichannel Amplifier

- 16 channels
- manual or remote channel selection
- 2-Hz to 100-kHz response
- 55-dB gain, manually or remotely adjusted
- calibration noise source built in

Many inputs — one output Many sound and vibration measurements can be simplified by use of a scanner that connects, in sequence or in any arbitrary order, the outputs from a number of transducers to a single analyzer. A scanner system can be set up to measure signals individually or to average all signals.

The 1566 scans up to 16 channels (up to 99 with a special additional unit), amplifies each by up to 55 dB, and provides a built-in pink-noise calibration source that speeds not only the check out of the scanner but also that of any analyzer connected to it. The 1566 is particularly useful with the 1921 Real-Time Analyzer. This combination can automatically analyze the spectrum from each transducer scanned or it can measure the space-averaged spectrum using 2, 4, 8, 10, 12, or 16 microphones. This feature makes possible automatic real-time sound-power measurements.

SPECIFICATIONS

Channels: 16 plus 1 for calibration, expandable to 99 (additional channels housed in a special unit). CONTROL: Active channel is selected manually or by external 1-2-4-8 BCD signal, or automatically scanned in sequence with range of channels to be scanned selected by thumbwheel switches; dwell time adjustable from 100 ms to 10 s or infinity (channel advance initiated by external signals); scan set to occur once or repetitively and started, stopped on active channel, or reset to lowest channel by pushbuttons or external closures to ground.

DISPLAY: Two high-intensity neon readout tubes display active channel number.

Frequency: 2 Hz to 100 kHz, flat within ±0.5 dB.

Sensitivity: 1.8 mV to 1.6 V for 1-V output; gain set in 1-dB increments by panel control or 1-2-4-8 BCD signal at standard DTL levels (logic 0 ≈ ground, logic 1 ⩾ + 3.5 V). Rear-panel adjustment provides 10-dB continuous control of gain for all channels for calibration. Each channel includes a 6-dB gain adjustment for transducer sensitivity equalization.

Maximum Input: 5 V rms, 7 V pk.

Impedance: INPUT, 100 kΩ. OUTPUT, 600 Ω.

Noise: <10 μV equivalent input noise (C weighted) in each channel when gain is maximum and source impedance is ⩽100 Ω.

Cross-Talk: Interchannel isolation >90 dB.

Calibration: Built-in pink-noise (±1 dB) source with symmetrical Gaussian distribution from 2 Hz to 100 kHz. Spectrum-level slope is −3 dB per octave. Noise signal applied to internal calibration channel is adjustable from 30 to 100 mV rms. Rear-panel noise output is fixed at 100 mV rms and can be loaded by 0.05 μF without affecting spectrum up to 100 kHz.

Supplied: Power cord, two 24-pin data plugs.

Available: 1560-P40 and -P42 Preamplifiers (1566 provides power for up to 99 of either), 1566-9500 Cable Set for connection to 1921 Real-Time Analyzer, microphones, vibration pickups.

Power: 100 to 125 or 200 to 250 V, 50 to 60 Hz, 30 W.

Mechanical: Bench or rack models. DIMENSIONS (wxhxd): Bench, 19.5x5x20 in. (495x127x508 mm); rack, 19x3.5x18.5 in. (483x89x470 mm). WEIGHT: Bench, 32 lb (15 kg) net, 47 lb (22 kg) shipping; rack, 26 lb (12 kg) net, 41 lb (19 kg) shipping.

Description	Catalog Number
1566 Multichannel Amplifier	
Bench Model	1566-9700
Rack Model	1566-9701
Cable Set	1566-9500

1396-B Tone-Burst Generator

- **fast, coherent switch for periodic waves**

- **dc to 2 MHz**

- **signal attenuated > 60 dB between bursts**

- **length of burst: 10 μs to 10 s, or continuous, or
  1 to 129 periods of the switched signal**

- **or burst length controllable by separate input**

The 1396-B Tone-Burst Generator fills the gap between steady-state cw testing and step-function, or pulse, testing of amplifiers, meters, etc. It is ideally suited for applications such as the test and calibration of sonar transducers and amplifiers, the measurement of distortion and transient response of amplifiers and loudspeakers, and routine testing of filters and ac meters. Still other uses are found in the measurement of room acoustics and automatic-gain-control circuits, in the synthesis of time ticks on standard-time radio transmissions, and in psychoacoustic instrumentation.

Description The 1396 acts as a switch that alternately interrupts and passes an input signal, thus chopping into bursts a sine wave, or continuous tone, applied to the input. The instrument times the burst duration and interval between bursts exactly by counting the number of cycles, or periods, of the input signal. Panel controls permit these intervals to be set to a wide range of values. The exact time at which the burst starts and stops can be controlled, thus the burst is phase-coherent with the input signal.

Alternately, timing can be based on a separate signal, the output can be turned on continuously for alignment or calibration, or single bursts can be generated with a front-panel pushbutton. The 1396-B can also operate with nonsinusoidal or aperiodic inputs.

SPECIFICATIONS

Signal Input (signal to be switched): AMPLITUDE: ±1 to ±10 V pk-pk (7 V rms with 0-V dc component) for proper operation. FREQUENCY RANGE: Dc to 2 MHz. INPUT IMPEDANCE: 50 kΩ, approx.

Timing Input (signal that controls switch timing): Same specifications as Signal Input except: INPUT IMPEDANCE: 20 kΩ, approx.

Signal Output: OUTPUT ON: Replica of Signal Input at approx same voltage level; dc coupled; down 3 dB at >1 MHz. Output current limits at >25 mA pk, decreasing to >15 mA at 2 MHz. Output source impedance typically 25 Ω, increasing above 0.2 MHz. Total distortion contribution <0.3% at 1 kHz and 10 kHz. OUTPUT OFF: Input-to-output transfer (feedthrough), <10 mV (<−60 dB re full output), dc to 1 MHz, increasing above 1 MHz. SPURIOUS OUTPUTS: Dc component and change in dc component due to on-off switching (pedestal) can be nulled with front-panel control. Output switching transients are typically 0.2 V pk-pk and 0.2 μs in duration (120-pF load).

On-Off Timing: Timing is phase-coherent with, and controlled by, either the signal at the Signal Input connector or a different signal applied to the Ext Timing connector. The on interval (duration of burst) and the off interval (between bursts) can be determined by cycle counting, timing, or direct external control. CYCLE-COUNT MODE: On and off intervals can be set independently, to be of 1, 2, 4, 8, 16, 32, 64, or 128 cycles (i.e., periods) duration or to be 2, 3, 5, 9, 17, 33, 65, or 129 cycles with +1 switch operated. TIMED MODE: The on and off times can be set independently from 10 μs to 10 s. They end at the first proper phase point of the controlling signal that occurs after the time interval set on the controls. One interval can be timed and the other counted, if desired. SWITCHING PHASE: For either of the above modes, the on-off switching always occurs at a phase of the controlling signal that is determined by the triggering controls. The Slope control allows triggering on either the positive or negative slope of the controlling signal and the Trigger Level control sets the level at which triggering occurs. DIRECT EXTERNAL CONTROL: A 10-V pulse applied to rear-panel connection will directly control switching.

Synchronizing Pulse: A dc-coupled aux output alternates between approx +8 V (output on) and −8 V (off). SOURCE RESISTANCE: ≈ 0.8 kΩ for pos output and ≈ 2 kΩ for neg.

Power: 100 to 125 or 200 to 250 V, 50 to 400 Hz, 16 W.

Mechanical: Convertible bench cabinet. DIMENSIONS (wx hxd): Bench, 8.5x5.63x10 in. (216x143x254 mm); rack, 19x 5.63x10 in. (483x143x254 mm). WEIGHT: Bench, 8 lb (3.7 kg) net, 12 lb (5.5 kg) shipping; rack, 11 lb (5 kg) net, 15 lb (7 kg) shipping.

Description	Catalog Number
1396-B Tone-Burst Generator	
Bench Model	1396-9702
Rack Model	1396-9703

1569 Automatic Level Regulator

- **2 Hz to 100 kHz**
- **50-dB control range**
- **acoustic-system component**

Constant level Use this regulator to hold a monitored signal amplitude steady (such as the sound level in a test chamber) while you sweep the frequency or some other parameter. The primary use is to control the excitation level in swept-frequency sound and vibration testing. The 1569 functions as an automatically controlled amplifier/attenuator between the oscillator and the power-amplifier-transducer chain.

The regulator senses a control voltage from a microphone, accelerometer, or other pickup monitoring the quantity to be controlled and adjusts its own attenuation to maintain that control voltage at constant level. Output from the 1569 is indicated on a panel meter with a scale that is linear in dB, showing you where the regulator is operating in its 50-dB control range. You can easily adjust the control rate to suit operating frequency and magnitude-phase relationships in your control loop.

In an entirely different mode of operation, the 1569 can be used to provide a leveled output, when driven by a poorly leveled signal source. In this mode, the control range is limited to the acceptable range for signal-input levels in the regulator, about 15 dB, whereas the range of outputs is much larger.

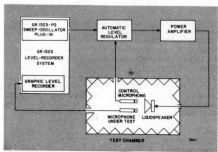

Typical measurement system using 1569.

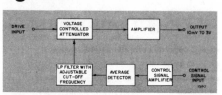

Diagram of 1569 Automatic Level Regulator.

SPECIFICATIONS

Operating Ranges: FREQUENCY: 2 Hz to 100 kHz. CONTROL RANGE: 50 dB. COMPRESSION RATIO: 25, i.e., 0.04 dB per dB.

Main Input: DRIVE VOLTAGE REQUIRED: For normal operation, 1 V; in voltage-leveler mode, 0.2 to 1 V. IMPEDANCE: 100 kΩ.

Output: VOLTAGE: 10 mV to 3 V. IMPEDANCE: 600 Ω. LOAD: Any impedance can be connected without affecting linear operation of output circuit.

Quality: NOISE LEVEL: Typically better than 65 dB below 3-V output in 100-kHz bandwidth. HARMONIC DISTORTION: <1% total for output levels <1 V.

Automatic Shut-Down Function: If drive input level drops below a critical voltage, output automatically drops to zero, to protect equipment connected to it.

Control-Signal Input: VOLTAGE: 5 mV to 4 V, required. IMPEDANCE: 25 MΩ.

Control Rates and Corresponding Min Operating Frequencies:

1000 dB/s	300 dB/s	100 dB/s	30 dB/s	10 dB/s	3 dB/s
600 Hz	200 Hz	60 Hz	20 Hz	6 Hz	2 Hz

Power: 100 to 125 or 200 to 250 V (switch selected), 50 to 60 Hz, 4 W.

Supplied: Power cord, mounting hardware with rack or bench models.

Available: 1560-P42 Preamplifier. Note: Power for preamp is available at rear-panel input connector. 1523 Graphic Level Recorder with 1523-P2 Sweep Oscillator Plug-in. Microphones and vibration pickups.

Mechanical: Rack-bench cabinet. DIMENSIONS (wxhxd): Bench, 19x5x12.87 in. (483x127x327 mm); rack, 19x3.5x 12.75 in. (483x89x324 mm). WEIGHT: 13 lb (6 kg) net, 30 lb (14 kg) shipping.

Description	Catalog Number
1569 Automatic Level Regulator	
Bench Model	1569-9700
Rack Model	1569-9701

1840-A Output Power Meter

- **20 Hz to 20 kHz**
- **0.1 mW to 20 W**
- **0.6-Ω to 32-kΩ input impedance**
- **true rms reading**

The 1840-A measures audio-frequency power into any desired magnitude of load impedance. Its important uses include the measurement of:

- Power output of oscillators, amplifiers, preamplifiers, transformers, transducers, and low-frequency lines.
- Output impedance, by adjustment of this load to yield maximum power indication.
- Frequency-response characteristics of amplifiers, transformers, and other audio-frequency devices.

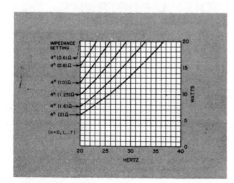

Power derating vs impedance setting and frequency. All 48 impedance settings are represented, as n = 0, 1, 2 . . . 7.

This instrument is basically a multi-tapped audio-frequency transformer with a fixed secondary load. Its two front-panel switches connect eight identical primary windings and six secondary taps in various combinations to provide a total of 48 different primary impedances.

The maximum power rating can be extended for any given impedance with the use of a simple T-network attenuator, design data for which are supplied with the instrument.

SPECIFICATIONS

Power: 0.1 mW to 20 W, 40 Hz to 20 kHz. Below 40 Hz, max rating is reduced by up to 50% (at 25 Hz), depending on impedance selected. See curve. Auxiliary dB scale reads from −15 to +43 dB re 1 mW.

Impedance: 0.6 Ω to 32 kΩ in two ranges; yielding 48 individual impedances spaced approximately $\sqrt[3]{2}$ apart.

Power Accuracy:
At 1 kHz, ±0.3 dB;
50 Hz to 6 kHz, ±0.5 dB;
30 Hz to 10 kHz, ±1 dB;
at 20 Hz, −1.5 dB max, −1 dB avg;
at 20 kHz, −5 dB max, ±1.5 dB avg.

Impedance Accuracy (at full-scale voltage):
At 1 kHz, ±6% max, −0.5% avg;
70 Hz to 2.5 kHz, ±7%;
2.5 kHz to 5 kHz, for Z < 10 kΩ, ±7%;
at 20 Hz, −15% max, −8% avg;
at 20 kHz, ±50% max, ±12% avg.

Waveform Error: Meter will indicate true rms with as much as 20% second and third harmonics present in the input signal.

Mechanical: Convertible bench cabinet. DIMENSIONS (wx hxd): 12x4x8 in. (305x102x203 mm). WEIGHT: 11 lb (5 kg) net, 17 lb (8 kg) shipping. Rack-adaptor panel height, 3.5 in. (89 mm).

Description	Catalog Number
1840-A Output Power Meter	1840-9701
480-P212 Relay-Rack Adaptor Set	0480-9822

Random-Noise Generators

Electrical noise is, by definition, any unwanted disturbance and its reduction in communications circuits is a constant aim of the engineer. Noise from a controlled source, however, is useful in studying the effectiveness of systems for detecting and recovering signals in noise. Well defined random noise is, moreover, a remarkably useful test signal that has, for many measurements, properties that are more useful than those of a single-frequency signal. Its wide spectrum sometimes permits one test with random noise to replace a series of single-frequency tests. Noise is also useful in simulating speech, music, or communications circuit traffic.

Noise is called random if its instantaneous amplitude at any future instant is unpredictable. Random noise is specified by its amplitude distribution and by its spectrum. Many types of naturally occurring electrical noise have the same distribution of amplitudes as do errors that

normally occur in experimental measurements — the normal or Gaussian distribution. In general-purpose noise generators the design objective is random noise that is Gaussian and has a uniform spectrum level over the specified frequency range.

The GenRad random-noise generators produce electrical noise at high output levels, each model having been designed for specific uses. The 1381 is useful for many audio-frequency applications, and also in vibration testing as its spectrum extends well into the subaudio range. The 1382 is intended for audio-frequency electrical, acoustical, and psychoacoustical applications. The 1390-B is useful at higher frequencies because its spectrum extends to 5 MHz. The 1383 generates wide-band noise of uniform spectrum level and is particularly useful for tests in video- and radio-frequency systems.

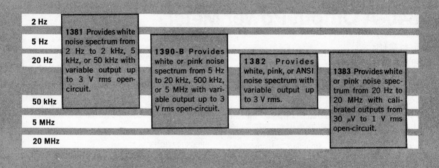

2 Hz	**1381** Provides white noise spectrum from 2 Hz to 2 kHz, 5 kHz, or 50 kHz with variable output up to 3 V rms open-circuit.			
5 Hz				
20 Hz		**1390-B** Provides white or pink noise spectrum from 5 Hz to 20 kHz, 500 kHz, or 5 MHz with variable output up to 3 V rms open-circuit.	**1382** Provides white, pink, or ANSI noise spectrum with variable output up to 3 V rms.	**1383** Provides white or pink noise spectrum from 20 Hz to 20 MHz with calibrated outputs from 30 μV to 1 V rms open-circuit.
50 kHz				
5 MHz				
20 MHz				

1381 and 1382 Random-Noise Generators

GR 1381

- 2 Hz to 2, 5, or 50 kHz, Gaussian distribution
- adjustable clipping
- 3-V rms output

GR 1382

- 20 Hz to 50 kHz, Gaussian distribution
- white, pink, or ANSI spectra
- 3-V rms output, balanced, unbalanced, or floating

Predictably random The 1381 and 1382 are companion instruments that generate truly random noise from a semiconductor source. Special precautions are taken to ensure a symmetrical, Gaussian amplitude distribution. Output level is adjustable from below 3 millivolts to 3 volts rms behind a 600-ohm source impedance. Each model is constructed in a 3½-inch-high, half-rack-

width cabinet, convenient for bench use and two can be mounted side-by-side in a relay rack.

Either of these noise generators can be used for simulation of noise in signal paths, as test-signal sources, or for demonstrations of statistical and correlation principles. The different features of the two offer a choice to match your needs.

Lowest frequency The 1381 generates noise that is flat down to 2 Hz and is intended for random-vibration tests and for general-purpose use in the audio and subaudio range. The upper-frequency limit (at −3 dB) can be switched to 2, 5, or 50 kHz. The output signal can be clipped symmetrically at 2, 3, 4, or 5 times the rms amplitude.

Pink or white The 1382 generates noise in the 20-Hz to 50-kHz band and is intended for electrical, acoustical, and psycho-acoustical tests. It offers three spectra, white (flat), pink (−3 dB per octave), and ANSI (see specifications). The output can be taken balanced or unbalanced, floating or grounded.

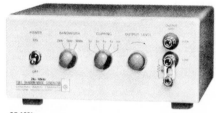

GR 1381

GR 1382

1381 and 1382 Random-Noise Generators (Cont.)

SPECIFICATIONS

Spectrum of 1381: SHAPES: Flat (constant energy per hertz of bandwidth) ±1 dB from 2 Hz to half of cutoff. CUTOFF FREQUENCY (down 3 dB): 2, 5, or 50 kHz, selected by switch. SPECTRAL DENSITY, at 3-V output level and for 1-Hz bandwidth: 64, 40, and 13 mV, approx, respectively for upper cutoff frequencies of 2, 5, and 50 kHz. SLOPE of amplitude vs frequency above upper cutoff: 12 dB/octave. See graph.

Spectrum of 1382: Choice of 3 shapes. WHITE NOISE (flat spectrum, constant energy per hertz bandwidth): ±1 dB, 20 Hz to 25 kHz, with 3-dB points at approx 10 Hz and 50 kHz; PINK NOISE (constant energy per octave bandwidth): ±1 dB, 20 Hz to 20 kHz; or ANSI NOISE, as specified in ANSI Standard S1.4-1961. See graph.

Waveform:

Voltage	Gaussian Probability-Density Function	Amplitude-Density Distribution of 1381/1382
0	0.0796	0.0796 ± 0.005
±σ	0.0484	0.0484 ± 0.005
±2σ	0.0108	0.0108 ± 0.003
±3σ	0.000898	0.000898 ± 0.0002
±4σ	0.0000274	0.0000274 ± 0.00002

These data measured in "windows" of 0.2σ, centered on the indicated values of voltage; σ is the standard deviation or rms value of the noise voltage.

Clipping: The output of the 1381 can be clipped internally to remove the occasional wide extremes of amplitude. Clipping, if desired, is adjustable to approx 2, 3, 4, or 5σ. Such clipping has negligible effect on the spectrum or the rms amplitude.

Output: VOLTAGE: >3 V rms max, open-circuit, for any bandwidth. CONTROL: Continuous adjustment from that level down approx 60 dB. IMPEDANCE: 600 Ω. Can be shorted without causing distortion. 1381 output is unbalanced; 1382 output is floating, can be connected balanced or unbalanced. TERMINALS: 1381 output at front-panel binding posts and rear-panel BNC connector; 1382 output at front-panel binding posts and rear-panel jacks for double plugs.

Supplied: Power cord, rack-mounting hardware with rack models.

Power: 100 to 125 or 200 to 250 V, 50 to 400 Hz, 6 W.

Mechanical: Convertible bench cabinet. DIMENSIONS (wx hxd): Bench, 8.5x3.87x9.87 in. (216x98x250 mm); rack, 19x3.5x9 in. (483x89x229 mm). WEIGHT: 7 lb (3.2 kg) net, 10 lb (4.6 kg) shipping.

Description	Catalog Number
Random-Noise Generator	
1381 (2 Hz to 50 kHz), Bench	**1381-9700**
1381 (2 Hz to 50 kHz), Rack	**1381-9701**
1382 (20 Hz to 50 kHz), Bench	**1382-9700**
1382 (20 Hz to 50 kHz), Rack	**1382-9701**

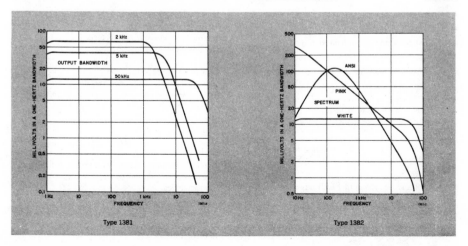

Type 1381   Type 1382

Random-Noise Generator with Pink-Noise Filter plugged in.

1390-B Random-Noise Generator

- **5 Hz to 5 MHz**
- **30 μV to 3 V**
- **±1-dB audio-spectrum-level uniformity**

This instrument generates wide-band noise of uniform spectrum level, particularly useful for noise and vibration testing in electrical and mechanical systems. The noise output of a gas-discharge tube is amplified and shaped with low-pass filters to provide wide spectral ranges with upper cutoff frequencies of 20 kHz, 500 kHz, and 5 MHz.

The output level is controlled by a continuous attenuator followed by a 4-step attenuator of 20 dB per step and is metered from over 3 volts to below 30 microvolts. When the attenuator is used, the output impedance remains essentially constant as you change the output level.

Frequency response Drive your device under test with the 1390-B and analyze output with any of several GR analyzers, manually or with a graphic level recorder. In contrast with the usual swept-single-frequency methods, this one makes your DUT handle a wide spectrum simultaneously. The distinction may be significant if the DUT is nonlinear.

Use the 1390-B as a broad-band signal source for:
- frequency response
- intermodulation and cross-talk tests
- simulation of telephone-line noise
- measurements on servo amplifiers
- noise interference tests on radar
- determining meter response characteristics
- setting transmission levels in communication circuits
- statistical demonstrations in classroom and lab

Make acoustic measurements:
- frequency response
- reverberation — use 1390-B with a GR analyzer as source of narrow-band noise
- sound attenuation of ducts, walls, panels, or floors
- acoustical properties of materials
- room acoustics

Use it with an amplifier to drive:
- a loudspeaker for structural fatigue tests in high-level acoustic fields
- a vibration shake-table

338

SPECIFICATIONS

Frequency Range: 5 Hz to 5 MHz.

Output: VOLTAGE: Max open-circuit output is at least 3 V for 20-kHz range, 2 V for 500-kHz range, and 1 V for 5-MHz range. IMPEDANCE: Source impedance for max output is approx 900 Ω. Output is taken from a 2500-Ω potentiometer. Source impedance for attenuated output is 200 Ω. One output terminal is grounded.

Spectrum: See spectrum-level curves and following table. Note: Spectrum level is shown with constant-Hz-bandwidth analysis, "white" noise being ideally flat. (Pink noise would slope down at 10 dB per decade.)

Range	Typical Spectrum Level (with 1-V rms output)	Spectrum Level Uniformity*
20 kHz	5 mV for 1-Hz band	within ±1 dB, 20 Hz to 20 kHz
500 kHz	1.2 mV for 1-Hz band	within ±3 dB, 20 Hz to 500 kHz
5 MHz	0.6 mV for 1 Hz band	within ±3 dB, 20 Hz to 500 kHz
		within ±8 dB, 500 kHz to 5 MHz

* Noise energy also beyond these limits. Level is down 3 dB at 5 Hz.

Typical spectrum-level characteristics.

Waveform: Noise source has good normal, or Gaussian, distribution of amplitudes for ranges of the frequency spectrum that are narrow compared with the band selected. Over wide ranges the distribution is less symmetrical because of dissymmetry introduced by the gas tube. Some clipping occurs on the 500-kHz and 5-MHz ranges.

Voltmeter: Rectifier-type averaging meter measures output. It is calibrated to read rms value of noise.

Attenuator: Multiplying factors of 1.0, 0.1, 0.01, 0.001, and 0.0001. Accurate to ±3% to 100 kHz, within ±10% to 5 MHz.

Available: Rack-adaptor set (19x7 in.); 1390-P2 Pink-Noise Filter.

Power: 105 to 125 or 210 to 250 V, 50 to 400 Hz, 50 W.

Mechanical: Convertible bench cabinet. DIMENSIONS (wx hxd): Bench, 12.75x7.5x9.75 in. (324x191x248 mm). WEIGHT: 12 lb (5.5 kg) net, 16 lb (7.5 kg) shipping.

Description	Catalog Number
1390-B Random-Noise Generator	
115-V Model	**1390-9702**
230-V Model	**1390-9703**
Rack Adaptor Set (7 in.)	**0480-9842**

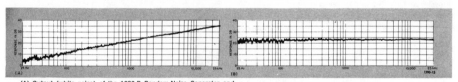

(A) Output (white noise) of the 1390-B Random-Noise Generator and (B) output (pink noise) after filtering by the 1390-P2 Pink-Noise Filter, as measured by a one-third-octave band analyzer.

1390-P2 Pink-Noise Filter

When white noise is used for frequency-response measurements in conjunction with a constant-percentage bandwidth analyzer (such as the GR 1564-A Sound and Vibration Analyzer or 1568-A Wave Analyzer), the amplitude-frequency characteristic of a flat system appears to slope upward with increasing frequency at a rate of 3 dB per octave, owing to the constantly increasing bandwidth (in hertz) of the analyzer. The 1390-P2 converts the audio-frequency output of the 1390-B from white noise to pink noise, which has constant energy per octave. Thus it flattens the response curves made with a constant-percentage-bandwidth analyzer.

SPECIFICATIONS

Frequency Response: Sloping −3 dB per octave from 20 Hz to 20 kHz, −6 dB per octave above 20 kHz. Output voltage is approx −5 dB with respect to the input voltage at 20 Hz and −35 dB at 20 kHz. It lies within 1 dB of the straight line connecting these two points on a graph of output in decibels vs log frequency.

Over-all Output Level: When the filter is used with the random-noise generator set for the 20-kHz range, the output voltage of the filter is approx 30 dB below its input, and the voltage level in each one-third-octave band is approx 17 dB below that. Thus, when the output meter of the generator indicates 3 V, the output of the filter is approx 0.1 V, and the level in each one-third-octave band is approx 15 mV.

Input Impedance: The filter should be driven from a source whose impedance is 1 kΩ or less. Input impedance is variable from 6.5 kΩ + load resistance at zero frequency to 6.7 kΩ at high frequencies.

Output Impedance: The filter should not be operated into a load of less than 20 kΩ. Internal output impedance is variable from 6.5 kΩ + source resistance at low frequencies to approx 200 Ω at high frequencies.

Max Input Voltage: 15 V rms.

Terminals: Input terminals are recessed banana pins on ¾-in. spacing at rear of unit. Output terminals are jack-top binding posts with ¾-in. spacing.

Mechanical: Plug-in unit housing. DIMENSIONS (wxhxd): 1.38x 5x2.87 in. (35x127x73 mm). WEIGHT: 6 oz (0.2 kg) net, 4 lb (1.9 kg) shipping.

Description	Catalog Number
1390-P2 Pink-Noise Filter	**1390-9602**

1383 Random-Noise Generator

- **20 Hz to 20 MHz, ±1.5 dB**
- **30-μV to 1-V output, open-circuit**
- **50-ohm output impedance**
- **meter and 10-dB-per-step attenuator**

This instrument generates wide-band noise of uniform spectrum level, particularly useful for tests in video- and radio-frequency systems.

The maximum output is one volt open circuit from a 50-ohm source. An 8-step attenuator of 10 dB per step permits reduction of the output level to 30 μV.

Use the 1383 as a broad-band noise source for

- intermodulation and cross-talk tests
- simulation of noise in carrier systems
- noise-interference tests in radar and telemetry
- determining noise bandwidth
- measuring noise figure
- setting transmission levels in communication circuits
- statistical demonstrations in classroom and lab
- determining meter response characteristics
- measuring noise temperature

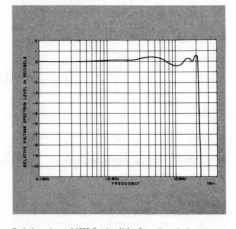

Typical spectrum of 1383 Random-Noise Generator output; energy-per-Hz bandwidth vs frequency.

SPECIFICATIONS

Spectrum: Flat (constant energy per hertz of bandwidth) ±1 dB from 20 Hz to 10 MHz, ±1.5 dB from 10 MHz to 20 MHz.

Waveform: Table shows amplitude-density-distribution specifications of generator compared with the Gaussian probability-density function, as measured in "windows" of 0.2σ, centered on the indicated values of voltage:

Voltage	Gaussian Prob. Dens. Function	Amplitude-Density Dist. of 1383 Random-Noise Gen.	
0	0.0796	0.0796	± 0.005
±σ	0.0484	0.0484	± 0.005
±2σ	0.0108	0.0108	± 0.003
±3σ	0.000898	0.000898	± 0.0003

(σ is the standard deviation or rms value of the noise voltage.)

Output: VOLTAGE ⩾1 V rms open circuit, at full output. CONTROL: Continuous control and 8-step attenuator of 10 dB/

step. METER: Indicates open-circuit output voltage ahead of 50 Ω. IMPEDANCE: 50 Ω. Can be shorted without causing distortion. TERMINALS: GR874® coaxial connector that can be mounted on either front or rear panel.

Power: 100 to 125 or 200 to 250 V, 50 to 400 Hz, 40 W.

Mechanical: Convertible bench cabinet. DIMENSIONS (wx hxd): Bench, 17x3.87x12.75 in. (432x98x324 mm); rack, 19x 3.5x10.75 in. (483x90x273 mm). WEIGHT: 14 lb (6.5 kg) net, 21 lb (10 kg) shipping.

Description	Catalog Number
1383 Random-Noise Generator	
Bench Model	1383-9700
Rack Model	1383-9701

1952 Universal Filter

- 4-Hz to 60-kHz tuning

- low-pass or high-pass,
  band-pass or band-reject, ganged for easy tuning

- high attenuation rate — 30 dB/octave

- line or battery operation

The 1952 Universal Filter will perform as a low-pass, high-pass, band-pass, or band-reject filter at the turn of a panel switch. It consists of low-pass and high-pass filters that can be employed singly, in cascade, or in parallel, to provide the assortment of over-all characteristics. The cut-off frequencies of the two filters can be controlled independently or ganged together to provide constant-percentage bandwidth for band-pass or band-reject tuning.

This filter is of value in many signal-conditioning applications. For example, it can be used to control system bandwidth for reduction of extraneous signals or to evaluate the effect of limited bandwidth upon signal intelligibility and data-transmission accuracy. As a high-pass filter it can reduce power-line-related components, as a low-pass filter control high-frequency noise, or as a notch filter eliminate single-frequency components. The 1952 can also act as part of a spectrum analyzer or distortion meter and, with a random-noise generator, produce controlled bands of noise as test signals.

SPECIFICATIONS

Frequency Range: CUT-OFF FREQUENCIES: Adjustable 4 Hz to 60 kHz in four ranges. PASS-BAND LIMITS: Low-frequency response to dc (approx 0.7 Hz in ac input coupling) in Low Pass and Band Reject modes. High-frequency response uniform ±0.2 dB to 300 kHz in High Pass and Band Reject modes. CONTROLS: Log freqency-dial calibration; accuracy ±2% of cut-off frequency (at 3-dB points).

Filters: FILTER CHARACTERISTICS: Filters are fourth-order (four-pole) Chebyshev approximations to ideal magnitude response. The nominal pass-band ripple is ±0.1 dB (±0.2 dB max); nominal attenuation at the calibrated cut-off frequency is 3 dB; initial attenuation rate is 30 dB per octave. Attenuation at twice or at one-half the selected frequency, as applicable, is at least 30 dB. TUNING MODES: Switch selected, Low Pass, High Pass, Band Pass, and Band Reject. GANGED TUNING: The two frequency controls can be ganged in Band Pass and Band Reject modes so the ratio of upper to lower cut-off frequencies remains constant as controls are adjusted. Range overlap is sufficient to permit tuning through successive ranges without the need to reset frequency controls if ratio of upper to lower cut-off frequencies is 1.5 or less. MINIMUM BANDWIDTH: 26% (approx ⅓ octave) in Band Pass mode. NULL TUNING: In Band Reject mode, setting the frequency controls for a critical ratio of upper to lower cut-off frequency (indicated on dials) gives a null characteristic

(point of infinite attenuation) that can be tuned from 5 Hz to 50 kHz.

Input: GAIN: 0 or −20 dB, switch selected. IMPEDANCE: 100 kΩ. COUPLING: Ac or dc, switch selected. Lower cut-off frequency (3 dB down) for ac coupling is about 0.7 Hz. An LC filter at input limits bandwidth to 300 kHz, thus reducing danger of overloading active circuits at frequencies above normal operating range.

Max Input Voltage: SINE WAVE: 3 V rms (8.5 V pk-pk); except with input attenuator at 20 dB, 30 V rms. DC COUPLED: ±4.2 V pk. AC COUPLED: Max peak level of ac component must not exceed ±4.2 V for specified performance; dc level, ±100 V. Peaks up to ±100 V are tolerated without damage.

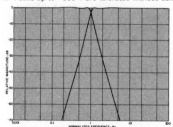

Low-pass and high-pass filter characteristics.

Output: IMPEDANCE: 600 Ω. LOAD: Any load can be connected without affecting linear operation of output circuit. TEMPERATURE COEFFICIENT of output offset voltage: Between 0 and +4 mV/°C.

Noise: <100 µV in an effective bandwidth of 50 kHz.

Distortion: Max harmonic distortion, with all components in the pass band, for a linear load, is less than 0.25% for open-circuit voltages up to 3 V and frequencies up to 50 kHz.

Available: Rechargeable batteries (two required) and 1560-P60 Battery Charger. Replacement battery: Gould 9.6V/225B with snaps, or equivalent.

Power: 100 to 125 or 200 to 250 V (switch selected), 50 to 60 Hz, 2.5 W. Or 19.2 V, approx 20 mA from rechargeable nickel-cadmium batteries (not supplied), about 10-h operation. Connections for external battery.

Mechanical: Bench or rack models. DIMENSIONS (wxhxd): Bench, 19x3.87x14.8 in. (483x98x376 mm); rack, 19x3.5x 13.63 in. (483x89x346 mm); charger, 4.25x3.75x8 in. (108x 95x203 mm). WEIGHT: 21 lb (10 kg) net, 25 lb (12 kg) shipping.

Description	Catalog Number
1952 Universal Filter	
Bench Model	1952-9801
Rack Model	1952-9811
Rechargeable Battery (2 req'd)	8410-1040
1560-P60 Battery Charger	
115 volts	1560-9660
230 volts	1560-9661

Index

343

344

345